Dimensions Math®
Teacher's Guide 5A

Authors and Reviewers

Cassandra Turner

Allison Coates

Jenny Kempe

Bill Jackson

Tricia Salerno

Singapore Math Inc.

Published by Singapore Math Inc.

19535 SW 129th Avenue
Tualatin, OR 97062
www.singaporemath.com

Dimensions Math® Teacher's Guide 5A
ISBN 978-1-947226-40-1

First published 2020
Reprinted 2020, 2021, 2022

Printed in China

Acknowledgments

Editing by the Singapore Math Inc. team.
Design and illustration by Cameron Wray with Carli Bartlett.

Contents

Chapter		Lesson	Page

Chapter		Lesson	Page

Dimensions Math® Curriculum

The **Dimensions Math®** series is a Pre-Kindergarten to Grade 5 series based on the pedagogy and methodology of math education in Singapore. The main goal of the **Dimensions Math®** series is to help students develop competence and confidence in mathematics.

The series follows the principles outlined in the Singapore Mathematics Framework below.

Pedagogical Approach and Methodology

- Through Concrete-Pictorial-Abstract development, students view the same concepts over time with increasing levels of abstraction.
- Thoughtful sequencing creates a sense of continuity. The content of each grade level builds on that of preceding grade levels. Similarly, lessons build on previous lessons within each grade.
- Group discussion of solution methods encourages expansive thinking.
- Interesting problems and activities provide varied opportunities to explore and apply skills.
- Hands-on tasks and sharing establish a culture of collaboration.
- Extra practice and extension activities encourage students to persevere through challenging problems.
- Variation in pictorial representation (number bonds, bar models, etc.) and concrete representation (straws, linking cubes, base ten blocks, discs, etc.) broaden student understanding.

Each topic is introduced, then thoughtfully developed through the use of a variety of learning experiences, problem solving, student discourse, and opportunities for mastery of skills. This combination of hands-on practice, in-depth exploration of topics, and mathematical variability in teaching methodology allows students to truly master mathematical concepts.

Singapore Mathematics Framework

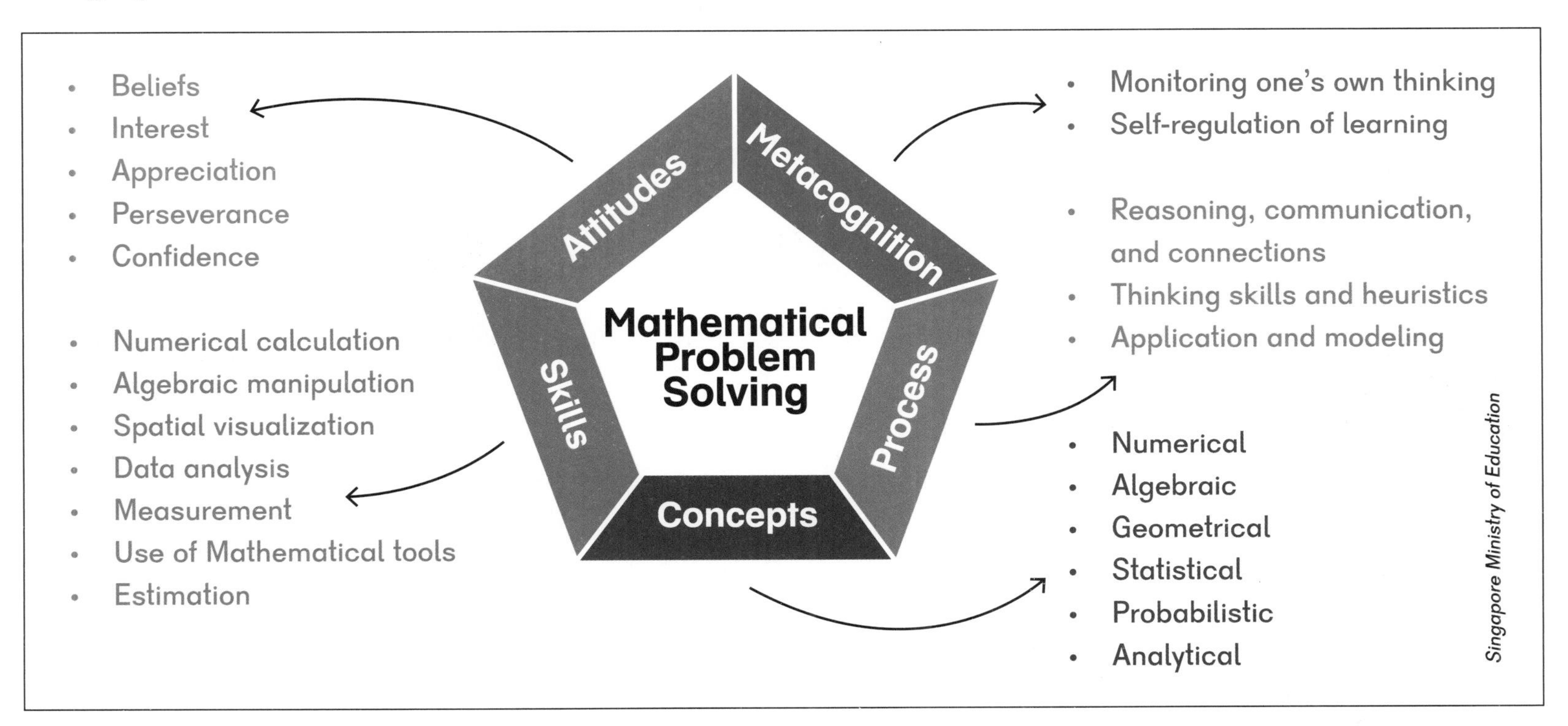

Dimensions Math® Program Materials

Textbooks

Textbooks are designed to help students build a solid foundation in mathematical thinking and efficient problem solving. Careful sequencing of topics, well-chosen problems, and simple graphics foster deep conceptual understanding and confidence. Mental math, problem solving, and correct computation are given balanced attention in all grades. As skills are mastered, students move to increasingly sophisticated concepts within and across grade levels.

Students work through the textbook lessons with the help of five friends: Emma, Alex, Sofia, Dion, and Mei. The characters appear throughout the series and help students develop metacognitive reasoning through questions, hints, and ideas.

A pencil icon at the end of the textbook lessons links to exercises in the workbooks.

Workbooks

Workbooks provide additional problems that range from basic to challenging. These allow students to independently review and practice the skills they have learned.

Teacher's Guides

Teacher's Guides include lesson plans, mathematical background, games, helpful suggestions, and comprehensive resources for daily lessons.

Tests

Tests contain differentiated assessments to systematically evaluate student progress.

Online Resources

The following can be downloaded from dimensionsmath.com.

- **Blackline Masters** used for various hands-on tasks.
- **Material Lists** for each chapter and lesson, so teachers and classroom helpers can prepare ahead of time.
- **Activities** that can be done with students who need more practice or a greater challenge, organized by concept, chapter, and lesson.
- **Standards Alignments** for various states.

Using the Teacher's Guide

This guide is designed to assist in planning daily lessons. It should be considered a helping hand between the curriculum and the classroom. It provides introductory notes on mathematical content, key points, and suggestions for activities. It also includes ideas for differentiation within each lesson, and answers and solutions to textbook and workbook problems.

Each chapter of the guide begins with the following.

- **Overview**

  Includes objectives and suggested number of class periods for each chapter.

- **Notes**

  Highlights key learning points, provides background on math concepts, explains the purpose of certain activities, and helps teachers understand the flow of topics throughout the year.

- **Materials**

  Lists materials, manipulatives, and Blackline Masters used in the Think and Learn sections of the guide. It also includes suggested storybooks. Many common classroom manipulatives are used throughout the curriculum. When a lesson refers to a whiteboard and markers, any writing materials can be used. Blackline Masters can be found at dimensionsmath.com.

The guide goes through the Chapter Openers, Daily Lessons, and Practices of each chapter, and cumulative reviews in the following general format.

- **Chapter Opener**

  Provides talking points for discussion to prepare students for the math concepts to be introduced.

- **Think**

  Offers structure for teachers to guide student inquiry. Provides various methods and activities to solve initial textbook problems or tasks.

- **Learn**

  Guides teachers to analyze student methods from Think to arrive at the main concepts of the lesson through discussion and study of the pictorial representations in the textbook.

- **Do**

  Expands on specific problems with strategies, additional practice, and remediation.

Activities

Allows students to practice concepts through individual, small group, and whole group hands-on tasks and games, including suggestions for outdoor play (most of which can be modified for a gymnasium or classroom).

Level of difficulty in the games and activities are denoted by the following symbols.

● Foundational activities
▲ On-level activities
★ Challenge or extension activities

Brain Works

Provides opportunities for students to extend their mathematical thinking.

Discussion is a critical component of each lesson. Teachers are encouraged to let students discuss their reasoning. As each classroom is different, this guide does not anticipate all situations. The following questions can help students articulate their thinking and increase their mastery:

- Why? How do you know?
- Can you explain that?
- Can you draw a picture of that?
- Is your answer reasonable? How do you know?
- How is this task like the one we did before? How is it different?
- What is alike and what is different about...?
- Can you solve that a different way?
- Yes! You're right! How do you know it's true?
- What did you learn before that can help you solve this problem?
- Can you summarize what your classmate shared?
- What conclusion can you draw from the data?

Each lesson is designed to take one day. If your calendar allows, you may choose to spend more than one day on certain lessons. Throughout the guide, there are notes to extend on learning activities to make them more challenging. Lesson structures and activities do not have to conform exactly to what is shown in the guide. Teachers are encouraged to exercise their discretion in using this material in a way that best suits their classes.

Textbooks are designed to last multiple years. Textbook problems with a ▢ (or a blank line for terms) are meant to invite active participation.

Dimensions Math® Scope & Sequence

PKA

Chapter 1
Match, Sort, and Classify

Red and Blue
Yellow and Green
Color Review
Soft and Hard
Rough, Bumpy, and Smooth
Sticky and Grainy
Size — Part 1
Size — Part 2
Sort Into Two Groups
Practice

Chapter 2
Compare Objects

Big and Small
Long and Short
Tall and Short
Heavy and Light
Practice

Chapter 3
Patterns

Movement Patterns
Sound Patterns
Create Patterns
Practice

Chapter 4
Numbers to 5 — Part 1

Count 1 to 5 — Part 1
Count 1 to 5 — Part 2
Count Back
Count On and Back
Count 1 Object
Count 2 Objects
Count Up to 3 Objects
Count Up to 4 Objects
Count Up to 5 Objects
How Many? — Part 1
How Many? — Part 2
How Many Now? — Part 1
How Many Now? — Part 2
Practice

Chapter 5
Numbers to 5 — Part 2

1, 2, 3
1, 2, 3, 4, 5 — Part 1
1, 2, 3, 4, 5 — Part 2
How Many? — Part 1
How Many? — Part 2
How Many Do You See?
How Many Do You See Now?
Practice

Chapter 6
Numbers to 10 — Part 1

0
Count to 10 — Part 1
Count to 10 — Part 2
Count Back
Order Numbers
Count Up to 6 Objects
Count Up to 7 Objects
Count Up to 8 Objects
Count Up to 9 Objects
Count Up to 10 Objects — Part 1
Count Up to 10 Objects — Part 2
How Many?
Practice

Chapter 7
Numbers to 10 — Part 2

6
7
8
9
10
0 to 10
Count and Match — Part 1
Count and Match — Part 2
Practice

PKB

Chapter 8
Ordinal Numbers

First
Second and Third
Fourth and Fifth
Practice

Chapter 9
Shapes and Solids

Cubes, Cylinders, and Spheres
Cubes
Positions
Build with Solids
Rectangles and Circles
Squares
Triangles

Dimensions Math® Scope & Sequence

Count Up to 10 Things — Part 2
Recognize the Numbers 6 to 10
Write the Numbers 6 and 7
Write the Numbers 8, 9, and 10
Write the Numbers 6 to 10
Count and Write the Numbers 1 to 10
Ordinal Positions
One More Than
Practice

Chapter 4
Shapes and Solids

Curved or Flat
Solid Shapes
Closed Shapes
Rectangles
Squares
Circles and Triangles
Where is It?
Hexagons
Sizes and Shapes
Combine Shapes
Graphs
Practice

Chapter 5
Compare Height, Length, Weight, and Capacity

Comparing Height
Comparing Length
Height and Length — Part 1
Height and Length — Part 2
Weight — Part 1
Weight — Part 2
Weight — Part 3
Capacity — Part 1
Capacity — Part 2
Practice

Chapter 6
Comparing Numbers Within 10

Same and More
More and Fewer
More and Less
Practice — Part 1
Practice — Part 2

KB

Chapter 7
Numbers to 20

Ten and Some More
Count Ten and Some More
Two Ways to Count
Numbers 16 to 20
Number Words 0 to 10
Number Words 11 to 15
Number Words 16 to 20
Number Order
1 More Than or Less Than
Practice — Part 1
Practice — Part 2

Chapter 8
Number Bonds

Putting Numbers Together — Part 1
Putting Numbers Together — Part 2
Parts Making a Whole
Look for a Part
Number Bonds for 2, 3, and 4
Number Bonds for 5
Number Bonds for 6
Number Bonds for 7
Number Bonds for 8
Number Bonds for 9
Number Bonds for 10
Practice — Part 1
Practice — Part 2
Practice — Part 3

Chapter 9
Addition

Introduction to Addition — Part 1
Introduction to Addition — Part 2
Introduction to Addition — Part 3
Addition
Count On — Part 1
Count On — Part 2
Add Up to 3 and 4
Add Up to 5 and 6
Add Up to 7 and 8
Add Up to 9 and 10
Addition Practice
Practice

Chapter 10
Subtraction

Take Away to Subtract — Part 1

Dimensions Math® Scope & Sequence

Compare Numbers to 20
Addition
Subtraction
Practice

Chapter 6
Addition to 20

Add by Making 10 — Part 1
Add by Making 10 — Part 2
Add by Making 10 — Part 3
Addition Facts to 20
Practice

Chapter 7
Subtraction Within 20

Subtract from 10 — Part 1
Subtract from 10 — Part 2
Subtract the Ones First
Word Problems
Subtraction Facts Within 20
Practice

Chapter 8
Shapes

Solid and Flat Shapes
Grouping Shapes
Making Shapes
Practice

Chapter 9
Ordinal Numbers

Naming Positions
Word Problems
Practice
Review 2

1B

Chapter 10
Length

Comparing Lengths Directly
Comparing Lengths Indirectly
Comparing Lengths with Units
Practice

Chapter 11
Comparing

Subtraction as Comparison
Making Comparison
    Subtraction Stories
Picture Graphs
Practice

Chapter 12
Numbers to 40

Numbers to 40
Tens and Ones
Counting by Tens and Ones
Comparing
Practice

Chapter 13
Addition and Subtraction Within 40

Add Ones
Subtract Ones
Make the Next Ten
Use Addition Facts
Subtract from Tens
Use Subtraction Facts
Add Three Numbers
Practice

Chapter 14
Grouping and Sharing

Adding Equal Groups
Sharing
Grouping
Practice

Chapter 15
Fractions

Halves
Fourths
Practice
Review 3

Chapter 16
Numbers to 100

Numbers to 100
Tens and Ones
Count by Ones or Tens
Compare Numbers to 100
Practice

Chapter 17
Addition and Subtraction Within 100

Add Ones — Part 1
Add Tens
Add Ones — Part 2
Add Tens and Ones — Part 1
Add Tens and Ones — Part 2
Subtract Ones — Part 1
Subtract from Tens
Subtract Ones — Part 2
Subtract Tens

Dimensions Math® Scope & Sequence

Dividing by 5 and 10
Practice C
Word Problems
Review 2

2B

Chapter 8
Mental Calculation

Adding Ones Mentally
Adding Tens Mentally
Making 100
Adding 97, 98, or 99
Practice A
Subtracting Ones Mentally
Subtracting Tens Mentally
Subtracting 97, 98, or 99
Practice B
Practice C

Chapter 9
Multiplication and Division of 3 and 4

The Multiplication Table of 3
Multiplication Facts of 3
Dividing by 3
Practice A
The Multiplication Table of 4
Multiplication Facts of 4
Dividing by 4
Practice B
Practice C

Chapter 10
Money

Making $1
Dollars and Cents
Making Change
Comparing Money
Practice A
Adding Money
Subtracting Money
Practice B

Chapter 11
Fractions

Halves and Fourths
Writing Unit Fractions
Writing Fractions
Fractions that Make 1 Whole
Comparing and Ordering Fractions
Practice
Review 3

Chapter 12
Time

Telling Time
Time Intervals
A.M. and P.M.
Practice

Chapter 13
Capacity

Comparing Capacity
Units of Capacity
Practice

Chapter 14
Graphs

Picture Graphs
Bar Graphs
Practice

Chapter 15
Shapes

Straight and Curved Sides
Polygons
Semicircles and Quarter-circles
Patterns
Solid Shapes
Practice
Review 4
Review 5

3A

Chapter 1
Numbers to 10,000

Numbers to 10,000
Place Value — Part 1
Place Value — Part 2
Comparing Numbers
The Number Line
Practice A
Number Patterns
Rounding to the Nearest Thousand
Rounding to the Nearest Hundred
Rounding to the Nearest Ten
Practice B

Dimensions Math® Scope & Sequence

The Multiplication Table of 9
Multiplying by 8 and 9
Dividing by 8 and 9
Practice B

Chapter 9
Fractions — Part 1

Fractions of a Whole
Fractions on a Number Line
Comparing Fractions with
Like Denominators
Comparing Fractions with
Like Numerators
Practice

Chapter 10
Fractions — Part 2

Equivalent Fractions
Finding Equivalent Fractions
Simplifying Fractions
Comparing Fractions — Part 1
Comparing Fractions — Part 2
Practice A
Adding and Subtracting
Fractions — Part 1
Adding and Subtracting
Fractions — Part 2
Practice B

Chapter 11
Measurement

Meters and Centimeters
Subtracting from Meters
Kilometers
Subtracting from Kilometers
Liters and Milliliters
Kilograms and Grams
Word Problems
Practice
Review 3

Chapter 12
Geometry

Circles
Angles
Right Angles
Triangles
Properties of Triangles
Properties of Quadrilaterals
Using a Compass
Practice

Chapter 13
Area and Perimeter

Area
Units of Area
Area of Rectangles
Area of Composite Figures
Practice A
Perimeter
Perimeter of Rectangles
Area and Perimeter
Practice B

Chapter 14
Time

Units of Time
Calculating Time — Part 1
Practice A
Calculating Time — Part 2
Calculating Time — Part 3
Calculating Time — Part 4
Practice B

Chapter 15
Money

Dollars and Cents
Making $10
Adding Money
Subtracting Money
Word Problems
Practice
Review 4
Review 5

4A

Chapter 1
Numbers to One Million

Numbers to 100,000
Numbers to 1,000,000
Number Patterns
Comparing and Ordering
Numbers
Rounding 5-Digit Numbers
Rounding 6-Digit Numbers
Calculations and Place Value
Practice

Chapter 2
Addition and Subtraction

Addition
Subtraction
Other Ways to Add and
Subtract — Part 1
Other Ways to Add and
Subtract — Part 2
Word Problems

Dimensions Math® Scope & Sequence

Chapter 11
Area and Perimeter

Area of Rectangles — Part 1
Area of Rectangles — Part 2
Area of Composite Figures
Perimeter — Part 1
Perimeter — Part 2
Practice

Chapter 12
Decimals

Tenths — Part 1
Tenths — Part 2
Hundredths — Part 1
Hundredths — Part 2
Expressing Decimals as Fractions in Simplest Form
Expressing Fractions as Decimals
Practice A
Comparing and Ordering Decimals
Rounding Decimals
Practice B

Chapter 13
Addition and Subtraction of Decimals

Adding and Subtracting Tenths
Adding Tenths with Regrouping
Subtracting Tenths with Regrouping
Practice A
Adding Hundredths
Subtracting from 1 and 0.1
Subtracting Hundredths
Money, Decimals, and Fractions
Practice B
Review 3

Chapter 14
Multiplication and Division of Decimals

Multiplying Tenths and Hundredths
Multiplying Decimals by a Whole Number — Part 1
Multiplying Decimals by a Whole Number — Part 2
Practice A
Dividing Tenths and Hundredths
Dividing Decimals by a Whole Number — Part 1
Dividing Decimals by a Whole Number — Part 2
Dividing Decimals by a Whole Number — Part 3
Practice B

Chapter 15
Angles

The Size of Angles
Measuring Angles
Drawing Angles
Adding and Subtracting Angles
Reflex Angles
Practice

Chapter 16
Lines and Shapes

Perpendicular Lines
Parallel Lines
Drawing Perpendicular and Parallel Lines
Quadrilaterals
Lines of Symmetry
Symmetrical Figures and Patterns
Practice

Chapter 17
Properties of Cuboids

Cuboids
Nets of Cuboids
Faces and Edges of Cuboids
Practice
Review 4
Review 5

5A

Chapter 1
Whole Numbers

Numbers to One Billion
Multiplying by 10, 100, and 1,000
Dividing by 10, 100, and 1,000
Multiplying by Tens, Hundreds, and Thousands
Dividing by Tens, Hundreds, and Thousands
Practice

Chapter 2
Writing and Evaluating Expressions

Expressions with Parentheses
Order of Operations — Part 1
Order of Operations — Part 2

Chapter 3
Multiplication and Division

Chapter 4
Addition and Subtraction of Fractions

Chapter 5
Multiplication of Fractions

Chapter 6
Division of Fractions

Chapter 7
Measurement

Chapter 8
Volume of Solid Figures

5B

Chapter 9
Decimals

Dimensions Math® Scope & Sequence

Conversion of Measures
Mental Calculation
Practice B

Chapter 10
The Four Operations of Decimals

Adding Decimals to Thousandths
Subtracting Decimals
Multiplying by 0.1 or 0.01
Multiplying by a Decimal
Practice A
Dividing by a Whole Number — Part 1
Dividing by a Whole Number — Part 2
Dividing a Whole Number by 0.1 and 0.01
Dividing a Whole Number by a Decimal
Practice B

Chapter 11
Geometry

Measuring Angles
Angles and Lines
Classifying Triangles
The Sum of the Angles in a Triangle
The Exterior Angle of a Triangle
Classifying Quadrilaterals
Angles of Quadrilaterals — Part 1
Angles of Quadrilaterals — Part 2
Drawing Triangles and Quadrilaterals
Practice

Chapter 12
Data Analysis and Graphs

Average — Part 1
Average — Part 2
Line Plots
Coordinate Graphs
Straight Line Graphs
Practice
Review 3

Chapter 13
Ratio

Finding the Ratio
Equivalent Ratios
Finding a Quantity
Comparing Three Quantities
Word Problems
Practice

Chapter 14
Rate

Finding the Rate
Rate Problems — Part 1
Rate Problems — Part 2
Word Problems
Practice

Chapter 15
Percentage

Meaning of Percentage
Expressing Percentages as Fractions
Percentages and Decimals
Expressing Fractions as Percentages
Practice A
Percentage of a Quantity
Word Problems
Practice B
Review 4
Review 5

Suggested number of class periods: 6–7

	Lesson	Page	Resources	Objectives
	Chapter Opener	p. 5	TB: p. 1	Investigate large numbers.
1	Numbers to One Billion	p. 6	TB: p. 2 WB: p. 1	Read, write, and interpret numbers to one billion.
2	Multiplying by 10, 100, and 1,000	p. 9	TB: p. 6 WB: p. 5	Multiply a whole number by 10, 100, and 1,000. Understand the relative size of the digits in each position on a place-value chart.
3	Dividing by 10, 100, and 1,000	p. 12	TB: p. 10 WB: p. 8	Divide a whole number by 10, 100, and 1,000.
4	Multiplying by Tens, Hundreds, and Thousands	p. 15	TB: p. 14 WB: p. 11	Multiply a whole number by a multiple of 10, 100, and 1,000.
5	Dividing by Tens, Hundreds, and Thousands	p. 19	TB: p. 18 WB: p. 14	Divide a whole number by a multiple of 10, 100, and 1,000.
6	Practice	p. 21	TB: p. 22 WB: p. 17	Practice concepts from the chapter.
	Workbook Solutions	p. 22		

In Dimensions Math 4A, students learned to understand, compare, and round numbers to 1 million. They learned to interpret each digit in terms of its place value.

In this chapter, students will work with numbers of up to nine digits. They will use mental math to multiply and divide numbers within 1 billion by 10, 100, or 1,000, and then by multiples of 10, 100, and 1,000.

Place Value to the Billions

In whole numbers, a period is every three digits, starting at the ones place. The first three periods are the ones period, the thousands period, and the millions period. Each period has the ones, tens, and hundreds place for that period. For example, the millions period consists of the one millions, ten millions, and hundred millions places. The next two periods are the billions and the trillions periods.

In the U.S., it is customary to separate periods of three digits with commas. One billion, for example, is written as 1,000,000,000. Other countries may use a dot or space to separate periods of numbers.

In the place-value system, the position of each digit determines its value. Each place represents a value ten times the value of the place to its right.

The values of each of the digits in the number 147,865,423, are:

1 hundred million, 4 ten millions, 7 millions,
8 hundred thousands, 6 ten thousands, 5 thousands,
4 hundreds, 2 tens, and 3 ones

The number 147,865,423 can be expressed as a sum of the values of the digits in each place, sometimes referred to as the expanded form of the number:

100,000,000 + 40,000,000 + 7,000,000 +
800,000 + 60,000 + 5,000 + 400 + 20 + 3

Calculations with Place Value

Building on their place value knowledge from earlier grades, students will become fluent in thinking about the various representations of a number that is a multiple of 10, 100, or 1,000. Students can think of tens, hundreds, and thousands as units. For example, 430 is 43 tens (the unit is tens) or 430 ones (the unit is ones).

Examples:

437 × 10
437 tens = 4,370 ones

437 × 100
437 hundreds = 4,370 tens = 43,700 ones

437 × 1,000
437 thousands = 4,370 hundreds
= 43,700 tens = 437,000 ones

Students will see that when we multiply a whole number by 10, 100, or 1,000, the product is ten, one hundred, or one thousand times as much, and we can append zeros to the original number:

437 × 1**0** = 437 **tens** = 4,37**0**
437 × 1**00** = 437 **hundreds** = 43,7**00**

When dividing, students will see similar patterns.

Examples:

437,000 ÷ 10 = $\frac{437{,}000}{10}$ = 43,700

437,000 ÷ 100 = $\frac{437{,}000}{100}$ = 4,370

437,000 ÷ 1,000 = $\frac{437{,}000}{1{,}000}$ = 437

When we divide by 10, 100, or 1,000, the value of each digit in the resulting quotient is $\frac{1}{10}$, $\frac{1}{100}$, or $\frac{1}{1{,}000}$ as much as its value in the original number. As a shortcut, when dividing by 10, we can cross off a zero from the original number:

437,000 ÷ 10 = $\frac{437{,}00\cancel{0}}{1\cancel{0}}$ = 43,700

437,00$\cancel{0}$ ÷ 1$\cancel{0}$ = 43,700

Similar patterns can be seen in dividing by 100 and 1,000:

$437{,}0\cancel{0}\cancel{0} \div 1\cancel{0}\cancel{0} = 4{,}370$
$437{,}\cancel{0}\cancel{0}\cancel{0} \div 1{,}\cancel{0}\cancel{0}\cancel{0} = 437$

Helping students to see 437,000 ÷ 1,000 as, “How many groups of 1,000 are in 437,000?” will help them conceptually understand why we cross out zeros.

In Lessons 4 and 5, students will apply this knowledge of multiplying and dividing by 10, 100, or 1,000 to multiply and divide by multiples of 10, 100, and 1,000.

Multiplication

When multiplying by multiples of 10, 100, and 1,000, students will learn to multiply the leading non-zero digits in each number together first. Next, they will multiply the result by the multiple of 10, 100, or 1,000.

Example:

24 × 600 = 24 × 6 × 100 or 24 × 6 hundreds

To solve, multiply 24 × 6 using a known strategy first:

24 × 6 = 120 + 24
20 4

24 × 6 = 144

Then multiply the result by 1 hundred:

144 × 100 = 14,400

Division

Students will learn a strategy for dividing a whole number by a multiple of 10, 100, or 1,000 that is a reverse of the procedure for multiplication.

Example:

42,000 ÷ 600

Because 600 = 6 × 100, divide by 100 first:

42,000 ÷ 100 = 420

Then divide the result by 6:

420 ÷ 6 = 70

Students can relate the division expression to fractions and what they know about simplifying fractions:

$\frac{42{,}0\cancel{0}\cancel{0}}{6\cancel{0}\cancel{0}} = \frac{420}{6} = 70$

Knowing how to do calculations like these will help students estimate answers to problems involving large numbers. They will continue to apply place-value concepts to calculations with larger numbers in the next chapter.

Materials

- Dry erase markers
- Ten-sided dice
- Whiteboards

Blackline Masters

- Mental Division Duel Scoring Sheet
- Mental Multiplication Duel Scoring Sheet
- Number Cards
- Race to 1 Billion Cards

Activities

Games and activities included in this chapter are designed to provide practice and extensions of place-value concepts. They can be used after students complete the **Do** questions, or any time review and practice are needed.

Objective

- Investigate large numbers.

Have students discuss the **Chapter Opener**. They can look at the numbers and read them, and then talk about where they have seen or heard of larger numbers.

Possible questions to ask students:

- “Have you heard the names of really large numbers?”
- “Is a zillion a number? Is a googol a number?”
- “What is the largest number you know?”

These are interesting questions to discuss and ponder. Answers are not required.

This introduction to large numbers can be a short discussion before beginning Lesson 1.

Objective

- Read, write, and interpret numbers to one billion.

Think

Have students look at the **Think** problem.

Ask students:

- "What place values do you know that are greater than the thousands place?"
- "Knowing what you know about place values and numbers, how could we read this number?"

Have students try to read the number as directed in (a).

Discuss student answers to (b).

Learn

Have students discuss the representation of the number on the chart.

Have students look at multiplication expressions for each place value. They should see, for example, that 9 one millions is the same as 9 × 1 million.

2

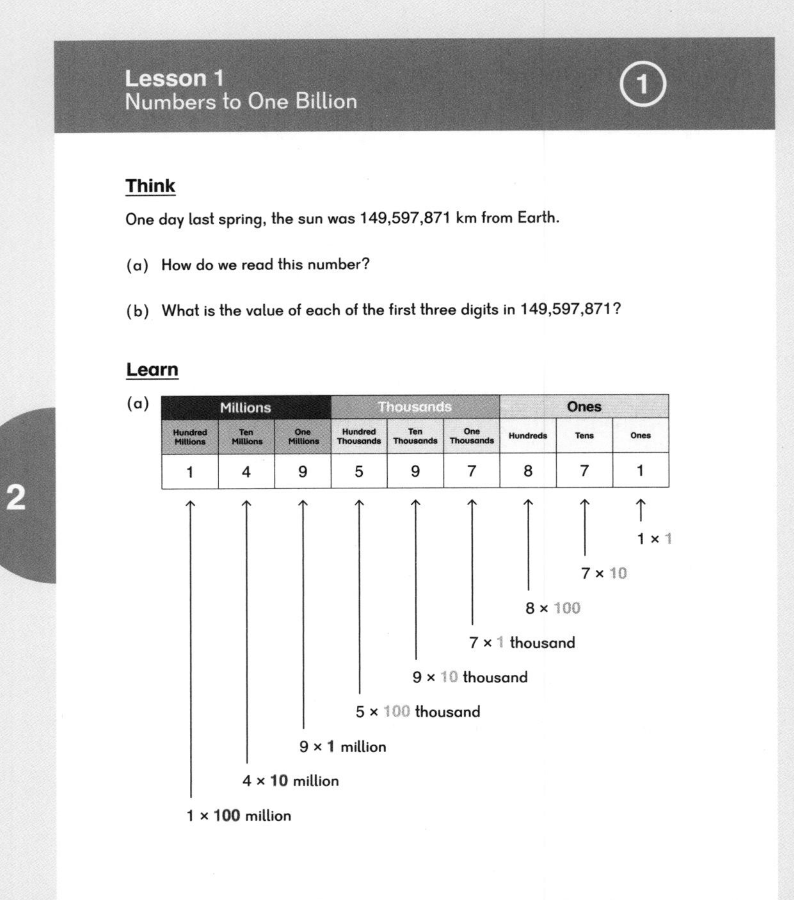

Lesson 1
Numbers to One Billion ①

Think

One day last spring, the sun was 149,597,871 km from Earth.

(a) How do we read this number?

(b) What is the value of each of the first three digits in 149,597,871?

Learn

(a)

Millions			Thousands			Ones		
Hundred Millions	Ten Millions	One Millions	Hundred Thousands	Ten Thousands	One Thousands	Hundreds	Tens	Ones
1	4	9	5	9	7	8	7	1

1 × 1
7 × 10
8 × 100
7 × 1 thousand
9 × 10 thousand
5 × 100 thousand
9 × 1 million
4 × 10 million
1 × 100 million

2 1-1 Numbers to One Billion

Discuss Mei's comment. Ensure that students understand the use of the term "period" to mean three place values starting with the ones.

Have students recall the term "expanded form" and ask them to write the number 149,597,871 in expanded form:

100,000,000 + 40,000,000 + 9,000,000 + 500,000 + 90,000 + 7,000 + 800 + 70 + 1

Ask students to name and write the number that is 1 more than 999, 1 more than 999,999, and 1 more than 999,999,999.

Alex introduces a new place for 1,000 millions, which is one billion. Just as one thousand thousands is one million, one thousand millions is one billion.

Do

❶—❼ Discuss the problems with students as necessary. Most students should be able to solve the problems independently.

❶ (b) Questions like these can be used and asked of any numbers to solidify understanding of place value. Periodically, ask students for the value of a specified digit in a given number.

❸ Because the numbers are large, ensure students are including all of the places when writing each number. In (a) for example, there is no given value for the thousands, hundreds, or ones places so the digits in each of these places will be zeros: 2,650,030.

For students who struggle with large numbers, provide a place-value chart, similar to the one at the top of the textbook page, and have them write the digits in the appropriate places.

3

Every three places is called a **period**. We can place a comma in between each period to make large numbers easier to read.

1 4 9, 5 9 7, 8 7 1

149 million — 597 thousand — 871

One hundred forty-nine million, five hundred ninety-seven thousand, eight hundred seventy-one

(b)

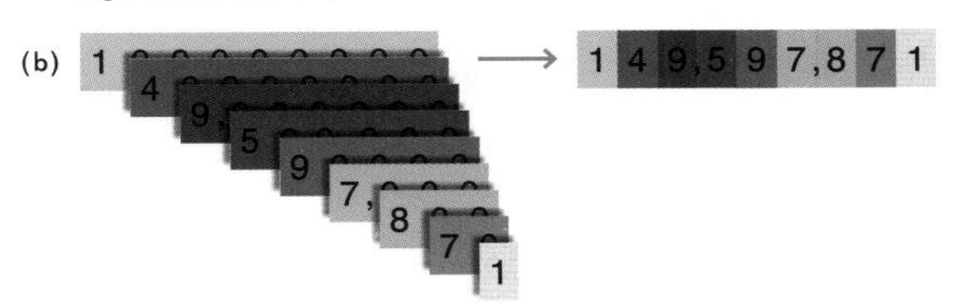

The value of the digit 1 in the hundred millions place is:
1 × 100,000,000 = 100,000,000.

The value of the digit 4 in the ten millions place is:
4 × 10,000,000 = 40,000,000.

The value of the digit 9 in the one millions place is:
9 × 1,000,000 = 9,000,000.

Ten hundred millions is one **billion**.
It is written as 1,000,000,000.

4

Do

❶ (a) Read the number shown on the place-value chart.

Millions			Thousands			Ones		
Hundred Millions	Ten Millions	One Millions	Hundred Thousands	Ten Thousands	One Thousands	Hundreds	Tens	Ones
5	8	3	6	4	2	1	7	9

(b) What are the values of the digits 3, 8, and 5?

3 × 1,000,000 = ▭ 3,000,000

8 × 10,000,000 = ▭ 80,000,000

5 × 100,000,000 = ▭ 500,000,000

❷ Write each number in words.

(a) 25,604,067
(a) Twenty-five million, six hundred four thousand, sixty-seven

(b) 372,805,005
(b) Three hundred seventy-two million, eight hundred five thousand, five

(c) 650,700,802
(c) Six hundred fifty million, seven hundred thousand, eight hundred two

(d) 909,021,014
(d) Nine hundred nine million, twenty one thousand, fourteen

❸ (a) 2,000,000 + 600,000 + 50,000 + 30 = ▭ 2,650,030

(b) 20,000,000 + 500,000 + 50,000 + 700 + 8 = ▭ 20,550,708

(c) 7,000,000 + 465,000 + 652 = ▭ 7,465,652

(d) 48,723,904 = ▭ + 723,000 + 904 — 48,000,000

❹ Ask students additional questions to solidify their understanding of place value.

For example:

- "36,000,000 = ______ hundred thousands?"
- "36,000,000 = ______ ten thousands?"
- "36,000,000 = ______ thousands?"

❻ As hints, ask students:

- "What digit can we look at to determine if a number is odd or even?"
- "What is the value of that digit for an even number? For an odd number?"
- "Can a nine-digit number have a zero in the hundred millions place?"
- "If you want the greatest number possible, which digit would it make sense to start with?"

Activity

▲ Greatest or Least?

Materials: Number Cards (BLM) 0–9 (multiple sets), whiteboards, dry erase markers

Play in groups of up to 4 players. On a whiteboard, players draw a nine-digit place-value chart and one extra box labeled "trash" as shown below.

Hundred Millions	Ten Millions	Millions	Hundred Thousands	Ten Thousands	Thousands	Hundreds	Tens	Ones

Trash

Players take turns drawing a number card and writing the number in different places on their game boards. Once the digit has been written, it cannot be changed. On any turn, players may write the digit in the box labeled "trash." After all players have drawn 10 cards and filled their game boards, the player with the greatest (or least) nine-digit number wins.

★ Challenge: Have students try to make the greatest odd number (or least even number).

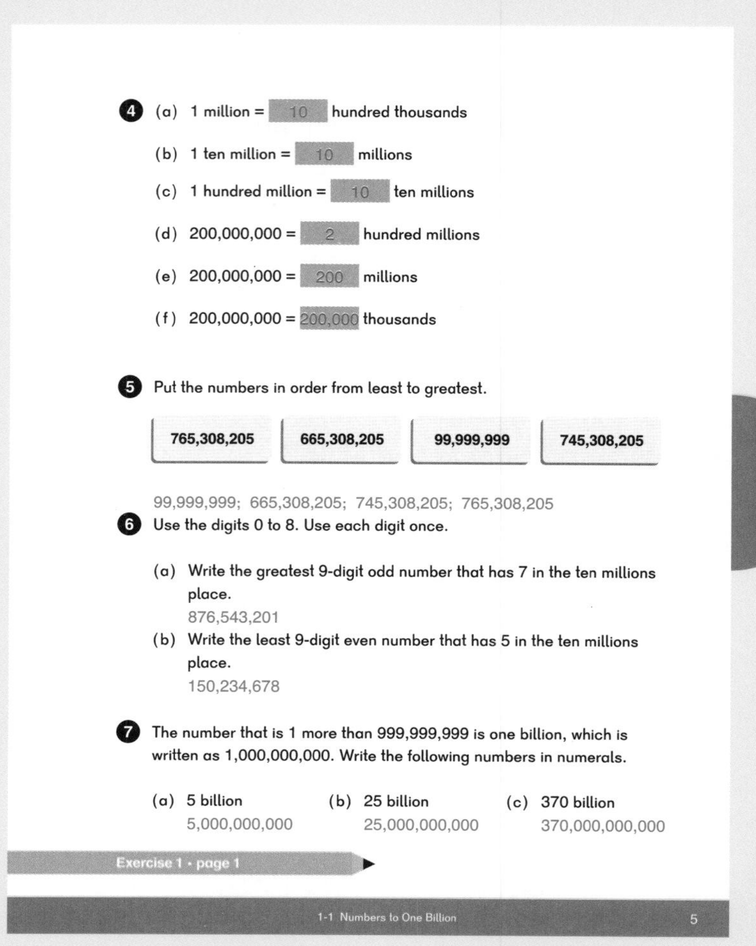

❹ (a) 1 million = 10 hundred thousands

(b) 1 ten million = 10 millions

(c) 1 hundred million = 10 ten millions

(d) 200,000,000 = 2 hundred millions

(e) 200,000,000 = 200 millions

(f) 200,000,000 = 200,000 thousands

❺ Put the numbers in order from least to greatest.

765,308,205 | 665,308,205 | 99,999,999 | 745,308,205

99,999,999; 665,308,205; 745,308,205; 765,308,205

❻ Use the digits 0 to 8. Use each digit once.

(a) Write the greatest 9-digit odd number that has 7 in the ten millions place.
876,543,201

(b) Write the least 9-digit even number that has 5 in the ten millions place.
150,234,678

❼ The number that is 1 more than 999,999,999 is one billion, which is written as 1,000,000,000. Write the following numbers in numerals.

(a) 5 billion
5,000,000,000

(b) 25 billion
25,000,000,000

(c) 370 billion
370,000,000,000

Exercise 1 • page 1

1-1 Numbers to One Billion 5

5

◀ Exercise 1 • page 1

Objectives

- Multiply a whole number by 10, 100, and 1,000.
- Understand the relative size of the digits in each position on a place-value chart.

Think

Pose the **Think** problems and have students solve them independently.

Discuss the strategies students used to find their answers.

Learn

Discuss the examples shown in **Learn** and have students compare their own answers with the ones shown in the textbook.

Ask students, “What patterns do you see in the pictures of the place-value discs?”

When a number is multiplied by 10, the value of each digit is multiplied by 10:

- 200 × 10 = 2,000
- 30 × 10 = 300
- 1 × 10 = 10

This multiplication results in each digit moving one place to the left on a place-value chart. Students can see why we append a zero when a number is multiplied by 10.

Since 100 = 10 × 10, students should see that 1,000 = 10 × 100, and that 1,000 = 10 × 10 × 10. When a number is multiplied by 100, each digit moves two places to the left and 2 zeros are appended. When a number is multiplied by 1,000, each digit moves 3 places to the left and so 3 zeros are appended.

6

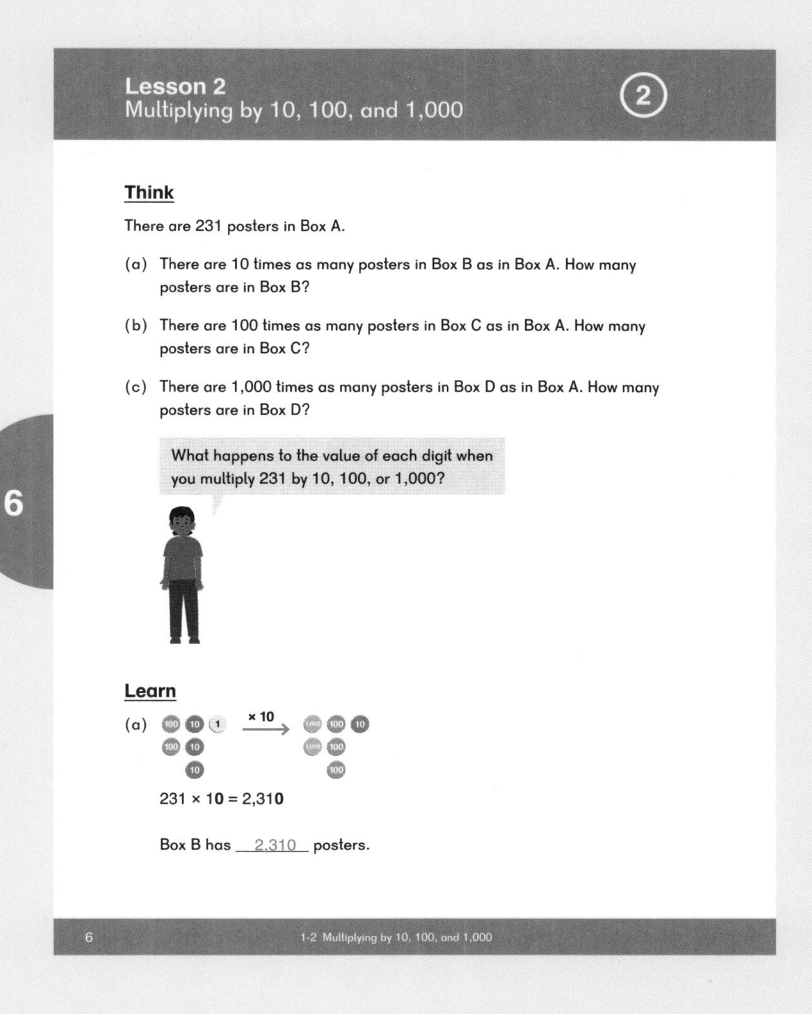

Lesson 2
Multiplying by 10, 100, and 1,000 ②

Think

There are 231 posters in Box A.

(a) There are 10 times as many posters in Box B as in Box A. How many posters are in Box B?

(b) There are 100 times as many posters in Box C as in Box A. How many posters are in Box C?

(c) There are 1,000 times as many posters in Box D as in Box A. How many posters are in Box D?

Learn

(a)

231 × 10 = 2,310

Box B has 2,310 posters.

6 1-2 Multiplying by 10, 100, and 1,000

Ask students:

- “What number is 231 tens?” (2,310)
- “What number is 231 hundreds?” (23,100)
- “231 hundreds has the same value as 231 × 100, so 231 thousands has the same value as what number multiplied by what number?” (231 × 1,000)
- “What is 231 × 100 × 100? Is that the same as asking, ‘What is the value of 23,100 hundreds?’” (2,310,000, yes)

Discuss Sofia's comments.

The answer to both of Dion's questions is 2,310,000. Students should note the number of zeros in 23,100 × 100 and how that relates to the number of zeros in the product.

Do

❶—❷ Discuss the problems and given place-value representations with students.

❶ If students need additional help, encourage them to think about these numbers as numbers of tens, hundreds, or thousands.

(a) 24 × 10 = 24 tens = 240
(b) 24 × 100 = 24 hundreds = 2,400
(c) 24 × 1,000 = 24 thousands = 24,000

❷ Encourage students to study the table. Ask students who are struggling which row of the table they should start on, how many rows they move down, and which row they would end on. For example, for 328 × 10, they start on the first row and move one place down, ending on the second row. Since they only moved one row down, each digit shifted only one place to the left, so they need to append one zero to 328 (3,280).

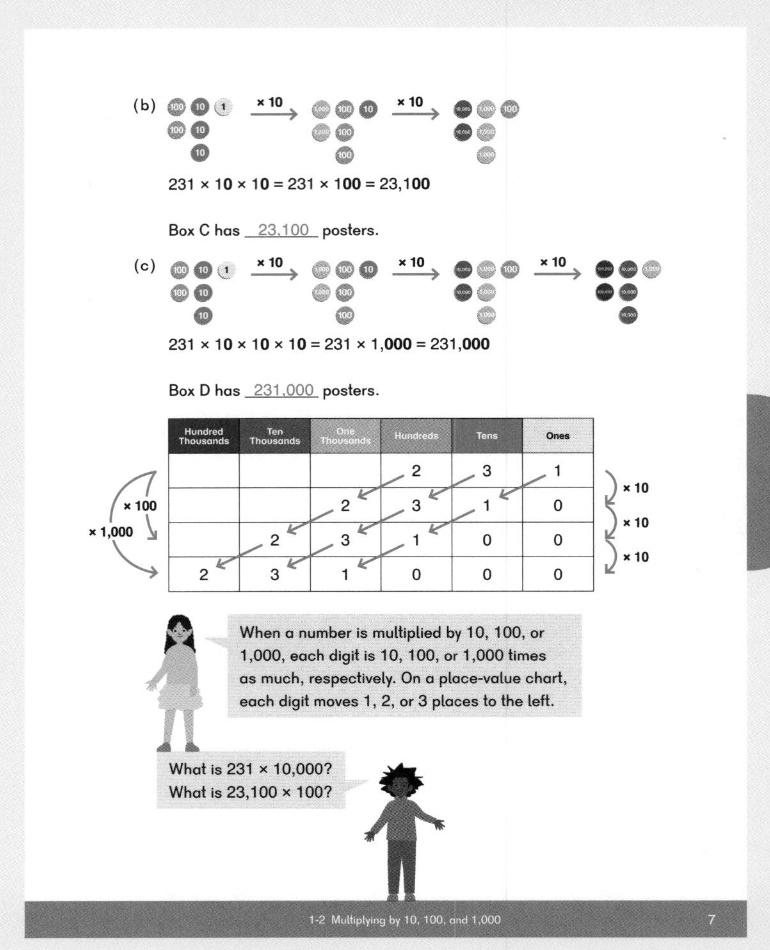

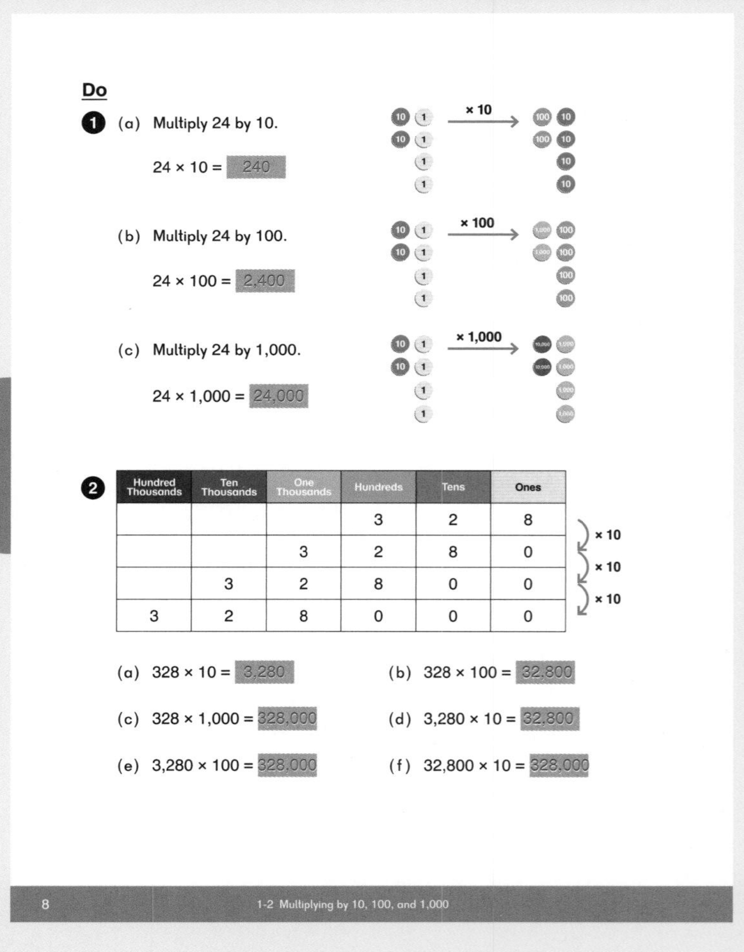

❸—❻ Students should be able to solve these problems independently.

❸ Ask students, "What patterns do you notice in these problems?"

❹ At this point, most students will simply append zeros according to the number of zeros in the factors 10, 100, or 1,000. For example, in (h), students will most likely append three zeros to 100,000 to get the answer 100,000,000.

Activity

▲ Mental Multiplication Duel

Materials: Number Cards (BLM) 0–9 (multiple sets), Mental Multiplication Duel Scoring Sheet (BLM)

Players take turns drawing a card and filling in the nine boxes with the numbers on the card or die. Once all of their nine boxes are filled in, players complete the multiplication equations and add the three quotients together.

The player with the greatest sum is the winner.

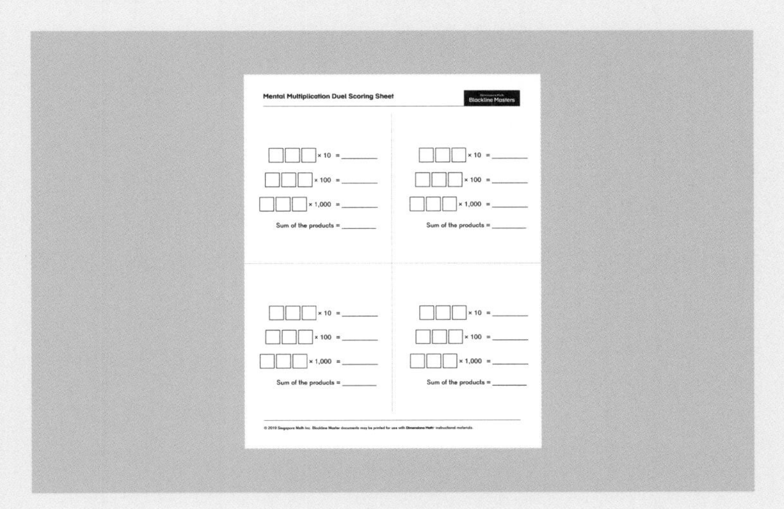
Mental Multiplication Duel Scoring Sheet

Blackline Masters

□□□ × 10 = ____
□□□ × 100 = ____
□□□ × 1,000 = ____
Sum of the products = ____

□□□ × 10 = ____
□□□ × 100 = ____
□□□ × 1,000 = ____
Sum of the products = ____

□□□ × 10 = ____
□□□ × 100 = ____
□□□ × 1,000 = ____
Sum of the products = ____

□□□ × 10 = ____
□□□ × 100 = ____
□□□ × 1,000 = ____
Sum of the products = ____

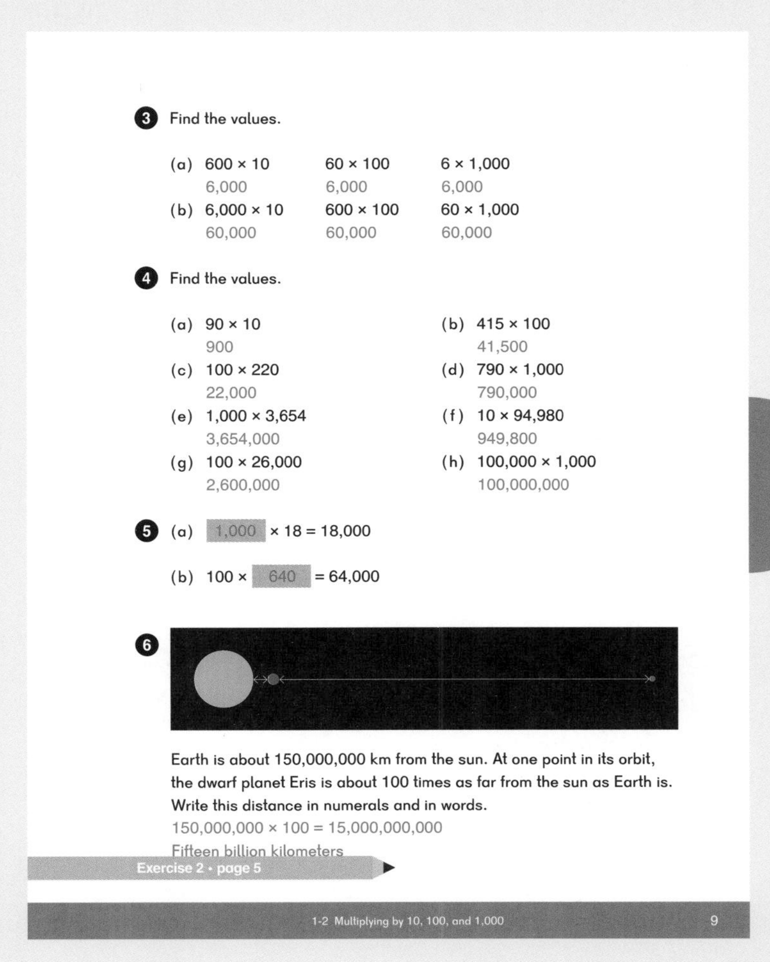
❸ Find the values.

(a) 600 × 10 — 6,000 | 60 × 100 — 6,000 | 6 × 1,000 — 6,000

(b) 6,000 × 10 — 60,000 | 600 × 100 — 60,000 | 60 × 1,000 — 60,000

❹ Find the values.

(a) 90 × 10 — 900

(b) 415 × 100 — 41,500

(c) 100 × 220 — 22,000

(d) 790 × 1,000 — 790,000

(e) 1,000 × 3,654 — 3,654,000

(f) 10 × 94,980 — 949,800

(g) 100 × 26,000 — 2,600,000

(h) 100,000 × 1,000 — 100,000,000

❺ (a) 1,000 × 18 = 18,000

(b) 100 × 640 = 64,000

❻ Earth is about 150,000,000 km from the sun. At one point in its orbit, the dwarf planet Eris is about 100 times as far from the sun as Earth is. Write this distance in numerals and in words.

150,000,000 × 100 = 15,000,000,000

Fifteen billion kilometers

Exercise 2 • page 5

1-2 Multiplying by 10, 100, and 1,000 9

9

Exercise 2 • page 5

Objective

- Divide a whole number by 10, 100, and 1,000.

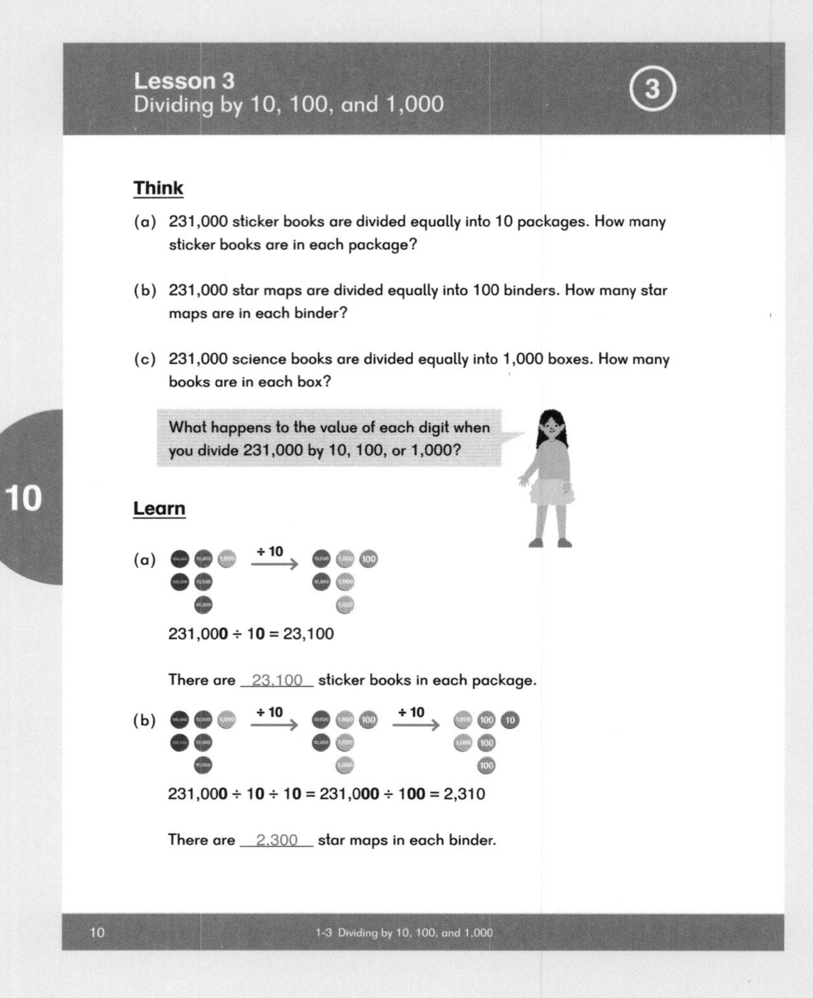

Lesson 3
Dividing by 10, 100, and 1,000

3

Think

(a) 231,000 sticker books are divided equally into 10 packages. How many sticker books are in each package?

(b) 231,000 star maps are divided equally into 100 binders. How many star maps are in each binder?

(c) 231,000 science books are divided equally into 1,000 boxes. How many books are in each box?

Learn

(a) ÷ 10

231,000 ÷ 10 = 23,100

There are 23,100 sticker books in each package.

(b) ÷ 10 ÷ 10

231,000 ÷ 10 ÷ 10 = 231,000 ÷ 100 = 2,310

There are 2,300 star maps in each binder.

10 1-3 Dividing by 10, 100, and 1,000

Think

Pose the **Think** problems and have students solve them independently.

Discuss the strategies students used to find their answers.

Learn

Discuss the examples shown in **Learn** and have students compare their own answers with the ones shown in the textbook.

Ask students, "What patterns do you see in the pictures of the discs?"

(a) Students should see that the value of each disc is $\frac{1}{10}$ of its previous value.

(c) When a number is divided by 10, the value of each digit is divided by 10.

For example:

- $200{,}000 \div 10 = 20{,}000$
- $30{,}000 \div 10 = 3{,}000$
- $1{,}000 \div 10 = 100$

This division results in each digit moving one place to the right on a place-value chart. Students can see that the 0 in the ones place is dropped.

Ask students, "How many places to the right on a place-value chart will each digit move when the number is divided by 100 or 1,000?"

Ask students why Alex can simplify by crossing off the same number of zeros in the numerator and denominator of his fraction expression.

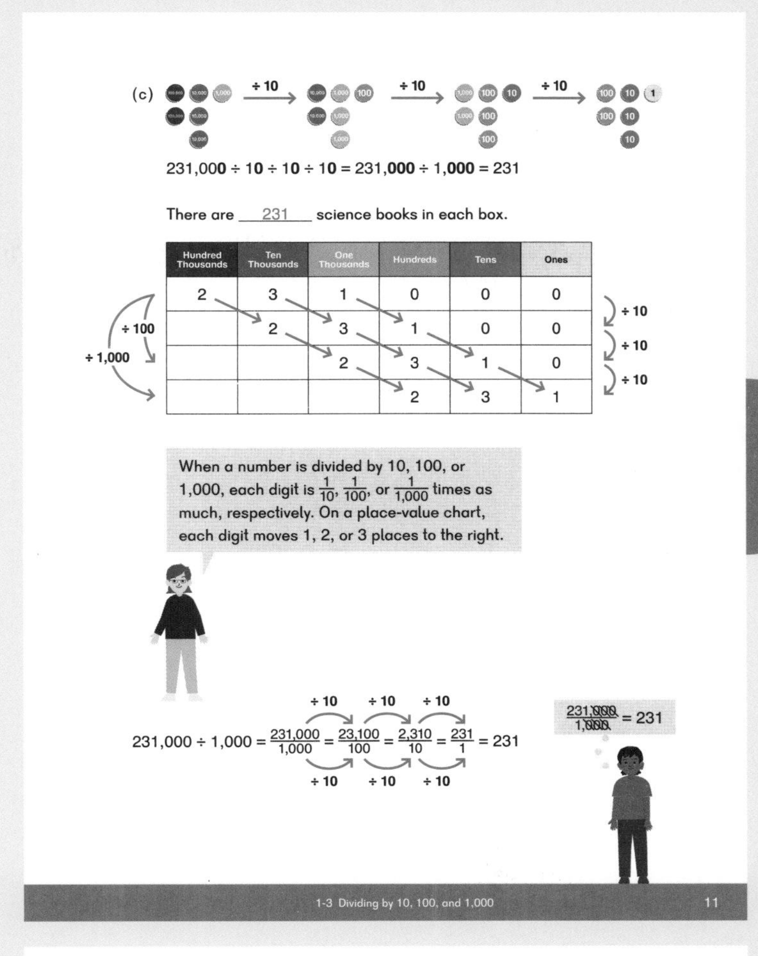

(c) ÷ 10 ÷ 10 ÷ 10

$231{,}000 \div 10 \div 10 \div 10 = 231{,}000 \div 1{,}000 = 231$

There are 231 science books in each box.

Hundred Thousands	Ten Thousands	One Thousands	Hundreds	Tens	Ones
2	3	1	0	0	0
	2	3	1	0	0
		2	3	1	0
			2	3	1

When a number is divided by 10, 100, or 1,000, each digit is $\frac{1}{10}$, $\frac{1}{100}$, or $\frac{1}{1{,}000}$ times as much, respectively. On a place-value chart, each digit moves 1, 2, or 3 places to the right.

$231{,}000 \div 1{,}000 = \frac{231{,}000}{1{,}000} = \frac{23{,}100}{100} = \frac{2{,}310}{10} = \frac{231}{1} = 231$

Do

❶—❷ Discuss the problems and place-value representations with students.

❷ Students should see from the place-value chart that when we divide by 100, we divide by 10 and then by 10 again.

When we divide by 1,000, we divide by 10 three times.

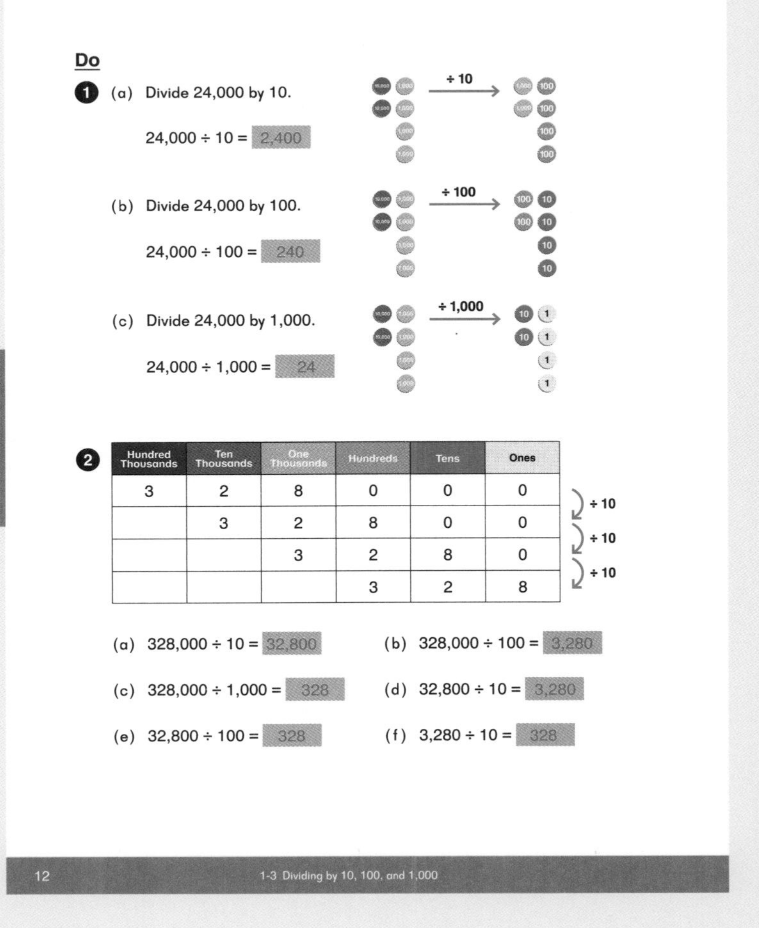

Do

❶ (a) Divide 24,000 by 10.

$24{,}000 \div 10 =$ 2,400

(b) Divide 24,000 by 100.

$24{,}000 \div 100 =$ 240

(c) Divide 24,000 by 1,000.

$24{,}000 \div 1{,}000 =$ 24

❷

Hundred Thousands	Ten Thousands	One Thousands	Hundreds	Tens	Ones
3	2	8	0	0	0
	3	2	8	0	0
		3	2	8	0
			3	2	8

(a) $328{,}000 \div 10 =$ 32,800 (b) $328{,}000 \div 100 =$ 3,280

(c) $328{,}000 \div 1{,}000 =$ 328 (d) $32{,}800 \div 10 =$ 3,280

(e) $32{,}800 \div 100 =$ 328 (f) $3{,}280 \div 10 =$ 328

❸—❼ Students should be able to solve these problems independently.

❸ Ask students, "What patterns do you notice in these problems? Look at both the rows and the columns."

❺ At this point, most students will simply be crossing off the same number of zeros in the divisor and the dividend and finding the resulting value, similar to Dion's and Mei's thoughts in ❹.

(a) Ask students:

- "What fraction of 36,000 is 3,600?" ($\frac{1}{10}$)
- "How many 3,600s make 36,000?" (10)

❼ 57,900,000,000 is read as "fifty-seven billion, nine hundred million."

Activity

▲ Mental Division Duel

Materials: Number Cards (BLM) 0–9 (multiple sets), Mental Division Duel Scoring Sheet (BLM)

Players take turns drawing a card and filling in the nine boxes with the numbers on the card. Once all of their nine boxes are filled in, players complete the division equations and add the three quotients together.

The player with the least sum is the winner.

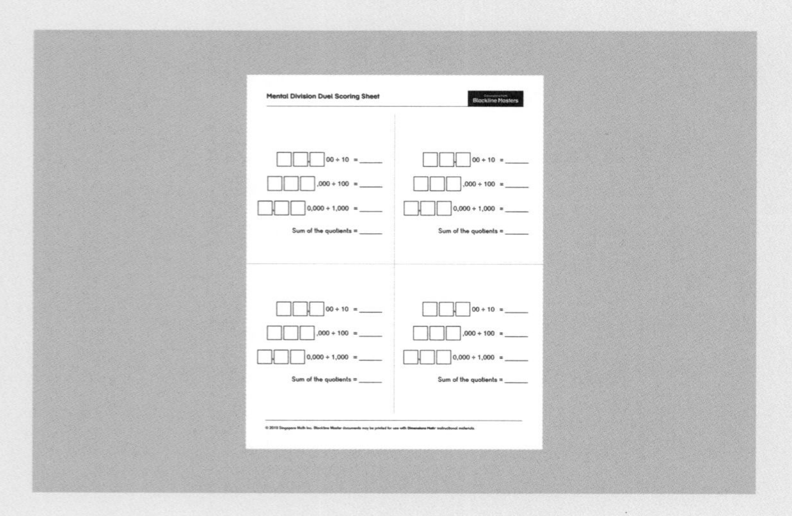
Mental Division Duel Scoring Sheet

Blackline Masters

☐☐☐00 ÷ 10 = ____
☐☐☐,000 ÷ 100 = ____
☐☐☐0,000 ÷ 1,000 = ____
Sum of the quotients = ____

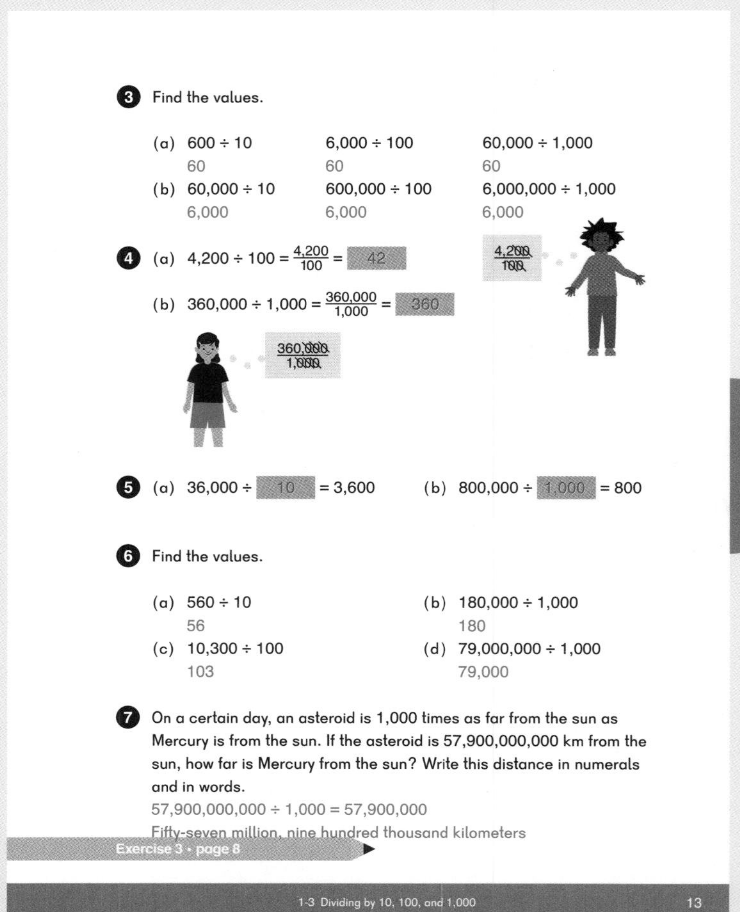
❸ Find the values.

(a) 600 ÷ 10 — 60; 6,000 ÷ 100 — 60; 60,000 ÷ 1,000 — 60

(b) 60,000 ÷ 10 — 6,000; 600,000 ÷ 100 — 6,000; 6,000,000 ÷ 1,000 — 6,000

❹ (a) 4,200 ÷ 100 = $\frac{4,200}{100}$ = 42

(b) 360,000 ÷ 1,000 = $\frac{360,000}{1,000}$ = 360

❺ (a) 36,000 ÷ 10 = 3,600 (b) 800,000 ÷ 1,000 = 800

❻ Find the values.

(a) 560 ÷ 10 — 56

(b) 180,000 ÷ 1,000 — 180

(c) 10,300 ÷ 100 — 103

(d) 79,000,000 ÷ 1,000 — 79,000

❼ On a certain day, an asteroid is 1,000 times as far from the sun as Mercury is from the sun. If the asteroid is 57,900,000,000 km from the sun, how far is Mercury from the sun? Write this distance in numerals and in words.

57,900,000,000 ÷ 1,000 = 57,900,000

Fifty-seven million, nine hundred thousand kilometers

Exercise 3 • page 8

13

Exercise 3 • page 8

Objective

- Multiply a whole number by a multiple of 10, 100, and 1,000.

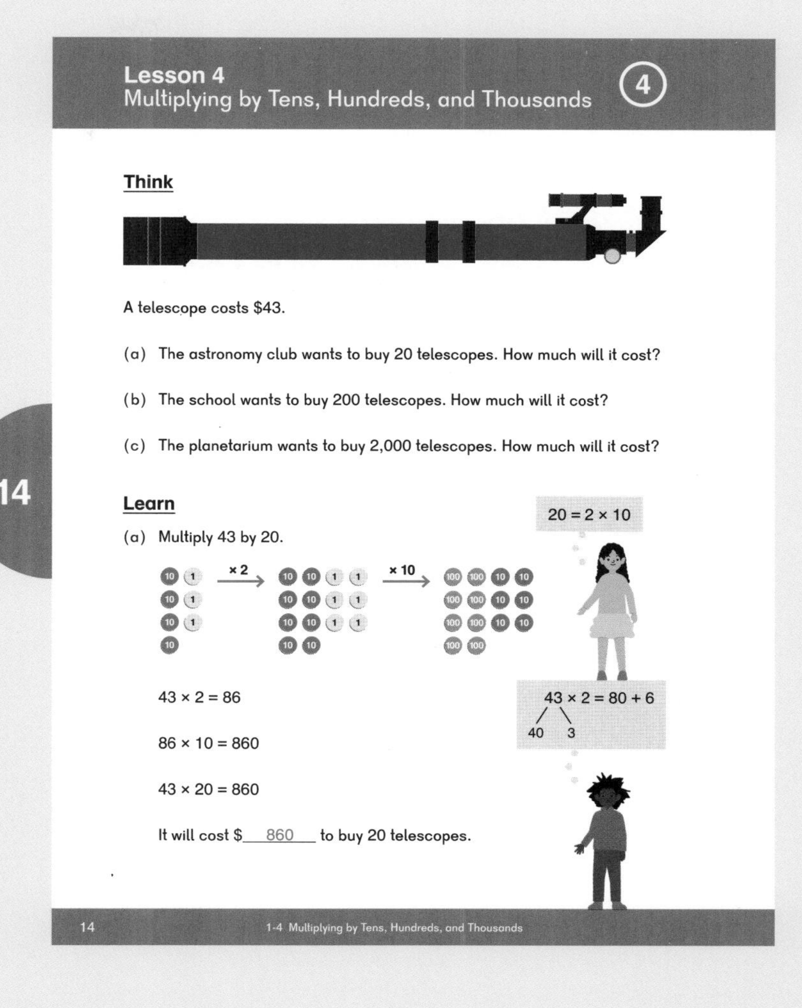

Lesson 4
Multiplying by Tens, Hundreds, and Thousands (4)

Think

A telescope costs $43.

(a) The astronomy club wants to buy 20 telescopes. How much will it cost?

(b) The school wants to buy 200 telescopes. How much will it cost?

(c) The planetarium wants to buy 2,000 telescopes. How much will it cost?

Learn

(a) Multiply 43 by 20.

$20 = 2 \times 10$

$43 \times 2 = 80 + 6$

$43 \times 2 = 86$

$86 \times 10 = 860$

$43 \times 20 = 860$

It will cost $ 860 to buy 20 telescopes.

14 1-4 Multiplying by Tens, Hundreds, and Thousands

14

Think

Pose the **Think** problems and have students solve them independently.

Discuss the strategies students used to find their answers.

Learn

Discuss the examples shown in **Learn** and have students compare their answers with the ones shown in the textbook.

Ask students, "What do the discs show?"

All three problems use the same strategy: multiply 43 by 2, and then multiply the product by 10, 100, or 1,000.

(a) Sofia and Dion think about 43×20 as 43×2 tens.

However, if they are calculating 430×2 mentally, they would likely do it by thinking of the answer to 43×2, so this is essentially the same strategy.

(b) 43 × 2 hundreds = 86 hundreds
86 hundreds = 8,600

(c) 43 × 2 thousands = 86 thousands
86 thousands = 86,000

In each of these problems, students find the value of 43 × 2 and then append the appropriate number of zeros to the product. From this, students should see that they can take off trailing zeros, do the computation (43 × 2), and append the correct number of zeros back at the end. The equations in **Learn** show why this works.

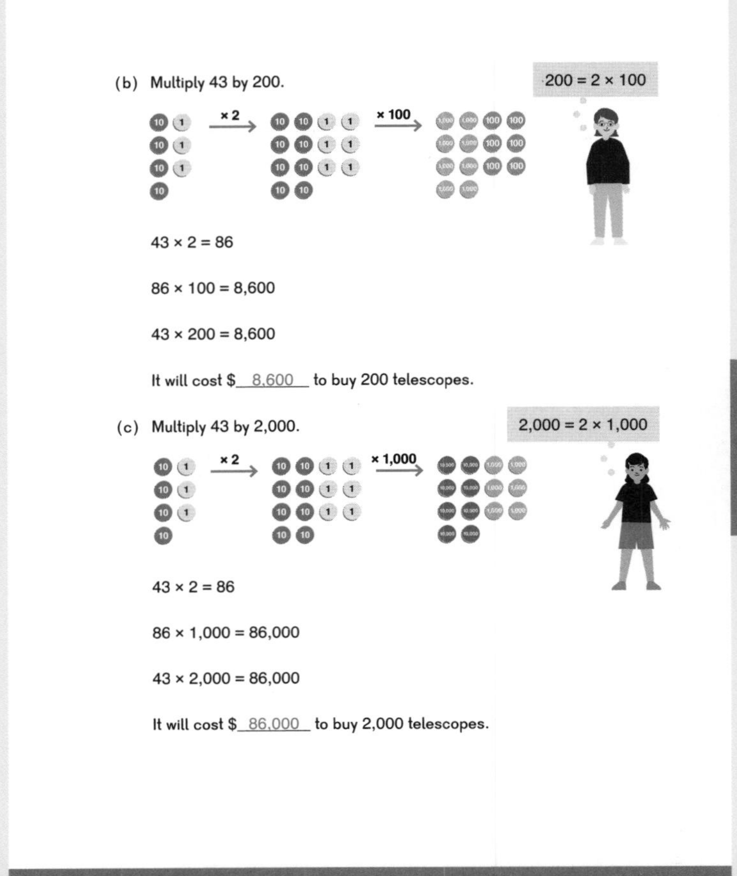

(b) Multiply 43 by 200.

200 = 2 × 100

43 × 2 = 86

86 × 100 = 8,600

43 × 200 = 8,600

It will cost $ 8,600 to buy 200 telescopes.

(c) Multiply 43 by 2,000.

2,000 = 2 × 1,000

43 × 2 = 86

86 × 1,000 = 86,000

43 × 2,000 = 86,000

It will cost $ 86,000 to buy 2,000 telescopes.

1-4 Multiplying by Tens, Hundreds, and Thousands 15

15

Do

❶–❷ Discuss the problems and steps in the calculations shown with students.

❶ Alex prompts students to compute 27 × 3 mentally.

Ask students to look for patterns in problems (a)–(c). They should notice that in each problem we are multiplying the numbers without the trailing zeros first. In all three instances, it is
27 × 3. Then we multiply the result of 81 by 10, 100, and 1,000. Students can see that this is the same as taking off trailing zeros, multiplying the numbers, and then appending back the trailing zeros.

(a) 27 × 30 is the same as 27 × 3 tens.

27 × 3 is 81, so the answer is 81 tens.

(b) Ask students, “If the answer to 27 × 3 is 81, then what is the answer to 27 × 3 hundreds?”

(c) Similarly, 27 × 3,000 is 27 × 3 thousands.

The products in these problems differ by the number of trailing zeros.

❷ Sofia knows that 400 = 4 × 100 and 800 = 8 × 100. She multiplies (4 × 8) × (100 × 100) so she can easily calculate 32 × 10,000.

16

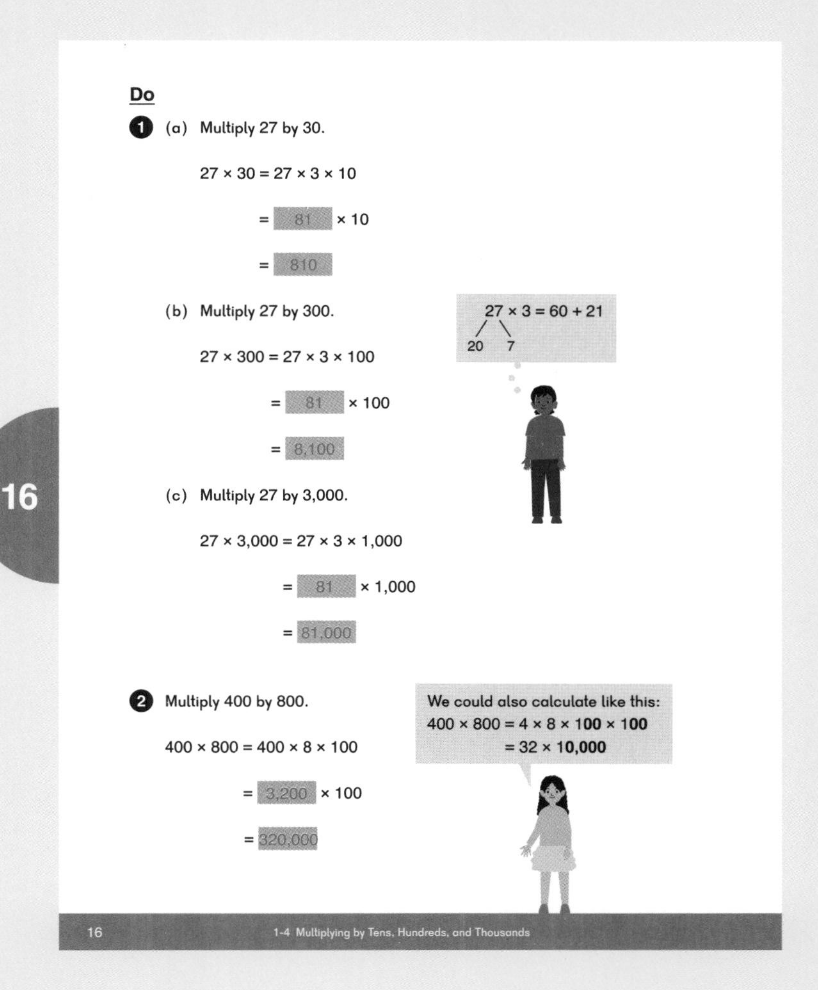

Do

❶ (a) Multiply 27 by 30.

27 × 30 = 27 × 3 × 10
= 81 × 10
= 810

(b) Multiply 27 by 300.

27 × 300 = 27 × 3 × 100
= 81 × 100
= 8,100

(c) Multiply 27 by 3,000.

27 × 3,000 = 27 × 3 × 1,000
= 81 × 1,000
= 81,000

27 × 3 = 60 + 21
20 7

❷ Multiply 400 by 800.

400 × 800 = 400 × 8 × 100
= 3,200 × 100
= 320,000

We could also calculate like this:
400 × 800 = 4 × 8 × **100 × 100**
= 32 × **10,000**

16 1-4 Multiplying by Tens, Hundreds, and Thousands

❸ Dion uses a strategy similar to Sofia's strategy in ❷.

5,000 × 4,000 can be thought of as
5 × 4 × 1,000 × 1,000 = 20 × 1,000 × 1,000.

Students can see this calculation by thinking of the result as 20 thousand thousands.

Students may think to check their answers by counting zeros in both products. Ensure that they realize that they must append the same number of zeros they take out. In this case, the product has 7 trailing zeros, but the two factors have only 6 trailing zeros. One zero comes from multiplying 5 by 4.

❹—❻ Students should be able to solve these problems independently.

❹ Ask students, "How are the problems in each row related?"

❺ At this point, most students will simply be removing trailing zeros from both factors, multiplying the factors, then appending the same number of zeros back at the end. From the previous part of the lesson, they should understand why this works.

(b) As in ❸, ensure students see that 5 × 100 × 4 × 10 results in 5 × 4 × 100 × 10, which is 20 × 1,000.

Students will need to think about the number of zeros in their final answers.

Exercise 4 • page 11

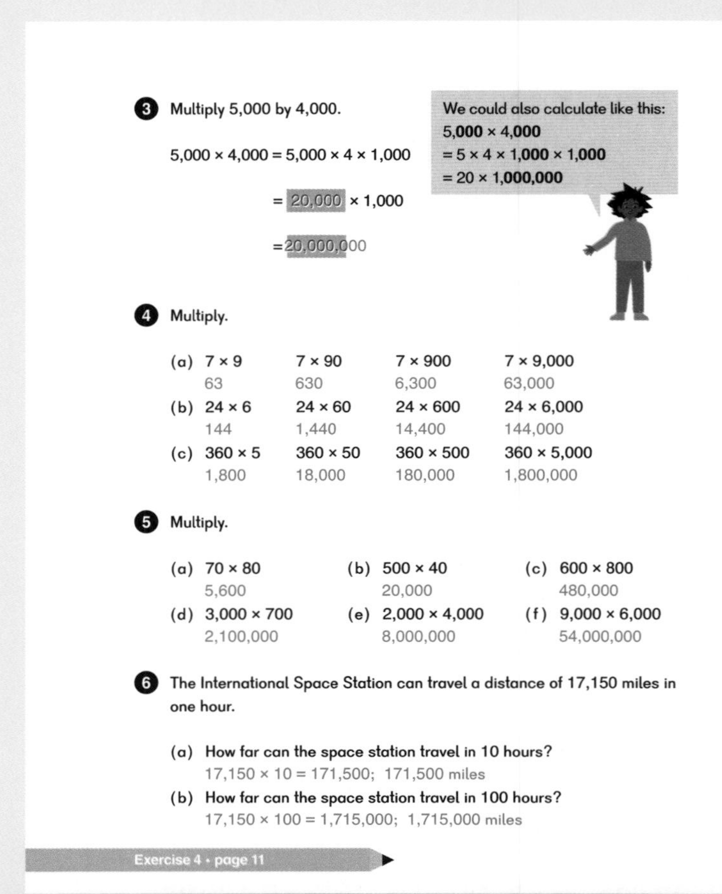

❸ Multiply 5,000 by 4,000.

5,000 × 4,000 = 5,000 × 4 × 1,000
= 20,000 × 1,000
= 20,000,000

We could also calculate like this:
5,000 × 4,000
= 5 × 4 × **1,000 × 1,000**
= 20 × **1,000,000**

❹ Multiply.

(a) 7 × 9 — 63; 7 × 90 — 630; 7 × 900 — 6,300; 7 × 9,000 — 63,000
(b) 24 × 6 — 144; 24 × 60 — 1,440; 24 × 600 — 14,400; 24 × 6,000 — 144,000
(c) 360 × 5 — 1,800; 360 × 50 — 18,000; 360 × 500 — 180,000; 360 × 5,000 — 1,800,000

❺ Multiply.

(a) 70 × 80 — 5,600
(b) 500 × 40 — 20,000
(c) 600 × 800 — 480,000
(d) 3,000 × 700 — 2,100,000
(e) 2,000 × 4,000 — 8,000,000
(f) 9,000 × 6,000 — 54,000,000

❻ The International Space Station can travel a distance of 17,150 miles in one hour.

(a) How far can the space station travel in 10 hours?
17,150 × 10 = 171,500; 171,500 miles
(b) How far can the space station travel in 100 hours?
17,150 × 100 = 1,715,000; 1,715,000 miles

Exercise 4 • page 11

1-4 Multiplying by Tens, Hundreds, and Thousands 17

17

Objective

- Divide a whole number by a multiple of 10, 100, and 1,000.

Think

Pose the **Think** problems and have students solve them independently.

Learn

Discuss the examples shown in **Learn** and have students compare their own answers with the ones shown in the textbook.

(a) Since students know how to divide by ten, they can divide 86,000 by 10 first, and then by 2. This is the same as dividing by 20.

Emma reminds students that division problems can be written as fractions, and we can simplify the fractions.

(b) Similar to (a), since 200 is the same as 100 × 2, we can divide by 200 by first dividing 86,000 by 100 and then dividing that result, 860, by 2.

As fractions can be understood as division, Mei shows how to use equivalent fractions to solve the problem.

(c) Since students also know how to divide by 1,000, we can divide 86,000 by 1,000 first, and then by 2.

Alex also thinks about simplifying fractions. When dividing by 1,000, he can cross off three zeros in the numerator and denominator.

18

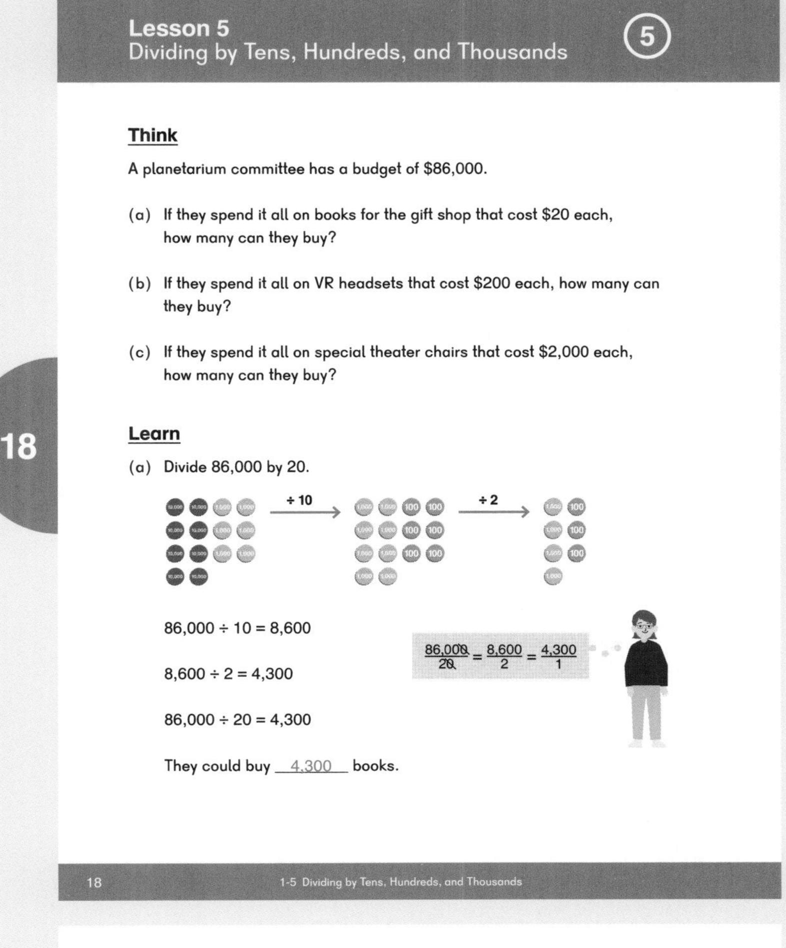

Lesson 5
Dividing by Tens, Hundreds, and Thousands (5)

Think

A planetarium committee has a budget of $86,000.

(a) If they spend it all on books for the gift shop that cost $20 each, how many can they buy?

(b) If they spend it all on VR headsets that cost $200 each, how many can they buy?

(c) If they spend it all on special theater chairs that cost $2,000 each, how many can they buy?

Learn

(a) Divide 86,000 by 20.

$86,000 \div 10 = 8,600$

$8,600 \div 2 = 4,300$

$86,000 \div 20 = 4,300$

They could buy 4,300 books.

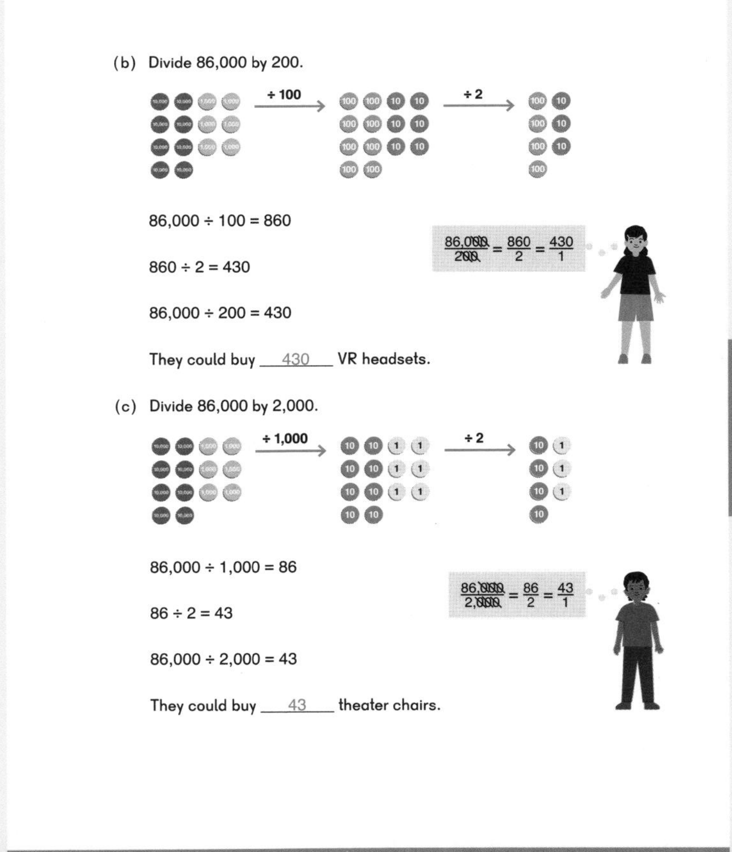

(b) Divide 86,000 by 200.

$86,000 \div 100 = 860$

$860 \div 2 = 430$

$86,000 \div 200 = 430$

They could buy 430 VR headsets.

(c) Divide 86,000 by 2,000.

$86,000 \div 1,000 = 86$

$86 \div 2 = 43$

$86,000 \div 2,000 = 43$

They could buy 43 theater chairs.

19

Do

❶—❸ Discuss the problems and steps in the calculations shown with students.

❶ (a) Point out to students that 12,000 ÷ 10 ÷ 3 means to first divide by 10, then divide that result by 3.

Sofia, Dion, and Emma calculate the first part of each expression by thinking about equivalent fractions. Crossing off the same number of zeros in the numerator and denominator has the same effect as dividing 12,000 by 10, 100, or 1,000.

❸ Mei splits 960 into 900 and 60 so she can easily divide by 3: 900 ÷ 3 = 300 and 60 ÷ 3 = 20.

960 ÷ 3 = 300 + 20 = 320

❹—❻ Students should be able to solve these problems independently.

❹ Ask students, "How are the problems in each row related?"

❺ At this point, most students will simply be crossing off the same number of trailing zeros in the divisor and the dividend, and then finding the quotient. They should understand why this works from the previous part of this lesson.

Example:

(e)

640,~~000~~ ÷ 4,~~000~~ = 640 ÷ 4

400   240

640 ÷ 4 = 100 + 60 = 160

Exercise 5 • page 14

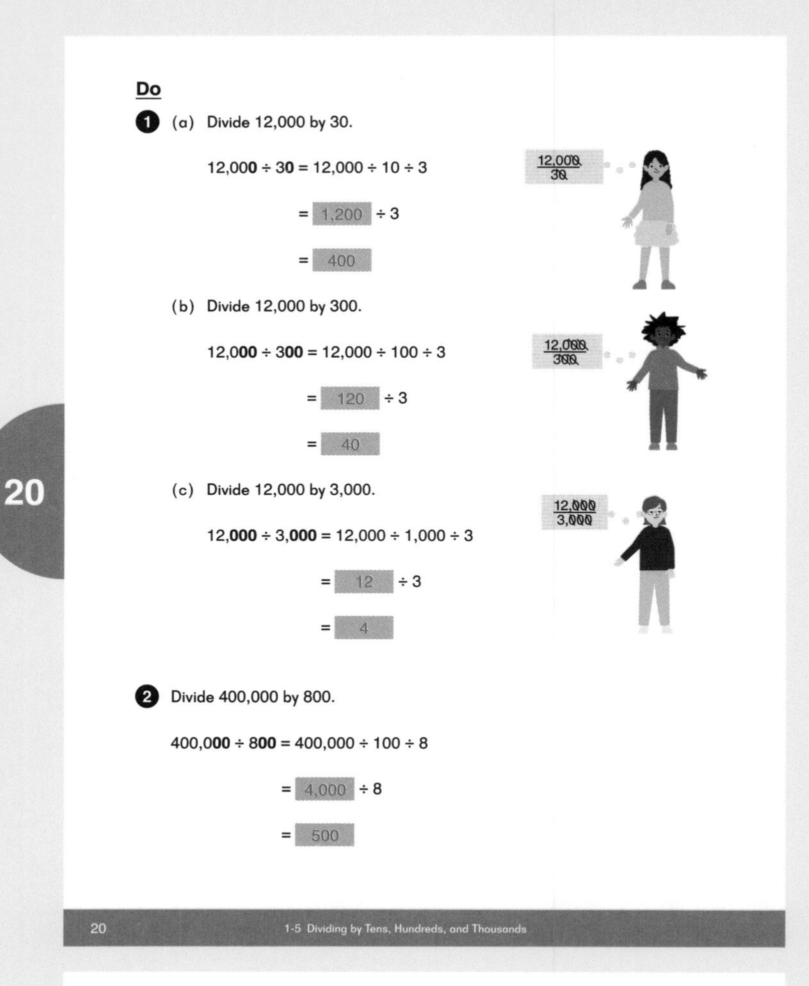

Do

❶ (a) Divide 12,000 by 30.

12,000 ÷ 30 = 12,000 ÷ 10 ÷ 3

= 1,200 ÷ 3

= 400

(b) Divide 12,000 by 300.

12,000 ÷ 300 = 12,000 ÷ 100 ÷ 3

= 120 ÷ 3

= 40

(c) Divide 12,000 by 3,000.

12,000 ÷ 3,000 = 12,000 ÷ 1,000 ÷ 3

= 12 ÷ 3

= 4

❷ Divide 400,000 by 800.

400,000 ÷ 800 = 400,000 ÷ 100 ÷ 8

= 4,000 ÷ 8

= 500

20 1-5 Dividing by Tens, Hundreds, and Thousands

20

❸ Divide 960,000 by 3,000.

960,000 ÷ 3,000 = 960,000 ÷ 1,000 ÷ 3

= 960 ÷ 3

= 320

❹ Divide.

(a) 56 ÷ 8 — 7; 560 ÷ 80 — 7; 56,000 ÷ 8,000 — 7; 56,000 ÷ 800 — 70

(b) 40 ÷ 5 — 8; 400 ÷ 50 — 8; 40,000 ÷ 50 — 800; 400,000 ÷ 500 — 800

❺ Divide.

(a) 240 ÷ 40 — 6
(b) 900 ÷ 90 — 10
(c) 4,800 ÷ 80 — 60
(d) 49,000 ÷ 700 — 70
(e) 640,000 ÷ 4,000 — 160
(f) 4,500,000 ÷ 9,000 — 500

❻ A spacecraft traveling to Mars can travel up to 1,600,000 km in 100 hours. How far can it travel in 1 hour?

1,600,000 ÷ 100 = 16,000

16,000 km

Exercise 5 • page 14

1-5 Dividing by Tens, Hundreds, and Thousands 21

21

Objective

- Practice concepts from the chapter.

Have students complete the practice in the textbook. They will continue to apply place-value concepts to calculations with larger numbers in the next chapter.

❷ (b) Titan: One million, two hundred twenty-one thousand, eight hundred thirty
Phoebe: Twelve million, nine hundred fifty-two thousand
Rhea: Five hundred twenty-seven thousand, forty
Hyperion: One million, four hundred eighty-one thousand, one hundred
Iapetus: Three million, five hundred sixty-one thousand, three hundred

Activity

★ Race to 1 Billion

Materials: Two ten-sided dice, Race to 1 Billion Cards (BLM)

On each turn, players roll the two dice and draw a card. They multiply the numbers on the dice together, then multiply that product by the number on the card. Players then write down the final product, which represents their score. On each subsequent turn, players add their products to their running totals. The first player to reach 1 billion is the winner.

Example play:

$3 \times 7 = 21$
$21 \times 10,000 = 210,000$

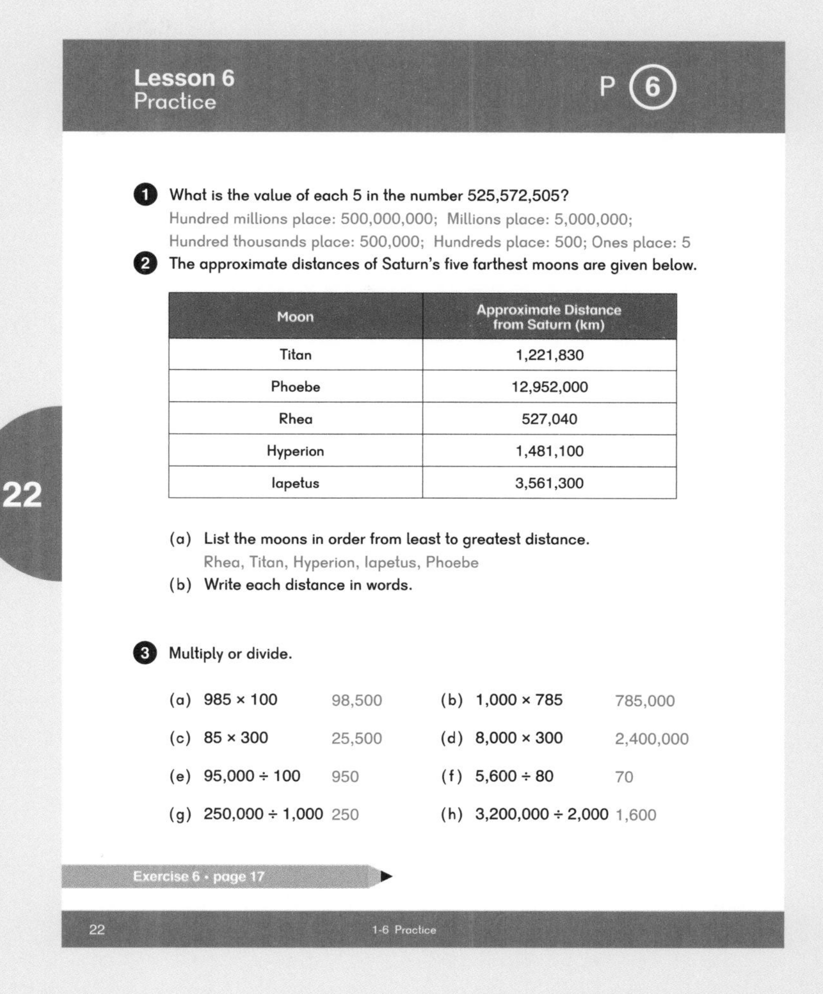

Lesson 6
Practice
P 6

❶ What is the value of each 5 in the number 525,572,505?
Hundred millions place: 500,000,000; Millions place: 5,000,000;
Hundred thousands place: 500,000; Hundreds place: 500; Ones place: 5

❷ The approximate distances of Saturn's five farthest moons are given below.

Moon	Approximate Distance from Saturn (km)
Titan	1,221,830
Phoebe	12,952,000
Rhea	527,040
Hyperion	1,481,100
Iapetus	3,561,300

(a) List the moons in order from least to greatest distance.
Rhea, Titan, Hyperion, Iapetus, Phoebe
(b) Write each distance in words.

❸ Multiply or divide.

(a) 985×100 98,500 (b) $1,000 \times 785$ 785,000
(c) 85×300 25,500 (d) $8,000 \times 300$ 2,400,000
(e) $95,000 \div 100$ 950 (f) $5,600 \div 80$ 70
(g) $250,000 \div 1,000$ 250 (h) $3,200,000 \div 2,000$ 1,600

Exercise 6 • page 17

22 1-6 Practice

Exercise 6 • page 17

Brain Works

★ 20 Questions

A student chooses any number up to 1 million. Other students get a total of 20 guesses to determine the number.

They can ask yes/no questions such as:

- "Is it greater than [some number]?"
- "Is it less than [some number]?"
- "Is the number [even, odd]?"
- "Is the [ones, tens, hundreds, etc.] place [greater than, less than] the [ones, tens, hundreds, etc.] place?"
- "Is the [ones, tens, hundreds, etc.] place [even, odd]?"

20 proper questions should be enough to determine the answer every time.

Chapter 1 Whole Numbers

Exercise 1

Basics

1. (a) Write the number that is 1 more than 999,999 in numerals and in words.
   1,000,000
   One million
   (b) Write the number that is 1 more than 9,999,999 in numerals and in words.
   10,000,000
   Ten million
   (c) Write the number that is 1 more than 99,999,999 in numerals and in words.
   100,000,000
   One hundred million

2.

Millions			Thousands			Ones		
Hundred Millions	Ten Millions	One Millions	Hundred Thousands	Ten Thousands	One Thousands	Hundreds	Tens	Ones
7	4	2	9	1	6	3	8	5

(a) Write the number in numerals and in words.
742,916,385
Seven hundred forty-two million, nine hundred sixteen thousand, three hundred eighty-five

(b) The value of the digit 2 is 2 × 1,000,000 = 2,000,000

(c) The value of the digit 4 is 4 × 10,000,000 = 40,000,000

(d) The value of the digit 7 is 7 × 100,000,000 = 700,000,000

Practice

3. 609,304,049

(a) Write the number in words.
Six hundred nine million, three hundred four thousand, forty-nine

(b) The value of the digit in the one millions place is 9,000,000.

(c) The value of the digit in the one thousands place is 4,000.

(d) Write the names of all the places with the digit 0.
ten millions place, ten thousands place, hundreds place

(e) One hundred million more than 609,304,049 is 709,304,049.

(f) Ten million less than 609,304,049 is 599,304,049.

4. Write the numbers in numerals.

Two million, four hundred forty-seven thousand, sixteen	2,447,016
Seventy-four million, three hundred seven	74,000,307
Eighty-two million, eighty-two	82,000,082
Four hundred six million, fifty-seven thousand, three	406,057,003

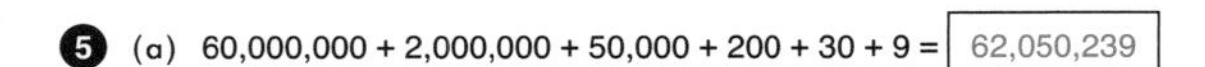

5. (a) 60,000,000 + 2,000,000 + 50,000 + 200 + 30 + 9 = 62,050,239

(b) 400,000,000 + 600,000 + 5,000 + 30 = 400,605,030

(c) 203,800,062 = 200,000,000 + 3,800,000 + 62

(d) 5,500,555 = 500 + 5,000,000 + 55 + 500,000

6. Write the numbers in order from greatest to least.

680,125,823 **680,125,283** **680,521,823** **608,125,823**

680,521,823 680,125,823 680,125,283 608,125,823

7. Write >, <, or = in each ◯.

(a) 80,000,000 + 60,000 (<) 50,000 + 400,000,000 + 900,000

(b) Six hundred twenty millions (>) 60 hundred thousands

(c) Eight hundred millions (=) 800,000 thousands

(d) 60,832,000 − 10,000 (<) 59,823,000 + 10,000,000

Challenge

8. (a) 4 millions = 40 hundred thousands

(b) 4 millions = 400 ten thousands

(c) 4 millions = 4,000 thousands

(d) 4 millions = 40,000 hundreds

(e) 4 ten millions = 4,000 ten thousands

(f) 4 hundred millions = 4,000 hundred thousands

(g) 4 hundred millions = 400,000 thousands

9. Write the numbers in numerals.

430 thousand thousands	430,000,000
9,860 ten thousands	98,600,000
60 thousand thousands, 40 hundred hundreds	60,400,000
8 ten thousands, 56 hundred thousands, 8 ones	5,680,008
8,000 ones + 12,000 tens + 4 millions	4,128,000
4,000 tens + 3,000 thousands + 6,000 ones + 50,000 ten thousands	503,046,000

Exercise 2 • pages 5–7

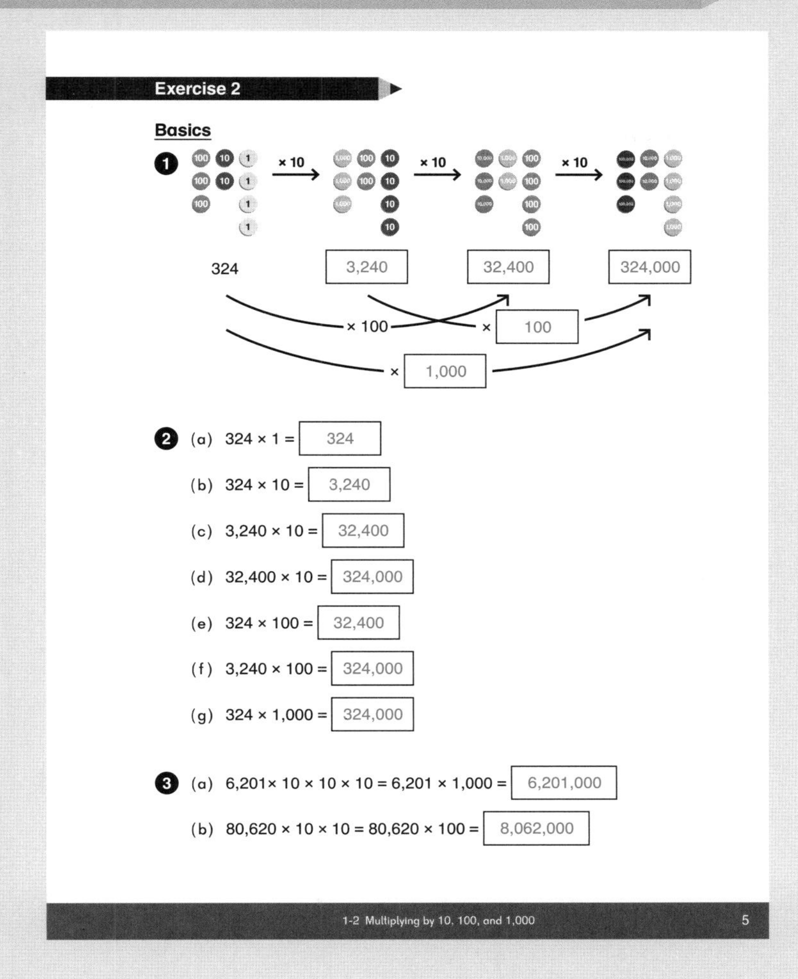

Exercise 2

Basics

1. 324 → × 10 → 3,240 → × 10 → 32,400 → × 10 → 324,000

   324 × 100 → 32,400; 3,240 × 100 → 324,000

   324 × 1,000 → 324,000

2. (a) 324 × 1 = 324

   (b) 324 × 10 = 3,240

   (c) 3,240 × 10 = 32,400

   (d) 32,400 × 10 = 324,000

   (e) 324 × 100 = 32,400

   (f) 3,240 × 100 = 324,000

   (g) 324 × 1,000 = 324,000

3. (a) 6,201× 10 × 10 × 10 = 6,201 × 1,000 = 6,201,000

   (b) 80,620 × 10 × 10 = 80,620 × 100 = 8,062,000

1-2 Multiplying by 10, 100, and 1,000 5

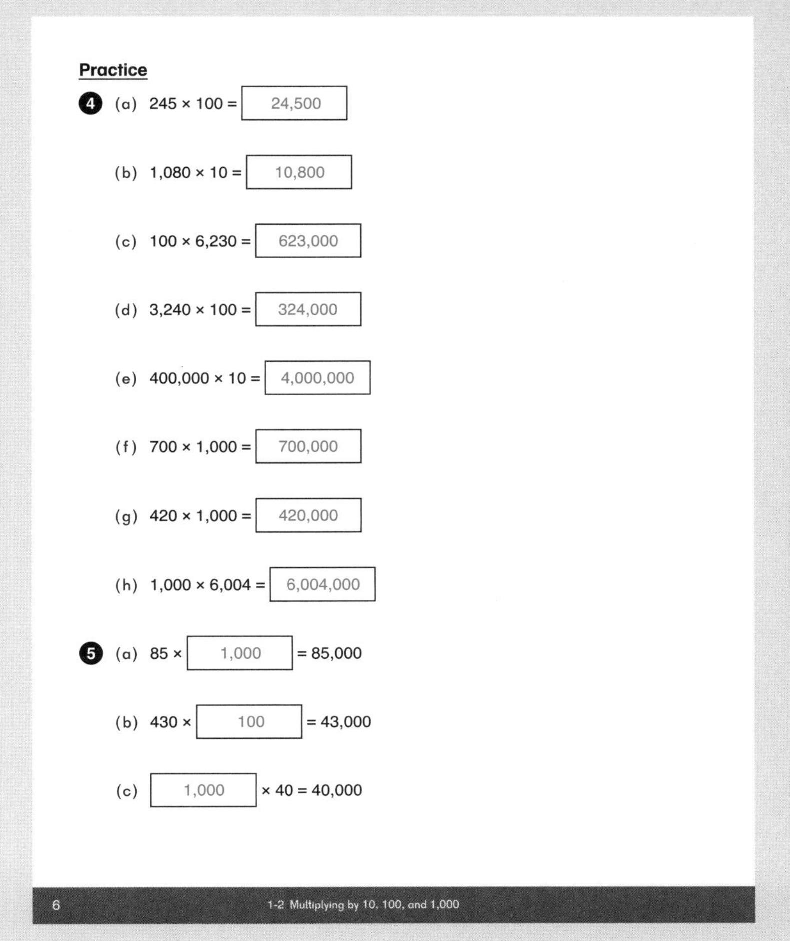

Practice

4. (a) 245 × 100 = 24,500

   (b) 1,080 × 10 = 10,800

   (c) 100 × 6,230 = 623,000

   (d) 3,240 × 100 = 324,000

   (e) 400,000 × 10 = 4,000,000

   (f) 700 × 1,000 = 700,000

   (g) 420 × 1,000 = 420,000

   (h) 1,000 × 6,004 = 6,004,000

5. (a) 85 × 1,000 = 85,000

   (b) 430 × 100 = 43,000

   (c) 1,000 × 40 = 40,000

6 1-2 Multiplying by 10, 100, and 1,000

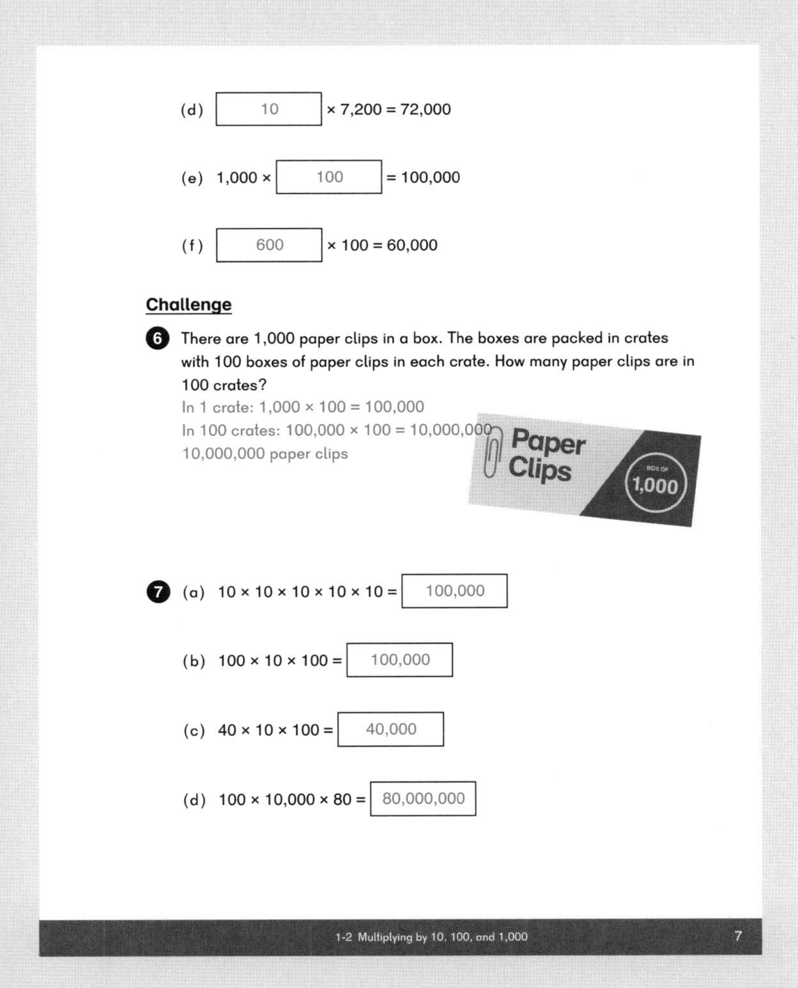

   (d) 10 × 7,200 = 72,000

   (e) 1,000 × 100 = 100,000

   (f) 600 × 100 = 60,000

Challenge

6. There are 1,000 paper clips in a box. The boxes are packed in crates with 100 boxes of paper clips in each crate. How many paper clips are in 100 crates?

   In 1 crate: 1,000 × 100 = 100,000

   In 100 crates: 100,000 × 100 = 10,000,000

   10,000,000 paper clips

7. (a) 10 × 10 × 10 × 10 × 10 = 100,000

   (b) 100 × 10 × 100 = 100,000

   (c) 40 × 10 × 100 = 40,000

   (d) 100 × 10,000 × 80 = 80,000,000

1-2 Multiplying by 10, 100, and 1,000 7

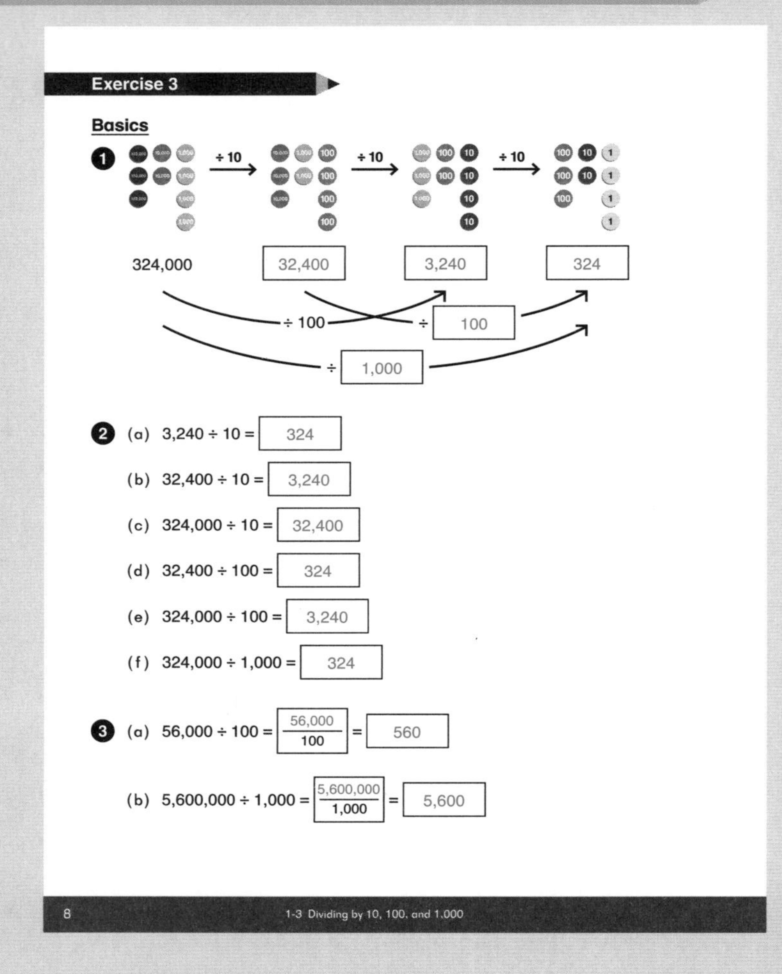

Exercise 3

Basics

1. 324,000 → ÷ 10 → 32,400 → ÷ 10 → 3,240 → ÷ 10 → 324

   ÷ 100 ; ÷ 100 ; ÷ 1,000

2. (a) 3,240 ÷ 10 = 324

   (b) 32,400 ÷ 10 = 3,240

   (c) 324,000 ÷ 10 = 32,400

   (d) 32,400 ÷ 100 = 324

   (e) 324,000 ÷ 100 = 3,240

   (f) 324,000 ÷ 1,000 = 324

3. (a) 56,000 ÷ 100 = $\frac{56,000}{100}$ = 560

   (b) 5,600,000 ÷ 1,000 = $\frac{5,600,000}{1,000}$ = 5,600

Practice

4. (a) 1,300 ÷ 10 = 130

   (b) 8,200 ÷ 100 = 82

   (c) 98,000 ÷ 100 = 980

   (d) 62,000 ÷ 10 = 6,200

   (e) 400,000 ÷ 10 = 40,000

   (f) 720,000 ÷ 100 = 7,200

   (g) 920,000 ÷ 1,000 = 920

   (h) 3,090,000 ÷ 100 = 30,900

5. (a) 8,500,000 ÷ 100 = 85,000

   (b) 620,000 ÷ 10 = 62,000

   (c) 4,500,000 ÷ 1,000 = 4,500

6. A supplier paid $71,000 for 1,000 portable photo printers. How much did the supplier pay for each portable photo printer?

   71,000 ÷ 1,000 = 71

   $71

Challenge

7. For a Box Tops for Education program, purchasing 1,000 participating products with Box Tops logos and scanning the receipts is worth $100. If 630 students each uploaded 100 Box Top scans, how much money will the school receive?

   630 × 100 = 63,000

   Number of thousands: 63,000 ÷ 1,000 = 63

   63 × $100 = $6,300

   $6,300

8. (a) 100,000,000 ÷ 10 ÷ 10 ÷ 10 ÷ 10 = 10,000

   (b) 20,000,000 ÷ 10 ÷ 100 = 20,000

   (c) 3,400,000 ÷ 1,000 ÷ 100 = 34

   (d) 700,000,000 ÷ 10,000 ÷ 100 = 700

Exercise 4

Basics

1. (a) 31 × 5 ones = 155 ones = 155
   (b) 31 × 5 tens = 155 tens = 1,550
   (c) 31 × 5 hundreds = 155 hundreds = 15,500
   (d) 31 × 5 thousands = 155 thousands = 155,000

2. (a) 28 × 4 = 112
   (b) 28 × 40 = 28 × 4 × 10
   = 112 × 10
   = 1,120
   (c) 28 × 400 = 28 × 4 × 100
   = 112 × 100
   = 11,200
   (d) 28 × 4,000 = 28 × 4 × 1,000
   = 112 × 1,000
   = 112,000

3. (a) 5 × 8 = 40
   (b) 5,000 × 8 = 8 × 5,000
   = 40,000
   (c) 5,000 × 8,000 = 5,000 × 8 × 1,000
   = 40,000 × 1,000
   = 40,000,000

Practice

4. (a) 35 × 20 = 700
   (b) 350 × 2 = 700
   (c) 35 × 200 = 7,000
   (d) 350 × 20 = 7,000
   (e) 35 × 2,000 = 70,000
   (f) 3,500 × 20 = 70,000
   (g) 3,500 × 200 = 700,000
   (h) 3,500 × 2,000 = 7,000,000

5. (a) 7 × 400 = 2,800
   (b) 5 × 8,000 = 40,000
   (c) 41 × 6,000 = 246,000
   (d) 25 × 40,000 = 1,000,000
   (e) 800 × 9,000 = 7,200,000
   (f) 7,000 × 800 = 5,600,000
   (g) 32,000 × 400 = 12,800,000
   (h) 2,100 × 500 = 1,050,000
   (i) 25,000 × 600 = 15,000,000
   (j) 10,600 × 900 = 9,540,000

6. New Zealand has a population of about 4 million people. There are about 20 times as many sheep in New Zealand as people. About how many sheep are in New Zealand?
   4,000,000 × 20 = 80,000,000
   About 80,000,000 sheep

Exercise 5

Basics

1 (a) 850 ÷ 5 = 85 tens ÷ 5

= 17 tens

= 170

(b) 8,500 ÷ 5 = 85 hundreds ÷ 5

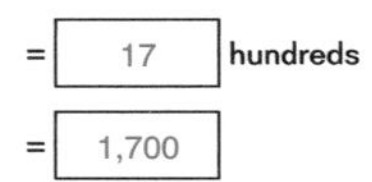

= 17 hundreds

= 1,700

(c) 85,000 ÷ 5 = 85 thousands ÷ 5

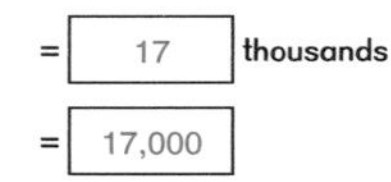

= 17 thousands

= 17,000

2 (a) 40,000 ÷ 8,000 = 40,000 ÷ 1,000 ÷ 8

= 40 ÷ 8

= 5

(b) 40,000 ÷ 800 = 40,000 ÷ 100 ÷ 8

= 400 ÷ 8

= 50

(c) 40,000 ÷ 80 = 40,000 ÷ 10 ÷ 8

= 4,000 ÷ 8

= 500

3 (a) 56,000 ÷ 700 = $\frac{56,000}{700}$ = $\frac{560}{7}$ = 80

(b) 5,600,000 ÷ 7,000 = $\frac{5,600,000}{7,000}$ = $\frac{5,600}{7}$ = 800

(c) 80,000 ÷ 500 = $\frac{80,000}{500}$ = $\frac{800}{5}$ = 160

(d) 960,000 ÷ 80 = $\frac{960,000}{80}$ = $\frac{96,000}{8}$ = 12,000

Practice

4 (a) 96 ÷ 6 = 16

(b) 9,600 ÷ 600 = 16

(c) 960,000 ÷ 600 = 1,600

(d) 960,000 ÷ 6,000 = 160

(e) 9,600,000 ÷ 6,000 = 1,600

5 (a) 630,000 ÷ 9,000 = 70

(b) 32,000 ÷ 400 = 80

(c) 4,800,000 ÷ 6,000 = 800

(d) 810,000,000 ÷ 9,000 = 90,000

(e) 360,000,000 ÷ 600 = 600,000

(f) 300,000 ÷ 600 = 500

(g) 100,000 ÷ 4,000 = 25

(h) 120,000 ÷ 5,000 = 24

6 A grocer paid $4,500 for 300 bushels of apples. How much did 1 bushel of apples cost?

4,500 ÷ 300 = 15

$15

Exercise 6 • pages 17–18

Exercise 6

Check

1. (a) The digit 7 is in the ___ten millions___ place in the number 378,903,400.

   (b) The digit ___0___ is in the ten thousands place in the number 24,302,627.

   (c) The value of the digit 2 in 542,390,108 is ___2,000,000___.

   (d) 3,000,000 has ___3,000___ thousands.

   (e) 53,900,000 has ___5,390___ ten thousands.

   (f) The value of the digit 6 in 460 ten thousands is ___600,000___.

   (g) 100 more than one million is the number ___1,000,100___.

   (h) 1 less than one million is the number ___999,999___.

   (i) 1 billion is ___1,000___ times more than 1 million.

   (j) 6,500,000 is 100 times as great as ___65,000___.

2. Write >, <, or = in each ◯.

   (a) 5,983,426 (>) 5,983,416

   (b) Seventy million, six hundred forty-seven thousand (<) 240,674,000

   (c) 80,000 + 40,000,000 + 900 (<) 40,800,000 + 9,000

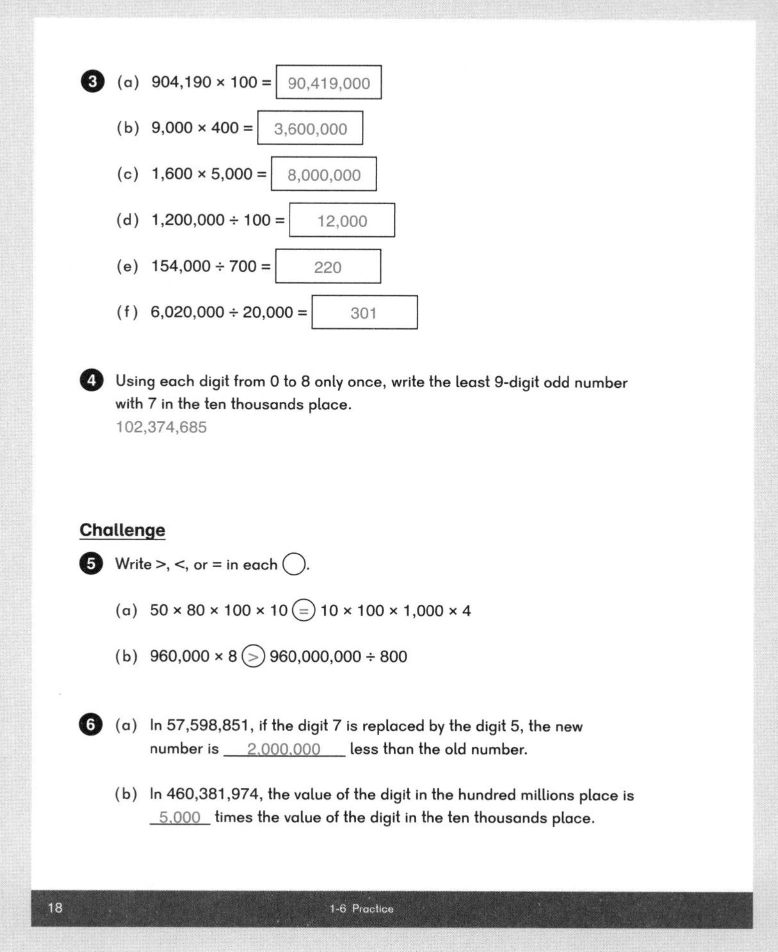

3. (a) 904,190 × 100 = 90,419,000

   (b) 9,000 × 400 = 3,600,000

   (c) 1,600 × 5,000 = 8,000,000

   (d) 1,200,000 ÷ 100 = 12,000

   (e) 154,000 ÷ 700 = 220

   (f) 6,020,000 ÷ 20,000 = 301

4. Using each digit from 0 to 8 only once, write the least 9-digit odd number with 7 in the ten thousands place.
   102,374,685

Challenge

5. Write >, <, or = in each ◯.

   (a) 50 × 80 × 100 × 10 (=) 10 × 100 × 1,000 × 4

   (b) 960,000 × 8 (>) 960,000,000 ÷ 800

6. (a) In 57,598,851, if the digit 7 is replaced by the digit 5, the new number is ___2,000,000___ less than the old number.

   (b) In 460,381,974, the value of the digit in the hundred millions place is ___5,000___ times the value of the digit in the ten thousands place.

Notes

Suggested number of class periods: 7–8

	Lesson	Page	Resources	Objectives
	Chapter Opener	p. 33	TB: p. 23	Investigate writing expressions.
1	Expressions with Parentheses	p. 34	TB: p. 24 WB: p. 19	Use parentheses to group operations in an expression.
2	Order of Operations — Part 1	p. 37	TB: p. 28 WB: p. 22	Evaluate expressions with multiple types of operations using the order of operations.
3	Order of Operations — Part 2	p. 40	TB: p. 32 WB: p. 25	Evaluate expressions with parentheses using the order of operations.
4	Other Ways to Write and Evaluate Expressions	p. 42	TB: p. 34 WB: p. 28	Write and evaluate expressions. Informally use the distributive property to make calculations simpler.
5	Word Problems — Part 1	p. 46	TB: p. 38 WB: p. 31	Solve multi-step word problems involving whole numbers. Review use of bar models to solve word problems.
6	Word Problems — Part 2	p. 49	TB: p. 41 WB: p. 36	Solve challenging multi-step word problems involving whole numbers.
7	Practice	p. 52	TB: p. 44 WB: p. 41	Practice concepts from the chapter.
	Workbook Solutions	p. 55		

In Dimensions Math 1A–4B, students learned how to solve mental math problems informally using arithmetic properties, as outlined below.

Students have learned they can add in any order, but when subtracting, they must begin with the whole:

$4 + 5 + 6 = 4 + 6 + 5$

$25 - 4 - 3 \neq 4 - 25 - 3$

Students have also learned they can multiply factors in any order, but when dividing, they must begin with the whole.

$4 \times 5 \times 8 = 8 \times 5 \times 4$

$36 \div 4 \neq 4 \div 36$

Expressions and Equations

An equation is a statement in which there are two or more expressions that are equal in value.

Examples of equations:

$10 + 20 = 30$	$\frac{6}{2} = 3$
$4 \times 5 = 20$	$4 \div 3 = \frac{4}{3} = 1\frac{1}{3}$
$6 \div 2 = 3$	$13 - 3 = 2 \times 5$

An expression is a mathematical statement that uses numbers and operations to show a value. Students first learned the difference between expressions and equations in Dimensions Math 3A Chapter 2.

Examples of expressions:

30	$6 \div 2$
$10 + 20$	$\frac{2}{6}$
4×5	4^2

Students have been finding the value of (or evaluating) expressions since Dimensions Math Kindergarten.

Example from *Dimensions Math Textbook 1B*:

Expressions can contain multiple operations. Students will learn to find the value of expressions with multiple operations by applying order of operations. In Lesson 1, they will begin by using parentheses to indicate which operations should be calculated first.

Order of Operations for Evaluating Expressions

The order of operations is a set of conventions that explains how to evaluate an expression containing multiple operations.

According to the order of operations, multiplication and division expressions are computed first, from left to right. Next, addition and subtraction expressions are computed. If the expression includes parentheses, the value in parentheses is computed first, applying order of operations.

This order of computations is referred to as "precedence." Addition and subtraction have lower precedence than multiplication and division.

Students may choose to underline calculations as they are performed to help them see the flow of operations and each resulting step.

Example:

$80 - \underline{10 \div 2} \times 3$
$= 80 - \underline{5 \times 3}$
$= 80 - 15$
$= 65$

Note that in the example on the previous page, division is calculated before multiplication because the division expression appears first when computing from left to right.

In some cases, steps in an expression can be combined.

Example:

$2 \times (\underline{36 \div 4}) \times (\underline{6 - 2})$
$= \underline{2 \times 9} \times 4$
$= 18 \times 4$
$= 72$

To help avoid confusion, encourage students who need additional help to write each step independently:

$2 \times (\underline{36 \div 4}) \times (6 - 2)$
$= 2 \times 9 \times (\underline{6 - 2})$
$= \underline{2 \times 9} \times 4$
$= 18 \times 4$
$= 72$

By the third step, since multiplication can be done in any order, encourage students to use their mental calculation skills and notice that they can rearrange the factors as follows: $2 \times 4 \times 9 = 8 \times 9 = 72$.

Teachers should not teach the mnemonic PEMDAS, or "Please Excuse My Dear Aunt Sally" for Parentheses, Exponents, Multiplication, Division, Addition, and Subtraction. This mnemonic confuses students as it implies that we always calculate multiplication before division, and addition before subtraction. Additionally, it focuses students on following procedural rules instead of understanding expressions in general.

For example, when calculating $24 \div 3 \times 2$ from left to right, the answer is 16, which is correct. However, when multiplying first, then dividing, the answer is 4, which is incorrect.

As another example, when calculating $15 - 5 + 7$ from left to right, the answer is 17, which is correct. However, when adding first, then subtracting, the answer is 3, which is incorrect.

Rules for exponents in order of operations are covered in Dimensions Math 6A.

Properties of Operations

Students have informally learned the commutative and associative properties of addition and multiplication when working with number bonds in addition and multiplication equations.

Addition and multiplication are commutative. For any number a and b:

$a + b = b + a$
$a \times b = b \times a$

Examples:

$2 + 7 = 7 + 2$
$4 \times 21 = 21 \times 4$

Addition and multiplication are associative. For any numbers a, b, and c:

$a + (b + c) = (a + b) + c$
$a \times (b \times c) = (a \times b) \times c$

Examples:

$7 + (3 + 5)$
$= 7 + 8$
$= 15$

$(7 + 3) + 5$
$= 10 + 5$
$= 15$

$(5 \times 4) \times 3$
$= 20 \times 3$
$= 60$

$5 \times (4 \times 3)$
$= 5 \times 12$
$= 60$

A combination of both properties allows addition and multiplication to be done in any order. For example, $2 + 7 + 8$ can be solved by adding 2 and 8 first, then adding 7 to the sum. $4 \times 21 \times 25$ can be solved by multiplying 4 and 25 first, then multiplying the product by 21.

Multiplication is distributive. For any number a, b, and c:

$(a + b) \times c = a \times c + b \times c$
$a \times (b + c) = a \times b + a \times c$
$(a - b) \times c = a \times c - b \times c$
$a \times (b - c) = a \times b - a \times c$

Students have used the distributive property informally:

- When multiplying a number with two or more digits by one digit.
- When finding partial products and then adding the products.
- When solving other types of problems using mental calculations.

Examples:

$$\begin{aligned} 32 \times 3 &= (30 + 2) \times 3 \\ &= 30 \times 3 + 2 \times 3 \\ &= 90 + 6 \end{aligned}$$

$$\begin{aligned} 4 \times 98 &= 4 \times (100 - 2) \\ &= 4 \times 100 - 4 \times 2 \\ &= 400 - 8 \\ &= 392 \end{aligned}$$

Word Problems

Students have been drawing and interpreting bar models to solve word problems since Dimensions Math 2A. Bar models allow students to solve algebraic problems even before they are able to write algebraic equations. Many of the problems will involve determining equal units for two or more quantities, and finding the value of one unit. Students can write expressions where they combine several steps into one expression to explain their methods, as shown in the answer overlays, however, they are not required to combine all the steps into a single expression.

Note: The calculations required in bar model lessons are designed to encourage students to continue to practice their mental calculation skills.

Materials

- Dry-erase markers
- Deck of playing cards with face cards removed
- Whiteboards

Blackline Masters

- Shaded Dots
- Stars

Activities

Games and activities included in this chapter are designed to provide practice with chapter concepts. They can be used after students complete the **Do** questions, or any time review and practice are needed.

Objective

- Investigate writing expressions.

Lesson Materials

- Shaded Dots (BLM)

Provide students with Shaded Dots (BLM) and have them discuss the Chapter Opener.

Review the terms "expressions" and "equations" with students.

Discuss Dion's and Mei's thoughts.

Students should see that Dion groups the dots as 2 groups of 9 with a middle row of 7. Point out that Dion did not say, "I found 2 groups of 9 first, then added 7."

Mei calculates the number of green dots differently. Point out that she did not say, "I found 4 groups of 4 equals 16, then found 3 groups of 3 equals 9. Then I added 16 and 9 together to get 25."

Have students try to find other ways to group the dots.

For example, they may see:

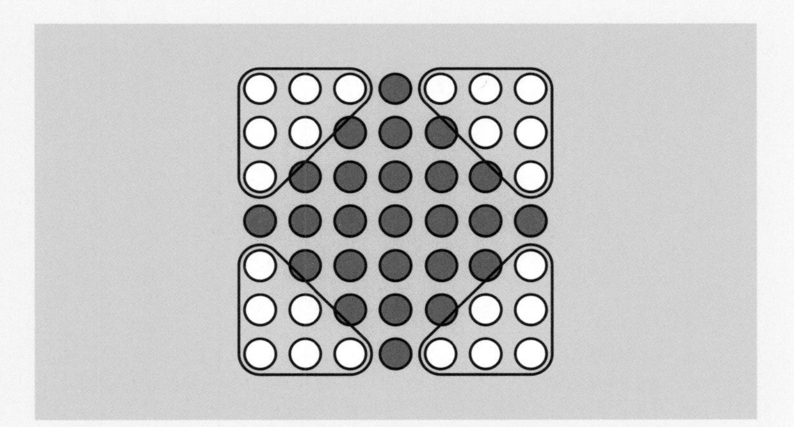

Challenge students to explain their solutions. For example, they may say, "I saw 7 groups of 7 in all and I subtracted 4 groups of 6 white dots on the corners."

Objective

- Use parentheses to group operations in an expression.

Think

Pose the **Think** problem and discuss the given bar model.

Alex challenges students to write a single expression for the computations. Have students think about how they can combine their steps into one expression.

Record student expressions on the board and discuss their solutions.

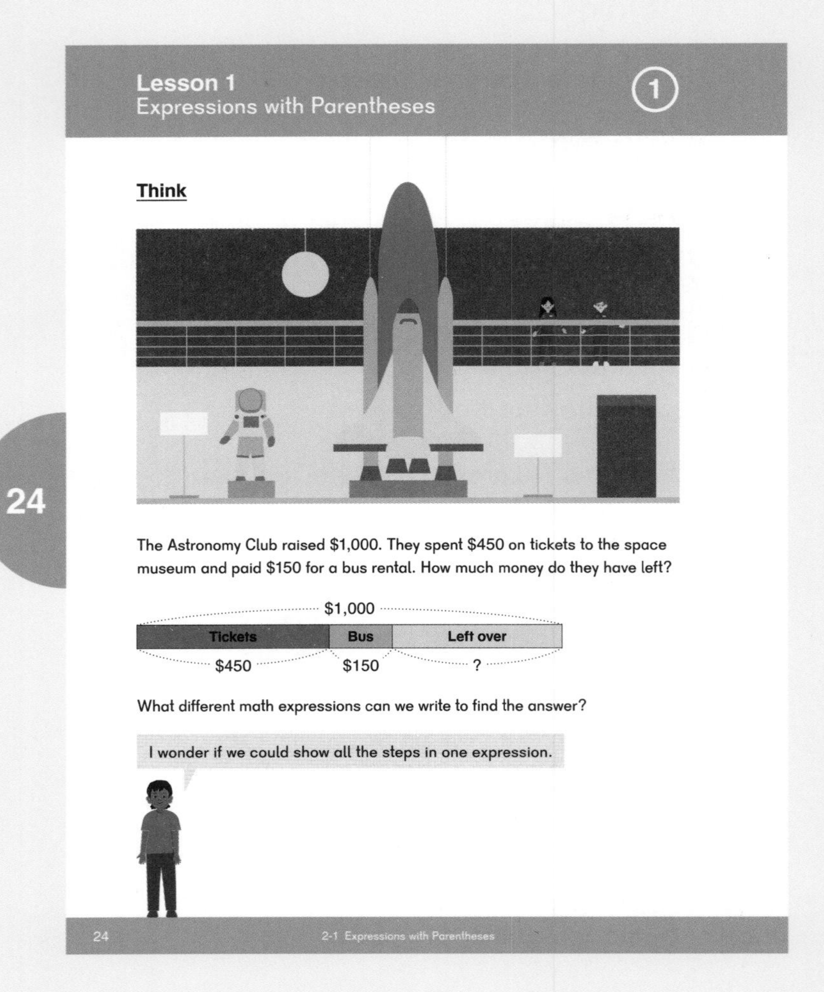

Learn

Have students compare their expressions from **Think** with the ones shown in the textbook. Discuss each friend's comment.

Method 1

We begin with the whole and then subtract each of the parts. Written as one expression, the whole comes first, and we calculate from left to right.

The two steps can be shown with a single expression: 1,000 – 450 – 150, starting with the amount of money the Astronomy Club had at first and subtracting each amount spent, one amount at a time.

1,000 – 150 – 450 is also correct.

Method 2

We add the two expenses first, and then subtract the sum from the total. The two steps can be shown with a single expression if we use parentheses: 1,000 – (450 + 150). The parentheses indicate that the addition should be done first.

The answer to Sofia's question is "no," because the value of the expression would be 700, not 400. Sofia's expression shows that she is subtracting 450 from the total, and then adding 150.

Ask students to think of a story for Sofia's expression. For example, "The Astronomy Club spent $450 on telescopes, and then received $150 from a donation."

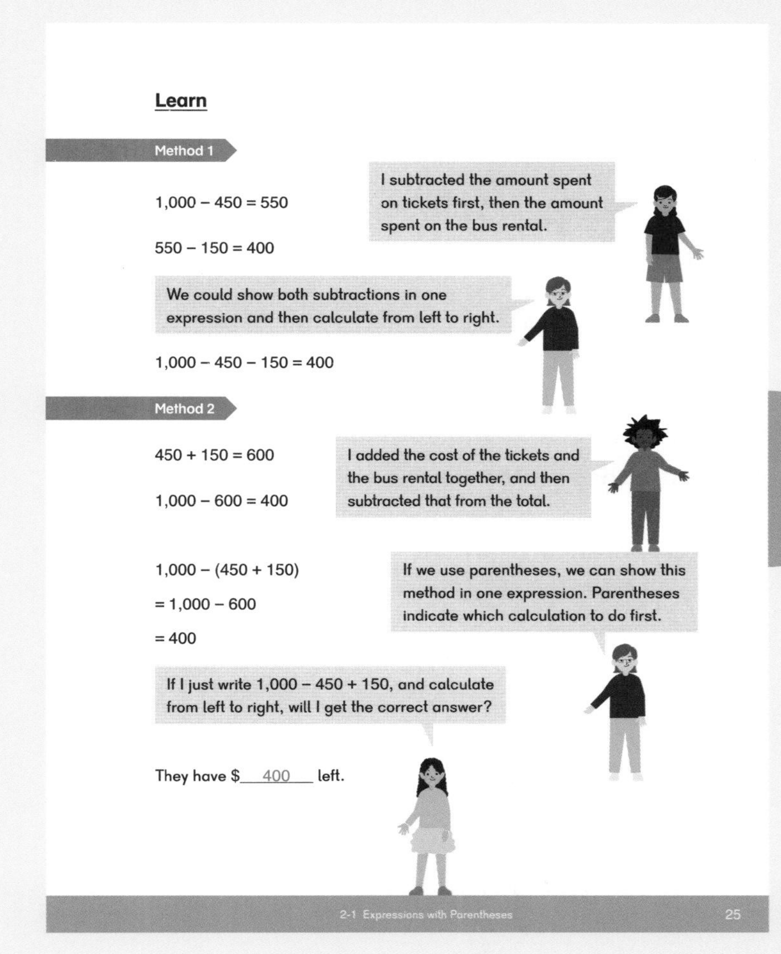

Do

❶—❷ Discuss the problems and calculation steps with students.

In calculating the (a) and (b) expressions in each problem, students will see that the answers differ.

❸—❻ Students should be able to solve these problems independently.

❺—❻ Sofia and Dion provide hints on how to write a single expression to solve the problems.

Exercise 1 • page 19

26

Do

❶ (a) 100 − 50 + 2

= 50 + 2

= 52

(b) 100 − (50 + 2)

= 100 − 52

= 48

Calculate from left to right.
If there are parentheses, calculate what is in parentheses first.

❷ (a) 56 ÷ 2 + 5

= 28 + 5

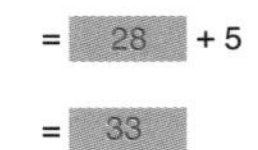

= 33

(b) 56 ÷ (2 + 5)

= 56 ÷ 7

= 8

❸ Find the values.

(a) 40 − (5 + 5)
30

(b) 430 − (100 − 20)
350

(c) 460 + (780 − 250)
990

26 2-1 Expressions with Parentheses

❹ Find the values.

(a) 9 × (86 − 16)
630

(b) 800 ÷ (20 + 60)
10

(c) 1,000 ÷ (48 ÷ 6)
125

❺ Rita had a $100 bill. She bought a shirt that cost $25 and a sweater that cost $18. Write an expression with parentheses to find the amount of change she received, and then find the value.

Money she had − (cost of shirt + cost of sweater)

100 − (25 + 18) = 57
$57

27

❻ A chair costs $33 and a chair cushion costs $7. They are sold as a set. Mr. Tomas spent $240 on chair and cushion sets. Write an expression with parentheses to find the number of sets he bought, and then find the value.

Money he spent ÷ (cost of chair + cost of cushion)

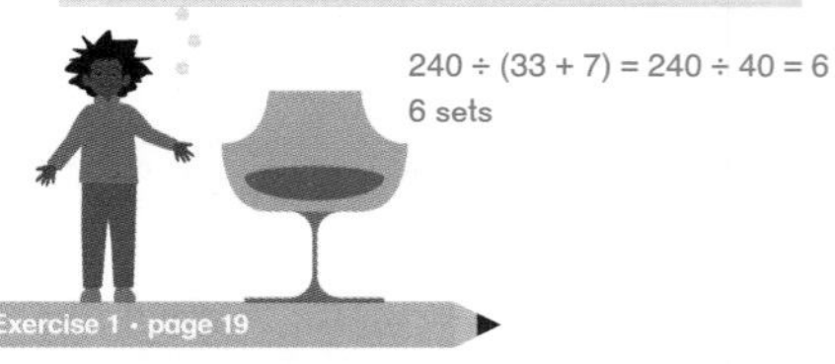

240 ÷ (33 + 7) = 240 ÷ 40 = 6
6 sets

Exercise 1 • page 19

2-1 Expressions with Parentheses 27

Objective

- Evaluate expressions with multiple types of operations using the order of operations.

Lesson Materials

- Shaded Dots (BLM)
- Stars (BLM)

Think

Pose the **Think** problem. Discuss Emma's solution and ask students why she used the expressions 5 × 5, 4 × 3, and 25 − 12. Have them try to combine Emma's steps into a single expression to show the number of yellow stars on the poster.

Learn

Have students compare their expression for Emma's method from **Think** with the ones shown in the textbook.

Mei reminds students that they can use parentheses to clarify which expression is calculated first.

Dion sees that the answer is the same, regardless of whether or not parentheses are used.

Introduce the term "order of operations." Explain that mathematicians have developed rules, just like rules in a board game, to ensure that everyone gets the same answer when finding the value of an expression.

When we apply order of operations to evaluate this expression, we subtract the product of 4 × 3 from the product of 5 × 5, to get 13 as the answer.

Have students relate Sofia's equation with the stars she has circled on her poster.

Provide students with Stars (BLM) and have them circle other groups that they see and write a single expression.

28

Lesson 2
Order of Operations — Part 1 ②

Think

Emma saw a poster with stars on it and thought of a way to find the total number of yellow stars without counting them one by one.

I found the total stars using multiplication and then subtracted 4 groups of 3 red stars.
5 × 5 = 25
4 × 3 = 12
25 − 12 = 13

Write one math expression that shows all the steps in her solution.

28 2-2 Order of Operations — Part 1

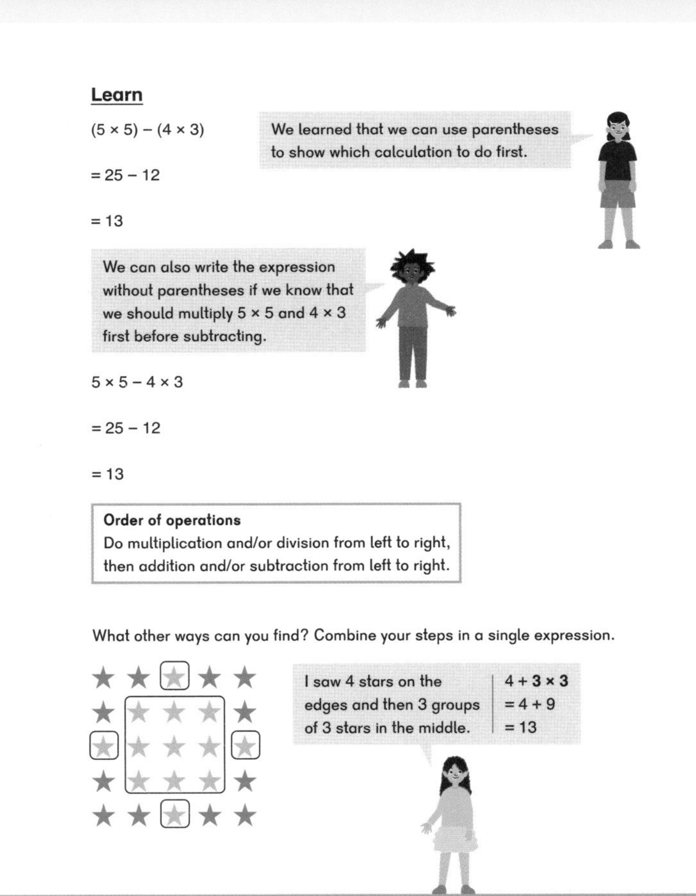

Learn

(5 × 5) − (4 × 3)

= 25 − 12

= 13

5 × 5 − 4 × 3

= 25 − 12

= 13

Order of operations
Do multiplication and/or division from left to right, then addition and/or subtraction from left to right.

What other ways can you find? Combine your steps in a single expression.

2-2 Order of Operations — Part 1 29

29

Do

❶—❷ Students should be able to solve these problems independently.

❶ Discuss the problems and given calculation steps with students. Ask students to come up with stories for each of these expressions.

Examples:

(a) I had \$100, received \$50 more for working, and spent \$2 on candy.

(b) I had \$100, spent \$50 on shoes, and then found \$2 in my pocket.

(c) A store has 10 boxes of 5 pears each. They are split into two orders.

(d) 10 pears are split into 5 boxes equally. I buy 2 boxes of them.

(e) I had 100 baseball cards. I gave 50 cards to each of my two friends.

(f) I had 100 baseball cards. My friend shared his 50 cards equally with me.

(g) There were 56 stamps in my stamp collection book. I gave away 8 pages of 5 stamps each and then bought 12 more stamps.

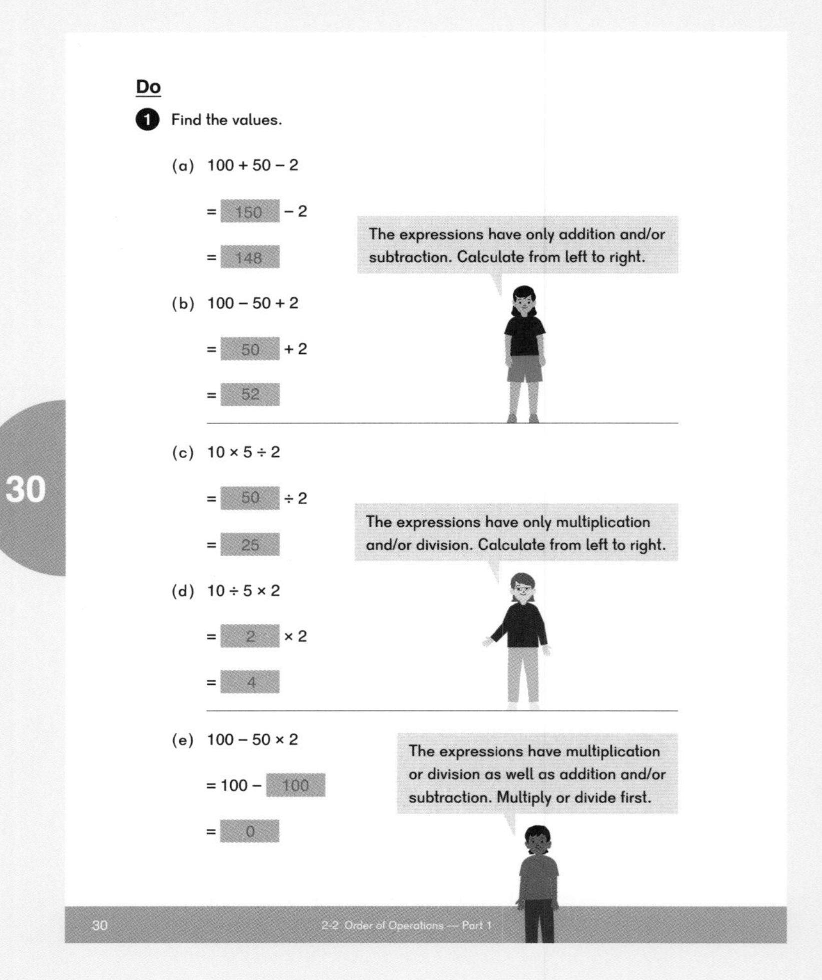

❷ If students struggle, have them show the order in which the calculations are performed by underlining them in each step.

Examples:

(c) $\underline{3 \times 50} + 4 \times 30$
$= 150 + \underline{4 \times 30}$
$= 150 + 120$
$= 270$

(f) $22 + \underline{8 \div 2} - 2$
$= \underline{22 + 4} - 2$
$= 26 - 2$
$= 24$

❸ If needed, students can use Shaded Dots (BLM) from the **Chapter Opener** to circle the dots and write their expressions.

Some sample solutions students might find:

5×5

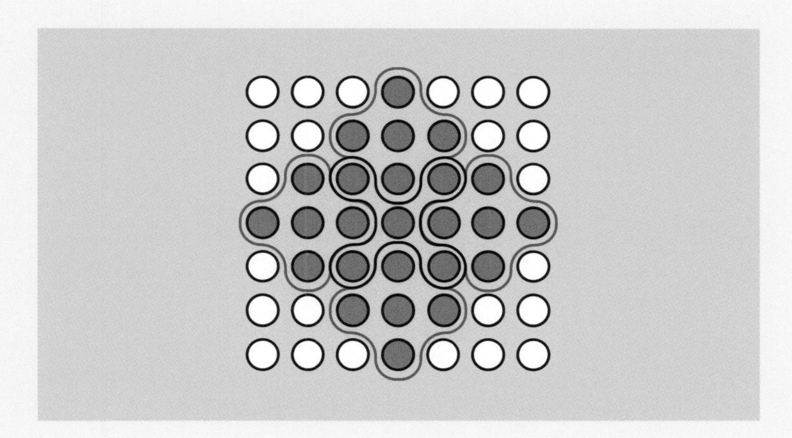

$4 \times 4 + 3 \times 3$

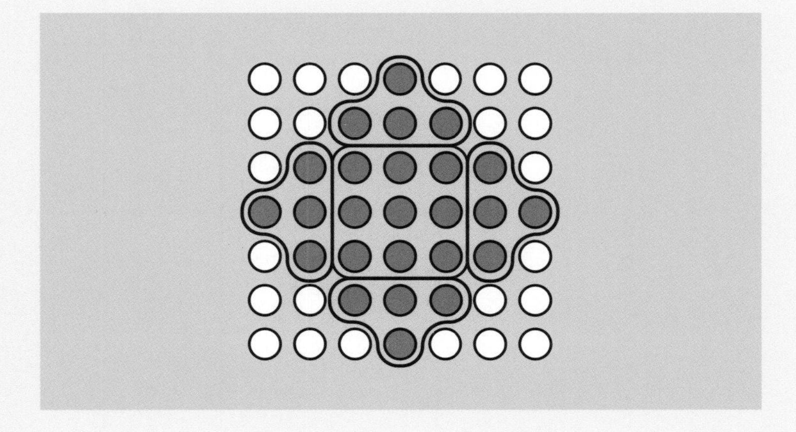

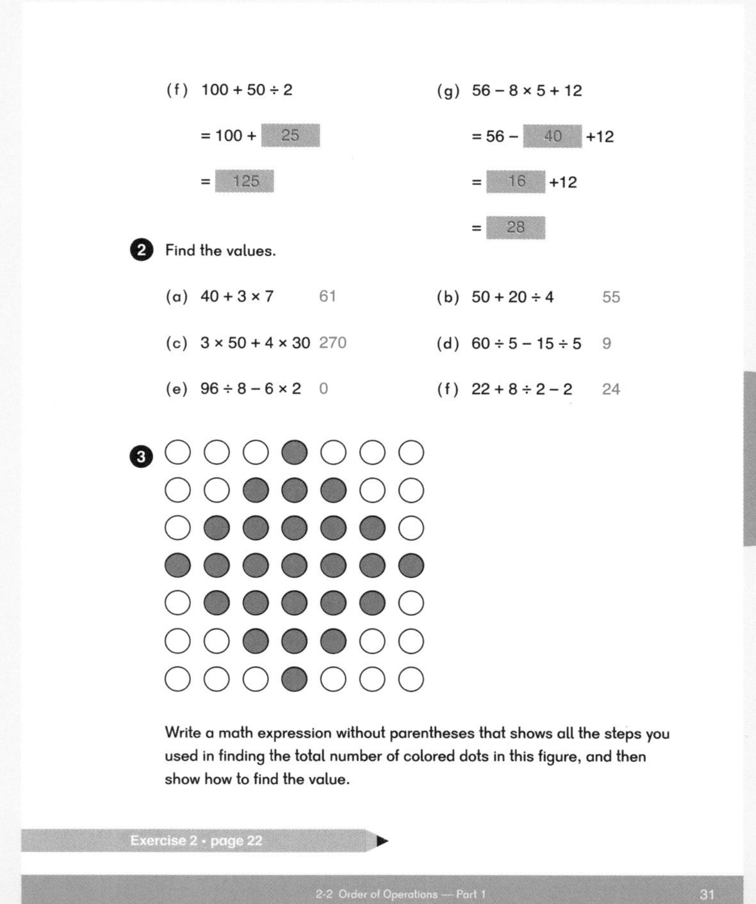

(f) $100 + 50 \div 2$
$= 100 + 25$
$= 125$

(g) $56 - 8 \times 5 + 12$
$= 56 - 40 + 12$
$= 16 + 12$
$= 28$

❷ Find the values.

(a) $40 + 3 \times 7$ 61
(b) $50 + 20 \div 4$ 55
(c) $3 \times 50 + 4 \times 30$ 270
(d) $60 \div 5 - 15 \div 5$ 9
(e) $96 \div 8 - 6 \times 2$ 0
(f) $22 + 8 \div 2 - 2$ 24

❸ Write a math expression without parentheses that shows all the steps you used in finding the total number of colored dots in this figure, and then show how to find the value.

Exercise 2 • page 22

2-2 Order of Operations — Part 1 31

$4 \times 4 + 3 \times 3$

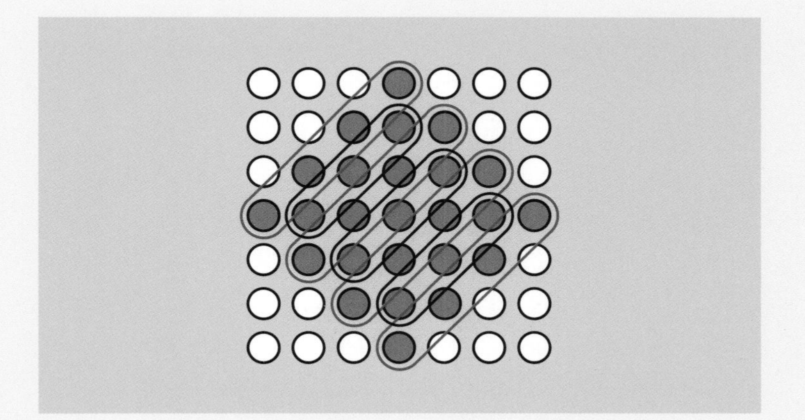

Exercise 2 • page 22

Lesson 3 Order of Operations — Part 2

Objective

- Evaluate expressions with parentheses using the order of operations.

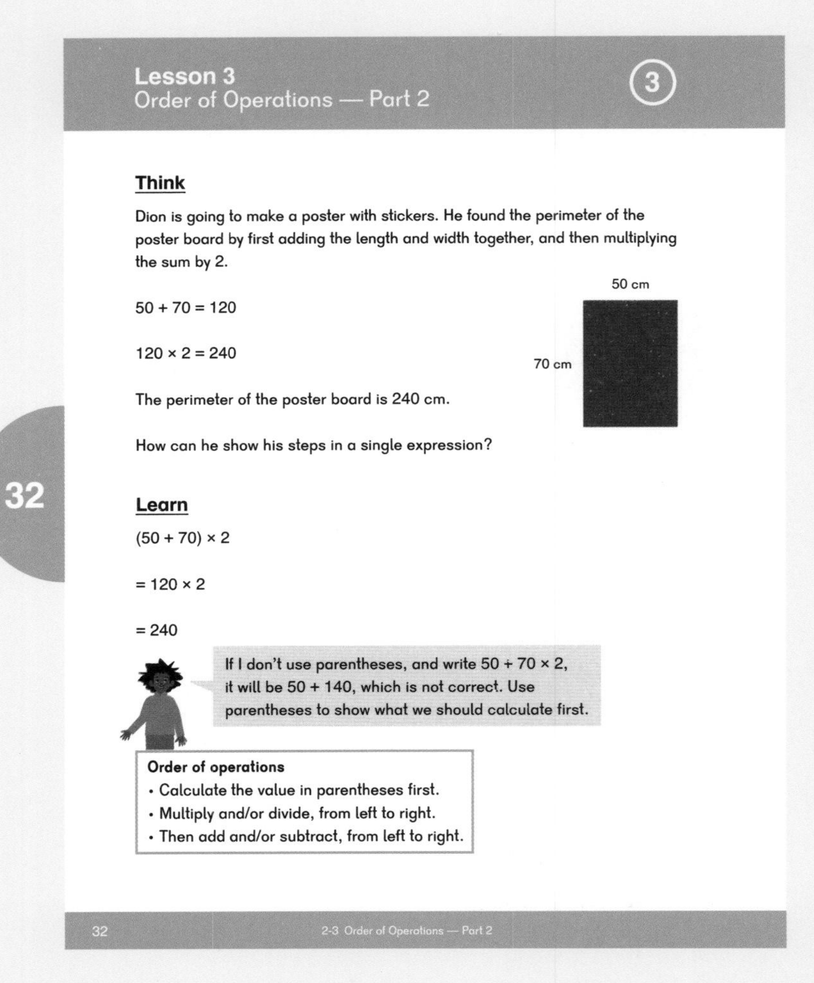

Lesson 3
Order of Operations — Part 2 ③

Think

Dion is going to make a poster with stickers. He found the perimeter of the poster board by first adding the length and width together, and then multiplying the sum by 2.

50 + 70 = 120

120 × 2 = 240

The perimeter of the poster board is 240 cm.

How can he show his steps in a single expression?

Learn

(50 + 70) × 2

= 120 × 2

= 240

Order of operations
- Calculate the value in parentheses first.
- Multiply and/or divide, from left to right.
- Then add and/or subtract, from left to right.

32 2-3 Order of Operations — Part 2

Think

Pose the **Think** problem and have students work independently.

Discuss student solutions.

Learn

Have students compare their own solutions with the methods shown in the textbook.

Discuss Dion's comment. Students should see that we can ensure that calculations are done in the correct order by adding parentheses to expressions. Parentheses indicate the calculation that should be done first.

Do

1. Discuss the problems and given calculation steps with students.

   Ask students, "What should we think about when deciding what operation to do first in each problem?"

   For (a), we would look at the first multiplication or division step, going left to right. For (b), we would look for any multiplication or division step in the parentheses first.

2. Students should be able to solve these problems independently.

   Where possible, students may combine steps. For example:

   (d) $40 \div 2 \times 4 - 3 \times 5$
   $= 20 \times 4 - 15$
   $= 80 - 15$
   $= 65$

   Students who need additional help should show the order in which the calculations are performed by underlining them in each step. For example:

   (b) $30 + \underline{10 \times 6} - 34 \div 2$
   $= 30 + 60 - \underline{34 \div 2}$
   $= \underline{30 + 60} - 17$
   $= 90 - 17$
   $= 73$

   (g) $8 \times (10 - \underline{36 \div 9}) + 2 - 2 \times 5 \times 5$
   $= 8 \times (\underline{10 - 4}) + 2 - 2 \times 5 \times 5$
   $= \underline{8 \times 6} + 2 - 2 \times 5 \times 5$
   $= 48 + 2 - \underline{2 \times 5} \times 5$
   $= 48 + 2 - \underline{10 \times 5}$
   $= \underline{48 + 2} - 50$
   $= 50 - 50$
   $= 0$

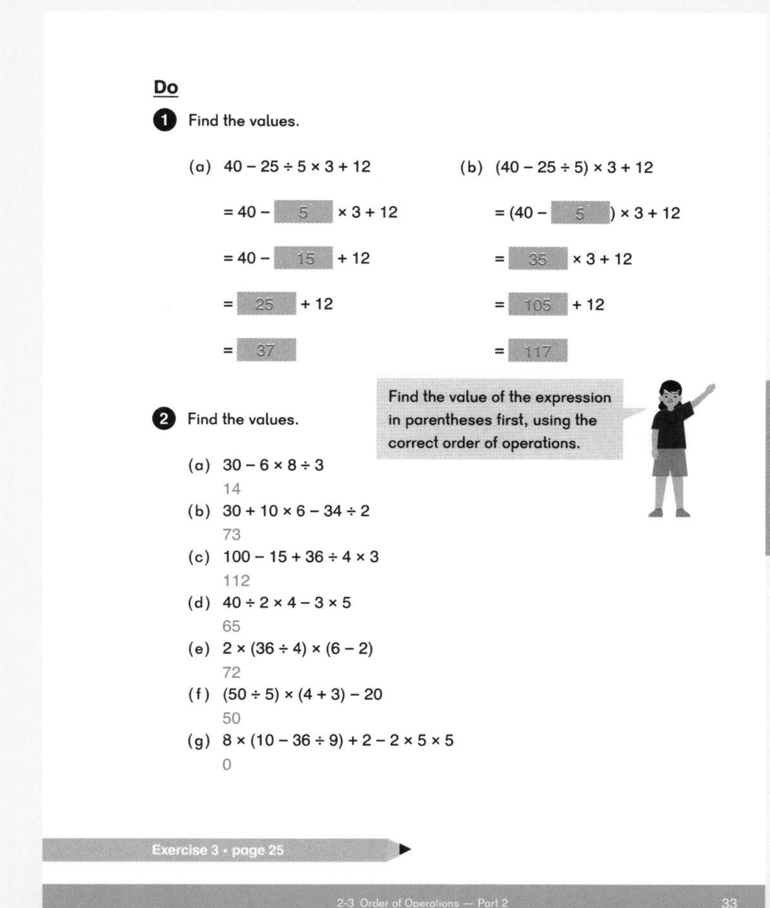

Do

1. Find the values.

(a) $40 - 25 \div 5 \times 3 + 12$
$= 40 - 5 \times 3 + 12$
$= 40 - 15 + 12$
$= 25 + 12$
$= 37$

(b) $(40 - 25 \div 5) \times 3 + 12$
$= (40 - 5) \times 3 + 12$
$= 35 \times 3 + 12$
$= 105 + 12$
$= 117$

2. Find the values.

(a) $30 - 6 \times 8 \div 3$
14
(b) $30 + 10 \times 6 - 34 \div 2$
73
(c) $100 - 15 + 36 \div 4 \times 3$
112
(d) $40 \div 2 \times 4 - 3 \times 5$
65
(e) $2 \times (36 \div 4) \times (6 - 2)$
72
(f) $(50 \div 5) \times (4 + 3) - 20$
50
(g) $8 \times (10 - 36 \div 9) + 2 - 2 \times 5 \times 5$
0

Exercise 3 • page 25

Exercise 3 • page 25

Objectives

- Write and evaluate expressions.
- Informally use the distributive property to make calculations simpler.

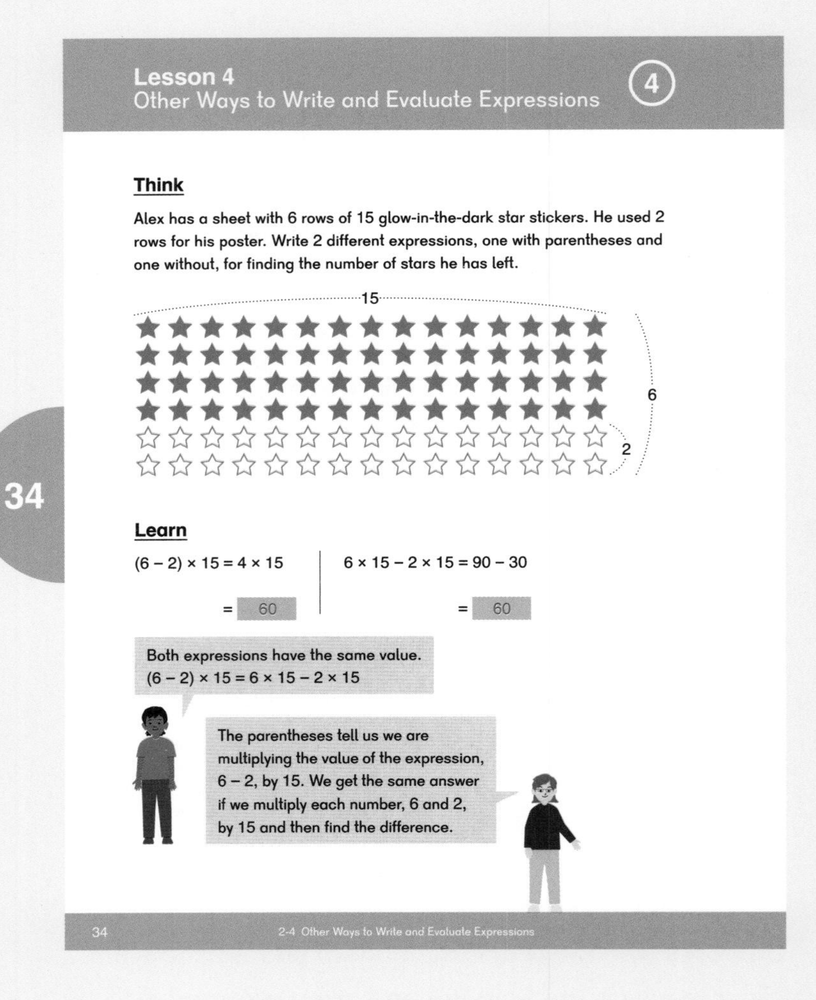

Think

Pose the **Think** problem. Ensure students understand they are writing two single expressions, one with parentheses, and one without, to find the number of stars Alex has left.

Learn

Have students compare their own solutions with the expressions shown in the textbook.

Have students explain the steps used to solve each expression in **Learn** and calculate each step.

In the first method, we subtract 2 groups of 15 from 6 groups of 15 to get 4 groups of 15 and then find the value. In the second method we find the value of 6 groups of 15 and 2 groups of 15 and then find the difference.

Ask students which calculation steps they found to be easier, the ones for the first expression or for the second expression.

Point out that it is acceptable to write $(6 \times 15) - (2 \times 15)$ even though the parentheses are not needed. The parentheses do make it easier to see what calculations are done first.

Do

❶–❹ Discuss the problems with students.

❶ Students should see a connection between this method and the use of number bonds to explain calculation strategies:

$$3 \times 46 = 3 \times 40 + 3 \times 6 = 120 + 18$$

(number bond: 46 → 40 and 6)

The number bond is now shown as an expression:

$3 \times (40 + 6)$

❷ Ask students:

- "What expression can be used to represent the difference between 50 and 1?"
- "What is 4 times that amount?"

Students have encountered problems like this when using mental math methods for multiplying numbers close to a multiple of 10.

For example:

$49 \times 4 = 50$ groups of $4 - 1$ group of 4

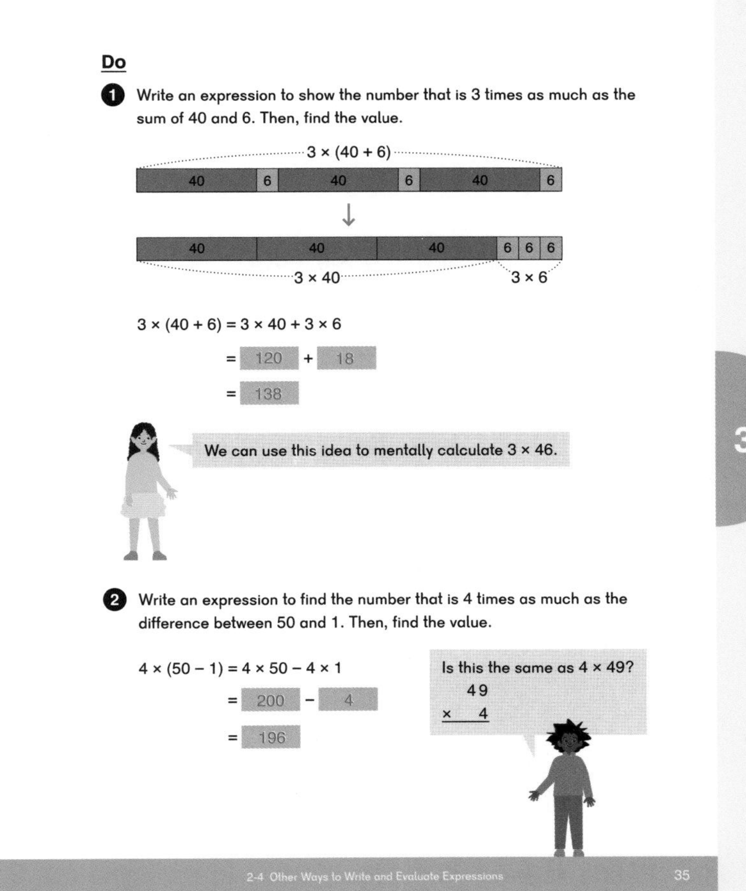

❸ Emma, Alex, and Mei show 3 different ways of calculating 4 × 27. Emma's thought and Alex's thought can be expressed as a number bond.

Emma:

$$4 \times 27 = 4 \times 20 + 4 \times 7 = 80 + 28 = 108$$

(number bond: 27 → 20 and 7)

Alex:

$$4 \times 27 = 4 \times 25 + 4 \times 2 = 100 + 8 = 108$$

(number bond: 27 → 25 and 2)

Mei thinks 27 is 3 less than 30. She can calculate 4 groups of 30 – 4 groups of 3.

$4 \times 30 - 4 \times 3 = 120 - 12 = 108$

Ask students which method was easier for them and why.

❹–❺ Students should see that they can simplify the calculations and solve some problems mentally.

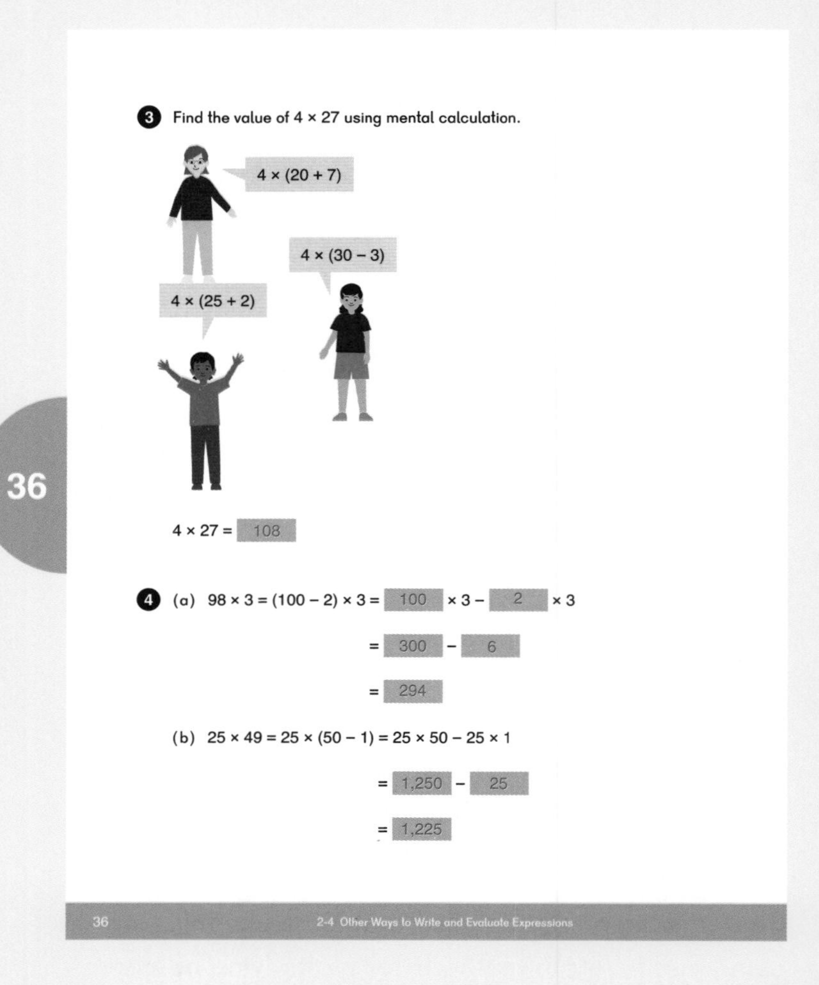

❺—❻ Students should be able to solve these problems independently.

❻ Encourage students to think about the numbers in each expression rather than immediately calculating. They should see that they can figure out which sign goes in the circle without fully working the problems. For example, since we are calculating (14 + 27) and then multiplying by either 6 or 8, we can see that (14 + 27) multiplied by 6 is less than (14 + 27) multiplied by 8.

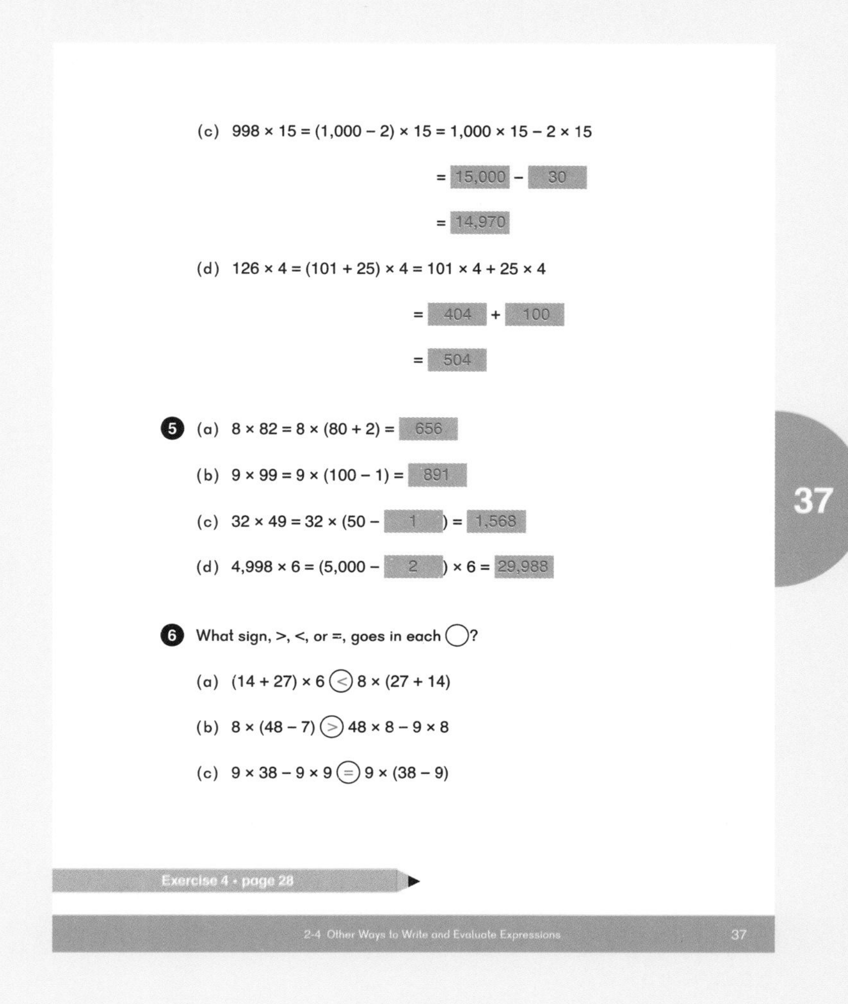

(c) $998 \times 15 = (1,000 - 2) \times 15 = 1,000 \times 15 - 2 \times 15$

$= 15,000 - 30$

$= 14,970$

(d) $126 \times 4 = (101 + 25) \times 4 = 101 \times 4 + 25 \times 4$

$= 404 + 100$

$= 504$

5 (a) $8 \times 82 = 8 \times (80 + 2) = 656$

(b) $9 \times 99 = 9 \times (100 - 1) = 891$

(c) $32 \times 49 = 32 \times (50 - 1) = 1,568$

(d) $4,998 \times 6 = (5,000 - 2) \times 6 = 29,988$

6 What sign, >, <, or =, goes in each ◯?

(a) $(14 + 27) \times 6$ (<) $8 \times (27 + 14)$

(b) $8 \times (48 - 7)$ (>) $48 \times 8 - 9 \times 8$

(c) $9 \times 38 - 9 \times 9$ (=) $9 \times (38 - 9)$

Exercise 4 • page 28

2-4 Other Ways to Write and Evaluate Expressions 37

Exercise 4 • page 28

Activities

▲ Build It

Materials: Whiteboards, dry-erase markers

Students begin with a simple equation, such as $2 + 3 = 5$. Players take turns replacing one number with an expression equal to that number.

Sample play:

$2 + 3 = 5$
$2 + 3 = 10 - 5$
$8 \div 4 + 3 = 10 - 5$
$8 \div 4 + 3 = (2 \times 5) - 5$

Challenge students to continue for 8 rounds.

▲ Make 24

Materials: Deck of playing cards with face cards removed

Make 24 can be played with the whole class or in small groups. In each round, a player turns four cards faceup. Players race to find an expression that has a value of 24 using all four cards and any of the operations: +, −, ×, or ÷.

The first player to use all the cards to find an expression equal to 24 collects the four cards.

If no one can find an expression that makes 24, the cards are shuffled back into the deck. When all of the cards have been played, the player with the most cards wins.

Objectives

- Solve multi-step word problems involving whole numbers.
- Review use of bar models to solve word problems.

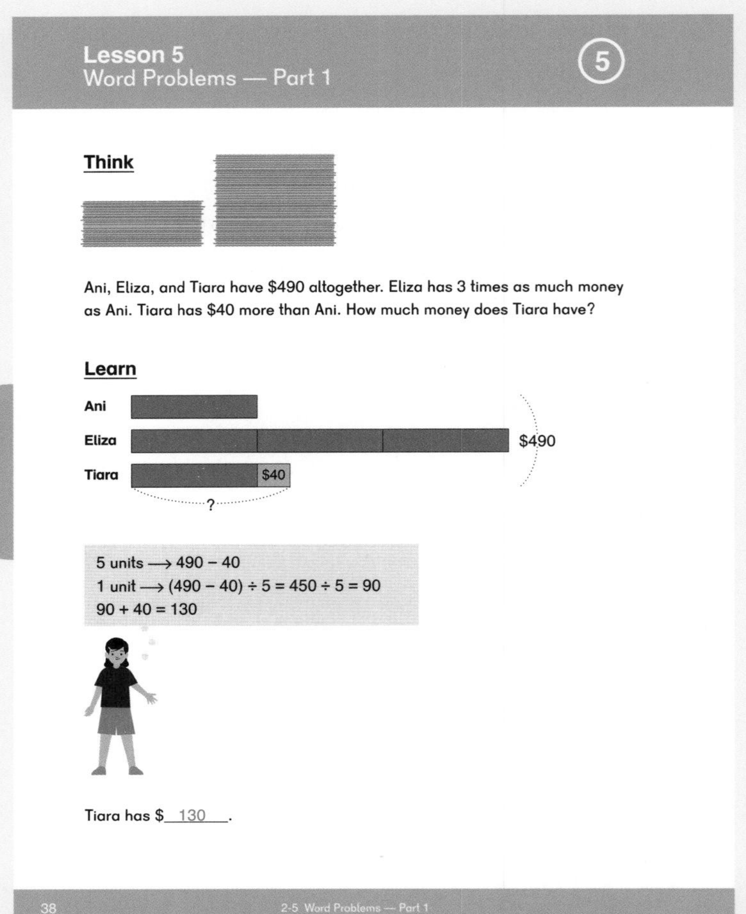

Think

Pose the **Think** problem and have students draw a bar model to help them find the amount of money Tiara has.

Learn

Have students compare their own solutions with the ones shown in the textbook.

Discuss Mei's calculations and how they relate to the bar model. She writes a single expression and combines some steps to find the value of one unit. Students should be able to interpret her calculations as written.

Do

❶–❸ Students should study the bar models in each problem and show the steps in their solutions. Encourage them to show more than one step in a single expression when possible.

❶ In the bar model, one unit represents a chair. 2 units represent a couch. So for 2 couches and 3 chairs, the model shows 4 units for the couches, and 3 for the chairs. Since the problem states that he spent $270 more on couches than chairs, and the bar model shows 1 more unit for couches than chairs, we know that 1 unit is 270.

1 unit ⟶ 270
7 units ⟶ 7 × 270 = $1,890

❷ The weights of both Suitcase B and Suitcase C are being compared to the weight of Suitcase A, so we can draw a bar for Suitcase A first, and then the bars for Suitcase B and Suitcase C, and mark the differences in weight.

From the model, Emma uses the weight of Suitcase A as the unit. To find the value of 1 unit, she needs to make equal units. To do this, she can subtract 15 lb from Suitcase A, and add 6 lb to suitcase B. So the weight of the 3 equal units of Suitcase A is 75 – 15 + 6.

Mei uses the weight of suitcase C as the unit, since that is what the problem asks us to find. From the model, she sees that to have 3 equal units, she needs to subtract 6 lb from Suitcase A and both 6 lb and 15 lb from Suitcase B. So the weight of 3 equal units of Suitcase C is 75 – 6 – 15 – 6 , which is the same as subtracting 15 once and 6 twice: 75 – 15 – (2 × 6).

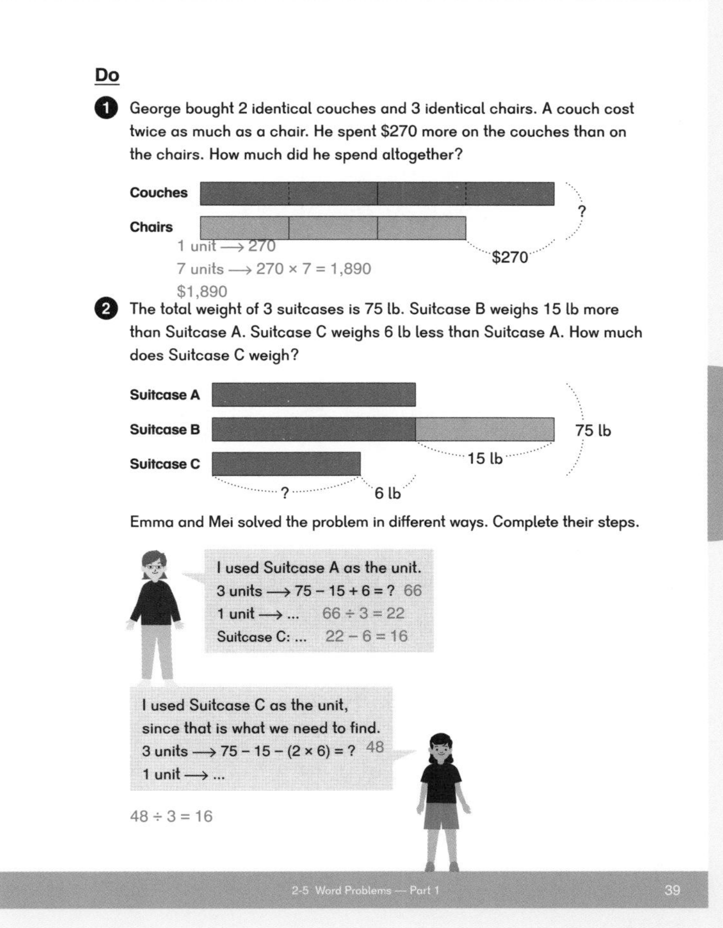

Do

❶ George bought 2 identical couches and 3 identical chairs. A couch cost twice as much as a chair. He spent $270 more on the couches than on the chairs. How much did he spend altogether?

❷ The total weight of 3 suitcases is 75 lb. Suitcase B weighs 15 lb more than Suitcase A. Suitcase C weighs 6 lb less than Suitcase A. How much does Suitcase C weigh?

Emma and Mei solved the problem in different ways. Complete their steps.

2-5 Word Problems — Part 1 39

❸ The cost of a printer is being compared to the cost of a laptop. The model shows a combined bar with all 5 printers in a row.

If we consider 1 unit the cost of a printer, then the cost of each laptop is 1 unit plus \$420. The bar model shows 6 units + 5 smaller units of \$420.

6 units ⟶ 6,000 – (5 × 420) = 6,000 – 2,100 = \$3,900
1 unit ⟶ 3,900 ÷ 6 = \$650

Alternatively, we can consider 1 unit the cost of a laptop, then add \$420 to the cost of a printer to make 6 equal units.

6 units ⟶ 6,000 + 420 = \$6,420
1 unit ⟶ 6,420 ÷ 6 = \$1,070

Printer: 1,070 – 420 = \$650

Alternate bar model:

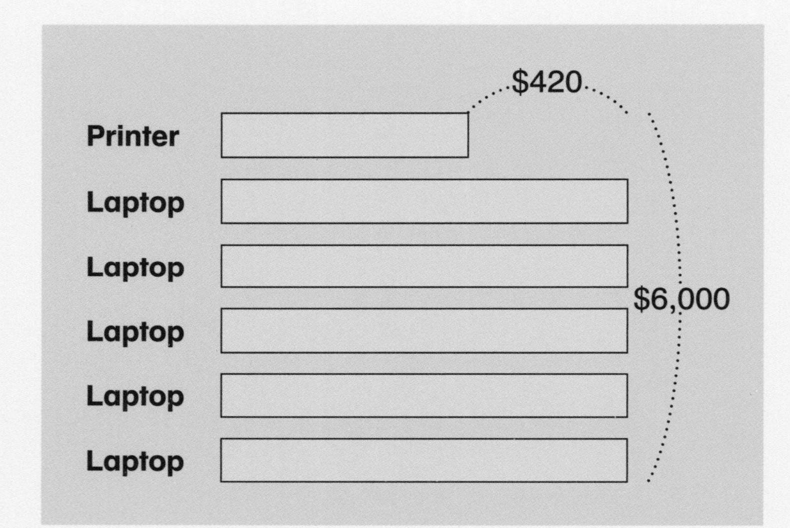

❹–❺ Students should draw bar models as needed.

❹

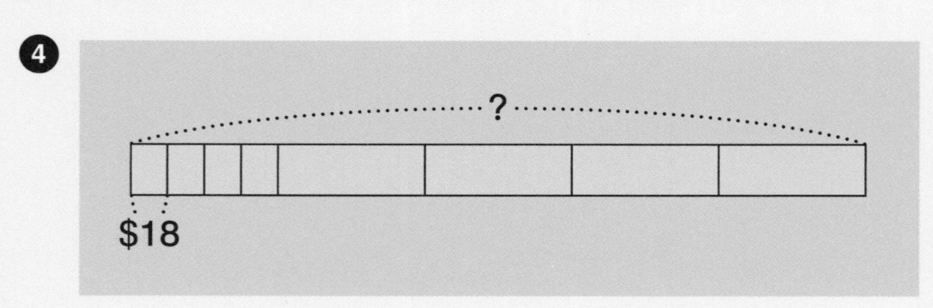

1 unit ⟶ 4 × 18
5 units ⟶ 5 × 4 × 18 = 360

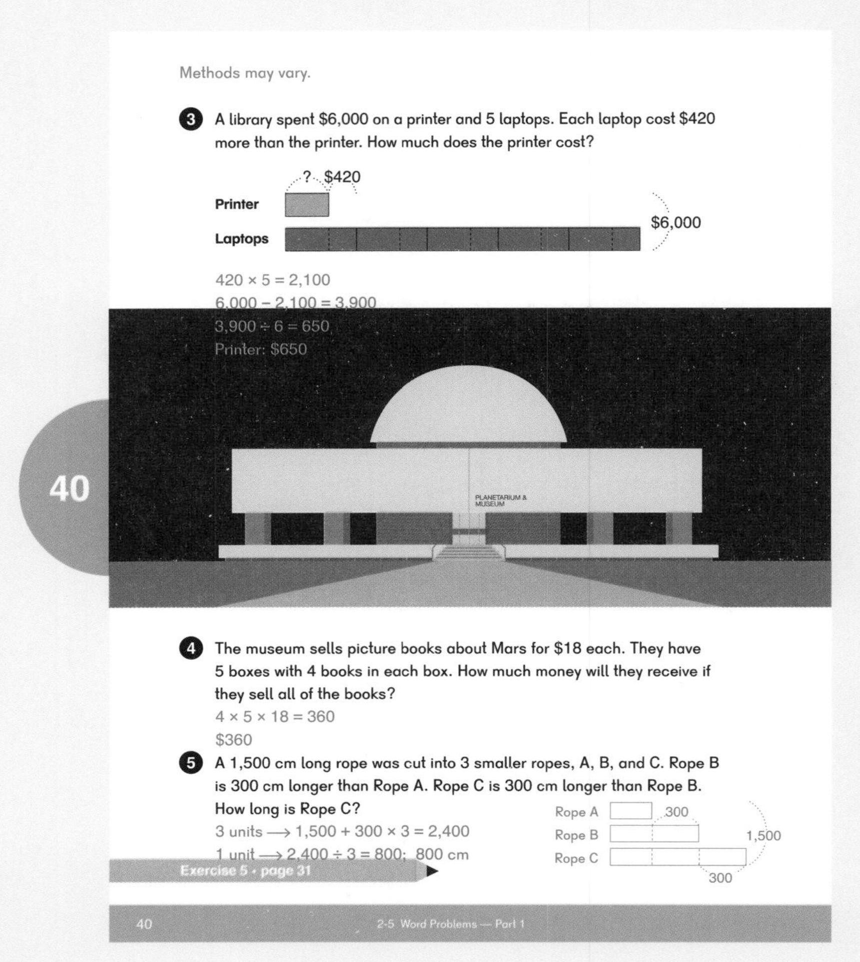

Methods may vary.

❸ A library spent \$6,000 on a printer and 5 laptops. Each laptop cost \$420 more than the printer. How much does the printer cost?

420 × 5 = 2,100
6,000 – 2,100 = 3,900
3,900 ÷ 6 = 650
Printer: \$650

❹ The museum sells picture books about Mars for \$18 each. They have 5 boxes with 4 books in each box. How much money will they receive if they sell all of the books?
4 × 5 × 18 = 360
\$360

❺ A 1,500 cm long rope was cut into 3 smaller ropes, A, B, and C. Rope B is 300 cm longer than Rope A. Rope C is 300 cm longer than Rope B. How long is Rope C?
3 units ⟶ 1,500 + 300 × 3 = 2,400
1 unit ⟶ 2,400 ÷ 3 = 800; 800 cm

Exercise 5 • page 31

40 2-5 Word Problems — Part 1

❺ If Rope A is the unit:

3 units ⟶ 1,500 – (3 × 300) = 600 cm
1 unit ⟶ 600 ÷ 3 = 200 cm

Rope C: 200 + (2 × 300) = 800 cm

Exercise 5 • page 31

Objective

- Solve challenging multi-step word problems involving whole numbers.

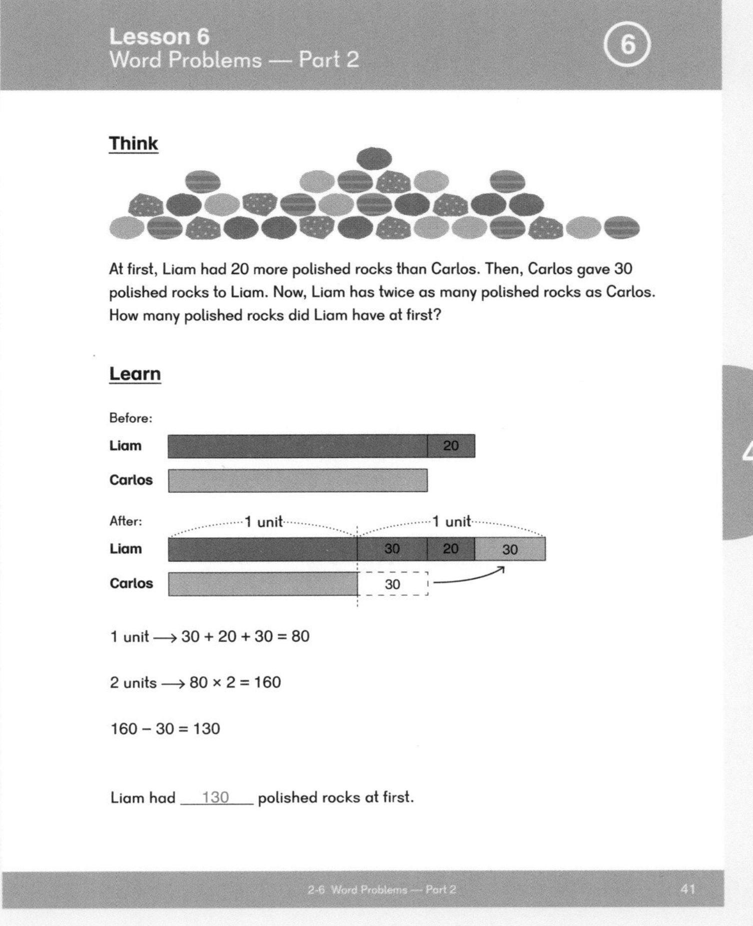

Lesson 6
Word Problems — Part 2 (6)

Think

At first, Liam had 20 more polished rocks than Carlos. Then, Carlos gave 30 polished rocks to Liam. Now, Liam has twice as many polished rocks as Carlos. How many polished rocks did Liam have at first?

Learn

Before:
Liam 20
Carlos

After:
1 unit 1 unit
Liam 30 20 30
Carlos 30

1 unit ⟶ 30 + 20 + 30 = 80

2 units ⟶ 80 × 2 = 160

160 − 30 = 130

Liam had 130 polished rocks at first.

2-6 Word Problems — Part 2 41

Think

Pose the **Think** problem and have students draw a bar model.

Ask questions, such as:

- "Do the quantities change? How can we show that the quantities change with bar models?"
- "Could we draw the situation at the end, Liam with twice as many rocks as Carlos, and then work backwards to show the situation at first?"
- "What would the units represent?"
- "What do you need to find? What information is given in the problem?"

Discuss student solutions.

Learn

Discuss the bar model and the solution shown in **Learn**.

The Before model shows that Liam has 20 more rocks than Carlos.

The After model shows that Liam has twice as many rocks as Carlos. Carlos's rocks are represented by 1 unit and Liam's are represented by 2 units.

Liam originally has 20 more rocks than Carlos. When Carlos gives 30 rocks to Liam, Liam has 50 more rocks (20 + 30) than what Carlos originally had, and Carlos has 30 less rocks than what he originally had.

From the model we can see that Liam has 30 + 20 + 30 more rocks than Carlos in the end. Because the facts state that Liam has twice as many rocks as Carlos at the end, 1 unit must be equal to 30 + 20 + 30.

Liam ends up with 2 units. He started with 30 less than 2 units.

Do

❶–❹ Students should study the bar models in each problem and understand how they relate to the information in the problem.

Students should show the steps in their solutions.

❶ The dark green in the wheat and rye bar models represents the weight of the containers. Even though the problem does not tell us the weight of the containers, we can find this weight by thinking in terms of part whole models, where the rye and container are both parts. We can then find the weight of the container after we find the weight of the rye.

Sofia subtracts to find the difference in weight.

2 units ⟶ 90 – 50 = 40 kg
1 unit ⟶ 40 ÷ 2 = 20 kg

Or

1 unit ⟶ (90 – 50) ÷ 2 = 20 kg

❷ In order for Jasmine and her sister to have the same amount, Jasmine must give $\frac{1}{2}$ of a unit to her sister. Dion points out that the value of 1 unit is therefore twice the amount Jasmine gave her sister.

Jasmine starts out with 2 units.
2 units ⟶ 2 × 2 × \$45

❸ Students should see from the model that the second bouquet has 2 more sunflowers than the first bouquet.

2 sunflowers or 2 S units ⟶ 24 – 18 = \$6
1 S unit ⟶ (24 – 18) ÷ 2 = 6 ÷ 2 = \$3

Each sunflower costs \$3.

Using the first bouquet:

2 gerberas or 2 G units ⟶ 18 – (2 × 3) = \$12
1 G unit ⟶ 12 ÷ 2 = \$6

Each gerbera costs \$6.

42

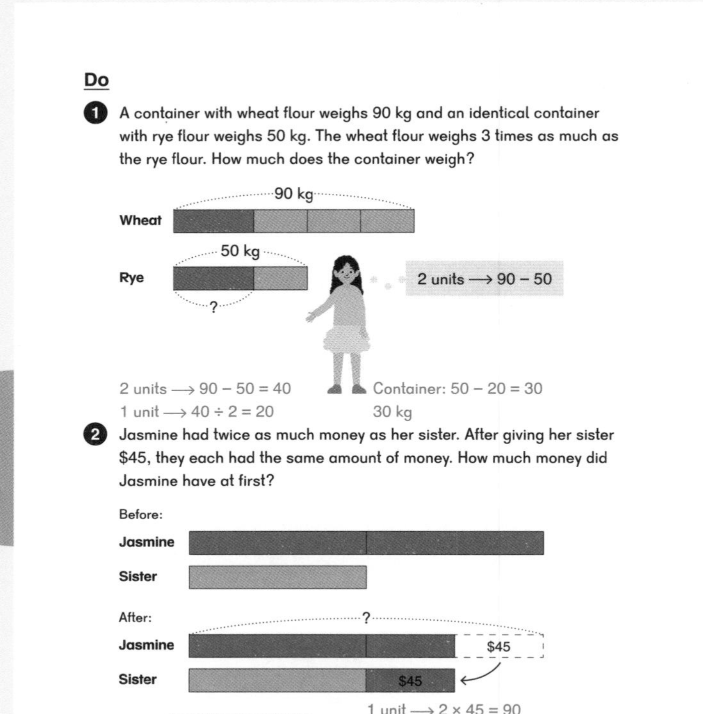

1 unit ⟶ 2 × 45

1 unit ⟶ 2 × 45 = 90
2 units ⟶ 90 × 2 = 180
\$180

❸

A bouquet of 2 gerberas and 2 sunflowers costs \$18. A bouquet of 2 gerberas and 4 sunflowers costs \$24. How much does one sunflower cost? How much does one gerbera cost?

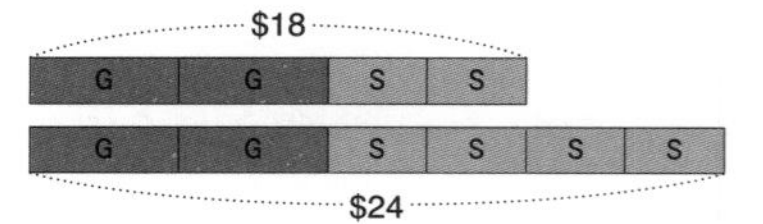

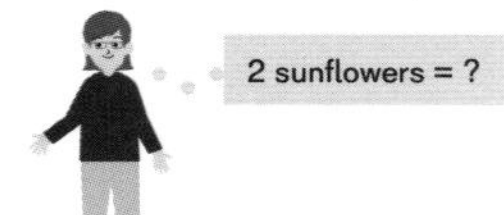

2 sunflowers: 24 – 18 = 6
1 sunflower: 6 ÷ 2 = 3; \$3
2 gerberas: 18 – 6 = 12
1 gerbera: 12 ÷ 2 = 6; \$6

43

❹ Emma and Alex have 980 coins altogether. Emma has 4 times as many coins as Alex. How many coins would she have to give Alex for them to have the same number of coins?

10 units ⟶ 980; 1 unit ⟶ 98; 98 × 3 = 294 ? 294 coins

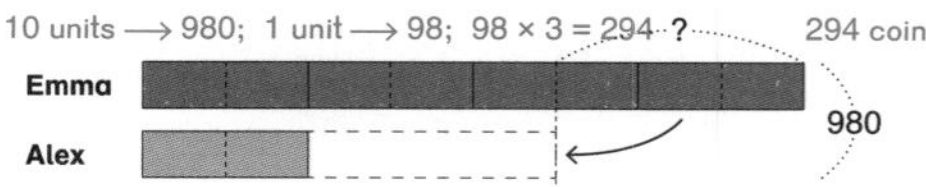

❺ A jug and a bottle had a combined total of 950 mL of water. After 50 mL of water was poured from the bottle to the jug, the jug had 4 times as much water as the bottle. How much water was in each container at first?

bottle: 190 + 50 = 240; 240 mL
jug: 950 – 240 = 710; 710 mL

Exercise 6 • page 36

4. The problem says that Emma has 4 times as many coins as Alex. We can therefore draw a model showing 4 units for Emma and 1 unit for Alex.

However, for the friends to have an equal number of coins in the end, Emma has to give half of the difference to Alex.

The difference is 3 units. Half of this is $1\frac{1}{2}$ units. To show half of the difference, we can divide each unit into half, so now Emma has 8 smaller units and Alex has 2 smaller units. The difference is now 6 units, and Emma has to give 3 of those units to Alex for them to have the same amount.

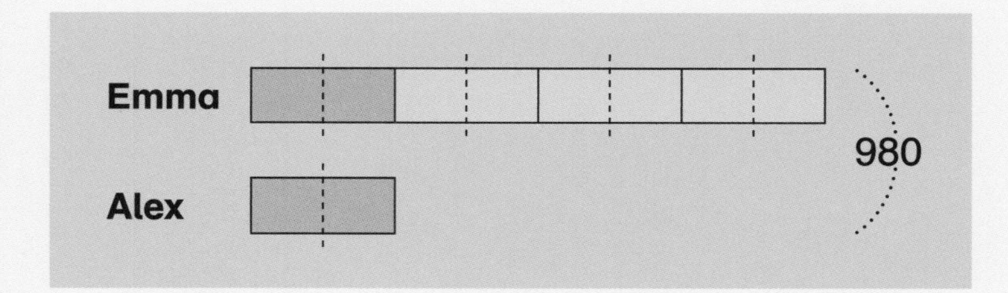

10 units ⟶ 980 coins
1 unit ⟶ 980 ÷ 10 = 98 coins
3 units ⟶ 98 × 3 = 294 coins

5. Since we are told that the jug has 4 times as much water as the bottle in the end, it is easier to draw this situation first.

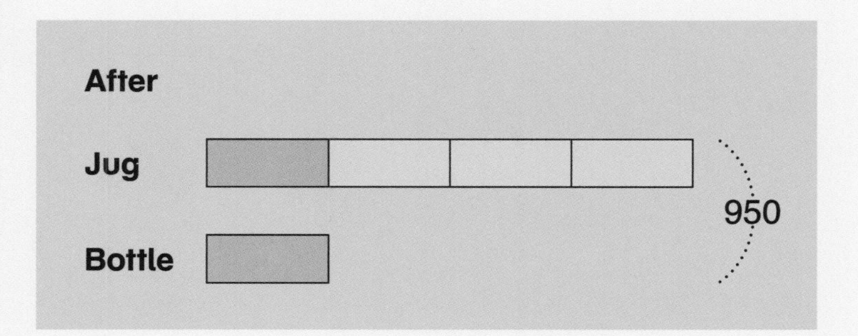

We can work backwards and show 50 mL being transferred from the bottle to the jug.

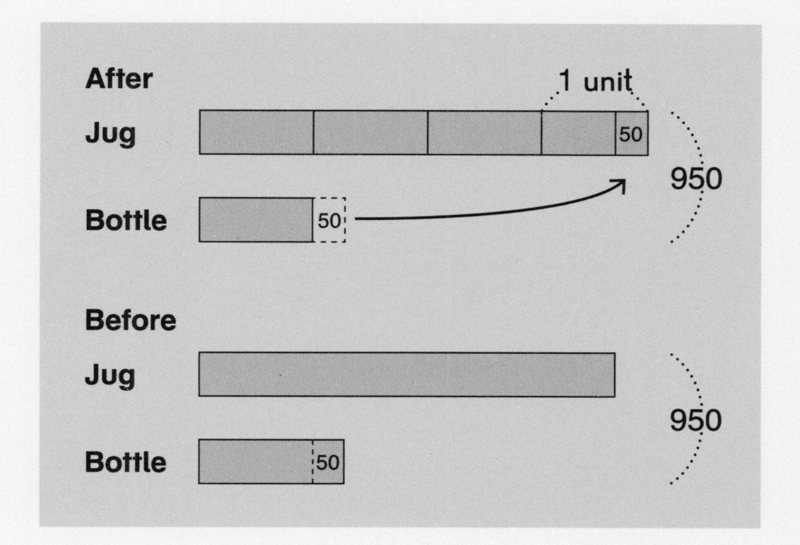

The total amount of liquid does not change, so we know that five units is 950 mL and can find 1 unit.

5 units ⟶ 950 mL
1 unit ⟶ 950 ÷ 5 = 190 mL

At the beginning, the bottle had 50 more liters than 1 unit.

Bottle: 190 + 50 = 240 mL
Jug: 950 – bottle, so 950 – 240 = 710 mL

Exercise 6 • page 36

Objective

- Practice concepts from the chapter.

After students complete the practice in the textbook, have them continue to practice skills using activities from the chapter.

44

Lesson 7
Practice

P 7

1. What sign, >, <, or =, goes in each ◯?

(a) (7 × 1,000,000) + (8 × 10,000) (<) 760,000,000

(b) (50 + 30) × 9 (=) 9 × (100 − 20)

(c) 7 × (100 − 8) (<) 98 × 7

(d) 500,000 × 400 − 500,000 × 40 (>) 500,000 × 320

2. Find the values.

(a) 3,000 − (575 + 128)
3,000 − 703 = 2,297

(b) (600 + 1,400) ÷ 40
2,000 ÷ 40 = 50

(c) 235 + 37 × 6
235 + 222 = 457

(d) 5,000 − 800 ÷ 4
5,000 − 200 = 4,800

(e) (1,200 − 400) × (45 − 5 × 3)
800 × (45 − 15) = 800 × 30 = 24,000

(f) (40 ÷ 5 − 6) + 90 ÷ 9 × 7
(8 − 6) + 10 × 7 = 2 + 70 = 72

(g) 2,000 × (25 + 15 × 2)
2,000 × (25 + 30) = 2,000 × 55 = 110,000

(h) (60,000 + 20,000) × 90 ÷ (1,500 − 700)
80,000 × 90 ÷ 800 = 7,200,000 ÷ 800 = 9,000

44 2-7 Practice

45

3. The friends below wrote some of their steps when they calculated 5 + 90 ÷ 5 × 2 − 6. Whose answer is correct? What did the others do wrong?

5 + 90 ÷ 5 × 2 − 6 = 95 ÷ 5 × 2 − 6 = 19 × 2 − 6 = 32	5 + 90 ÷ 5 × 2 − 6 = 5 + 90 ÷ 10 − 6 = 5 + 9 − 6 = 8	5 + 90 ÷ 5 × 2 − 6 = 5 + 18 × 2 − 6 = 5 + 36 − 6 = 35

Alex added first, which is incorrect.

Dion multiplied first, which is incorrect.

Sofia calculated in the correct order.

4.

Abigail got 50 glow-in-the-dark stickers and 2 packs of 20 neon stickers from the planetarium gift shop. She gave 15 stickers to each of her 2 brothers and 5 stickers to each of her 5 friends. How many stickers does she have left?

Total stickers: 50 + 2 × 20 = 90
Stickers given away: 2 × 15 + 5 × 5 = 55
Stickers left: 90 − 55 = 35

2-7 Practice 45

5

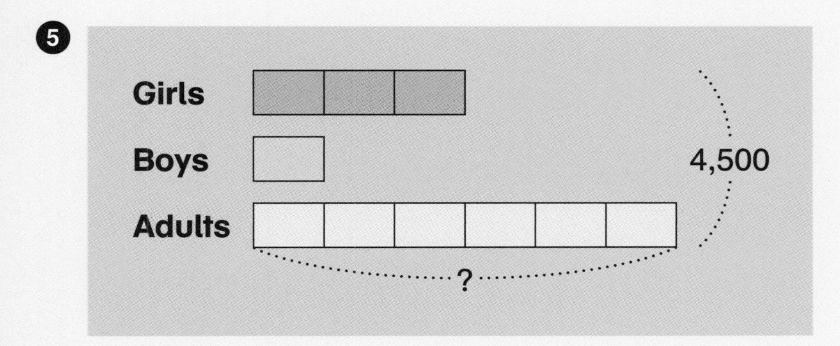

6

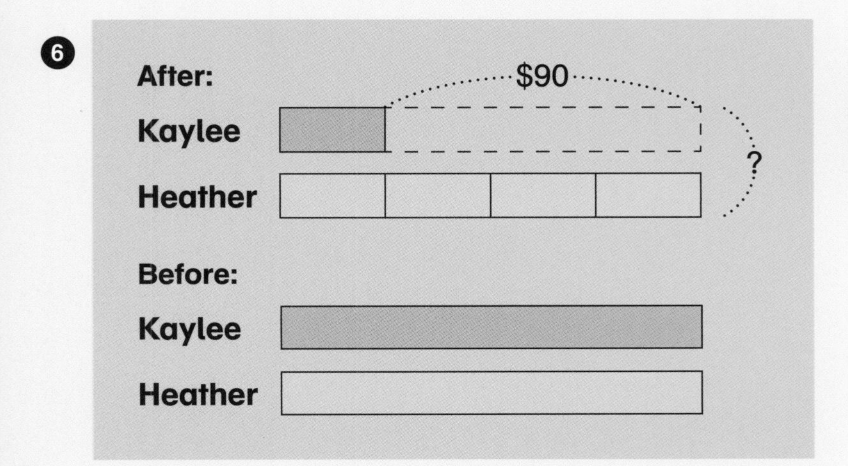

7

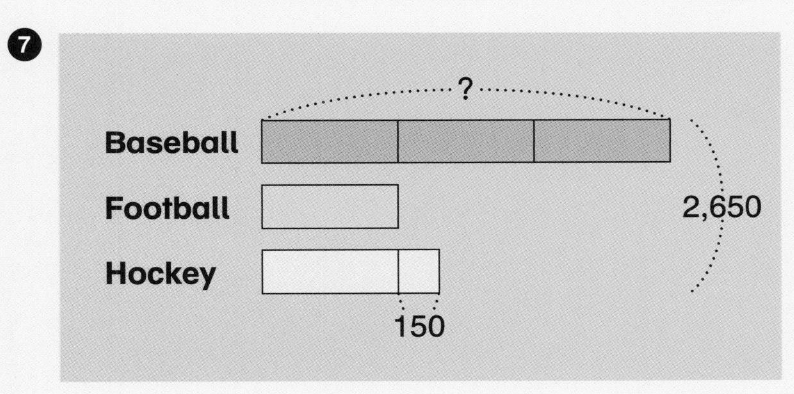

8

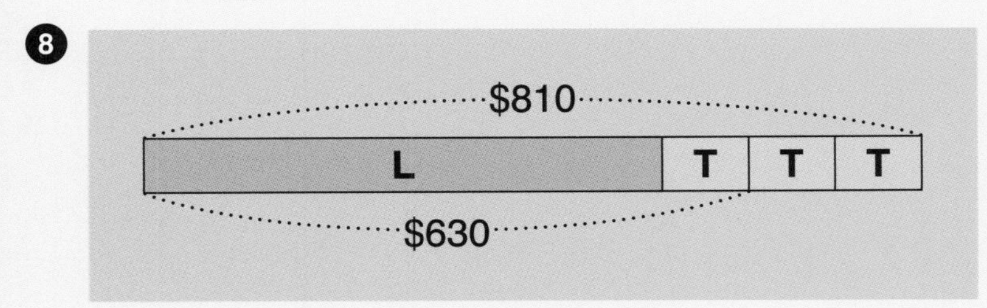

46

5

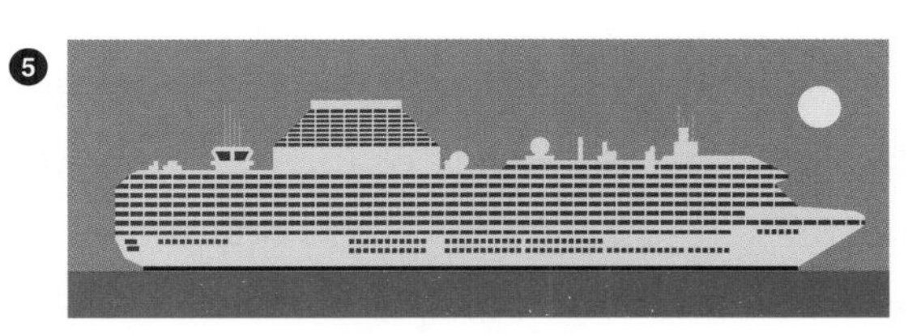

There are 3 times as many girls as boys on a cruise ship. There are twice as many adults as girls. There are 4,500 people altogether on the cruise ship. How many adults are there?
4,500 ÷ 10 × 6; 2,700 adults

6 Kaylee and Heather had the same amount of money at first. After Kaylee spent $90, Heather had 4 times as much money as Kaylee. How much money did they have altogether at first?
90 ÷ 3 × 8 = 240; $240

7 Ryan collected 2,650 baseball cards, football cards, and hockey cards. He has 3 times as many baseball cards as football cards. He has 150 more hockey cards than football cards. How many baseball cards does he have? 1 unit ⟶ (2,650 − 150) ÷ 5 = 500
3 units ⟶ 500 × 3 = 1,500;
1,500 baseball cards

8 A laptop and 3 tablets cost $810. A laptop and 1 tablet cost $630. How much does one laptop cost? How much does one tablet cost?
2 tablets: 810 − 630 = 180
1 tablet: 180 ÷ 2 = 90; $90; 1 laptop: 630 − 90 = 540; $540

9 Box A and Box B contained a total of 18,000 nails. After 2,500 nails were transferred from Box A to Box B, Box A had 3,000 more nails than Box B. How many nails did Box A have at first? 2 units ⟶ 18,000 − 3,000 = 15,000
1 unit ⟶ 15,000 ÷ 2 = 7,500
7,500 + 3,000 + 2,500 = 13,000

Exercise 7 • page 41

46 2-7 Practice

9

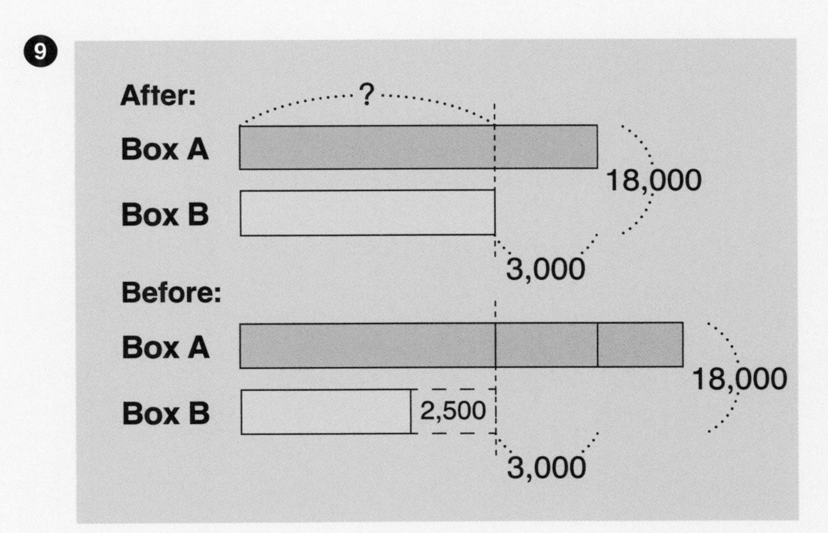

Exercise 7 • page 41

Brain Works

★ Order and Operate

Using the digits 1–4 and any of the four operations and parentheses to create expressions, how many whole number solutions can you find?

Rules:

- Number order cannot be changed.
- Numbers can be groups.
- Numbers can be combined to make two-digit numbers.
- All numbers must be used in each solution.

Note: The solutions can be any whole numbers.

Some sample solutions:

$12 - 3 \times 4 = 0$
$1 \times 2 + 3 - 4 = 1$
$1 + 2 + 3 - 4 = 2$
$1 + 2 \times 3 - 4 = 3$
$(1 + 2) \times 3 - 4 = 5$ or $12 - 3 - 4 = 5$
$(1 + 23) \div 4 = 6$ or $\frac{1}{2} \times (3 \times 4) = 6$
$12 \div 3 + 4 = 8$
$12 \times 3 \div 4 = 9$
$1 + 2 + 3 + 4 = 10$
$1 + (2 \times 3) + 4 = 11$
$12 - 3 + 4 = 13$
$1 \times 2 + 3 \times 4 = 14$
$1 + 2 + 3 \times 4 = 15$
$12 \div 3 \times 4 = 16$
$\frac{1}{2} \times 34 = 17$

Chapter 2 Writing and Evaluating Expressions

Exercise 1

Basics

In general, calculate from left to right.
Find the value in parentheses first.

1 75 craft sticks are required to make a large box, and 25 craft sticks are required to make a small box. Aisha is making sets that include one large and one small box. How many sets could she make with 500 craft sticks?

Total craft sticks ÷ Number of craft sticks per set

= 500 ÷ (75 + 25)

= 500 ÷ 100

= 5

2 

(a) 800 − 120 + 250

= 680 + 250

= 930

(b) 800 − (120 + 250)

= 800 − 370

= 430

(c) 320 ÷ 4 × 5

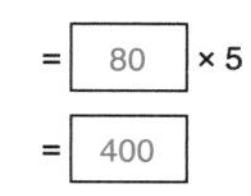

= 80 × 5

= 400

(d) 320 ÷ (4 × 5)

= 320 ÷ 20

= 16

Practice

3 Find the values.

(a) 400 − 53 − 27
320

(b) 400 − (53 − 27)
374

(c) 81 ÷ 9 ÷ 3
3

(d) 81 ÷ (9 ÷ 3)
27

(e) 180 ÷ (2 × 3)
30

(f) 4 × (60 − 22)
152

(g) 10,000 ÷ (48 ÷ 6)
1,250

(h) 640,000 ÷ (7,000 − 3,000)
160

4 Jamal had a package of 200 pipe cleaners. He made 3 woven baskets. Each basket used 35 pipe cleaners. Write an expression to find the number of pipe cleaners he has left, and then find the value.
200 − (3 × 35) = 95
95 pipe cleaners

Challenge

5 In each of the following, use each of the numbers 9, 3, and 3 once to make the equations true. Solutions may vary.

(a) 9 × 3 ÷ 3 = 9

(b) 9 ÷ 3 − 3 = 0

(c) 9 × (3 − 3) = 0

(d) 3 × (9 ÷ 3) = 9

(e) 9 − 3 − 3 = 3

(f) 9 ÷ (3 × 3) = 1

(g) 9 + (3 − 3) = 9

(h) 3 − 3 + 9 = 9

Exercise 2

Basics

In general, calculate from left to right.
Do multiplication and/or division first.
Then do addition and/or subtraction.

1 Jett is making 2 boxes and 3 picture frames using craft sticks. Each box requires 125 sticks and each picture frame requires 75 sticks. How many craft sticks does he need?

Number of sticks for box + Number of sticks for frame
= 2 × 125 + 3 × 75
= [250] + [225]
= [475]

2 (a) 15 + 500 ÷ 2
= 15 + [250]
= [265]

(b) 4 × 2 − 10 ÷ 5
= [8] − [2]
= [6]

(c) 54 − 8 × 5 + 10
= 54 − [40] + 10
= [14] + 10
= [24]

(d) 75 − 420 ÷ 7 + 3 × 15
= 75 − [60] + [45]
= [15] + [45]
= [60]

Practice

3 Find the values.

(a) 64 − 3 × 9
37

(b) 200 − 125 ÷ 25
195

(c) 200 + 25 × 4
300

(d) 75 ÷ 5 − 4 × 3
3

(e) 30 + 24 ÷ 4 − 2
34

(f) 88 + 18 ÷ 3 − 4 × 6
70

(g) 10 + 12 × 8 − 108 ÷ 9 + 6
100

(h) 5,000 − 360,000 ÷ 400 + 12,000
16,100

4 At a banquet, there are 45 tables that can seat 6 people and 82 tables that can seat 8 people. Write an expression to find the total number of seats, and then find the value.
45 × 6 + 82 × 8 = 926
926 tables

Challenge

5 Write +, −, or × between each number to make each equation true.

(a) 5 × 5 × 5 − 5 × 5 = 100
Answers may vary.

(b) 1 + 2 + 3 + 4 + 5 + 6 + 7 + 8 × 9 = 100

Exercise 3

Basics

In general, calculate from left to right.
If there are parentheses, find the value in parentheses first.
Do multiplication and/or division first, then addition and/or subtraction.

1 (a) $105 - 15 \div 3 \times 6 + 4 \div 2$

$= 105 - \boxed{5} \times 6 + 4 \div 2$

$= 105 - \boxed{30} + 4 \div 2$

$= 105 - 30 + \boxed{2}$

$= \boxed{75} + 2$

$= \boxed{77}$

(b) $(105 - 15 \div 3) \times (6 + 4) \div 2$

$= (105 - \boxed{5}) \times (6 + 4) \div 2$

$= \boxed{100} \times (6 + 4) \div 2$

$= 100 \times \boxed{10} \div 2$

$= \boxed{1{,}000} \div 2$

$= \boxed{500}$

(c) $(105 - 15) \div 3 \times (6 + 4 \div 2)$

$= \boxed{90} \div 3 \times (6 + 4 \div 2)$

$= 90 \div 3 \times (6 + \boxed{2})$

$= 90 \div 3 \times \boxed{8}$

$= \boxed{30} \times 8$

$= \boxed{240}$

(d) $105 - (15 \div 3) \times (6 + 4) \div 2$

$= 105 - \boxed{5} \times (6 + 4) \div 2$

$= 105 - 5 \times \boxed{10} \div 2$

$= 105 - \boxed{50} \div 2$

$= 105 - \boxed{25}$

$= \boxed{80}$

Practice

2 Find the values.

(a) $80 \div 8 \times 2 - 6 \div 2$
17

(b) $80 \div (8 \times 2 - 6) \div 2$
4

(c) $25 + 25 \div 5 \times 5 \div 25 - 5$
21

(d) $4 \times 4 \times (4 + 4 \div 4) \div 4 - 4 \times 4 + 4$
8

(e) $9{,}000 \div (1{,}800 \div 30 \times 20 \div 4)$
30

3 Andrei has 1,000 craft sticks. He used 250 craft sticks to make a boat. Then he made some birdhouses that each required 35 sticks for the base and 15 sticks for the roof. He used all of his craft sticks. Write an expression to find the number of birdhouses he made, and then find the value.
$(1{,}000 - 250) \div (35 + 15) = 15$
15 birdhouses

Challenge

4 Write +, −, ×, or ÷ in the ◯ to make each equation true.

(a) 12 − 8 ÷ 4 (×) 3 = 6

(b) 12 ÷ (8 (+) 4) + 4 = 5

(c) (12 − 8 (−) 4) × 4 = 0

(d) 12 (÷) (8 (÷) 4 × 2) = 3

5 Write +, −, ×, ÷, or ( ) between the numbers to make each equation true.
Solutions may vary.

(a) (4 + 4) − (4 + 4) = 0

(b) (4 + 4) ÷ (4 + 4) = 1

(c) 4 ÷ 4 + 4 ÷ 4 = 2

(d) (4 + 4 + 4) ÷ 4 = 3

(e) 4 × (4 − 4) + 4 = 4

(f) (4 × 4 + 4) ÷ 4 = 5

(g) (4 + 4) ÷ 4 + 4 = 6

(h) 4 + 4 − 4 ÷ 4 = 7

(i) 4 + 4 + 4 − 4 = 8

(j) 4 ÷ 4 + 4 + 4 = 9

Exercise 4

Basics

1 Charlotte made 11 large picture frames and 11 small picture frames using craft sticks. The large picture frames each required 75 sticks and the small frames each required 35 sticks. We can find the total number of craft sticks she used in two different ways:

11 × (75 + 35)   or   11 × 75 + 11 × 35

= 11 × [110]   = 825 + [385]

= [1,210]   = [1,210]

Write the missing numbers.

11 × (75 + 35) = [11] × 75 + 11 × [35]

2 3,998 × 45 = (4,000 − 2) × 45

= [4,000] × 45 − [2] × 45

= [180,000] − [90]

= [179,910]

3 25 × 59 = 25 × (60 − 1)

= 25 × [60] − 25 × [1]

= [1,500] − [25]

= [1,475]

4 125 × 8 = (100 + [25]) × 8

= [100] × 8 + [25] × 8

= [800] + [200]

= [1,000]

Practice

5 Find the values. Think of ways to simplify the calculation first.

Methods may vary.

(a) 7 × 199
= 7 × 200 − 7 × 1
= 1,400 − 7
= 1,393

(b) 4 × 9,125
= 4 × 9,000 + 4 × 100 + 4 × 25
= 36,000 + 400 + 100
= 36,500

(c) 25 × 38
= 25 × 30 + 25 × 8
= 750 + 200
= 950

(d) 42 × 32 + 42 × 68
= 42 × (32 + 68)
= 42 × 100
= 4,200

6 Write >, <, or = in the ◯ to make each equation true.

(a) 78 × 54 (=) 78 × 50 + 78 × 4

(b) 8 × 38 − 8 × 9 (>) 8 × 28

(c) 63 × 5 (>) (60 × 5) − (3 × 5)

(d) (700 − 3) × 7 (=) 7 × 697

(e) 3,009 × 9 (<) 3,000 × 9 × 9 + 9

(f) 27 × 8 + 6 × 8 (>) (27 + 8) × 6

Challenge

7 (a) 7,925 × 8 = (8,000 − 100 + [25]) × 8

= [8,000] × 8 − [100] × 8 + [25] × 8

= [64,000] − [800] + [200]

= [63,400]

(b) 4,799 × 6 = (5,000 − [200] − 1) × 6

= [5,000] × 6 − [200] × 6 − [1] × 6

= [30,000] − [1,200] − [6]

= [28,794]

Exercise 5 • pages 31–35

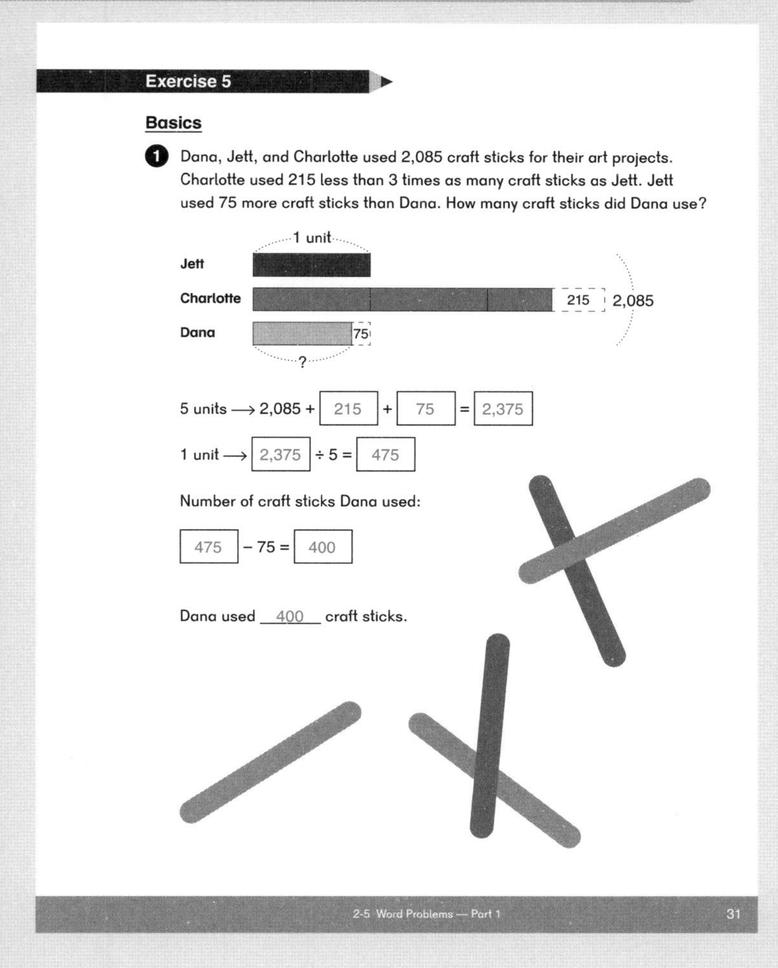

Exercise 5

Basics

1. Dana, Jett, and Charlotte used 2,085 craft sticks for their art projects. Charlotte used 215 less than 3 times as many craft sticks as Jett. Jett used 75 more craft sticks than Dana. How many craft sticks did Dana use?

5 units ⟶ 2,085 + 215 + 75 = 2,375

1 unit ⟶ 2,375 ÷ 5 = 475

Number of craft sticks Dana used:

475 − 75 = 400

Dana used 400 craft sticks.

2-5 Word Problems — Part 1 31

2. Holly and Carlos together have \$137. Ella and Carlos together have \$261. Ella has 3 times as much money as Holly. How much money does Carlos have?

\$137

Carlos	Holly

\$261

Carlos	Ella

? 1 unit

2 units ⟶ 261 − 137 = 124

1 unit ⟶ 124 ÷ 2 = 62

Amount Carlos has: 137 − 62 = 75

Carlos has \$ 75 .

3. An armchair cost \$122 more than a couch. Andrei bought 2 armchairs and 1 couch for \$1,078. How much did the couch cost?

Couch
Armchair \$1,078
Armchair
\$122

3 units ⟶ 1,078 − (2 × 122) = 834

1 unit ⟶ 834 ÷ 3 = 278

The couch cost \$ 278 .

32 2-5 Word Problems — Part 1

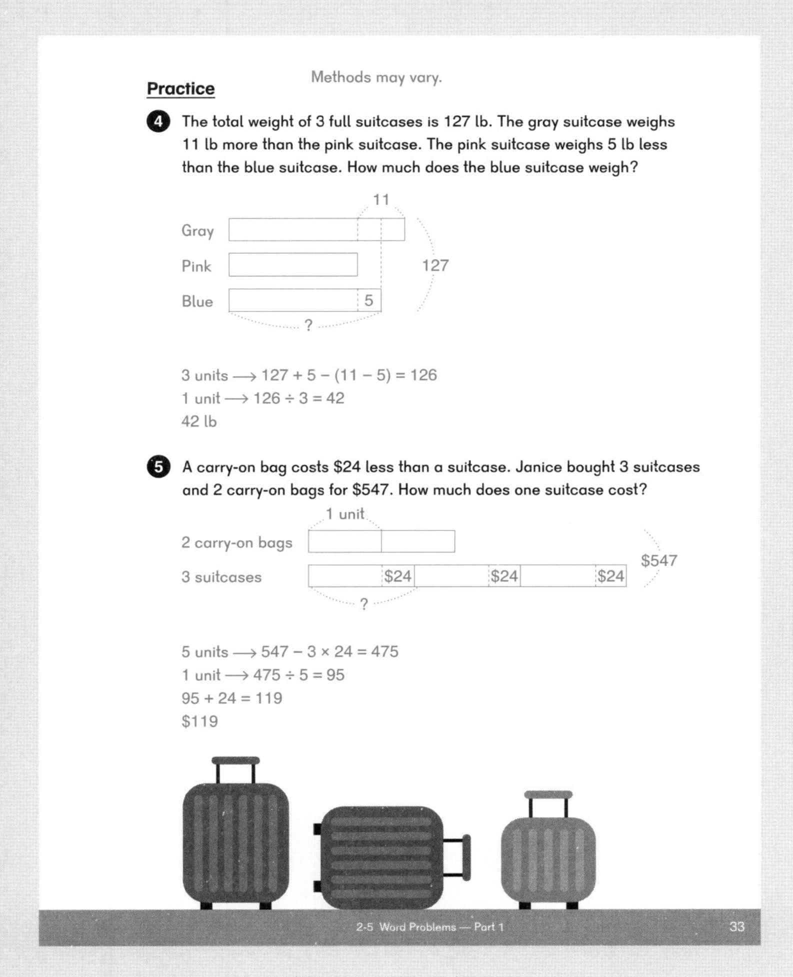

Practice

Methods may vary.

4. The total weight of 3 full suitcases is 127 lb. The gray suitcase weighs 11 lb more than the pink suitcase. The pink suitcase weighs 5 lb less than the blue suitcase. How much does the blue suitcase weigh?

3 units ⟶ 127 + 5 − (11 − 5) = 126
1 unit ⟶ 126 ÷ 3 = 42
42 lb

5. A carry-on bag costs \$24 less than a suitcase. Janice bought 3 suitcases and 2 carry-on bags for \$547. How much does one suitcase cost?

5 units ⟶ 547 − 3 × 24 = 475
1 unit ⟶ 475 ÷ 5 = 95
95 + 24 = 119
\$119

2-5 Word Problems — Part 1 33

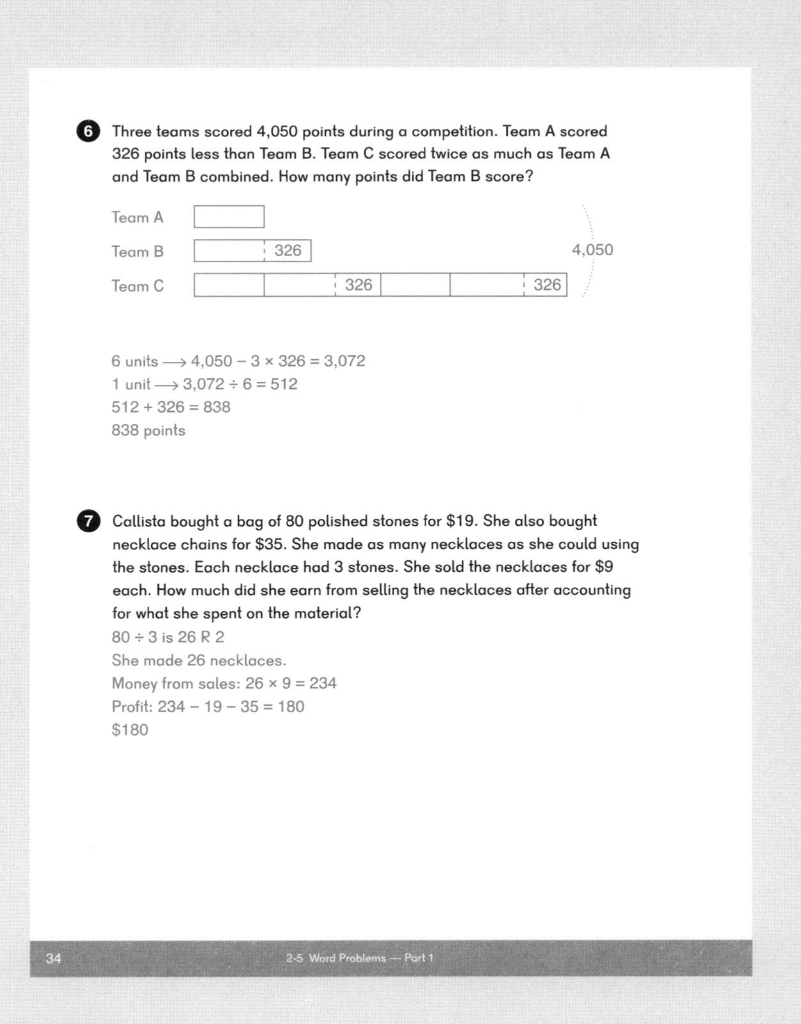

6. Three teams scored 4,050 points during a competition. Team A scored 326 points less than Team B. Team C scored twice as much as Team A and Team B combined. How many points did Team B score?

6 units ⟶ 4,050 − 3 × 326 = 3,072
1 unit ⟶ 3,072 ÷ 6 = 512
512 + 326 = 838
838 points

7. Callista bought a bag of 80 polished stones for \$19. She also bought necklace chains for \$35. She made as many necklaces as she could using the stones. Each necklace had 3 stones. She sold the necklaces for \$9 each. How much did she earn from selling the necklaces after accounting for what she spent on the material?

80 ÷ 3 is 26 R 2
She made 26 necklaces.
Money from sales: 26 × 9 = 234
Profit: 234 − 19 − 35 = 180
\$180

34 2-5 Word Problems — Part 1

Challenge

8 Mia, Xavier, and Micah have a total of $248. Mia and Xavier together have $165. Xavier and Micah together have $128. How much money do each of them have?

Overlap: (165 + 128) – 248 = 45
Xavier: $45
Mia: 165 – 45 = 120
Mia: $120
Micah: 128 – 45 = 83
Micah: $83

9 In a pet store, five goldfish cost as much as two tropical fish. If 10 goldfish cost $20, how many tropical fish could someone buy for $40?

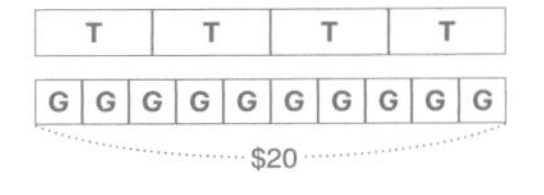

5 goldfish ⟶ 2 tropical fish
10 goldfish ⟶ 4 tropical fish
$20 ⟶ 10 goldfish
$40 ⟶ 20 goldfish
20 goldfish ⟶ 8 tropical fish
8 tropical fish

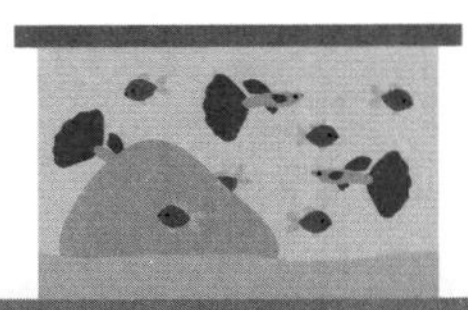

Exercise 6 • pages 36–40

Exercise 6

Basics

1 Maria collected 630 more ornaments than her cousin. After she gave 90 ornaments to her cousin, she had 3 times as many ornaments as her cousin. How many ornaments did Maria have at first?

Since we know that Maria had 3 times as many ornaments as her cousin after she gave ornaments to her cousin, we can draw that model first.

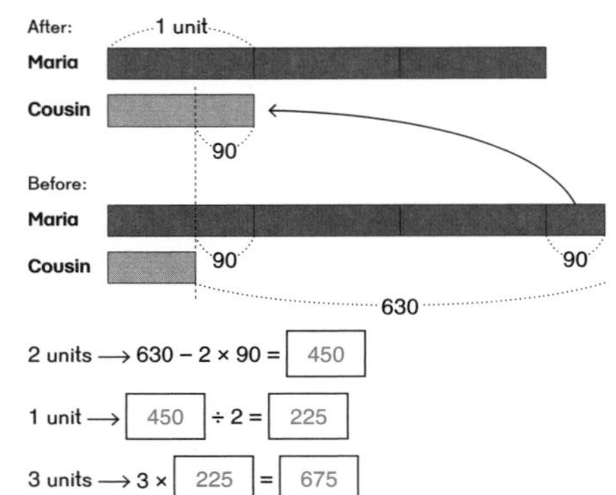

2 units ⟶ 630 – 2 × 90 = 450

1 unit ⟶ 450 ÷ 2 = 225

3 units ⟶ 3 × 225 = 675

Number of ornaments Maria had before:

675 + 90 = 765

Maria had 765 ornaments at first.

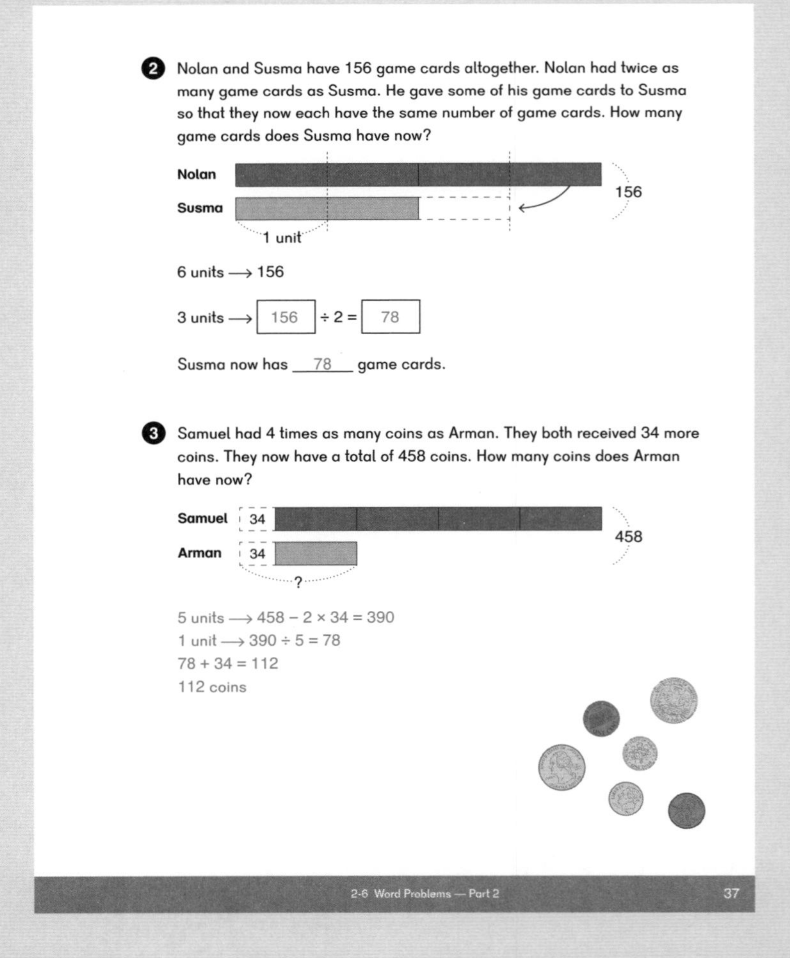

2 Nolan and Susma have 156 game cards altogether. Nolan had twice as many game cards as Susma. He gave some of his game cards to Susma so that they now each have the same number of game cards. How many game cards does Susma have now?

6 units ⟶ 156

3 units ⟶ 156 ÷ 2 = 78

Susma now has 78 game cards.

3 Samuel had 4 times as many coins as Arman. They both received 34 more coins. They now have a total of 458 coins. How many coins does Arman have now?

5 units ⟶ 458 – 2 × 34 = 390
1 unit ⟶ 390 ÷ 5 = 78
78 + 34 = 112
112 coins

Practice

Methods may vary.

4 2 dresses and 4 shirts cost \$64. 2 dresses and 7 shirts cost \$85. How much do 3 dresses and 3 shirts cost?

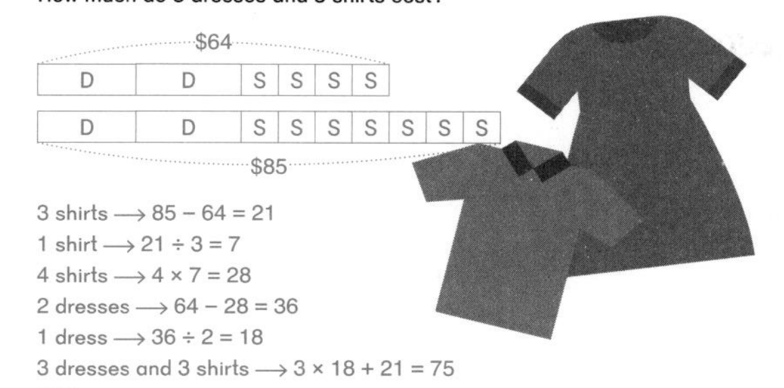

3 shirts ⟶ 85 − 64 = 21
1 shirt ⟶ 21 ÷ 3 = 7
4 shirts ⟶ 4 × 7 = 28
2 dresses ⟶ 64 − 28 = 36
1 dress ⟶ 36 ÷ 2 = 18
3 dresses and 3 shirts ⟶ 3 × 18 + 21 = 75
\$75

5 Sharif and his sister had the same amount of money. After Sharif spent \$75 and his sister spent \$37, his sister had 3 times as much money as Sharif. How much money did Sharif have at first?

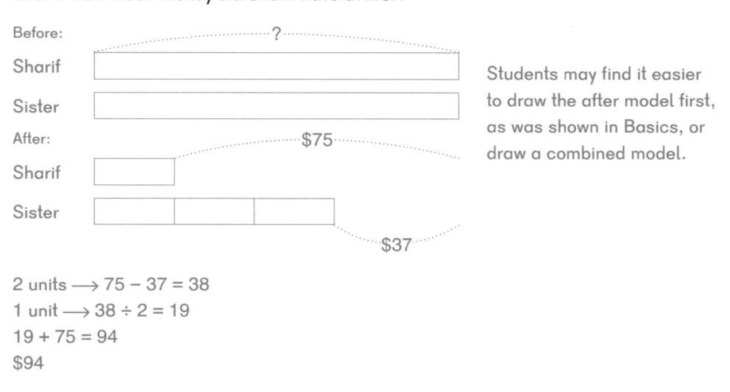

Students may find it easier to draw the after model first, as was shown in Basics, or draw a combined model.

2 units ⟶ 75 − 37 = 38
1 unit ⟶ 38 ÷ 2 = 19
19 + 75 = 94
\$94

6 Nora and Renata had an equal number of polished stones at first. After Nora received 65 more stones and Renata lost 23 stones, Nora had three times as many stones as Renata. How many stones did they have altogether at first?

After:
Nora
Renata
Before:
Nora 65
Renata 23

Students may instead draw the before model first.

2 units ⟶ 65 + 23 = 88
1 unit ⟶ 88 ÷ 2 = 44
2 × (44 + 23) = 134
134 stones

7 Tank A had 4 times as much water as Tank B. After 30 L of water was transferred from Tank A to Tank B, Tank B had 24 more L of water than Tank A. How much water is in both tanks altogether?

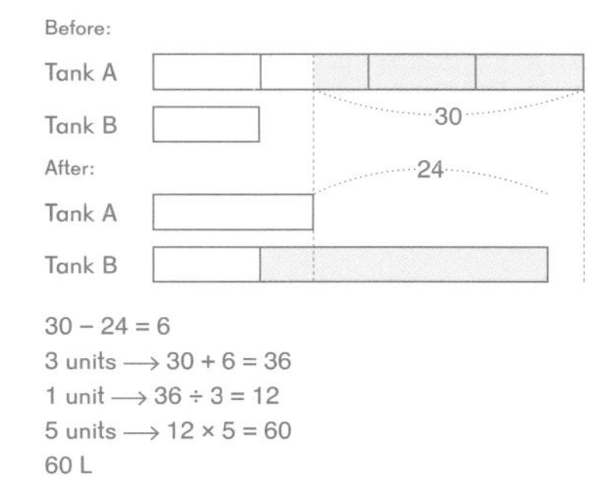

30 − 24 = 6
3 units ⟶ 30 + 6 = 36
1 unit ⟶ 36 ÷ 3 = 12
5 units ⟶ 12 × 5 = 60
60 L

Challenge

8 4 children collected a total of 529 seashells. Then, Logan found 26 more seashells. Mila doubled her seashells. Noah lost 42 seashells. Olivia lost half of her seashells. All 4 children now have an equal number of seashells. How many seashells did Noah have to begin with?

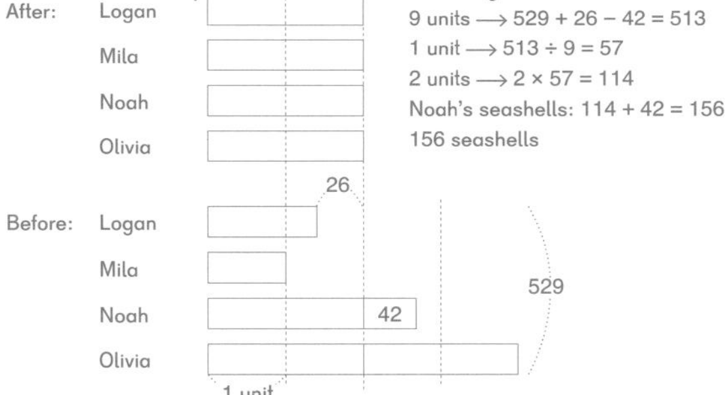

9 units ⟶ 529 + 26 − 42 = 513
1 unit ⟶ 513 ÷ 9 = 57
2 units ⟶ 2 × 57 = 114
Noah's seashells: 114 + 42 = 156
156 seashells

9 3 friends divided some strawberries equally. After they each ate 4 strawberries, the total number of strawberries left was equal to the amount each friend had at the beginning. How many strawberries were there at first?

Each person ate 4 strawberries, which is 12 strawberries altogether.

After: 12
Before:

2 units ⟶ 12
1 unit ⟶ 12 ÷ 2 = 6
3 units ⟶ 3 × 6 = 18
18 strawberries

Exercise 7

Check

1. Find the values.

(a) 72 ÷ (5 + 4) × 6
48

(b) 42 ÷ 7 × 3 − 11 + 9
16

(c) 76 + 24 ÷ 12 × 7 − 26
64

(d) 11 + 56 ÷ 8 × 24
179

(e) 36 ÷ (28 − 2 × 8) ÷ 3
1

(f) 44 − 24 ÷ 4 + 3 × 5
53

(g) 101 + 8 × (12 − 4) − 3 + 15
177

2. (a) 42 × 87 = 42 × 90 − 42 × [3]

(b) 113 × 456 + 113 × 544 = 113 × [1,000]

(c) 312 × 3,002 = 312 × [3,000] + [312] × 2

3. Use each of the given numbers once to make each equation true.
Solutions may vary.

(a) 1, 2, 3, 4

([1] + [2]) + ([4] − [3]) = 4

(b) 2, 3, 4, 5

([5] − [4]) + ([2] × [3]) = 7

(c) 1, 2, 4, 5, 7

[4] × ([1] + [2]) = [5] + [7]

4. 2 ropes are the same length. After cutting 50 m from Rope A and 14 m from Rope B, Rope B is 3 times as long as Rope A. Find the length of Rope B.

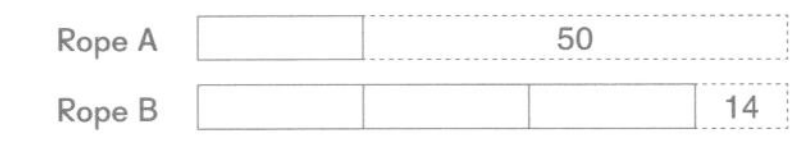

2 units ⟶ 50 − 14 = 36
1 unit ⟶ 36 ÷ 2 = 18
Rope B: 3 × 18 + 14 = 68
68 m

5. Diego spent $3,100 on a laptop, a VR headset, and a gaming mouse. The laptop cost $1,900 more than the mouse and VR headset combined. The VR headset cost 3 times as much as the mouse. How much did the VR headset cost?

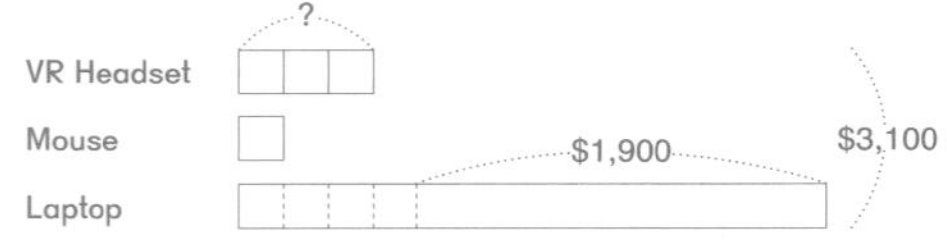

8 units ⟶ 3,100 − 1,900 = 1,200
1 unit ⟶ 1,200 ÷ 8 = 150
3 units ⟶ 3 × 150 = 450
$450

6. Patrick had 2,000 ducks and chickens on his farm. He had 3 times as many chickens as ducks. After selling some chickens, he now has twice as many ducks as chickens. How many chickens did he sell?

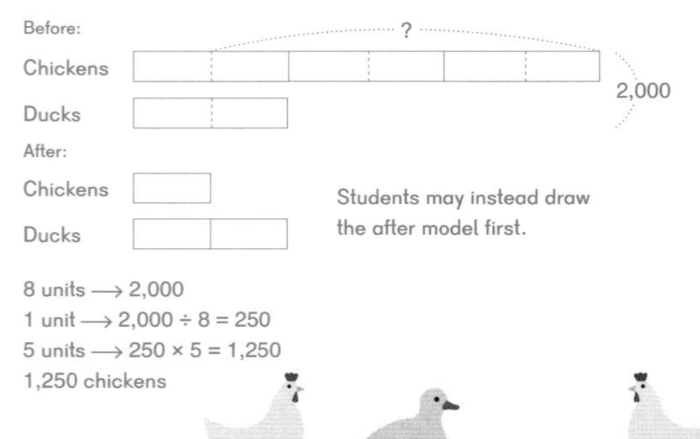

8 units ⟶ 2,000
1 unit ⟶ 2,000 ÷ 8 = 250
5 units ⟶ 250 × 5 = 1,250
1,250 chickens

Challenge

7. 4 stools cost as much as 3 chairs. 5 stools cost $28 more than 2 chairs. How much do 2 stools and 2 chairs cost?

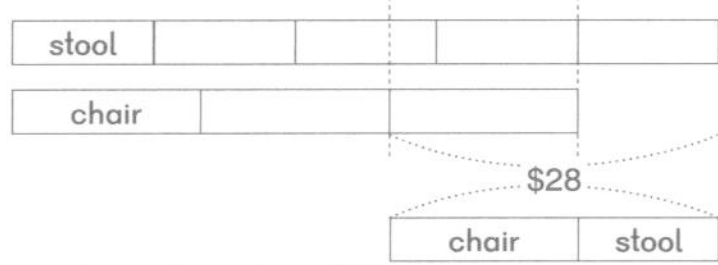

1 chair + 1 stool ⟶ $28
2 chairs + 2 stools ⟶ 2 × $28 ⟶ $56
$56

8. Write +, −, ×, ÷, or ( ) between the numbers to make each equation true.
Solutions may vary.

(a) (5 + 5) ÷ 5 − 5 ÷ 5 = 1

(b) (5 + 5 + 5 − 5) ÷ 5 = 2

(c) 5 − 5 ÷ 5 − 5 ÷ 5 = 3

(d) (5 + 5 + 5 + 5) ÷ 5 = 4

(e) 5 + 5 − 5 + 5 − 5 = 5

(f) 5 + 5 − 5 + 5 ÷ 5 = 6

(g) 5 + 5 ÷ 5 + 5 ÷ 5 = 7

(h) 5 + (5 + 5 + 5) ÷ 5 = 8

(i) 5 + (5 × 5 − 5) ÷ 5 = 9

(j) (5 × 5 + 5 × 5) ÷ 5 = 10

Suggested number of class periods: 9–10

	Lesson	Page	Resources	Objectives
	Chapter Opener	p. 69	TB: p. 47	Investigate multiplication of multi-digit numbers.
1	Multiplying by a 2-digit Number — Part 1	p. 70	TB: p. 48 WB: p. 45	Review multiplying two-digit and three-digit numbers by a two-digit number. Review estimation strategies.
2	Multiplying by a 2-digit Number — Part 2	p. 74	TB: p. 52 WB: p. 49	Multiply up to a five-digit number by a two-digit number.
3	Practice A	p. 77	TB: p. 56 WB: p. 52	Practice multiplying by a two-digit number.
4	Dividing by a Multiple of Ten	p. 78	TB: p. 57 WB: p. 56	Divide a two-digit or three-digit number by a multiple of ten.
5	Divide a 2-digit Number by a 2-digit Number	p. 80	TB: p. 60 WB: p. 59	Divide a two-digit number by a two-digit divisor.
6	Divide a 3-digit Number by a 2-digit Number — Part 1	p. 82	TB: p. 63 WB: p. 61	Divide a three-digit number by a two-digit divisor resulting in a one-digit quotient.
7	Divide a 3-digit Number by a 2-digit Number — Part 2	p. 84	TB: p. 66 WB: p. 63	Divide a three-digit number by a two-digit divisor resulting in a two-digit quotient.
8	Divide a 4-digit Number by a 2-digit Number	p. 87	TB: p. 70 WB: p. 66	Divide a four-digit number by a two-digit divisor.
9	Practice B	p. 90	TB: p. 74 WB: p. 69	Practice dividing by a two-digit divisor.
	Workbook Solutions	p. 91		

In Dimensions Math 4A, students learned how to use the standard algorithm to multiply up to a three-digit number by a two-digit number and to divide up to a four-digit number by a one-digit number.

In this chapter, students will extend the multiplication algorithm to multiply a four-digit or five-digit number by a two-digit number. They will then learn to divide up to a five-digit dividend by a two-digit divisor using the standard algorithm.

Multiplication Algorithm

In Lesson 1, students will review multiplication of two-digit and three-digit numbers by a two-digit number. Students will use rounding, multiplying by tens, and mental math to estimate products.

For multiplication problems that require regrouping, the regrouped numbers are not always shown in the textbook. Students can write the regrouped digits as needed.

```
   1 1
   2̸ 2̸
  6,817
×    23
 20,451  ←  6,817 × 3
136,340  ←  6,817 × 20
156,791
```

Students can cross off the regrouping marks after they have completed multiplying by the ones, and record the regrouping for multiplying by the tens above the crossed off numbers.

Students who can work mentally with the regrouped numbers do not need to write the regrouped digits.

Students who need additional practice with lining up numbers by the correct place value can practice either on graph paper or wide-ruled notebook paper turned sideways, so that the lines make columns.

Students should be comfortable with all the steps in the multiplication algorithm, including regrouping.

For a more basic review of the multiplication algorithm, reference Dimensions Math 4A Chapter 4, and Dimensions Math 3A Chapter 5.

Area Models

An area model is a way to see the partial products and can be shown to students if needed. Students calculate the area of smaller portions of the entire rectangle and add them together to find the area of the whole shape.

For example, when multiplying 6,817 × 23:

	6,000	800	10	7
20	6,000 × 20 = 120,000	800 × 20 = 16,000	10 × 20 = 200	7 × 20 = 140
3	6,000 × 3 = 18,000	800 × 3 = 2,400	10 × 3 = 30	7 × 3 = 21

```
   6,817
×     23
      21  ←  7 × 3        ⎫
      30  ←  10 × 3       ⎪
   2,400  ←  800 × 3      ⎬ 6,817 × 3
  18,000  ←  6,000 × 3    ⎭
     140  ←  7 × 20       ⎫
     200  ←  10 × 20      ⎪
  16,000  ←  800 × 20     ⎬ 6,817 × 20
 120,000  ←  6,000 × 20   ⎭
 156,791
```

Using an area model and partial products for large multi-digit computations is cumbersome, and students should master the standard algorithm.

Division Algorithm

Lessons 4 – 8 focus on the division algorithm. Students will learn the terms "dividend" (the number being divided) and "divisor" (the number the dividend is divided by). Students will apply their knowledge of multiplication to estimate quotients in division problems.

Estimation in division problems can be challenging, especially for students still struggling with basic multiplication and division facts. Estimation requires more number sense than rounding to a given place. Students will use their knowledge of multiplication facts to find a convenient multiple of the divisor in order to estimate.

The goal is for students to find numbers close to those in the problem to find an estimate, and to use that estimate to check if their answers are reasonable. Estimation is an important skill for students to develop prior to dividing by two-digit divisors.

Example: $98 \div 32$

Students can estimate $90 \div 30 = 3$.

The answer should be about 3.

The division algorithm requires an understanding of all four operations, as well as place value, regrouping, and estimation. The division algorithm for dividing by two-digit numbers is a set of steps involving estimation when dividing, repeated for each place value in the dividend.

For a more basic review of the division algorithm with single digit divisors, reference Dimensions Math 3A Chapter 6.

Since Dimensions Math 1B, students have considered both sharing and grouping interpretations for division. In the sharing interpretation, $84 \div 3$ can be thought of as sharing 84 into 3 groups, with 28 in each group. In the grouping interpretation, $84 \div 3$ can be thought of as grouping 84 by 3, which gives 28 groups.

When students learned the algorithm for dividing by a one-digit number, they used a sharing model with the place-value discs. In these lessons they will use a grouping model when using place-value discs, since, for example, dividing 98 into 32 groups is cumbersome.

In Lessons 4 – 6, students will begin with place-value discs by making groups, with each group containing the number of the divisor.

Example: $98 \div 32$

Estimate: $90 \div 30 = 3$. The answer will be ≈ 3.

There are 3 groups of 32 with two 1-discs remaining.

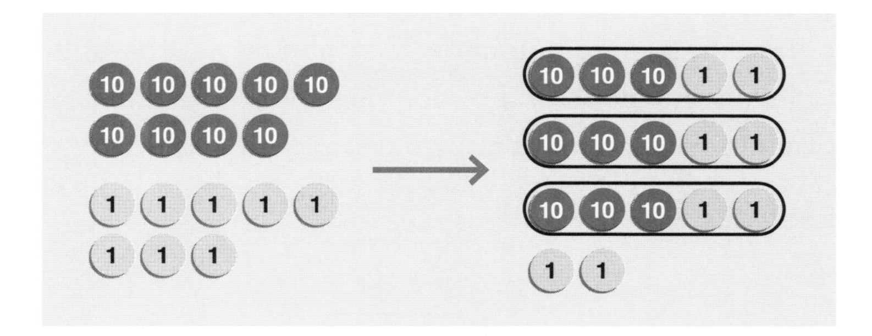

Students will relate the discs to the algorithm:

```
32)98
```

Since the estimated quotient was 3, we can start with 3 groups of 32, or $32 \times 3 = 96$.

The product, 96, is less than the dividend, 98.

```
     3
32)98
   96  ←  32 × 3
    2  ←  98 − 96
```

Students can check their work:

$32 \times 3 + 2 = 98$

If using a sharing interpretation of division for the algorithm, we cannot divide 9 tens into 32 groups, so we regroup 9 tens into ones and divide 96 into 32 groups. There will be 3 in each group.

Students will first divide a two-digit number by a two-digit number, which results in a one-digit quotient. Next they will divide a three-digit number by a two-digit number where the quotient is one-digit quotient.

They will then divide a three-digit number by a two-digit number where the quotient is a two-digit number, which adds a step to the algorithm (dividing tens, and then ones). Then, they divide a four-digit number by a two-digit number where the quotient is a three or two-digit number. They should now be able to follow the steps of the recursive algorithm and divide any sized number by a two-digit number.

Example: 9,478 ÷ 45

```
45)9,478
```

Because there are insufficient thousands in 9,478 to create 45 groups of thousands, we regroup the thousands as hundreds and divide 94 hundreds by 45. We can put 2 hundreds each into 45 groups and have 4 hundreds remaining.

Divide the hundreds:

Estimate 94 hundreds ÷ 45 ≈ 2 hundreds.

```
      2
 45)9,478
    90      ←  45 × 2 hundreds
    ---
     4      ←  94 hundreds – 90 hundreds
```

The remaining 4 hundreds are regrouped as 40 tens.

40 tens + 7 tens = 47 tens

Divide the tens:

Estimate 47 tens ÷ 45 ≈ 1 ten.

```
      21
 45)9,478
    90
    ---
     47
     45     ←  45 × 1 ten
    ---
      2     ←  47 tens – 45 tens
```

The remaining 2 tens are regrouped as 20 ones.

20 ones + 8 ones = 28 ones

```
      210
 45)9,478
    90
    ---
     47
     45
    ---
      28
```

We are left with 28 ones and cannot put a whole number into each of 45 groups. Write a 0 in the ones place of the quotient.

In this chapter, any remainders will be expressed as whole numbers. In Chapter 4, remainders will be expressed as fractions.

9,478 ÷ 45 is 210 with a remainder of 28.

Materials

- Place-value discs
- Whiteboards

Blackline Masters

- Multiplication Puzzle
- Number Cards

Activities

Games and activities included in this chapter are designed to provide practice with multiplication and division. The included activities can be used after students complete the **Do** questions, or anytime additional practice is needed.

Notes

Objective

- Investigate multiplication of multi-digit numbers.

Have students discuss the **Chapter Opener**, then have them write expressions for the friends' questions.

Ask students:

- "What is different about the numbers used on this page for multiplication from what you have learned before?"
- "What have you learned before that could help us think about solving the problems on this page?"
- "Can you find the answer to any of the problems using mental math?"

Sofia: 300 × 45
Alex: 480 ÷ 12
Emma: 250 × 20
Mei: 400 ÷ 50 × 200

Chapter 3

Multiplication and Division

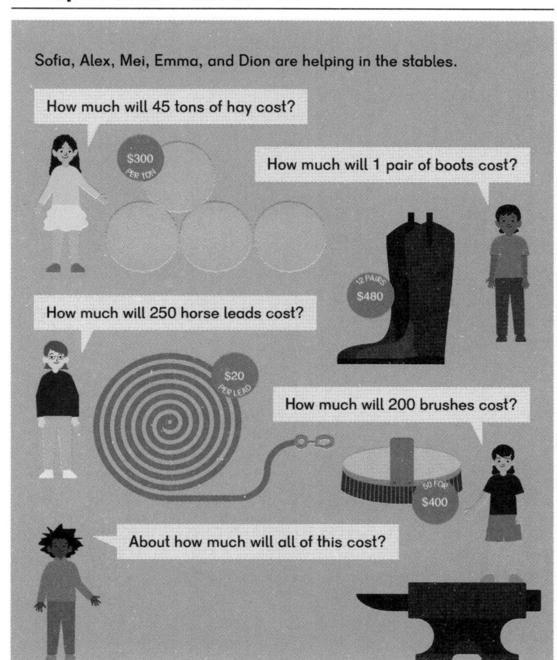

47

47

Objectives

- Review multiplying two-digit and three-digit numbers by a two-digit number.
- Review estimation strategies.

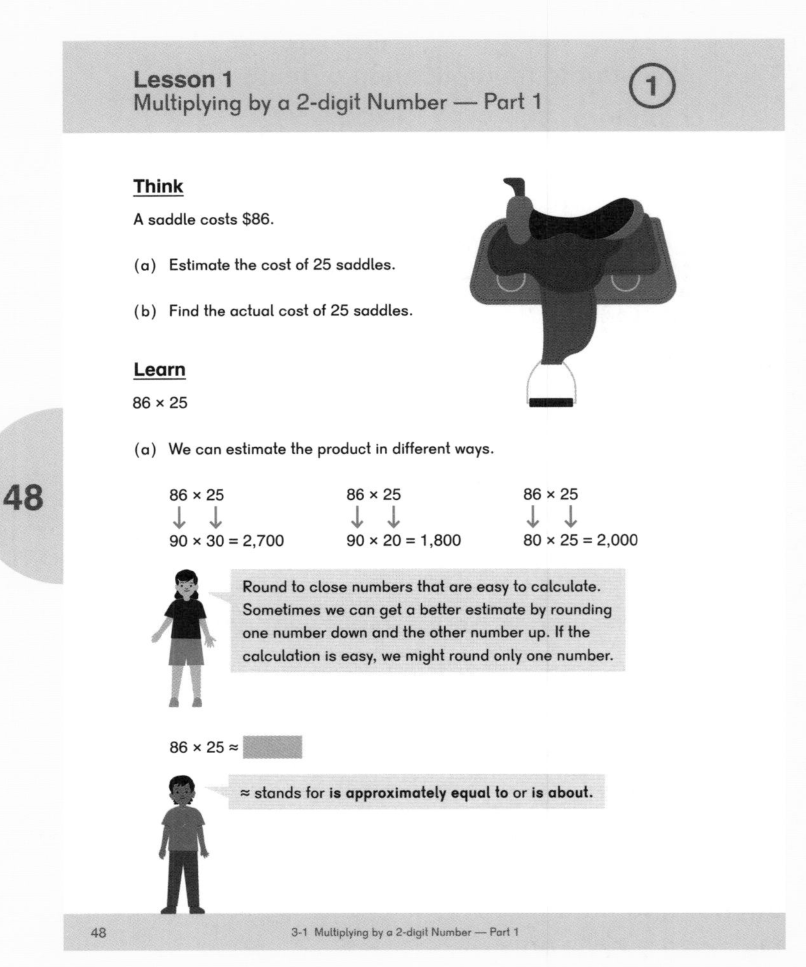

48

Think

Pose the **Think** problem and have students estimate, then find the cost of the saddles.

Discuss student estimates and the exact cost of the saddles.

Learn

Have students compare their estimates from **Think** with the ones shown in the textbook.

Mei reminds students how they have estimated answers in previous levels.

Discuss the three estimates in (a) and ask students if they think each will be greater than or less than the actual product.

Alex introduces the symbol used for estimation. Ask students what is alike and what is different between this symbol and the equals sign.

(b) Discuss the steps as they are modeled in **Learn**. Mei reminds students of one way to record the regrouped numbers.

If students struggle with the regrouping marks, have them write the regrouping marks with two different colored pencils.

For example:

$$
\begin{array}{rll}
1 & & \\
3 & & \\
86 & & \\
\times\ 25 & & \\
\hline
430 & \leftarrow & 86 \times 5 \\
1{,}720 & \leftarrow & 86 \times 20 \\
\hline
2{,}150 & &
\end{array}
$$

Ask students why Dion says, “We can first write a 0 in the ones place.” Ensure they understand that a 0 is not just a place holder. We are multiplying by a number of tens, so the partial product will be a number of tens.

Have students discuss Emma’s questions.

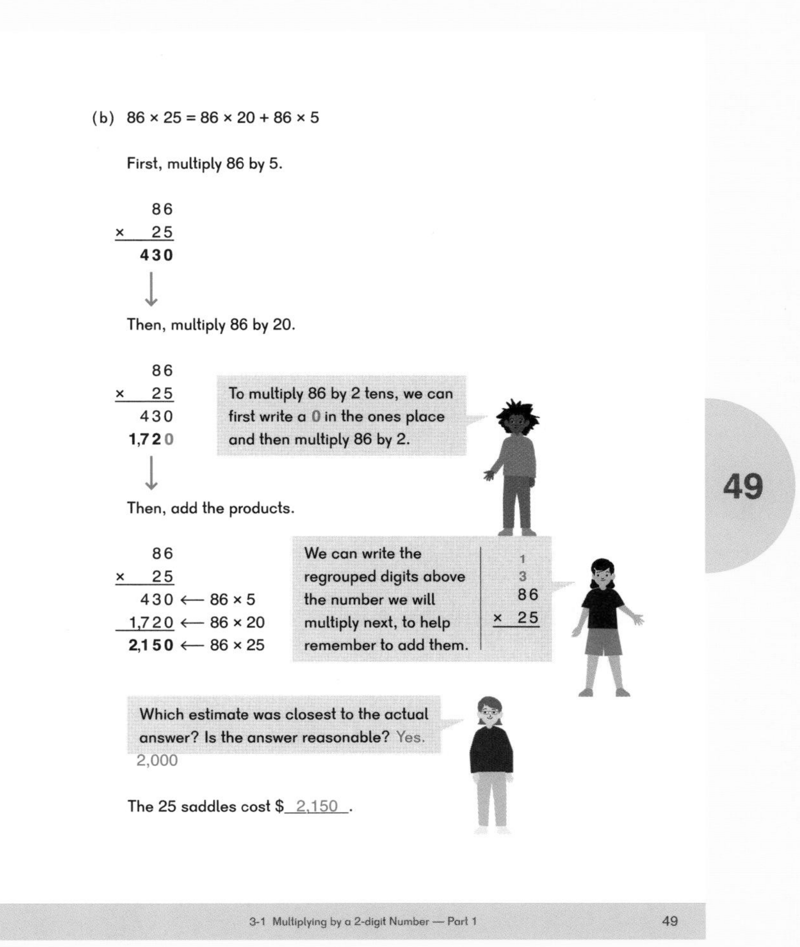
(b) 86 × 25 = 86 × 20 + 86 × 5

First, multiply 86 by 5.

$$
\begin{array}{r}
86 \\
\times\ 25 \\
\hline
430
\end{array}
$$

Then, multiply 86 by 20.

$$
\begin{array}{r}
86 \\
\times\ 25 \\
\hline
430 \\
1{,}720
\end{array}
$$

To multiply 86 by 2 tens, we can first write a 0 in the ones place and then multiply 86 by 2.

Then, add the products.

$$
\begin{array}{rll}
86 & & \\
\times\ 25 & & \\
\hline
430 & \leftarrow & 86 \times 5 \\
1{,}720 & \leftarrow & 86 \times 20 \\
\hline
2{,}150 & \leftarrow & 86 \times 25
\end{array}
$$

We can write the regrouped digits above the number we will multiply next, to help remember to add them.

$$
\begin{array}{r}
1 \\
3 \\
86 \\
\times\ 25 \\
\hline
\end{array}
$$

Which estimate was closest to the actual answer? Is the answer reasonable? Yes. 2,000

The 25 saddles cost $ 2,150 .

3-1 Multiplying by a 2-digit Number — Part 1 49

49

Do

❶—❸ Students should estimate first before finding an answer. Throughout the problems, ask students to share some of their estimates. Have students compare their estimates to their answers to confirm that their answers are reasonable.

If students struggle with the regrouping marks, have them write the regrouping marks with two different colored pencils.

❶ (b)–(c) Ask students, “Will the product be greater than 1,000? 10,000? 100,000?”

Alex and Sofia provide suggestions on estimating the product. Sofia knows her product will be between 42,000 and 36,000, and closer to 36,000.

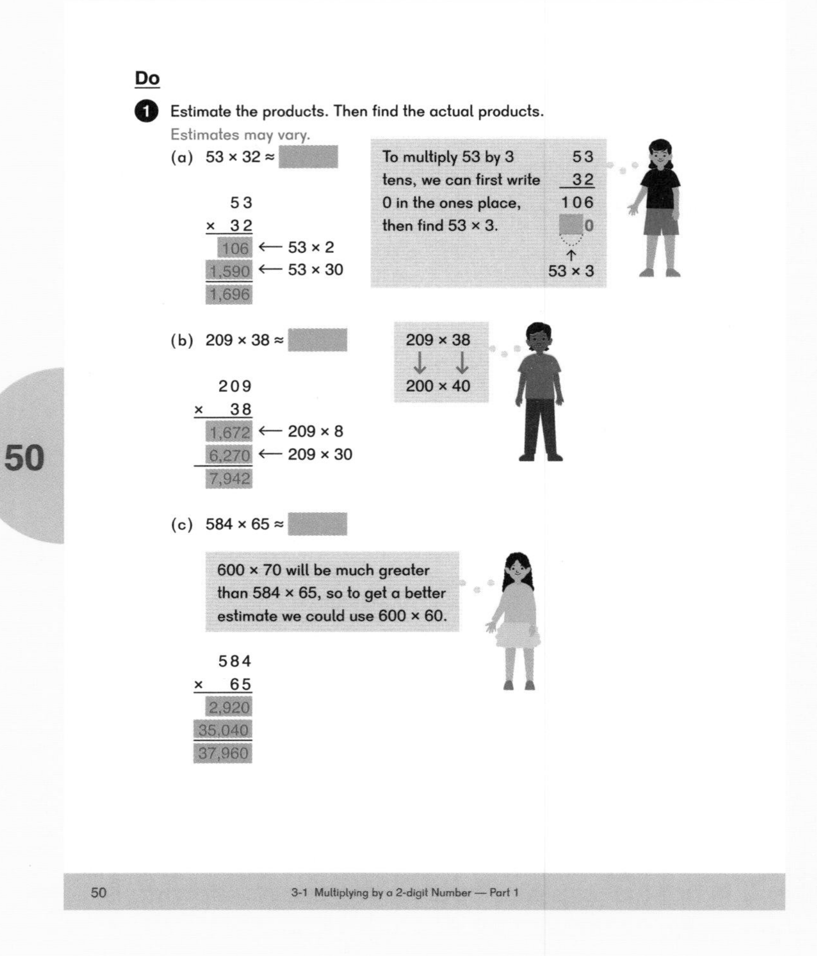

2 Students should be able to solve these problems independently.

(j) This is the first time students have been asked to multiply 3 two-digit numbers together. For an estimate, students might think of 20 × 20 × 40. That estimate will be high, and students should be able to see that.

To find the product, most students will multiply using the algorithm. They can multiply any two of the three numbers together first.

For example:

23 × 15 = 345
345 × 37 = 12,765

Or:

23 × 37 = 851
851 × 15 = 12,765

3 Discuss the different methods Mei, Emma, and Alex used to estimate.

Pose Dion's question. They will check their estimate in (b).

2 Estimate the products and then find the actual products.

(a)	48 × 72 3,456	(b)	97 × 68 6,596
(c)	57 × 45 2,565	(d)	94 × 36 3,384
(e)	307 × 44 13,508	(f)	760 × 89 67,640
(g)	235 × 84 19,740	(h)	706 × 14 9,884
(i)	387 × 58 22,446	(j)	23 × 15 × 37 12,765

3 A ton of alfalfa costs $350. Mei, Emma, and Alex estimated the cost of 25 tons of alfalfa in different ways.

Mei
350 × 25 ≈ 400 × 30
= $12,000

Emma
350 × 25 ≈ 400 × 20
= $8,000

Alex
350 × 25 ≈ 300 × 30
= $9,000

Which estimate do you think will be closest to the actual cost?

(a) Find the actual cost of 25 tons of alfalfa.
350 × 25 = 8,750; $8,750

(b) Explain why Emma's and Alex's estimates were closer to the actual cost than Mei's estimate.
Mei rounded both numbers up, one to the nearest hundred, and one to the nearest ten, so her estimate was much greater than the actual cost. Emma and Alex both rounded one number down and one number up, so their estimates were closer to the actual cost.

Exercise

51

Exercise 1 • page 45

Activity

▲ Greatest and Least

Materials: Number Cards (BLM) 1–9

Use five of the digits 1–9 once to find the greatest possible product.

Do the same to find the least possible product.

Greatest answer: 975 × 86
Least answer: 245 × 13

Objective

- Multiply up to a five-digit number by a two-digit number.

Think

Pose the **Think** problem and have students estimate, then find the money the stable will receive.

Ask students, “How is this problem different from the multiplication you have done already?“ (We are multiplying by a four-digit number.)

Learn

Have students compare their solutions from **Think** with the ones shown in the textbook.

(a) Because Emma has rounded both factors for her estimate down, her estimated product will be less than the actual product.

Encourage students to think of how they could solve Mei’s estimate of 8,000 × 25 mentally. (Students may think 8 × 25 cents or 8 quarters.)

Discuss Alex’s question.

(b) Some students may benefit by using grid paper or lined paper rotated 90 degrees to help them keep their digits aligned.

Discuss the steps as they are modeled in **Learn**. Sofia reminds students that they can record the regrouped numbers as they calculate.

Have students discuss Emma’s question.

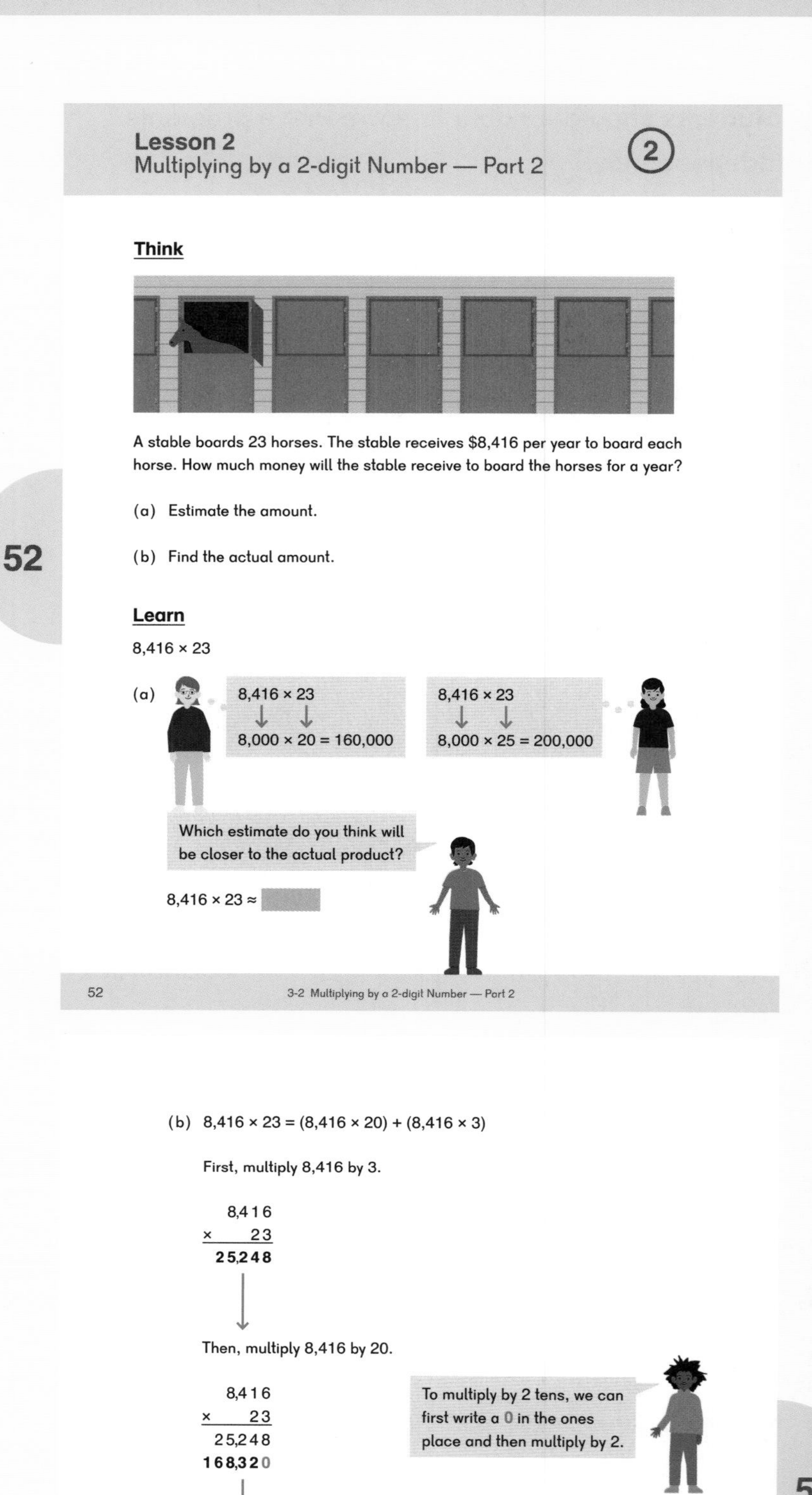

Do

❶—❹ As in the previous lesson, students should estimate first before finding an actual product.

❶ Ask students:

- "What will the ones digit be in the product? How do you know?" (For example, in problem (a), students should see that the ones digit will be 8 because 2 × 4 = 8.)
- "Will the number be even or odd?"
- "Will the actual answer be a number in the thousands, ten thousands, hundred thousands, or millions?"
  (Using Mei's estimate in (a), students should estimate that the product will be 2,400 × 3 tens = 7,200 tens or 72,000. Students might find it easier to estimate 2,000 × 30, realizing that their estimate will be much less than the actual product.)

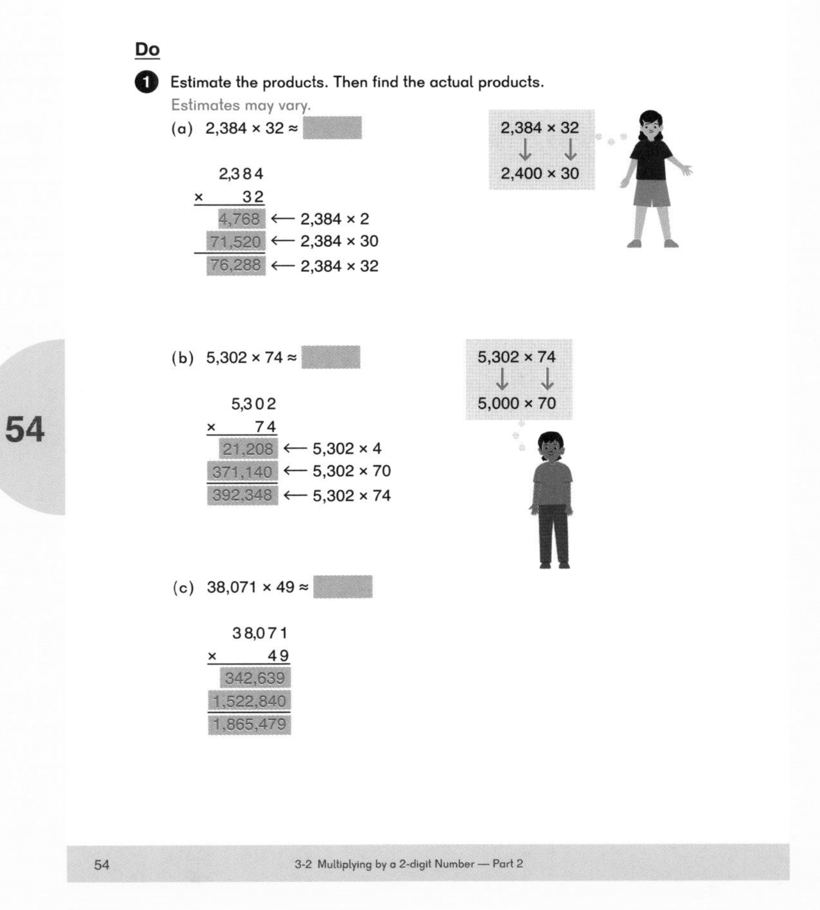

❷—❹ Students should be using the standard algorithm independently at this point.

❷ Encourage students to look carefully at the two factors in each expression.

(a) Students can multiply 5,438 × 5, then multiply that product by 10. By now they know what it means to append a zero: 5,438 × 50 = (5,438 × 5) × 10, rather than writing a line of zeroes as their calculation in the ones place.

In (c), students can multiply 83 × 56, then append two zeros to that product because they are multiplying by 100:

83 × 5,600 = (83 × 56) × 100

❹ Examples of possible student estimates:

- 100 × 30 + 200 × 10 = 3,000 + 2,000
- 100 × 40 + 200 × 10 = 4,000 + 2,000

Exercise 2 • page 49

❷ Estimate the products and then find the actual products.

Estimates may vary.

(a) 5,438 × 50
271,900

(b) 70 × 6,908
483,560

(c) 83 × 5,600
464,800

(d) 3,470 × 25
86,750

(e) 6,804 × 68
462,672

(f) 7,566 × 98
741,468

❸

Horseshoes come in boxes of 20 pairs. The farmer bought 328 boxes.

(a) How many pairs of horseshoes did he buy?
328 × 20 = 6,560; 6,560 pairs

(b) If horseshoes cost $6 per pair, how much did the farmer spend altogether?
6,560 × 6 = 39,360; $39,360

❹ It costs $112 per month to shoe a show horse, and $139 to shoe a draft horse.

(a) Estimate the monthly cost to shoe 35 show horses and 12 draft horses.

(b) Find the actual monthly cost.
35 × 112 = 3,920
12 × 139 = 1,668
3,920 + 1,668 = 5,588
$5,588

Exercise 2 • page 49

Objective

- Practice multiplying by a two-digit number.

After students complete the **Practice** in the textbook, have them continue estimating and multiplying using activities from the chapter.

❹ Students should think about how many trailers are needed to transport 12 horses.

Three 4-horse trailers would cost about 3 × $50,000 or $150,000.

Six 2-horse trailers would cost about 6 × $16,000 or $96,000.

Activity

★ Multiplication Puzzle

Materials: Multiplication Puzzle (BLM)

To prepare, print Multiplication Puzzle (BLM) on cardstock for each student or pair of students and cut out triangles along the bold lines.

Students match the sides of the triangles with an expression to the corresponding product. Encourage them to use estimation strategies.

The puzzle will form a triangle when complete.

56

Lesson 3
Practice A

P ③

❶ Estimate the values and then find the actual values.
Estimates may vary. Actual values provided.

(a) 36 × 63 2,268	(b) 75 × 208 15,600	(c) 5,019 × 32 160,608
(d) 6,819 × 48 327,312	(e) 17 × 2,175 36,975	(f) 4,087 × 46 188,002
(g) 99 × 9,999 989,901	(h) 5,630 × 78 439,140	(i) 7,092 × 48 340,416
(j) 60,812 × 82 4,986,584	(k) 16 × 125 × 8 16,000	(l) 32 × 7 × 128 28,672

❷ Mr. Johnson made a down payment of $1,500 for a car. He will make monthly car payments of $325 for 48 months. Estimate and then find the total cost of the car.
325 × 48 = 15,600; 15,600 + 1,500 = 17,100
$17,100

❸ A horse blanket costs $89 and a grooming kit costs $15. The owner wants to buy 25 of each item. Estimate and then find the actual cost.
89 × 25 = 2,225; 15 × 25 = 375; 2,225 + 375 = 2,600
$2,600

❹ The stable wants to be able to transport 12 horses at a time. A 4-horse trailer costs $48,900. A 2-horse trailer costs $16,400.

(a) Would it cost less to buy 4-horse trailers only or to buy 2-horse trailers only? 4-horse: 12 ÷ 4 = 3; 48,900 × 3 = 146,700
2-horse: 12 ÷ 2 = 6; 16,400 × 6 = 98,400; 2-horse trailers

(b) What would be the difference in cost?
146,700 − 98,400 = 48,300; $48,300

Exercise 3 • page 52

56 3-3 Practice A

Solution:

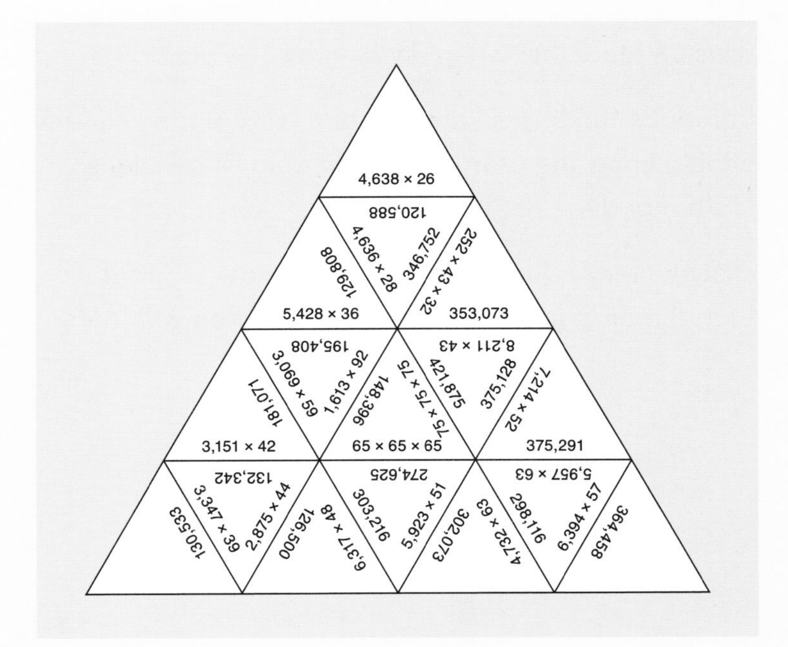

Exercise 3 • page 52

Objective

- Divide a two-digit or three-digit number by a multiple of ten.

Lesson Materials

- Place-value discs

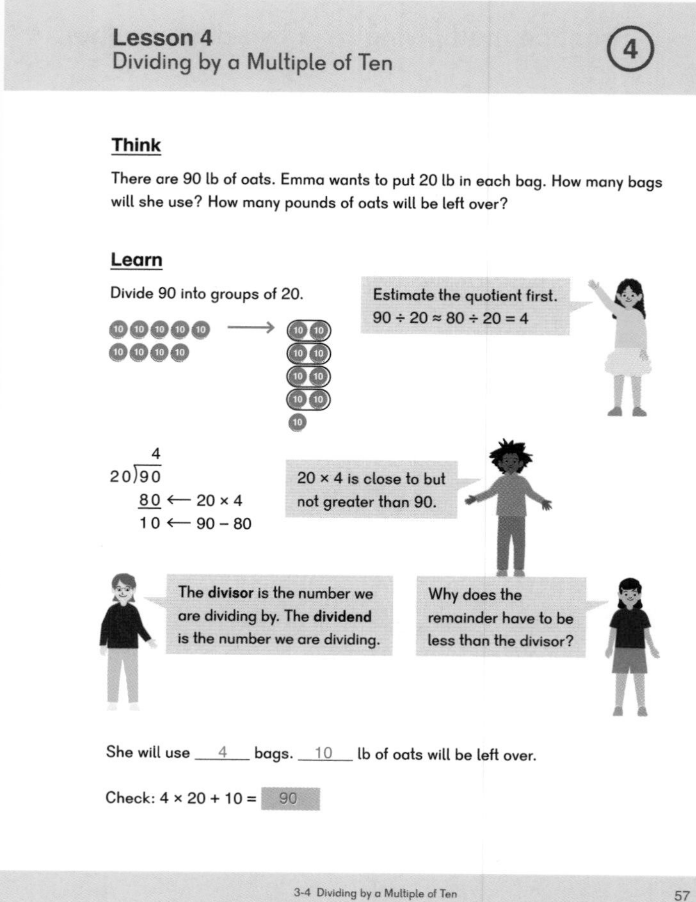

57

Think

Provide students with place-value discs and pose the **Think** problem. Have students estimate the quotient first.

Ask students:

- "Are we sharing into 20 groups or grouping by 20?" (Grouping by 20.)
- "How can we show that with the place-value discs?"

Learn

Have students relate what they did with the place-value discs to the steps in the written algorithm in **Learn**.

Remind students that they know how to use the division algorithm when dividing by one digit.

Introduce the terms "divisor" and "dividend." Students should know the term "quotient" from Dimensions Math 3 and 4.

Discuss Mei's question. If the remainder is greater than the divisor, another bag can be filled with oats.

Do

❶–❹ Discuss these problems and the friends' comments with students. Students who struggle can use place-value discs. By ❺ students should be able to work the problems independently.

❶ Discuss Alex's comments on estimating the quotient first.

❷ Discuss Emma's comments. Dion prompts students to consider that 150 ÷ 40 is the same as considering tens as the unit: 15 tens ÷ 4 tens. To check, we can say that there are 3 groups of 4 tens (12 tens) and 3 tens left over to make 15 tens.

❹ Discuss Alex's comments on estimating the quotient. Ask students why he is thinking about 70 × 9 = 630. (While his estimated quotient of 9 is reasonable, it results in a product greater than the dividend. He tries a lesser estimated quotient, 8.)

❺ All the quotients are single digits. Most of the problems could be solved mentally.

❻ Note that 5 R 29 means they will need 6 buses to transport all 279 people.

Exercise 4 • page 56

58

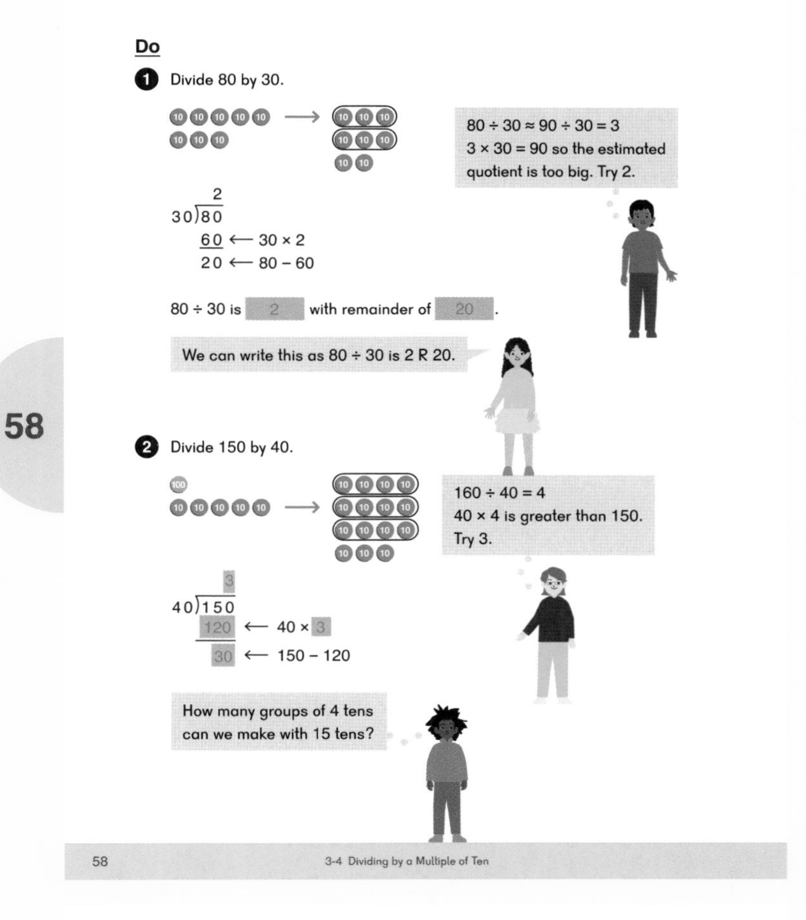
Do

❶ Divide 80 by 30.

80 ÷ 30 ≈ 90 ÷ 30 = 3
3 × 30 = 90 so the estimated quotient is too big. Try 2.

30)80 → 2; 60 ← 30 × 2; 20 ← 80 − 60

80 ÷ 30 is 2 with remainder of 20.

We can write this as 80 ÷ 30 is 2 R 20.

❷ Divide 150 by 40.

160 ÷ 40 = 4
40 × 4 is greater than 150.
Try 3.

40)150 → 3; 120 ← 40 × 3; 30 ← 150 − 120

How many groups of 4 tens can we make with 15 tens?

58 3-4 Dividing by a Multiple of Ten

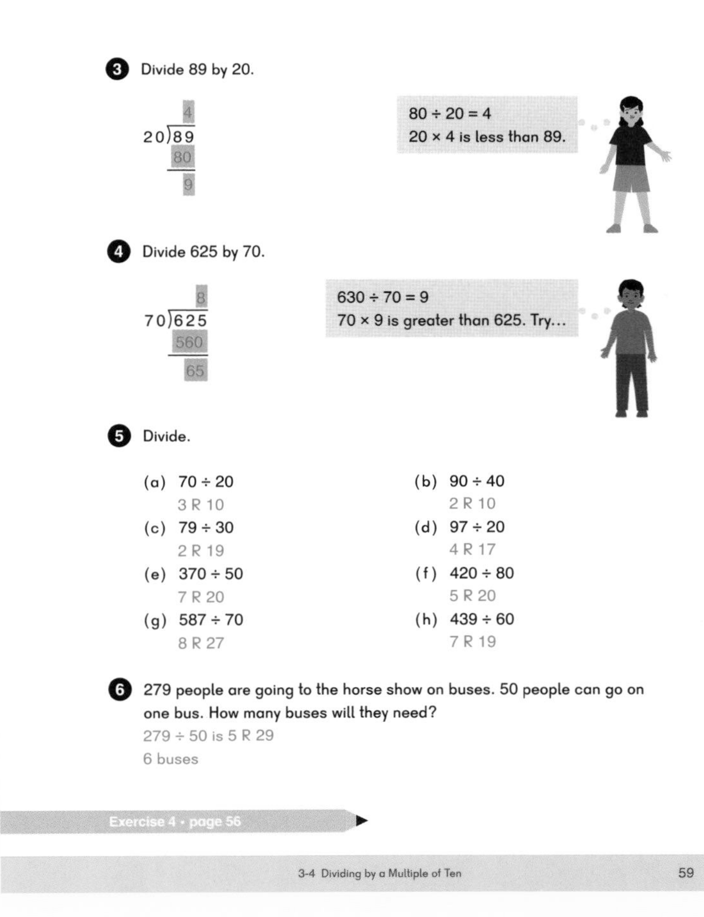
❸ Divide 89 by 20.

20)89 → 4; 80; 9

80 ÷ 20 = 4
20 × 4 is less than 89.

❹ Divide 625 by 70.

70)625 → 8; 560; 65

630 ÷ 70 = 9
70 × 9 is greater than 625. Try...

❺ Divide.

(a) 70 ÷ 20 — 3 R 10
(b) 90 ÷ 40 — 2 R 10
(c) 79 ÷ 30 — 2 R 19
(d) 97 ÷ 20 — 4 R 17
(e) 370 ÷ 50 — 7 R 20
(f) 420 ÷ 80 — 5 R 20
(g) 587 ÷ 70 — 8 R 27
(h) 439 ÷ 60 — 7 R 19

❻ 279 people are going to the horse show on buses. 50 people can go on one bus. How many buses will they need?
279 ÷ 50 is 5 R 29
6 buses

Exercise 4 • page 56

3-4 Dividing by a Multiple of Ten 59

59

Objective

- Divide a two-digit number by a two-digit divisor.

Lesson Materials

- Place-value discs: ones and tens

60

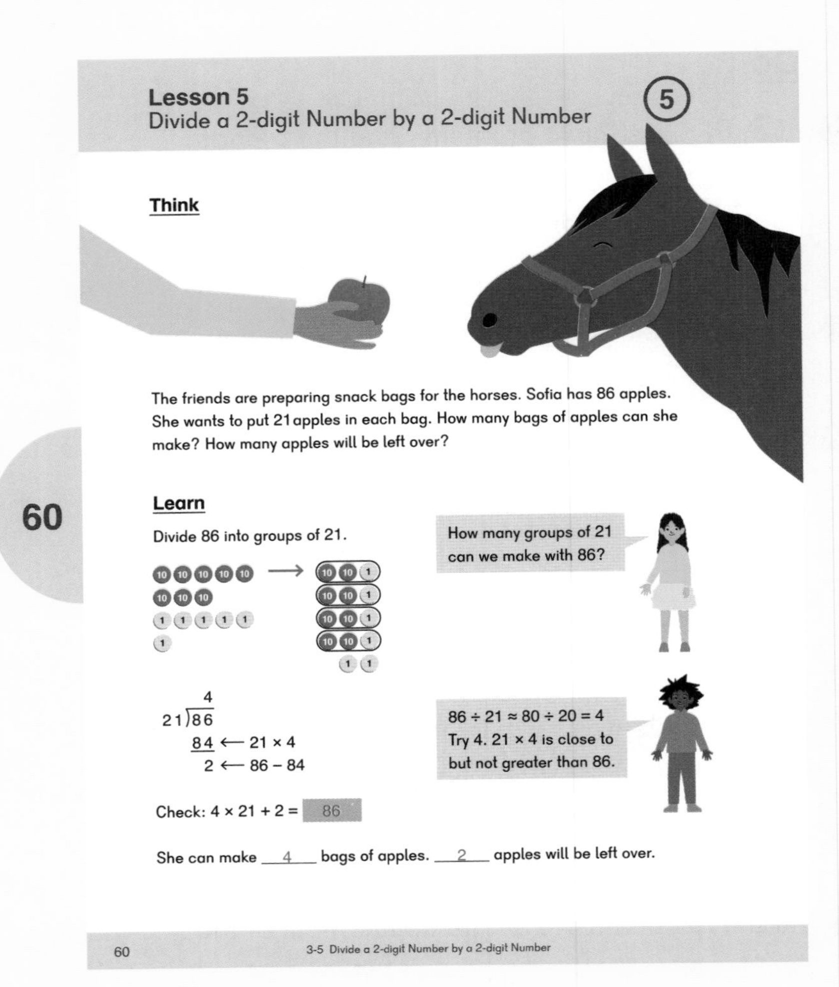

Lesson 5
Divide a 2-digit Number by a 2-digit Number

5

Think

The friends are preparing snack bags for the horses. Sofia has 86 apples. She wants to put 21 apples in each bag. How many bags of apples can she make? How many apples will be left over?

Learn

Divide 86 into groups of 21.

How many groups of 21 can we make with 86?

$$\begin{array}{r} 4 \\ 21\overline{)86} \\ \underline{84} \leftarrow 21 \times 4 \\ 2 \leftarrow 86 - 84 \end{array}$$

$86 \div 21 \approx 80 \div 20 = 4$
Try 4. 21×4 is close to but not greater than 86.

Check: $4 \times 21 + 2 =$ 86

She can make 4 bags of apples. 2 apples will be left over.

60 3-5 Divide a 2-digit Number by a 2-digit Number

Think

Provide students with place-value discs and pose the **Think** problem. Have students estimate the quotient first.

Ask students:

- "Are we sharing into 21 groups or grouping by 21?" (Grouping by 21.)
- "How is this problem similar to or different from the ones we did in the previous lesson?" (The divisor is not a multiple of ten, but we can still use the same procedure to divide.)
- "How can we show how to solve the problem with the discs?"

Learn

Work through the **Think** problem with students as demonstrated in **Learn**.

Discuss Dion's comments. Ask students why his comments are important. (It is useful to use estimates to find the first digit in the quotient. In this case, his estimate happens to be the exact quotient.)

When Dion calculates using his estimated quotient, 4 × 21, the remainder, 2, is less than the divisor, 21, so he knows he is done.

Do

❶—❷ Discuss these problems with students as they work through them. By ❹ students should be able to work the problems independently.

❶ Emma provides a suggested estimate for the first step of the division algorithm.

Mei reminds students how to check an answer when there is a quotient and a remainder.

❷ Discuss Sofia's comments. The division algorithm with 2 or more digits is a process involving estimation, and it is not unusual for the estimates to be too high or too low. Even if the first and second attempts are not the exact quotient, using estimates still brings students closer to the correct quotient.

Ask students:

- "Why didn't Sofia's estimate work?" (When she calculates using her estimated quotient, 4, the product of 4 and 16 results in a remainder, 17, that is greater than the divisor, 16.)
- "What can we figure out from a remainder of more than 16?" (She can make another group of 16: $5 \times 16 = 80$.)

❸ Students should check while calculating that the remainder is less than the divisor.

❺ (b) Ensure students understand that the answer is not the remainder, but the difference between the divisor, 15, and the remainder, 11. If necessary, ask students, "How many more hay cubes would Alex need to add to the remainder to get another bag of 15 hay cubes?"

Exercise 5 • page 59

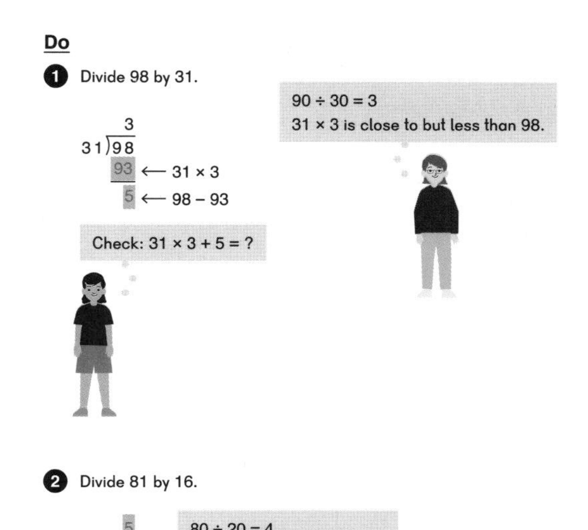

❷ Divide 81 by 16.

$$\begin{array}{r} 5 \\ 16\overline{)81} \\ 80 \\ \hline 1 \end{array}$$

80 ÷ 20 = 4

$16\overline{)81}$ → 4, 64, 17 → $16\overline{)81}$ → 5

The remainder is greater than 16 so the estimated quotient is too small. Try 5.

❸ Divide.

(a) 78 ÷ 26
3
(b) 84 ÷ 12
7
(c) 85 ÷ 17
5
(d) 89 ÷ 43
2 R 3
(e) 98 ÷ 24
4 R 2
(f) 95 ÷ 13
7 R 4
(g) 83 ÷ 37
2 R 9
(h) 85 ÷ 27
3 R 4
(i) 95 ÷ 16
5 R 15
(j) 89 ÷ 24
3 R 17

Check your answers.

❹ Carlton Horse Barn stables 91 horses. Their daily exercise sessions are divided equally among the 13 trainers. How many horses does each trainer exercise each day?
91 ÷ 13 = 7, 7 horses

❺ Alex has 86 hay cubes. He wants to put 15 hay cubes in each bag.

(a) How many bags of hay cubes can he make?
86 ÷ 15 is 5 R 11; 5 bags
(b) How many more hay cubes does he need to make another bag?
4 more hay cubes

Exercise 5 • page 59

Objective

- Divide a three-digit number by a two-digit divisor resulting in a one-digit quotient.

Lesson Materials

- Place-value discs: ones, tens, and hundreds

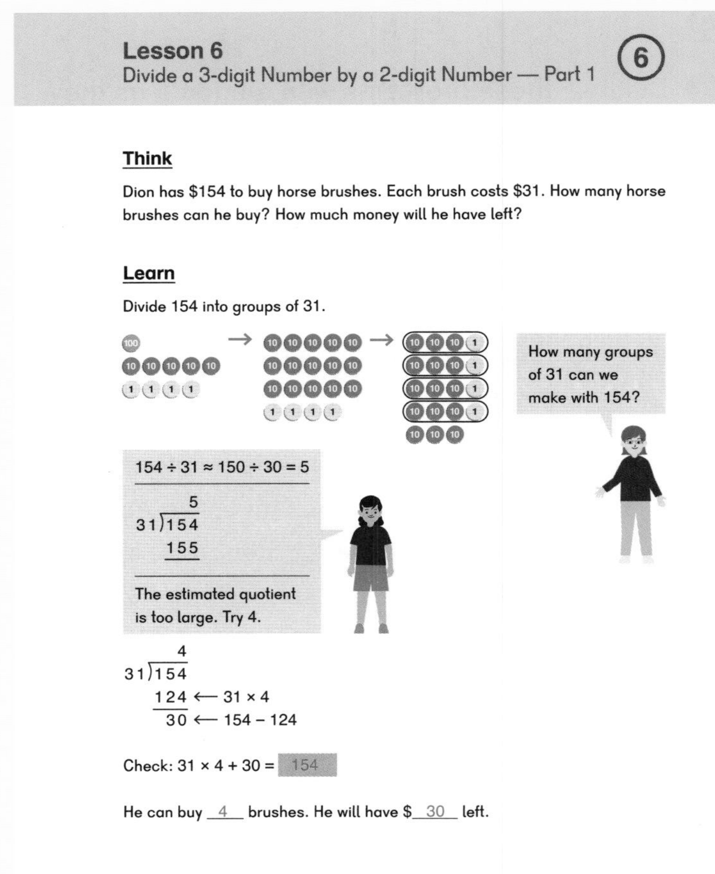

Lesson 6
Divide a 3-digit Number by a 2-digit Number — Part 1 (6)

Think

Dion has $154 to buy horse brushes. Each brush costs $31. How many horse brushes can he buy? How much money will he have left?

Learn

Divide 154 into groups of 31.

154 ÷ 31 ≈ 150 ÷ 30 = 5

$31\overline{)154}$ = 5; 155

The estimated quotient is too large. Try 4.

$31\overline{)154}$ = 4
124 ⟵ 31 × 4
30 ⟵ 154 − 124

Check: 31 × 4 + 30 = 154

He can buy 4 brushes. He will have $ 30 left.

3-6 Divide a 3-digit Number by a 2-digit Number — Part 1 63

Think

Provide students with place-value discs and pose the **Think** problem. Have students estimate the quotient first. They can work in groups to find their answers.

Ask students, based on their estimates:

- "How is this problem similar to or different from the ones we did in the previous lesson?"
- "How many digits will the quotient have?"

Learn

Work through the **Think** problem with students as demonstrated in **Learn**.

Mei estimates the quotient of 5. Ask students what she means when she says the estimated quotient is too large. (When she multiplies 31 × 5, the product is greater than the dividend.)

Do

❶–❹ Discuss these questions as students work through them. Discuss the friends' estimated quotients and comments. Students should see that they may need to try more than one reasonable estimate to find the quotient.

❷ Dion's estimated quotient, 7, results in a product that is greater than the dividend. He tries a lesser estimated quotient, 6.

❸ Emma's estimated quotient, 6, results in a remainder, 33, that is greater than the divisor, 26. She can make another group of 26: 7 × 26 = 182. So she tries a larger estimate, 7.

❹ Mei's first two estimated quotients were too large.

Ask students if there is a better estimate. (200 ÷ 25 = 8 or 180 ÷ 30 = 6)

Students should see that sometimes they may have to try more than one estimated quotient.

❺–❻ Students should be able to solve the problems independently. Encourage them to estimate mentally before doing the actual calculations.

❻ 15 boxes × 21 sugar cubes = 315 sugar cubes in all.

315 cubes divided into 45 bags = 7 cubes in each bag.

Exercise 6 • page 61

64

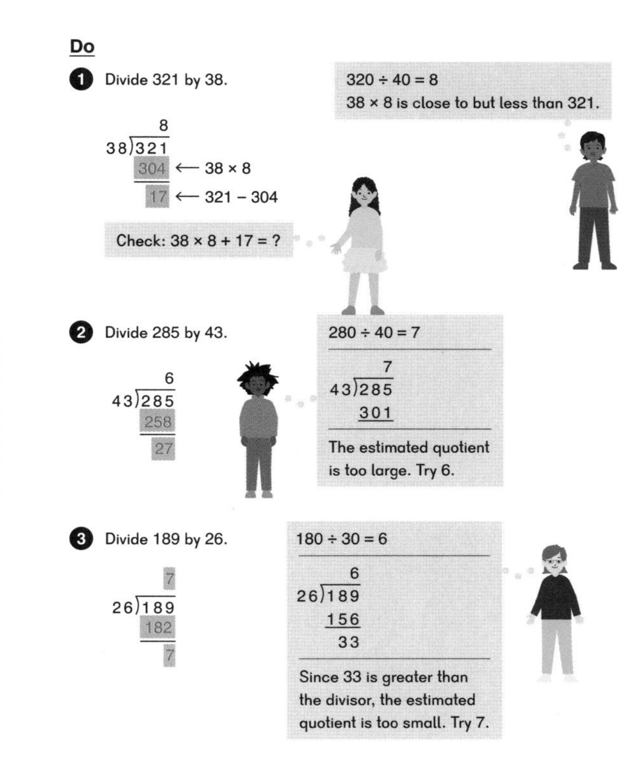

Do

❶ Divide 321 by 38.

```
     8
38)321
   304  ← 38 × 8
    17  ← 321 − 304
```

Check: 38 × 8 + 17 = ?

320 ÷ 40 = 8
38 × 8 is close to but less than 321.

❷ Divide 285 by 43.

```
     6
43)285
   258
    27
```

280 ÷ 40 = 7

```
     7
43)285
   301
```

The estimated quotient is too large. Try 6.

❸ Divide 189 by 26.

```
     7
26)189
   182
     7
```

180 ÷ 30 = 6

```
     6
26)189
   156
    33
```

Since 33 is greater than the divisor, the estimated quotient is too small. Try 7.

64 3-6 Divide a 3-digit Number by a 2-digit Number — Part 1

65

❹ Divide 183 by 24.

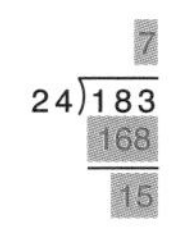

```
     7
24)183
   168
    15
```

180 ÷ 20 = 9
The estimated quotient is too large.
If we try 8 it is still too large. Try 7.

```
     9         8         7
24)183    24)183    24)183
   216       192       168
```

❺ Divide.

(a) 128 ÷ 25
5 R 3
(b) 147 ÷ 21
7
(c) 379 ÷ 53
7 R 8
(d) 237 ÷ 39
6 R 3
(e) 163 ÷ 18
9 R 1
(f) 358 ÷ 72
4 R 70
(g) 640 ÷ 92
6 R 88
(h) 308 ÷ 31
9 R 29

❻ Mei has 15 boxes that each contain 21 sugar cubes. She wants to put them equally into 45 bags. How many sugar cubes should she put in each bag? 15 × 21 = 315
315 ÷ 45 = 7
7 sugar cubes

Exercise 6 • page 61

3-6 Divide a 3-digit Number by a 2-digit Number — Part 1 65

Objective

- Divide a three-digit number by a two-digit divisor resulting in a two-digit quotient.

Think

Pose the **Think** problem and have students estimate the answer first.

Ask students, based on their estimates:

- "Are we sharing into 16 groups or grouping by 16?" (Sharing into 16 groups.)
- "How is this problem similar to or different from the ones we did in the previous lesson?" (We are dividing three-digit dividends.)
- "How many digits will the quotient have?" (Two digits.)

Learn

Work through the **Think** problem with students as demonstrated in **Learn**.

We cannot put 5 hundreds into 16 groups, so we rename the 5 hundreds as tens and then divide 57 tens by 16.

Sofia tells us that since we are dividing tens, the quotient will be tens and should go in the tens place.

Since 48 tens were divided into the 16 groups altogether, we need to find out how many tens are left over. Write 48 tens below 57 tens and subtract.

Ask students how many tens there are left to divide. (9 tens)

We can regroup 9 tens as 90 ones. There are now 96 ones to divide by 16.

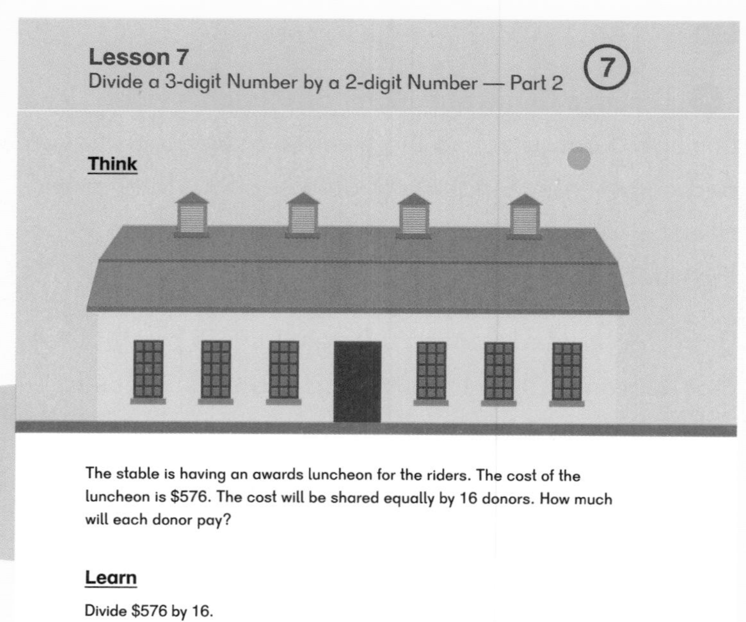

66

66 3-7 Divide a 3-digit Number by a 2-digit Number — Part 2

Regroup 5 hundreds as 50 tens, then divide 57 tens by 16.

```
     3
16)576
   48   ← 16 × 3 tens = 48 tens
    9   ← 57 tens − 48 tens
```

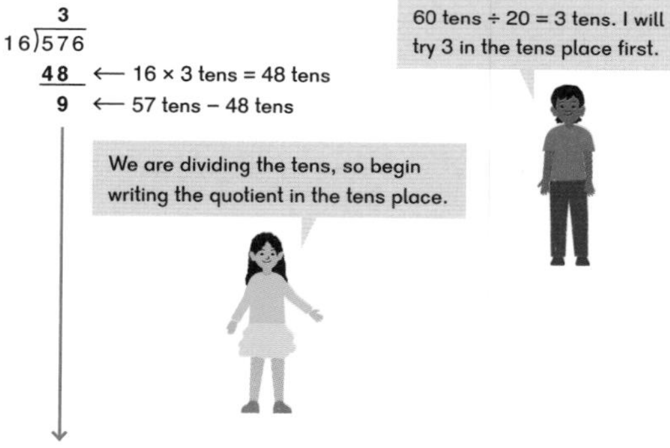

Regroup 9 tens as 90 ones, then divide 96 ones by 16.

```
    36
16)576
   48
    96
    96  ← 16 × 6 ones
     0  ← 96 ones − 96 ones
```

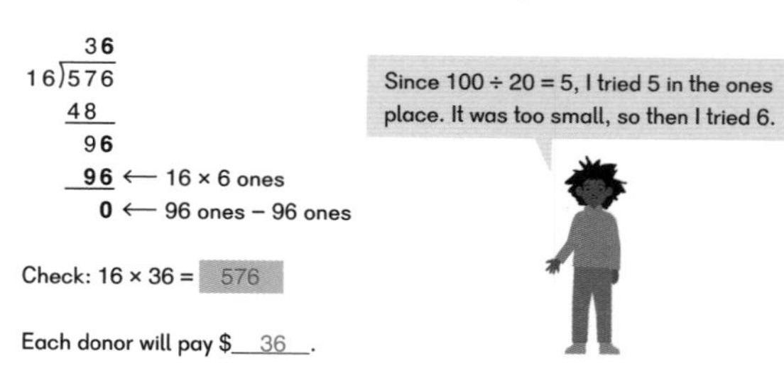

Check: 16 × 36 = 576

Each donor will pay $ 36 .

67

3-7 Divide a 3-digit Number by a 2-digit Number — Part 2 67

Do

❶–❹ Discuss the friends' comments as students work through the problems.

❶ Ask students to estimate to find out how many tens can be put in each group.

Emma sees that 12 × 2 tens = 24 tens. 24 tens is less than 28 tens.

To continue the division to find the ones digit, the remainder, 4 tens, can be regrouped as ones.

❸ Alex asks students to see that the 5 ones in the dividend cannot be evenly divided into 24 groups. Students write a 0 in the ones place. Encourage students to check their work. 30 × 24 + 5 = 725.

If students forget to write a 0 in the ones place, ask them what the 3 in the quotient represents. (Each group gets 30.)

Students can avoid this mistake by estimating first, then checking with multiplication.

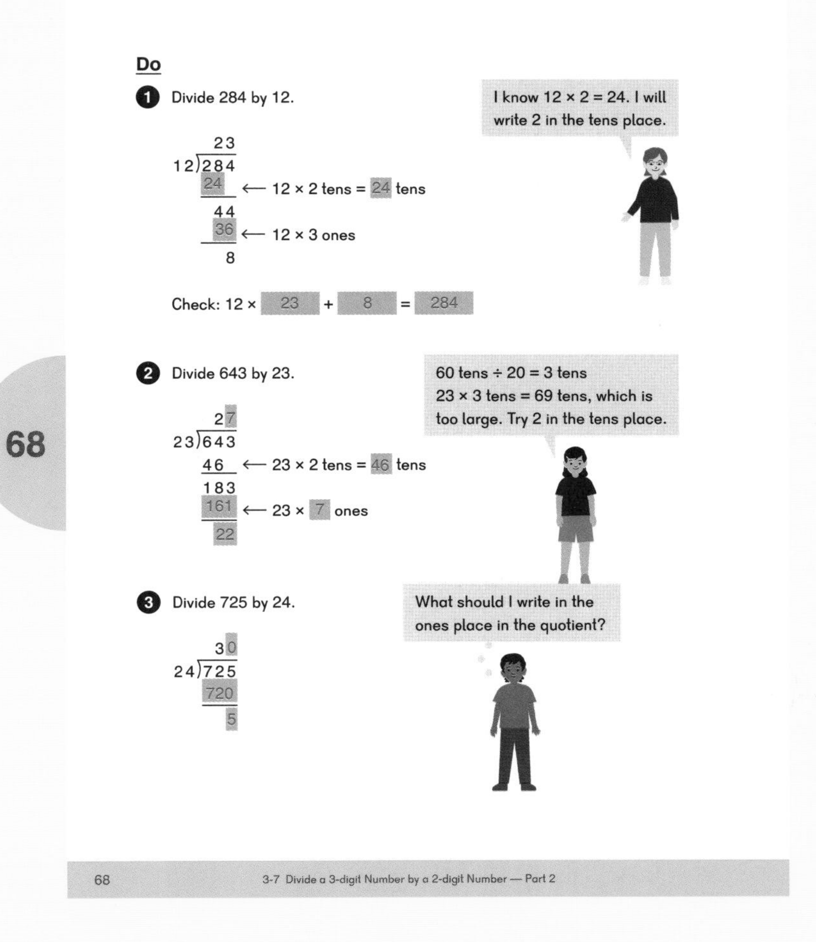

68

Do

❶ Divide 284 by 12.

I know 12 × 2 = 24. I will write 2 in the tens place.

$$\begin{array}{r} 23 \\ 12\overline{)284} \\ \underline{24} \\ 44 \\ \underline{36} \\ 8 \end{array}$$

← 12 × 2 tens = 24 tens

← 12 × 3 ones

Check: 12 × 23 + 8 = 284

❷ Divide 643 by 23.

60 tens ÷ 20 = 3 tens
23 × 3 tens = 69 tens, which is too large. Try 2 in the tens place.

$$\begin{array}{r} 27 \\ 23\overline{)643} \\ \underline{46} \\ 183 \\ \underline{161} \\ 22 \end{array}$$

← 23 × 2 tens = 46 tens

← 23 × 7 ones

❸ Divide 725 by 24.

What should I write in the ones place in the quotient?

$$\begin{array}{r} 30 \\ 24\overline{)725} \\ \underline{720} \\ 5 \end{array}$$

68 3-7 Divide a 3-digit Number by a 2-digit Number — Part 2

❹ Discuss Sofia's question and then ask students:

- "How many digits will there be in the quotient?"
- "What place will the first digit be in the quotient?"

(a) The hundreds are regrouped as tens (46 tens). There are still not enough tens to divide evenly by 57. We can regroup 46 tens as 460 ones.

The quotient will begin in the ones place. It will be a one-digit number.

(b) The hundreds are regrouped and are greater than the divisor (92 tens ÷ 43). The quotient will begin in the tens place. It will be a two-digit number.

❺—❼ Students should be able to solve the problems independently.

Exercise 7 • page 63

❹ Determine whether each quotient will be a 1-digit number or a 2-digit number, then divide.

(a) 464 ÷ 57 1 digit
8 R 8

(b) 926 ÷ 43 2 digits
21 R 23

(c) 330 ÷ 27 2 digits
12 R 6

(d) 705 ÷ 47 2 digits
15

Are the first two digits in the dividend greater than or less than the divisor?

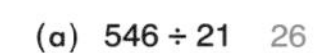

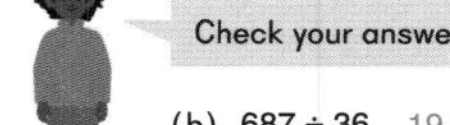

❺ Explain the mistakes below. Then do each calculation correctly.

(a)

```
   33        34
27)919    27)919
   81        81
   109       109
    81       108
    28         1
```

The remainder (28) is one greater than the divisor (27). One more group of 27 can be made.

(b)

```
   61        70
12)845    12)845
   72        84
   12         5
   12
    0
```

The tens digit of the quotient should have been 7.

❻ Divide.

Check your answers.

(a) 546 ÷ 21 26

(b) 687 ÷ 36 19 R 3

(c) 726 ÷ 24 30 R 6

(d) 900 ÷ 18 50

❼ 17 people are sharing the cost of a meal at a restaurant equally. The bill, including tip, is $544. How much money should each person pay?
544 ÷ 17 = 32
$32

Exercise 7 • page 63

Objective

- Divide a four-digit number by a two-digit divisor.

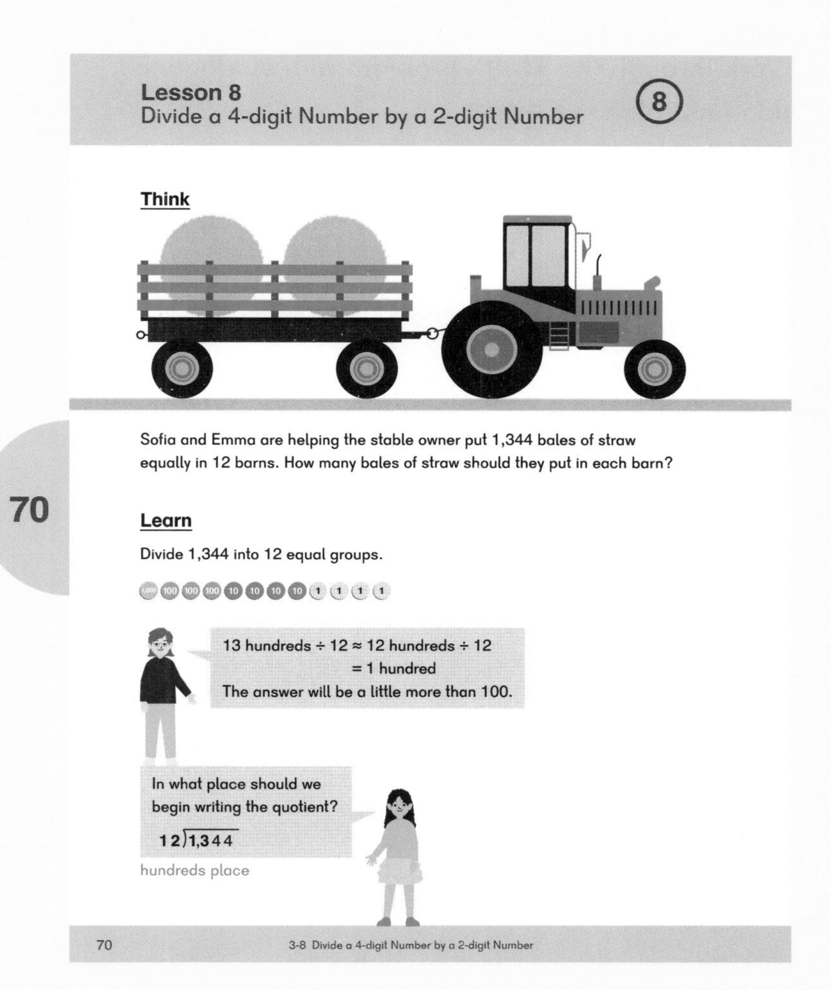

70

Lesson 8
Divide a 4-digit Number by a 2-digit Number

8

Think

Sofia and Emma are helping the stable owner put 1,344 bales of straw equally in 12 barns. How many bales of straw should they put in each barn?

Learn

Divide 1,344 into 12 equal groups.

13 hundreds ÷ 12 ≈ 12 hundreds ÷ 12
= 1 hundred
The answer will be a little more than 100.

In what place should we begin writing the quotient?

12)1,344

hundreds place

70 3-8 Divide a 4-digit Number by a 2-digit Number

Think

Pose the **Think** problem. Have students estimate the quotient first.

Learn

Have students compare their solutions from **Think** with the one shown in the textbook.

Discuss Emma's estimate.

Mei prompts students to think about where to start writing the quotient. Because we regroup 1 thousand as 10 hundreds, we have 13 hundreds. We can make 12 groups of 1 hundred out of 13 hundreds, so the first digit in the quotient will be in the hundreds place.

Work through the **Think** problem with students as demonstrated in **Learn**.

The process for dividing remains the same. Walk students through the process as needed, by asking questions.

Ask students:

- After dividing the hundreds: "How many hundreds are there left to divide?" (13 hundreds − 12 hundreds = 1 hundred)
- "What do we need to do with the 1 hundred?" (Regroup it as 10 tens and add 4 more tens.)
- "How many tens are there to divide by 12?" (14 tens)
- "What is 14 tens ÷ 12?" (1 ten with a remainder of 2 tens.)
- "Where do we record the 1 ten in the quotient?" (In the tens place.)
- "Where do we write the 12 tens?" (Below the 14 tens.)
- "How many tens are left to divide?" (14 tens − 12 tens = 2 tens)
- "What do we need to do with the 2 tens?" (Regroup them as 20 ones and add 4 more ones.)
- "How many ones are there to divide by 12?" (24 ones)

Regroup 1 thousand as 10 hundreds and divide 13 hundreds by 12.

```
     1
12)1,344
   12    ← 12 × 1 hundred = 12 hundreds
    1    ← 13 hundreds − 12 hundreds
```

Regroup 1 hundred as 10 tens and divide 14 tens by 12.

```
     11
12)1,344
   12
    14
    12   ← 12 × 1 ten
     2   ← 14 tens − 12 tens
```

Regroup 2 tens as 20 ones and divide the 24 ones by 12.

```
     112
12)1,344
   12
    14
    12
     24
     24  ← 12 × 2 ones
      0  ← 24 ones − 24 ones
```

Check: 12 × 112 = 1,344

They should put 112 bales of straw in each barn.

Do

❶–❺ Discuss these problems as students work through them. By ❻ students should be able to work the problems independently.

❶ Alex reminds students to regroup 4 thousands as 43 hundreds to be divided. We begin writing the quotient in the hundreds place.

❸ After regrouping the one hundred that was left as 10 tens and adding 2 more tens, there are still not enough tens remaining to divide evenly into 28 groups. Students should write a 0 in the tens place. Regroup the tens into ones.

They can then divide 124 by 28 and see that there are 4 ones in the quotient and 12 ones as the remainder.

❹ Emma prompts students to think about which place we will begin writing the quotient when we have to regroup twice, from thousands to hundreds and from hundreds to tens.

The quotient will begin in the tens place. It will be a two-digit number.

❺ For each problem, ask students:

- "How many digits will be in the quotient?"
- "Will the quotient be a number in the ones, tens, or hundreds?"
- "What place will the first digit be in the answer?"

❼ Note that 28 R 20 means Dion will need to work for 29 weeks to save $1,000.

Ensure students understand that he must work the entire extra week to save the full amount.

Exercise 8 • page 66

72

Do

❶ Divide 4,362 by 18.

Divide 43 hundreds by 18 and begin writing the quotient in the hundreds place.

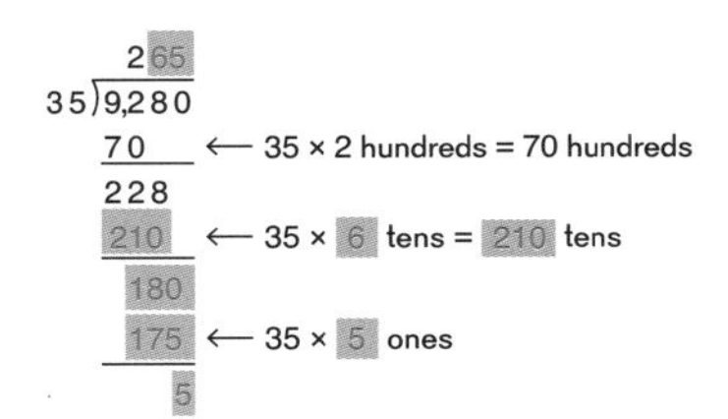

```
      242
18 ) 4,362
     36      ← 18 × 2 hundreds = 36 hundreds
      76
      72     ← 18 × 4 tens = 72 tens
       42
       36    ← 18 × 2 ones
        6
```

❷ Divide 9,280 by 35.

```
      265
35 ) 9,280
     70      ← 35 × 2 hundreds = 70 hundreds
     228
     210     ← 35 × 6 tens = 210 tens
      180
      175    ← 35 × 5 ones
        5
```

❸ Divide 8,524 by 28.

```
       3                   304
28 ) 8,524   →   28 ) 8,524
     84               84
      12               124
                       112
                        12
```

We cannot divide 12 tens into 28 groups of tens. What should we write in the tens place in the quotient?

0

❹ Divide 4,528 by 52.

```
       87
52 ) 4,528
     416
      368
      364
        4
```

We cannot divide 45 hundreds into 52 groups of hundreds. In what place should we begin writing the quotient?

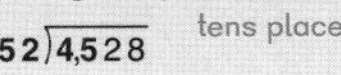

tens place

❺ Tell whether each quotient will be a 2-digit number or a 3-digit number. Then divide.

(a) 7,025 ÷ 21 3 digit
334 R 11

(b) 3,470 ÷ 45 2 digit
77 R 5

(c) 1,008 ÷ 25 2 digit
40 R 8

(d) 8,060 ÷ 62 3 digit
130

Are the first two digits in the dividend greater than or less than the divisor?

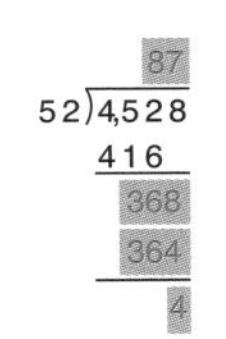

73

❻ Divide.

(a) 8,390 ÷ 34
246 R 26

(b) 8,875 ÷ 29
306 R 1

(c) 4,796 ÷ 57
84 R 8

(d) 4,340 ÷ 62
70

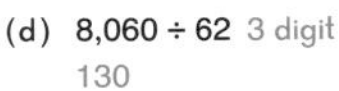

❼ Dion wants to save $1,000. How many weeks will it take him to save that much if he saves $35 each week?

1,000 ÷ 35 is 28 R 20
29 weeks

Exercise 8 • page 66

Objective

- Practice dividing by a two-digit divisor.

After students complete the **Practice** in the textbook, have them continue estimating and dividing using activities from the chapter.

Exercise 9 • page 69

74

Lesson 9
Practice B

P 9

1. Estimate the quotient and then find the actual quotient.

(a) 92 ÷ 50 1 R 42	(b) 78 ÷ 30 2 R 18	(c) 98 ÷ 40 2 R 18
(d) 98 ÷ 32 3 R 2	(e) 62 ÷ 16 3 R 14	(f) 142 ÷ 24 5 R 22
(g) 435 ÷ 70 6 R 15	(h) 650 ÷ 80 8 R 10	(i) 786 ÷ 30 26 R 6
(j) 362 ÷ 58 6 R 14	(k) 1,462 ÷ 47 31 R 5	(l) 2,205 ÷ 72 30 R 45
(m) 8,350 ÷ 18 463 R 16	(n) 6,204 ÷ 29 213 R 27	(o) 95,987 ÷ 96 999 R 83

2. 
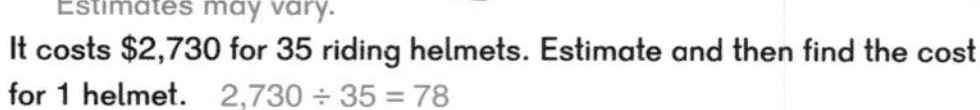
Estimates may vary.
It costs $2,730 for 35 riding helmets. Estimate and then find the cost for 1 helmet. 2,730 ÷ 35 = 78
$78

3. A flour mill produced 1,000 lb of flour. The workers put 300 lb of flour into 25-lb bags and the rest into 50-lb bags. How many of each kind of bag will they have?
25-lb bags: 300 ÷ 25 = 12; 1,000 – 300 = 700; 700
50-lb bags: 700 ÷ 50 lb = 14; 12 25-lb bags and 14 50-lb bags

4. A school paid $2,212 for 4 projectors and 8 tablets. A tablet cost three times as much as a projector. How much did each projector and each tablet cost? 8 tablets cost the same as 8 × 3 = 24 projectors
2,212 ÷ 28 = 79, 1 projector costs $79
79 ×3 = 237; 1 laptop costs $237

Exercise 9 • page 69

74 3-9 Practice B

Brain Works

★ How Many?

Divide 3,240 by a two-digit divisor. How many two-digit divisors can you find that result in a quotient without a remainder?

There are 16:

3,240 ÷ 10 = 324
3,240 ÷ 12 = 270
3,240 ÷ 15 = 216
3,240 ÷ 18 = 180
3,240 ÷ 20 = 162
3,240 ÷ 24 = 135
3,240 ÷ 27 = 120
3,240 ÷ 30 = 108
3,240 ÷ 36 = 90
3,240 ÷ 40 = 81
3,240 ÷ 45 = 72
3,240 ÷ 54 = 60
3,240 ÷ 60 = 54
3,240 ÷ 72 = 45
3,240 ÷ 81 = 40
3,240 ÷ 90 = 36

Chapter 3 Multiplication and Division

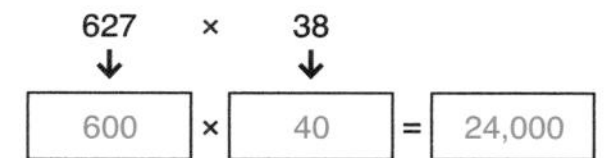

Basics

1 (a) Estimate the product of 627 and 38. Estimates may vary.

627 × 38

↓ ↓

600 × 40 = 24,000

(b) Find the product of 627 and 38.

		6	2	7	
×			3	8	
	5,	0	1	6	← 627 × 8
1	8,	8	1	0	← 627 × 30
2	3,	8	2	6	

2 (a) Sofia estimated the product of 819 and 26 to be 24,000. With what numbers could she have replaced each factor?

800 and 30

(b) Emma estimated the product of 819 and 26 to be 20,000. With what numbers could she have replaced each factor?

800 and 25

(c) Whose estimate will be closer to the actual product?

Emma's estimate

(d) Find the product of 819 and 26. 21,294

			8	1	9
×				2	6
		4,	9	1	4
	1	6,	3	8	0
	2	1,	2	9	4

Practice

3 One of these numbers is equal to 844 × 95. Use estimation to determine which one, and circle it.

8,110 72,210 80,180 101,820

4 Which of the following gives the greatest product? Circle it.

87 × 594 6 × 5,594 12 × 1,698

5 Estimate, and then find the exact product. Estimates may vary.

(a) 79 × 67 ≈

79 × 67 = 5,293

			7	9
×			6	7
		5	5	3
	4,	7	4	0
	5,	2	9	3

(b) 982 × 72 ≈

982 × 72 = 70,704

		9	8	2
×			7	2
	1,	9	6	4
6	8,	7	4	0
7	0,	7	0	4

(c) 638 × 48 ≈

638 × 48 = 30,624

(d) 88 × 608 ≈

88 × 608 = 53,504

6 The manager of an apartment complex bought new washing machines and dryers for each of the 52 apartments. The washing machines cost $398 each and the dryers cost $367 each. What was the total cost for all of the appliances he bought?

52 × (398 + 367) = 52 × 765 = 39,780

$39,780

7 (a) What is the ones digit of the product of 8 and 9?

2

(b) What is the ones digit of the product of 948 and 79?

2

Challenge

8 To find the answer to 897 × 24, Melissa multiplied 900 by 24 and then subtracted. What number did she subtract?

900 is 3 more than 897.

3 × 24 = 72

She subtracted 72.

9 Is the product of 26 × 19 × 87 odd or even? What is the ones digit of the product? Find the answer without doing the complete calculation.

Even, since one factor is even. 6 × 9 × 7 = 378, so the ones digit is 8.

Exercise 2 • pages 49–51

Exercise 2

Basics

1 (a) Estimate the product of 8,427 and 58.

Estimates may vary.

8,427 × 58

↓ ↓

8,000 × 60 = 480,000

(b) Find the product of 8,427 and 58.

		8,	4	2	7	
×				5	8	
	6	7,	4	1	6	⟵ 8,427 × 8
4	2	1,	3	5	0	⟵ 8,427 × 50
4	8	8,	7	6	6	

Practice

2 One of these numbers is equal to 1,899 × 89. Use estimation to determine which one, and circle it.

126,411 **169,011** **1,691,011** **16,480**

3 Which of the following give a product greater than 100,000? Circle them.

6,427 × 14 **7,873 × 39** **15 × 18,972**

4 Estimate and then find the exact product. Estimates may vary.

(a) 7,814 × 24 ≈

7,814 × 24 = 187,536

			7,	8	1	4
×					2	4
		3	1,	2	5	6
	1	5	6,	2	8	0
	1	8	7,	5	3	6

(b) 9,026 × 81 ≈

9,026 × 81 = 731,106

			9,	0	2	6
×					8	1
			9,	0	2	6
	7	2	2,	0	8	0
	7	3	1,	1	0	6

(c) 9,879 × 54 ≈

9,879 × 54 = 533,466

(d) 14,038 × 37 ≈

14,038 × 37 = 519,406

5 The manager of an apartment complex bought new refrigerators, ovens, and dishwashers for each of the 52 apartments. The refrigerators cost $598 each, the ovens cost $388 each, and the dishwashers cost $298 each. What is the total cost of all of these appliances?

52 × (598 + 388 + 298) = 52 × 1,284 = 66,768

$66,768

Challenge

6 Multiply.

(a) 879 × 406

356,874

(b) 4,027 × 36,040

145,133,080

Exercise 3 • pages 52–55

Exercise 3

Check

1. Multiply and use the answers to complete the cross number puzzle on the next page.

Across

C: $9{,}834 \times 93 = 914{,}562$

E: $489 \times 58 = 28{,}362$

H: $34{,}287 \times 17 = 582{,}879$

J: $4{,}788 \times 35 = 167{,}580$

I: $71{,}908 \times 34 = 2{,}444{,}872$

Down

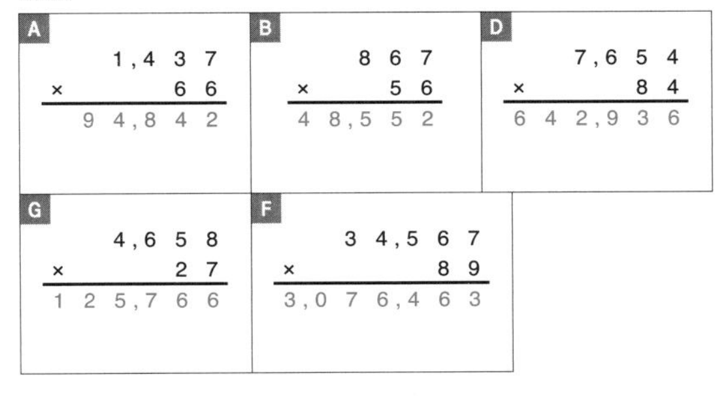

A: $1{,}437 \times 66 = 94{,}842$

B: $867 \times 56 = 48{,}552$

D: $7{,}654 \times 84 = 642{,}936$

G: $4{,}658 \times 27 = 125{,}766$

F: $34{,}567 \times 89 = 3{,}076{,}463$

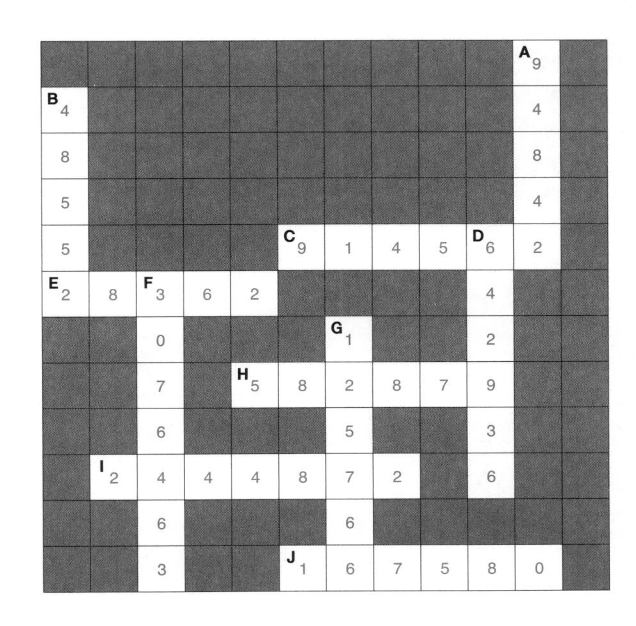

2. Write > or < in each ◯. Use estimation.

(a) 8,268 × 42 (>) 320,000 (b) 1,689 × 84 (<) 200 × 900

(c) 2,724 × 12 (>) 270 × 100 (d) 394 × 56 (<) 15,873 + 8,699

(e) 1,198 × 18 (<) 781 × 49 (f) 8,107 × 11 (>) 148,107 − 62,876

3. Alicia paid $1,690 per month for rent in the first year. The second year, her rent increased by $55 a month. How much did she pay in rent for those two years?

1,690 × 12 + (1,690 + 55) × 12 = 20,280 + 1,745 × 12 = 20,280 + 20,940 = 41,220

$41,220

4. The manager of an apartment complex bought water heaters for each of the 52 apartments. The water heaters each cost $1,398. It cost $832 to install each water heater. The electrician installing the water heaters gave a $3,400 discount on the total. What was the cost of buying and installing the water heaters?

52 × (1,398 + 832) − 3,400 = 112,560

$112,560

Challenge

5. Look for a pattern in the following problems. Find the product for the first problem. Can you can think of an easy way to find the next product by using the product of the previous expression? Explain. Then find the products for the rest for the problems.

5,812 × 37 = 215,044

5,815 × 37 = 215,155

5,818 × 37 = 215,266

5,821 × 37 = 215,377

5,824 × 37 = 215,488

One factor increases by 3 each time.
3 × 37 = 111
Add 111 to the previous product.

6. Find the missing digits.

(a)

```
      4, 5 1 3
  ×        9 7
  ------------
    3 1, 5 9 1
  4 0 6, 1 7 0
  ------------
  4 3 7, 7 6 1
```

(b)

```
      7, 0 6 5
  ×        4 3
  ------------
    2 1, 1 9 5
  2 8 2, 6 0 0
  ------------
  3 0 3, 7 9 5
```

Exercise 4 • pages 56–58

Exercise 4

Basics

1. Make groups of 4 tens.

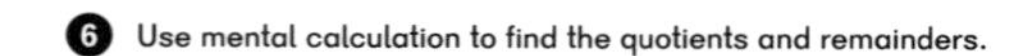

There are 3 groups of 4 tens with 1 ten left over.

130 ÷ 40 is 3 R 10

2. (a) Complete the following estimations for the quotient of 400 ÷ 70.

350 ÷ 70 = 5 | 420 ÷ 70 = 6

(b) Divide 400 by 70.

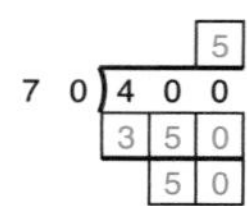

```
       5
70 ) 400
     350
      50
```

3. (a) Complete the following estimations for the quotient of 896 ÷ 90.

810 ÷ 90 = 9 | 900 ÷ 90 = 10

(b) Divide 896 by 90.

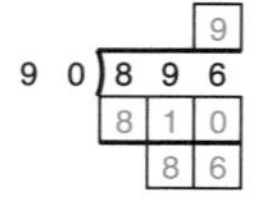

```
       9
90 ) 896
     810
      86
```


Practice

4. Divide.

(a) 762 ÷ 80

```
       9
80 ) 762
     720
      42
```

(b) 438 ÷ 70

```
       6
70 ) 438
     420
      18
```

(c) 385 ÷ 50
7 R 35

(d) 651 ÷ 90
7 R 21

(e) 700 ÷ 80
8 R 60

(f) 600 ÷ 70
8 R 40

5. 200 pieces of paper are distributed equally among 30 students. How many pieces of paper will each student get, and how many are left over?
200 ÷ 30 is 6 with a remainder of 20.
Each student will get 6 sheets of paper, and there will be 20 sheets left over.

6. Use mental calculation to find the quotients and remainders.

(a) 430 ÷ 70
6 R 10

(b) 180 ÷ 50
3 R 30

(c) 290 ÷ 30
9 R 20

(d) 420 ÷ 80
5 R 20

Challenge

7. What will be the ones digit of the remainder for each of these divisions?

(a) 789 ÷ 20
9

(b) 972 ÷ 70
2

8. Divide.

(a) 3,256 ÷ 20
162 R 16

(b) 40,287 ÷ 60
671 R 27

Exercise 5 • pages 59–60

Exercise 5

Basics

1 Divide 87 by 21.

Emma estimated: 80 ÷ 20 = 4

```
        4
2 1 ) 8 7
      8 4   ← 21 × 4
        3
```

2 Divide 86 by 24.

Dion estimated: 80 ÷ 20 = 4

```
        4                                3
2 4 ) 8 6    Too large,          2 4 ) 8 6
      9 6 ← 24 × 4   try 1 less. →      7 2 ← 24 × 3
                                        1 4
```

3 Divide 71 by 16.

Alex estimated: 60 ÷ 20 = 3

```
        3                                4
1 6 ) 7 1    Too small,          1 6 ) 7 1
      4 8 ← 16 × 3   try 1 more. →      6 4 ← 16 × 4
      2 3                                 7
```


Practice

4 Divide.

(a) 98 ÷ 31

```
          3
3 1 ) 9 8
      9 3
        5
```

(b) 71 ÷ 52

```
          1
5 2 ) 7 1
      5 2
      1 9
```

(c) 91 ÷ 13
7

(d) 61 ÷ 22
2 R 17

(e) 76 ÷ 23
3 R 7

(f) 58 ÷ 14
4 R 2

5 52 cards are dealt out to 12 players. How many cards does each player get? How many cards are left over?
52 ÷ 12 is 4 with a remainder of 4.
Each player gets 4 cards, and there are 4 cards left over.

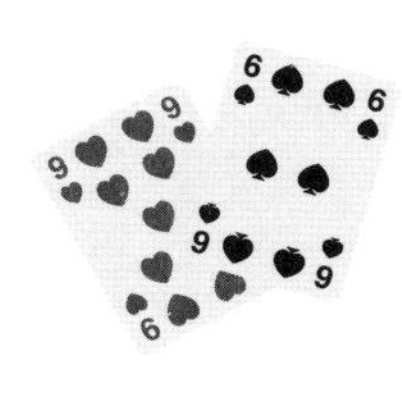

Exercise 6 • pages 61–62

Exercise 6

Basics

1 Divide 371 by 49.

Mei estimated: 350 ÷ 50 = 7

```
          7
4 9 ) 3 7 1
      3 4 3 ← 49 × 7
        2 8
```

2 Divide 345 by 38.

Sofia estimated: 320 ÷ 40 = 8

```
          8                                  9
3 8 ) 3 4 5    Too small,          3 8 ) 3 4 5
      3 0 4 ← 38 × 8  try 1 more. →       3 4 2 ← 38 × 9
        4 1                                   3
```

3 Divide 165 by 24.

Emma estimated: 160 ÷ 20 = 8

```
          8                        7                        6
2 4 ) 1 6 5  Too large,  2 4 ) 1 6 5  Too large,  2 4 ) 1 6 5
      1 9 2  try 7. →          1 6 8  try 6. →          1 4 4
                                                          2 1
```


Practice

4 Divide.

(a) 653 ÷ 86

```
            7
8 6 ) 6 5 3
      6 0 2
        5 1
```

(b) 511 ÷ 73

```
            7
7 3 ) 5 1 1
      5 1 1
          0
```

(c) 389 ÷ 47
8 R 13

(d) 815 ÷ 82
9 R 77

(e) 320 ÷ 53
6 R 2

(f) 406 ÷ 68
5 R 66

5 A farmer collected 195 eggs. He put some of them into 2 cartons of 12, and put the rest into cartons of 18. How many full cartons of 18 did he have?
195 − (2 × 12) = 171
171 ÷ 18 is 9 with a remainder of 9.
9 full cartons

Exercise 7 • pages 63–65

Exercise 7

Basics

1 Divide 893 by 28.

89 is greater than 28, so the quotient will start in the __tens__ place.

Divide 89 tens by 28.
90 tens ÷ 30 = 3 tens. Try 3 tens.

```
      3
2 8)8 9 3
    8 4     ← 28 × 3 tens
      5
```

Divide 53 by 28.
60 ÷ 30 = 2. Since 28 × 2 = 56, 2 is too large. Try 1.

```
      3 1
2 8)8 9 3
    8 4
      5 3
      2 8
      2 5
```

Check your answer: 28 × 31 + 25 = 868 + 25 = 893

2 Divide 852 by 21.

```
      4 0
2 1)8 5 2
    8 4
      1 2
```

Check your answer: 21 × 40 + 12 = 840 + 12 = 852

Practice

3 In each of the following problems, put a check mark in the place where the quotient will start.

(a) 24)590 — ✓ in the first (tens) place

(b) 43)902 — ✓ in the first (tens) place

(c) 63)570 — ✓ in the second (ones) place

(d) 56)553 — ✓ in the second (ones) place

4 Divide.

(a) 971 ÷ 29

```
      3 3
2 9)9 7 1
    8 7
    1 0 1
      8 7
      1 4
```

(b) 702 ÷ 29

```
      2 4
2 9)7 0 2
    5 8
    1 2 2
    1 1 6
        6
```

(c) 772 ÷ 37
20 R 32

(d) 945 ÷ 15
63

5 The area of a rectangle is 444 in². One side measures 1 foot. What is the length of the other side in inches?
444 ÷ 12 = 37
37 inches

Challenge

6 To divide 851 by 16, Alex first estimated that the tens digit of the quotient was 4. When he found it was too small (since the remainder was 21) he replaced the tens digit of the quotient with a 5. Instead of then erasing the 64 and multiplying 16 by 5 and then finding the new remainder, he subtracted 16 from the 21 and then proceeded. Does this work, and if so, why?

```
      5
      4̶ 3
1 6)8 5 1
    6 4
    2 1
    1 6
      5 1
      4 8
        3
```

It works. The 16 × 5 is 16 more than 16 × 4, so the remainder will be 16 less. Had he calculated 16 × 5 to get 80 and subtracted, he would have also gotten a remainder of 5.

Exercise 8 • pages 66–68

Exercise 8

Basics

1 (a) Divide 787 by 32.

```
       2 4
 3 2 ) 7 8 7
       6 4
       1 4 7
       1 2 8
         1 9
```

(b) Divide 7,876 by 32.

```
       2 4 6
 3 2 ) 7,8 7 6
       6 4
       1 4 7
       1 2 8
         1 9 6
         1 9 2
             4
```

(c) Check your answer for 7,876 ÷ 32:
$32 \times 246 + 4 = 7{,}872 + 4 = 7{,}876$

2 (a) Divide 941 by 23.

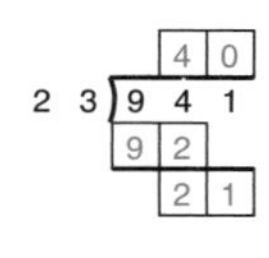

(b) Divide 9,413 by 23.

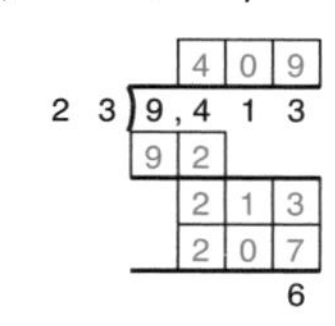

(c) Check your answer for 9,413 ÷ 23:
$23 \times 409 + 6 = 9{,}407 + 6 = 9{,}413$

3 (a) Divide 487 by 52.

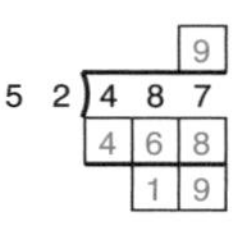

(b) Divide 4,872 by 52.

```
         9 3
 5 2 ) 4,8 7 2
       4 6 8
         1 9 2
         1 5 6
           3 6
```

(c) Check your answer for 4,872 ÷ 52:
$52 \times 93 + 36 = 4{,}836 + 36 = 4{,}872$

Practice

4 In each of the following problems, put a check mark in the place where the quotient will start.

(a)

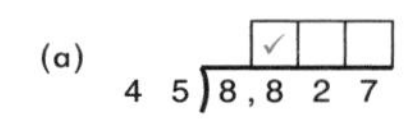

(b)

(c)

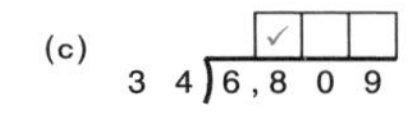

(d)

```
         ✓
 4 6 ) 4,2 3 2
```


5 Divide.

(a) 7,716 ÷ 19
406 R 2

(b) 8,072 ÷ 28
288 R 8

(c) 5,728 ÷ 63
90 R 58

(d) 9,285 ÷ 15
619

(e) 7,056 ÷ 85
83 R 1

(f) 8,297 ÷ 60
138 R 17

Exercise 9

Check

1. Divide.

(a) 889 ÷ 30
29 R 19

(b) 460 ÷ 53
8 R 36

(c) 982 ÷ 28
35 R 2

(d) 1,010 ÷ 11
91 R 9

(e) 8,932 ÷ 29
308

(f) 6,285 ÷ 18
349 R 3

2. Write > or < in each ◯. Use estimation.

(a) 937 ÷ 8 (>) 3,270 ÷ 40

(b) 5,938 ÷ 62 (<) 4,812 ÷ 36

(c) 8,908 ÷ 17 (<) 132 × 7

(d) 8,107 ÷ 11 (<) 128,107 – 72,876

3. Express 152 ounces as pounds and ounces.
152 ÷ 16 = 9 R 8
9 lb 8 oz

4. Lee's pickup truck can carry up to 1,500 lb. Lee weighs 195 lb and there are 45 lb of other contents in the truck. How many 94-pound bags of cement can the truck carry?
1,500 – 195 – 45 = 1,260
1,260 ÷ 94 is 13 R 38
13 bags

5. A rope 10 m long is cut into 4 parts. Part B is 4 times as long as Part A, and Part C is 4 times as long as part B. Part D is 55 cm long. How long is Part C?

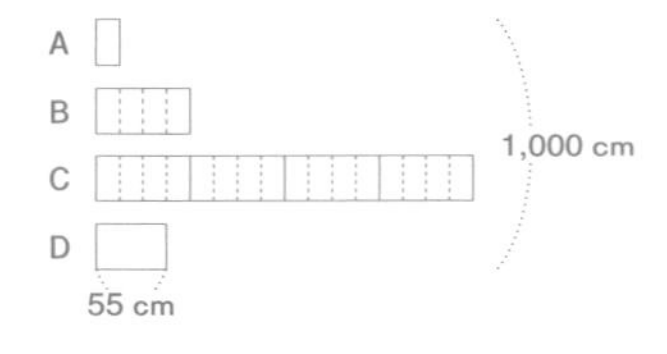

21 units ⟶ 1,000 – 55 = 945
1 unit ⟶ 945 ÷ 21 = 45
16 units ⟶ 16 × 45 = 720
720 cm

6. The manager of a new apartment complex with 12 apartments spent $8,190 on bathroom and kitchen sinks for each unit. Half of the units had 2 bathrooms. Each kitchen sink cost twice as much as each bathroom sink. What was the cost of 1 bathroom sink?
Number of bathroom sinks needed: 12 + 6 = 18
12 kitchen sinks cost the same as 24 bathroom sinks.
18 + 24 = 42
8,190 ÷ 42 = 195
$195

Challenge

7. When a 3 digit number is divided by 11, the remainder is greater than the quotient. What is the number?
The number is 109.
The remainder must be 10 or less. So the quotient must be 9 or less.
Try a quotient of 9 with a remainder of 10: 9 × 11 + 10 = 109
Try a quotient of 8 with a remainder of 10: 8 × 11 + 10 = 98, which is not a 3-digit number, which would also be the case for a remainder of 9 or any quotient less than 8.

8. When 165 is divided by a 2-digit divisor, the remainder is 30. What is the divisor?
165 = divisor × quotient + 30
165 – 30 = 135 must be divisible by the divisor.
The factors of 135 are 1, 3, 5, 9, 15, 27, 45, and 135.
The divisor cannot be less than the remainder.
The divisor must be 45.

9. Find the missing digits.

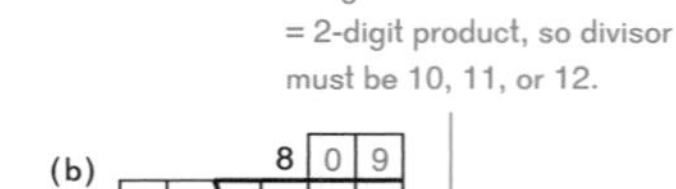

(a)

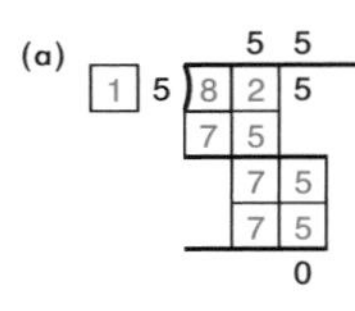

(b)

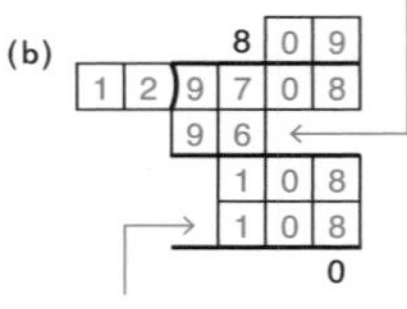

3 digits, so divisor must be 12 and the ones digit of the quotient must be 9.
Tens digit of quotient must be 0.

Suggested number of class periods: 10–11

	Lesson	Page	Resources	Objectives
	Chapter Opener	p. 103	TB: p. 75	Review addition and subtraction of fractions.
1	Fractions and Division	p. 104	TB: p. 76 WB: p. 73	Divide two whole numbers and express the remainder as a fraction or a mixed number.
2	Adding Unlike Fractions	p. 108	TB: p. 81 WB: p. 76	Add proper fractions with unlike denominators.
3	Subtracting Unlike Fractions	p. 111	TB: p. 85 WB: p. 79	Subtract fractions with unlike denominators.
4	Practice A	p. 113	TB: p. 88 WB: p. 82	Practice adding and subtracting fractions.
5	Adding Mixed Numbers — Part 1	p. 114	TB: p. 90 WB: p. 85	Add a mixed number and a fraction with unlike denominators.
6	Adding Mixed Numbers — Part 2	p. 117	TB: p. 94 WB: p. 87	Add mixed numbers with unlike denominators.
7	Subtracting Mixed Numbers — Part 1	p. 120	TB: p. 98 WB: p. 90	Subtract a fraction from a mixed number or whole number.
8	Subtracting Mixed Numbers — Part 2	p. 123	TB: p. 102 WB: p. 92	Subtract a mixed number from a mixed number or whole number.
9	Practice B	p. 126	TB: p. 106 WB: p. 94	Practice adding and subtracting mixed numbers.
	Review 1	p. 128	TB: p. 108 WB: p. 97	Review content from Chapters 1–4.
	Workbook Solutions	p. 130		

In Dimensions Math 4A, students learned:

- To find an equivalent fraction.
- To add and subtract fractions and mixed numbers with like and related denominators.
- To convert improper fractions to mixed numbers, and vice versa.
- That a fraction is a division expression.

In this chapter, students will learn to add and subtract fractions with unlike denominators, including mixed numbers.

In the same way that whole numbers count like objects (4 bears and 3 cats makes 7 animals), fractions count like units. These units are equal-sized parts of a whole number. In the fraction $\frac{3}{4}$, the denominator names the fractional unit, fourths, and the numerator counts the number of fractional units. For example, $\frac{3}{4}$ means 3 fourths.

Fractions with the same denominators have like fractional units and are often called "like fractions."

Fractions and Division

In Dimensions Math 4, students learned to interpret $\frac{2}{3}$ in two ways: as counting two parts that are each $\frac{1}{3}$ in size, and as a division expression: 2 divided by 3.
In Lesson 1, students review this concept, and apply it to larger improper fractions. For example, $13 \div 5$ is $\frac{13}{5}$, or $2\frac{3}{5}$. The solution of 2 with a remainder of 3 found by long division is now properly expressed as 2 and a fraction of the whole, $2\frac{3}{5}$.

Like and Unlike Fractions

To add or subtract fractions, the units specified by the denominators must be converted so that they are the same.

We can easily add $\frac{2}{7}$ and $\frac{5}{7}$, however, adding $\frac{2}{3}$ and $\frac{5}{7}$ requires additional steps. An analogy would be that while we can add 5 feet and 5 feet, we cannot add 5 feet and 5 meters without first converting to the same units. Similarly, to add fractions with different denominators, we need to make the units the same. We do so by finding equivalent fractions.

Addition and Subtraction with Unlike Denominators

When the denominators of two or more fractions are the same, they are called common denominators. Students have learned that fractions can only be added or subtracted when they have common denominators.

Unlike fractions are fractions that do not have common denominators. In Dimensions Math 4A, students learned to add related fractions in which one denominator was a simple multiple of the other, by finding an equivalent fraction for one fraction with the same denominator as the other.

Example: $\frac{1}{6} + \frac{1}{3} = \frac{1}{6} + \frac{2}{6} = \frac{3}{6} = \frac{1}{2}$

Now, students will learn to add fractions in which neither denominator is a multiple of the other, for example, $\frac{2}{6} + \frac{2}{10}$. They will need to find equivalent fractions with common denominators.

To find common denominators, students will use their knowledge of common multiples that they learned in Dimensions Math 4A.

Students will be shown two methods for finding common denominators. The first method is to list the multiples of each denominator until they find a common one, usually the least common one. They can list or think of the multiples of the larger number until they get to a number they recognize as a multiple of the smaller number. The second method is to make a common denominator by multiplying the two denominators together.

Addition example: $\frac{2}{6} + \frac{2}{10}$

Method 1

Multiples of 10: 10, 20, 30

Multiples of 6: 6, 12, 18, 24, 30

$\frac{2 \times 5}{6 \times 5} = \frac{10}{30}$

$\frac{2 \times 3}{10 \times 3} = \frac{6}{30}$

$\frac{2}{6} + \frac{2}{10} = \frac{10}{30} + \frac{6}{30} = \frac{16}{30} = \frac{8}{15}$

Method 2

$6 \times 10 = 60$

$\frac{2}{6} + \frac{2}{10} = \frac{2 \times 10}{6 \times 10} + \frac{2 \times 6}{10 \times 6} = \frac{20}{60} + \frac{12}{60}$

$= \frac{32}{60} = \frac{8}{15}$

Dimensions Math expects final answers to be expressed in simplest form.

Subtraction example: $\frac{9}{10} - \frac{1}{4}$

Method 1

Multiples of 10: 10, 20

Multiples of 4: 4, 8, 12, 16, 20

$\frac{9 \times 2}{10 \times 2} = \frac{18}{20}$

$\frac{1 \times 5}{4 \times 5} = \frac{5}{20}$

$\frac{18}{20} - \frac{5}{20} = \frac{13}{20}$

Method 2

$10 \times 4 = 40$

$\frac{9}{10} - \frac{1}{4} = \frac{9 \times 4}{10 \times 4} - \frac{1 \times 10}{4 \times 10} = \frac{36}{40} - \frac{10}{40}$

$= \frac{26}{40} = \frac{13}{20}$

Both methods will be shown for sums and differences.

Adding Mixed Numbers

Mixed numbers can be thought of as the sum of a whole number and a fraction:

$1\frac{4}{5} + 2\frac{1}{3} = 1 + \frac{4}{5} + 2 + \frac{1}{3}$

Students will be shown that they can approach these problems by either grouping whole numbers and fractions or by converting to improper fractions. In both cases, they will need to add unlike fractions by finding common denominators.

Students will be asked to estimate before calculating. For example, since $1 + 2 = 3$, and $\frac{4}{5}$ is close to 1, the estimate for $1\frac{4}{5} + 2\frac{1}{3}$ might be "more than 4."

Students begin by adding a mixed number and a fraction.

Example: $1\frac{4}{5} + \frac{1}{3}$

Estimate: More than 2.

Method 1

Find common denominators first, then add the fractions.

$1\frac{4}{5} + \frac{1}{3} = 1\frac{12}{15} + \frac{5}{15}$

$= 1\frac{17}{15}$

$= 2\frac{2}{15}$

Method 2

Change the mixed number to an improper fraction first, and then add.

$1\frac{4}{5} + \frac{1}{3} = \frac{9}{5} + \frac{1}{3}$

$= \frac{27}{15} + \frac{5}{15}$

$= \frac{32}{15}$

$= 2\frac{2}{15}$

Multiple methods are taught for grouping the whole numbers and fractions in these problems. For addition, these methods are straightforward. In each method, the final step is converting to a mixed number in simplest form.

Students may find that they use different methods based on the fractions in the equation. They will then extend these strategies to adding two mixed numbers.

Subtracting Mixed Numbers

To subtract mixed numbers, students may need to regroup a whole number into a fraction in order to have enough parts from which to subtract. They will first learn to subtract a fraction from a mixed number, and then a mixed number from a mixed number.

Example: $3\frac{1}{5} - 1\frac{1}{3}$

Method 1

Since students first learn to subtract a fraction from a mixed number in Lesson 7, this method is simply an extension of that. They first subtract the whole number part of the minuend, resulting in a fraction or a mixed number, and then subtract the fractional part.

$3\frac{1}{5} - 1\frac{1}{3} = 3\frac{1}{5} - 1 - \frac{1}{3} = 2\frac{1}{5} - \frac{1}{3}$

$$2\frac{1}{5} - \frac{1}{3} = 2\frac{3}{15} - \frac{5}{15}$$

(2 is split into 1 and $\frac{15}{15}$)

$$= 1\frac{18}{15} - \frac{5}{15}$$

$$= 1\frac{13}{15}$$

Method 2

Convert the mixed numbers to improper fractions, find equivalent fractions with common denominators, and then subtract:

$3\frac{1}{5} - 1\frac{1}{3} = \frac{16}{5} - \frac{4}{3} = \frac{48}{15} - \frac{20}{15} = \frac{28}{15} = 1\frac{13}{15}$

Unlike whole number calculations, mixed number calculations should not be written in a vertical format. The purpose of a vertical algorithm for whole number calculations is to emphasize the single digit calculations within a base-ten system.

Because fraction representation is not base ten, a vertical algorithm is not used.

Materials

- Dry erase sleeves
- Paper strips
- Whiteboards

Blackline Masters

- Closest to 7 Cards
- Greatest Sum
- Number Cards
- Smallest Difference
- Yohaku

Activities

Games and activities included in this chapter are designed to provide practice with adding and subtracting mixed numbers and can be used anytime practice is needed.

Objective

- Review addition and subtraction of fractions.

Have students discuss the friends' comments in the **Chapter Opener** about what students have learned about fractions.

Emma's statement gives students an idea of what they will learn to do in this chapter.

Chapter 4

Addition and Subtraction of Fractions

The friends are on a field trip to the bakery. They get to help the baker!

We will need to add and subtract fractions. What have we learned so far?

We can find equivalent fractions. $\frac{1}{2} = \frac{4}{8}$

We can add and subtract fractions like $\frac{1}{2}$ and $\frac{3}{4}$. $\frac{3}{4} + \frac{1}{2} = \frac{3}{4} + \frac{2}{4} = \frac{5}{4} = 1\frac{1}{4}$

I wonder how we can add or subtract fractions like $\frac{2}{3}$ and $\frac{3}{4}$.

75

Objective

- Divide two whole numbers and express the remainder as a fraction or a mixed number.

Lesson Materials

- Paper strips, all the same length, 2 each per student

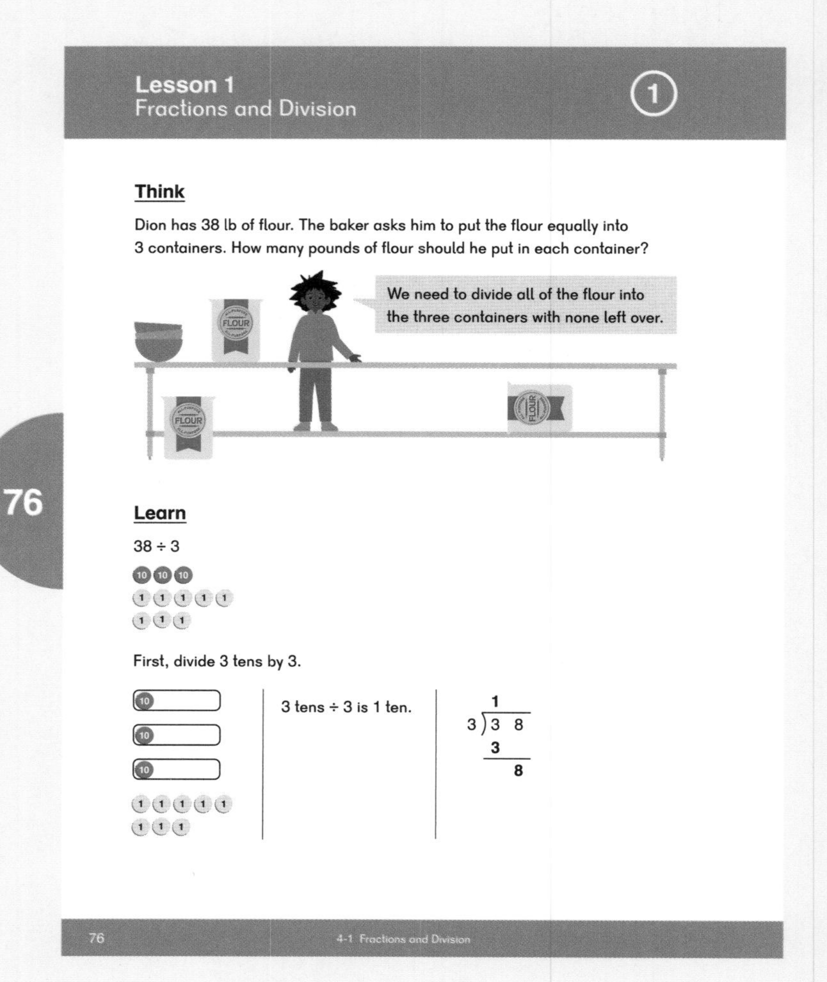

Think

Provide students with paper strips and pose the **Think** problem.

Ask students what they recall about fractions and division. Have them estimate the answer. They may use $30 \div 3 = 10$ or even $36 \div 3 = 12$, and see that the answer will be greater than either 10 or 12. Have them use the paper strips to represent the 2 remaining pounds of flour. They can fold, cut, or draw to show how the 2 lb of flour can be divided evenly among 3 containers.

Have students share how they solved the problem.

Learn

The **Learn** reminds students they can use the division algorithm, and that we can divide the remainder as well and express it as a fraction. The quotient is a mixed number.

Since the entire measurement quantity is being divided into 3 equal parts, the only way to express how much flour goes into each container is to use fractions. Later, students will also learn that they can use decimals in some cases.

Since 2 divided by 3 means 2 divided into 3 equal parts, or $\frac{2}{3}$, we can say that Dion should put $12\frac{2}{3}$ lb of flour into each container.

To check his answer, Alex thinks of fractions, which can be simplified:

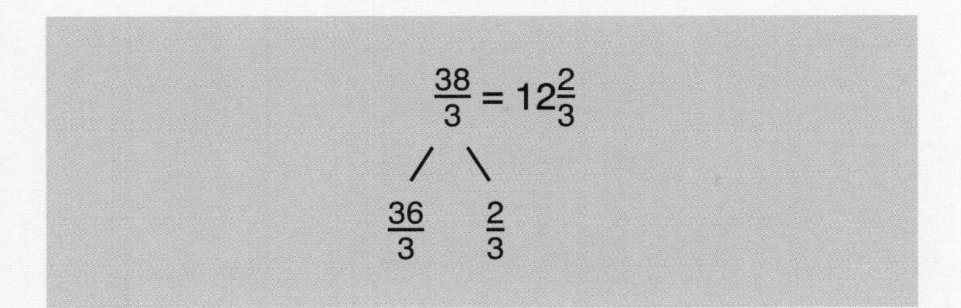

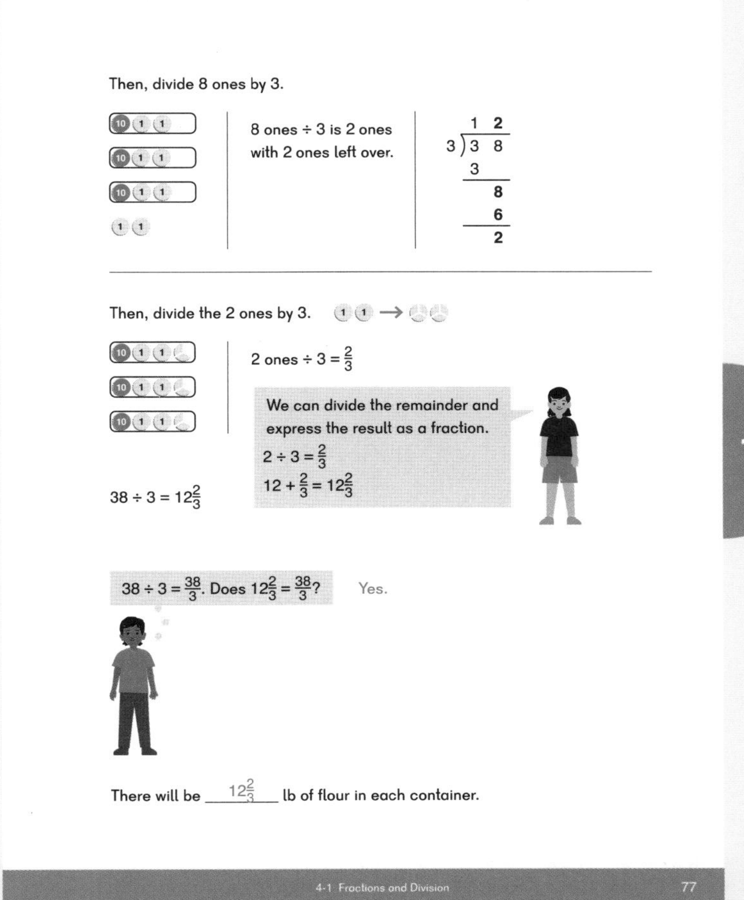

Do

1—6 Discuss the problems and given solutions with students.

1 (a) There are not enough wholes to place 1 whole in each group. We begin by dividing each whole into 6 equal parts, or sixths. There are 24 sixths in 4.

Divide the sixths into 6 equal groups. There are 4 sixths in each group. 4 sixths is equal to 2 thirds, or $\frac{2}{3}$.

(b) To divide 6 into 4 equal parts, we can begin by dividing each whole into 4 equal parts (fourths). There are 24 fourths in 6.

Regroup the fourths into 4 groups. There are 6 fourths in each group. 6 fourths is equal to $\frac{6}{4}$, or $1\frac{1}{2}$.

Students could also use division. They can see that $6 \div 4$ results in 1 whole in each group. The remainder can be expressed as $\frac{2}{4}$ or $\frac{1}{2}$.

2—5 Both the division algorithm and simplifying of fractions are shown as methods for division. Students should see how the two methods are related. The remainder, when divided by the dividend, is the fractional part of the quotient.

2 The bar representing 10 is divided into 4 equal-sized units. Each unit is $\frac{1}{4}$ of the whole (10). We can find $10 \div 4$ by:

- Dividing 10 by 4: $\frac{10}{4} = \frac{5}{2} = 2\frac{1}{2}$.
- Using the division algorithm to find a quotient and expressing the remainder as a fraction.

5 Discuss Alex's comment. Students may choose to solve problems similar to this one by simplifying in two steps: divide both the numerator and the denominator by 2, then divide the resulting numerator and denominator by 2 again.

78

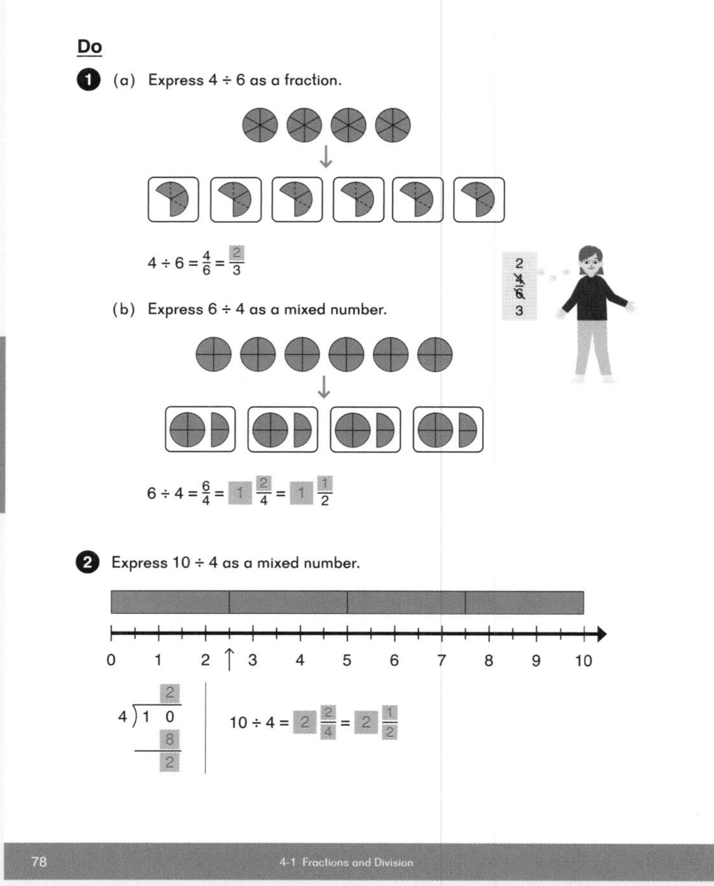

Do

1 (a) Express $4 \div 6$ as a fraction.

$4 \div 6 = \frac{4}{6} = \frac{2}{3}$

(b) Express $6 \div 4$ as a mixed number.

$6 \div 4 = \frac{6}{4} = 1\frac{2}{4} = 1\frac{1}{2}$

2 Express $10 \div 4$ as a mixed number.

0 1 2 3 4 5 6 7 8 9 10

$10 \div 4 = 2\frac{2}{4} = 2\frac{1}{2}$

78 4-1 Fractions and Division

79

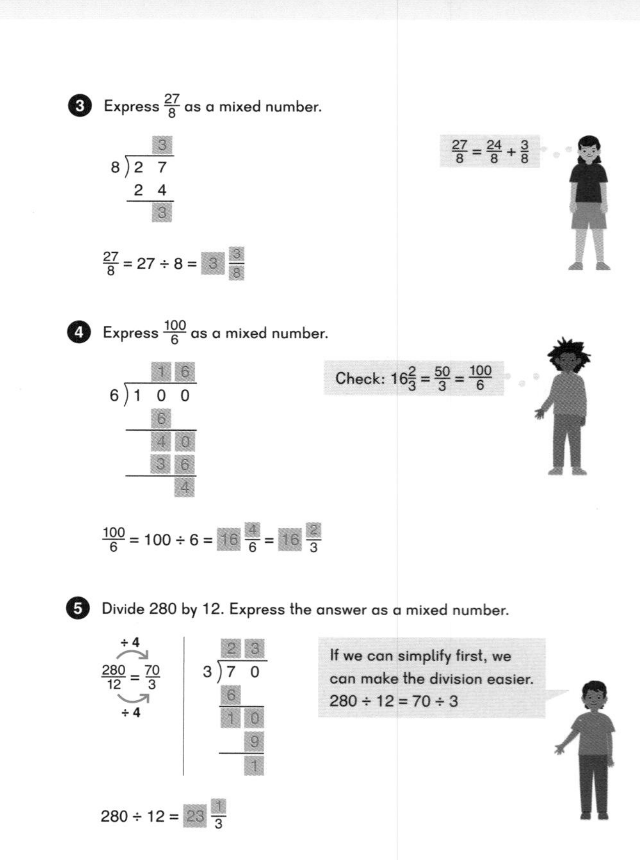

3 Express $\frac{27}{8}$ as a mixed number.

$\frac{27}{8} = \frac{24}{8} + \frac{3}{8}$

$\frac{27}{8} = 27 \div 8 = 3\frac{3}{8}$

4 Express $\frac{100}{6}$ as a mixed number.

Check: $16\frac{2}{3} = \frac{50}{3} = \frac{100}{6}$

$\frac{100}{6} = 100 \div 6 = 16\frac{4}{6} = 16\frac{2}{3}$

5 Divide 280 by 12. Express the answer as a mixed number.

$\frac{280}{12} = \frac{70}{3}$ (÷ 4)

If we can simplify first, we can make the division easier.
$280 \div 12 = 70 \div 3$

$280 \div 12 = 23\frac{1}{3}$

4-1 Fractions and Division 79

❻ Sofia and Dion demonstrate why simplifying fractions before calculating is a good choice for some numbers. The division algorithm may be time-consuming to use for 2,200 ÷ 80.

Remind students that if both the numerator and denominator are even, or both are multiples of 5, the fraction can be simplified. Once they have simplified to two-digit numbers, they can also easily check if the digits in the numerator and denominator have a sum of 3, and so are multiples of 3.

Once Dion simplifies to $\frac{55}{2}$, he can mentally decompose 55 into 54 + 1:

$$55 \div 2 = (54 \div 2) + (1 \div 2) = 27 + \frac{1}{2}$$

54 1

❼—❾ Students can use any method to solve the problems. They should be able to work these problems independently.

Activity

▲ Word Problem

Have students write a word problem using an expression from ❼. They can exchange the problem with another student to solve.

Exercise 1 • page 73

80

❻ Find the value of 2,200 ÷ 80. Express the answer as a mixed number in simplest form.

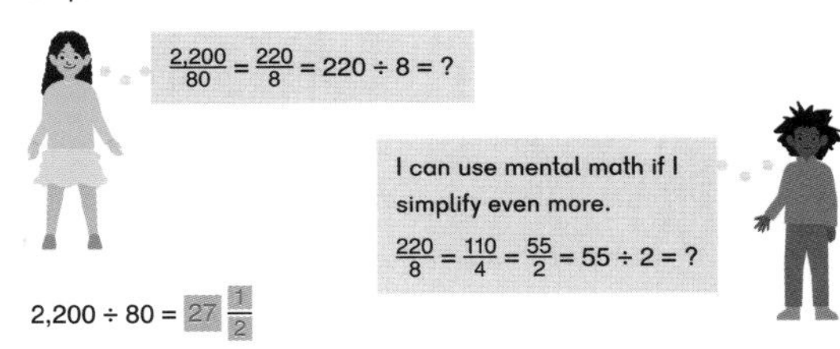

2,200 ÷ 80 = $27\frac{1}{2}$

❼ Divide. Express each answer as a fraction or mixed number in simplest form.

(a) 5 ÷ 7 $\frac{5}{7}$

(b) 9 ÷ 6 $1\frac{1}{2}$

(c) 56 ÷ 3 $18\frac{2}{3}$

(d) 82 ÷ 12 $6\frac{5}{6}$

(e) 120 ÷ 14 $8\frac{4}{7}$

(f) 338 ÷ 16 $21\frac{1}{8}$

❽ Express each fraction as a mixed number in simplest form.

(a) $\frac{8}{5}$ $1\frac{3}{5}$ (b) $\frac{13}{4}$ $3\frac{1}{4}$ (c) $\frac{88}{12}$ $7\frac{1}{3}$ (d) $\frac{40}{15}$ $2\frac{2}{3}$

❾ Emma cut 53 ft of ribbon into 3 equal length pieces. What is the length of each piece in feet? $53 \div 3 = 17\frac{2}{3}$

$17\frac{2}{3}$ ft

Exercise 1 • page 73

Lesson 2 Adding Unlike Fractions

Objective

- Add proper fractions with unlike denominators.

Think

Pose the **Think** problem. Students can draw a model or use equations to solve the problem.

Ask students what they recall about adding fractions. They should know that to add fractions, the fractions must have equal-sized units, or common denominators.

Have students share their solutions.

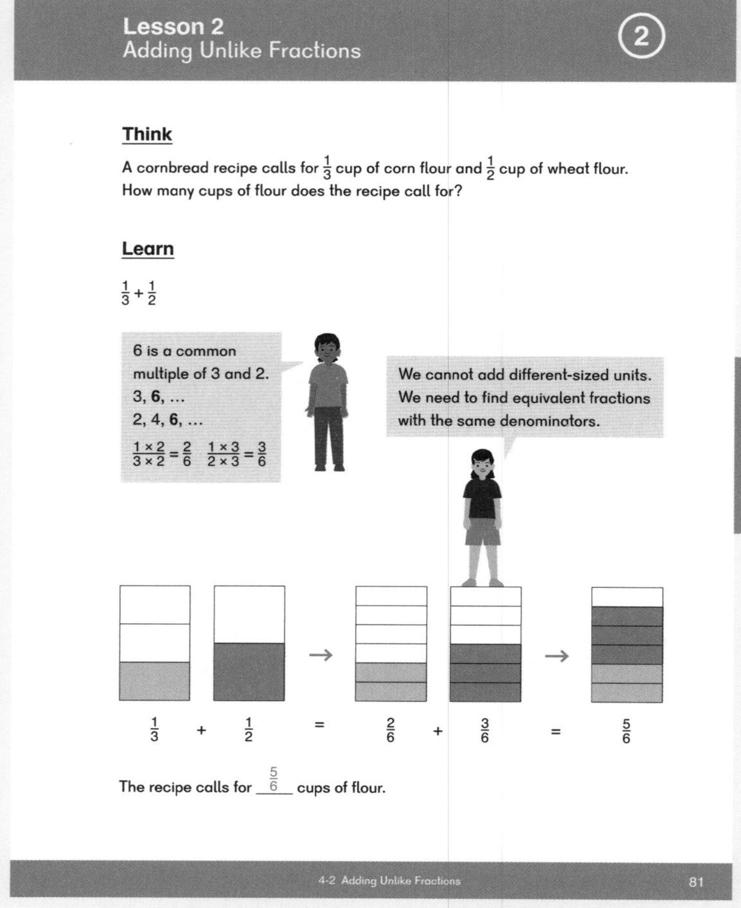

Lesson 2
Adding Unlike Fractions
2

Think

A cornbread recipe calls for $\frac{1}{3}$ cup of corn flour and $\frac{1}{2}$ cup of wheat flour. How many cups of flour does the recipe call for?

Learn

$\frac{1}{3}+\frac{1}{2}$

6 is a common multiple of 3 and 2.
3, **6**, ...
2, 4, **6**, ...
$\frac{1\times 2}{3\times 2}=\frac{2}{6}$ $\frac{1\times 3}{2\times 3}=\frac{3}{6}$

We cannot add different-sized units. We need to find equivalent fractions with the same denominators.

$\frac{1}{3}$ + $\frac{1}{2}$ = $\frac{2}{6}$ + $\frac{3}{6}$ = $\frac{5}{6}$

The recipe calls for $\frac{5}{6}$ cups of flour.

4-2 Adding Unlike Fractions 81

81

Learn

Have students compare their solutions from **Think** with the one shown in the textbook.

Discuss Mei's comment. Students have learned that to add fractions, the denominators must be the same.

Ask students:

- "What denominator can you use to express both fractions with common denominators?"
- "Why does Alex express the $\frac{1}{2}$ and $\frac{1}{3}$ as sixths?"

Do

❶–❻ Discuss the problems and given solutions with students. Students should give their final answers in simplest form.

❶ Ask students, “What number is the first common multiple of 3 and 6?”

Students should see that 6 is a multiple of 3. They only need to find an equivalent fraction for $\frac{1}{3}$ to add the fractions.

❷ Because neither 3 nor 4 is a multiple of the other, we first need to convert both fractions to equivalent fractions with common denominators.

❸ Discuss Dion’s comments. Ask students why his procedure always works. (Because when we multiply the numbers in the denominators, we always get a multiple of both: 10 is a multiple of both 2 and 5.)

❹ Emma asks students to estimate. Since $\frac{1}{4} + \frac{1}{4} = \frac{1}{2}$ and $\frac{1}{6} < \frac{1}{4}$, the answer will be less than $\frac{1}{2}$.

Discuss the two methods Mei and Alex use to find a common denominator. Ask students if one method is easier for them than the other.

Encourage students to think of the efficiency of each method and how that might be determined by the given denominators. For example, Dion’s idea of multiplying 2 and 5 was more efficient than listing multiples of each denominator.

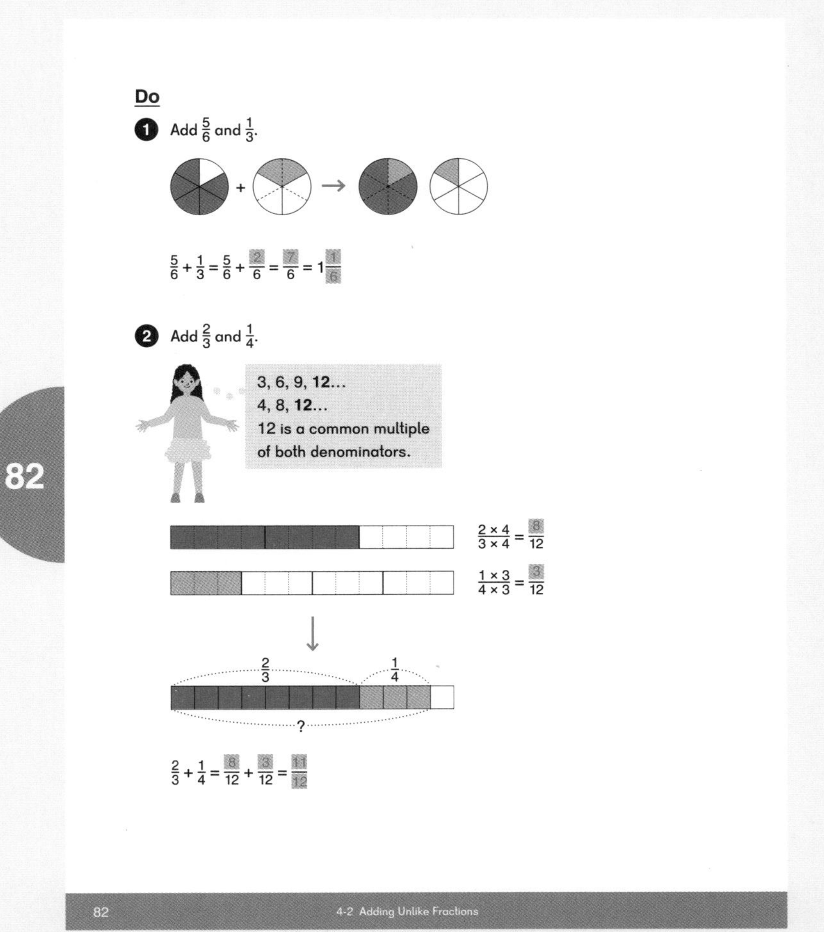

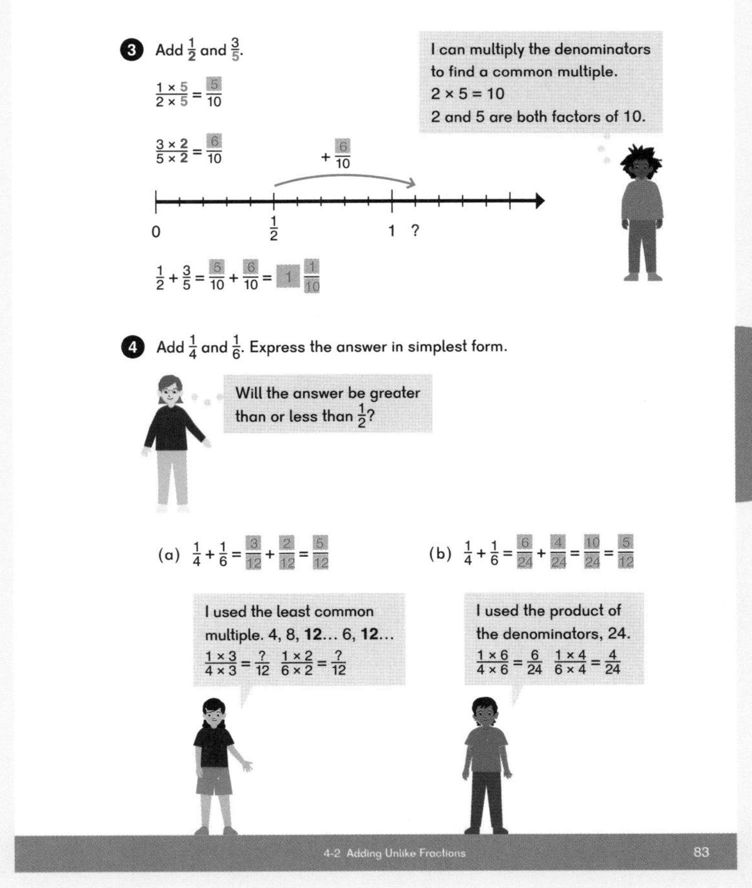

❻—❼ Students can use any method to solve the problems. They should be able to work these problems independently.

❻ (g) Since students have worked with multiples of 2 and 3 in **Think**, they should immediately see that 2, 3, and 6 share the common multiple of 6.

$\frac{3}{6} + \frac{2}{6} + \frac{1}{6} = \frac{6}{6} = 1$

(h) The common multiple is 20.

$\frac{6}{20} + \frac{16}{20} + \frac{15}{20} = \frac{37}{20} = 1\frac{17}{20}$

Activity

▲ Yohaku

Materials: Yohaku (BLM)

Fill in the empty cells with unit fractions. To solve, the fractions must result in the sum shown in each row and column.

If students need a hint, tell them to try different combinations of unit fractions where the denominators are factors of the denominator in the sum.

$\frac{1}{?}$	$\frac{1}{?}$	$\frac{5}{6}$
$\frac{1}{?}$	$\frac{1}{?}$	$\frac{5}{12}$
$\frac{7}{12}$	$\frac{2}{3}$	+

$\frac{1}{?}$	$\frac{1}{?}$	$\frac{13}{30}$
$\frac{1}{?}$	$\frac{1}{?}$	$\frac{11}{18}$
$\frac{4}{9}$	$\frac{3}{5}$	+

84

❺ Add $\frac{3}{10}$ and $\frac{5}{6}$. Express the answer in simplest form.

I used the least common multiple.
$\frac{3 \times 3}{10 \times 3} = \frac{?}{30}$ $\frac{5 \times 5}{6 \times 5} = \frac{?}{30}$

I used the product of the denominators.
$\frac{3 \times 6}{10 \times 6} = \frac{?}{60}$ $\frac{5 \times 10}{6 \times 10} = \frac{?}{60}$

$\frac{3}{10} + \frac{5}{6} = 1\frac{2}{15}$

❻ Add. Express each answer in simplest form.

(a) $\frac{1}{2} + \frac{1}{7}$ $\frac{9}{14}$

(b) $\frac{1}{6} + \frac{3}{10}$ $\frac{7}{15}$

(c) $\frac{1}{10} + \frac{2}{5}$ $\frac{1}{2}$

(d) $\frac{2}{3} + \frac{5}{8}$ $1\frac{7}{24}$

(e) $\frac{9}{6} + \frac{6}{9}$ $2\frac{1}{6}$

(f) $\frac{5}{3} + \frac{3}{2}$ $3\frac{1}{6}$

(g) $\frac{1}{2} + \frac{1}{3} + \frac{1}{6}$ 1

(h) $\frac{3}{10} + \frac{4}{5} + \frac{3}{4}$ $1\frac{17}{20}$

❼ Mei ran $\frac{3}{4}$ mi on Monday, $\frac{1}{2}$ mi on Tuesday, and $\frac{1}{3}$ mi on Wednesday. How far did she run on the three days altogether?
$\frac{9}{12} + \frac{6}{12} + \frac{4}{12} = 1\frac{7}{12}$; $1\frac{7}{12}$ miles

Exercise 2 • page 76

84 4-2 Adding Unlike Fractions

Answers:

$\frac{1}{3}$	$\frac{1}{2}$	$\frac{5}{6}$
$\frac{1}{4}$	$\frac{1}{6}$	$\frac{5}{12}$
$\frac{7}{12}$	$\frac{2}{3}$	+

$\frac{1}{3}$	$\frac{1}{10}$	$\frac{13}{30}$
$\frac{1}{9}$	$\frac{1}{2}$	$\frac{11}{18}$
$\frac{4}{9}$	$\frac{3}{5}$	+

★ Challenge students to write their own Yohaku and have a classmate solve it.

Exercise 2 • page 76

Lesson 3 Subtracting Unlike Fractions

Objective

- Subtract fractions with unlike denominators.

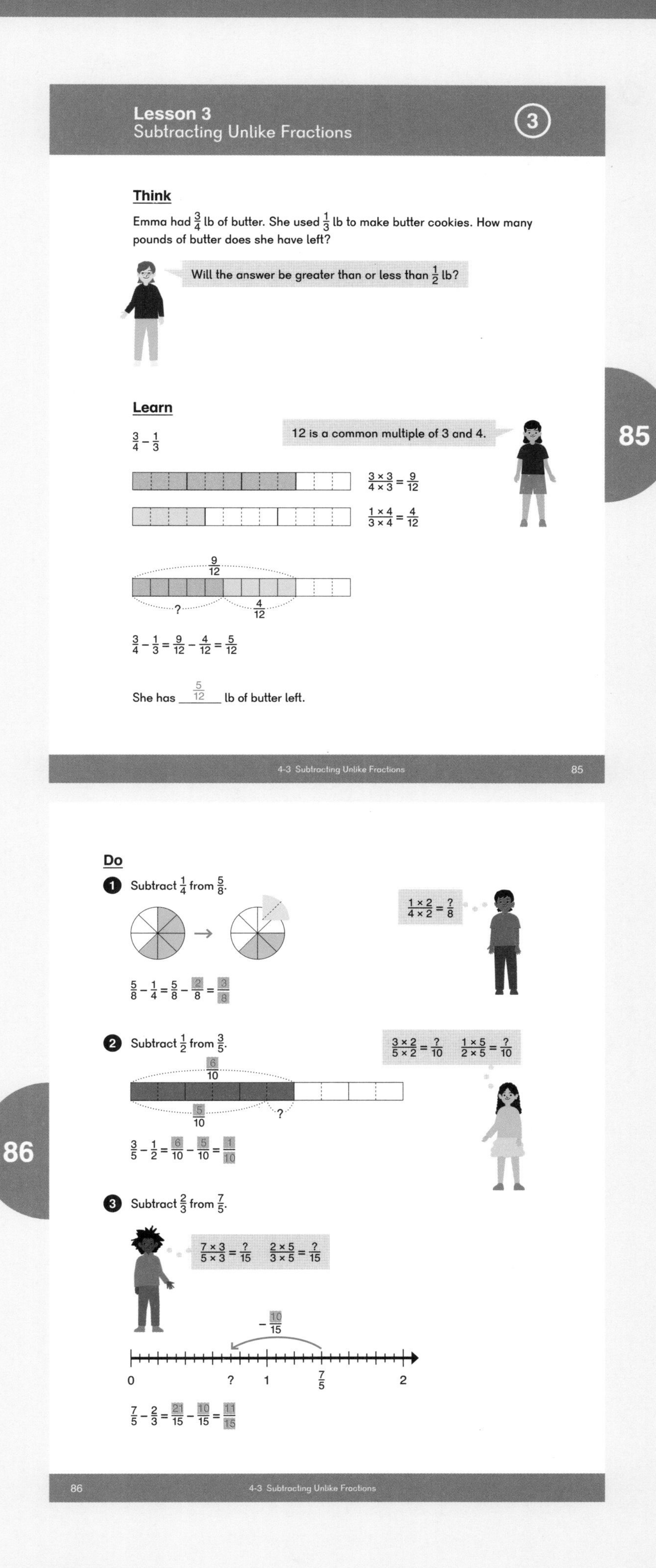
Lesson 3
Subtracting Unlike Fractions

Think

Emma had $\frac{3}{4}$ lb of butter. She used $\frac{1}{3}$ lb to make butter cookies. How many pounds of butter does she have left?

Will the answer be greater than or less than $\frac{1}{2}$ lb?

Learn

$\frac{3}{4} - \frac{1}{3}$

12 is a common multiple of 3 and 4.

$\frac{3 \times 3}{4 \times 3} = \frac{9}{12}$

$\frac{1 \times 4}{3 \times 4} = \frac{4}{12}$

$\frac{3}{4} - \frac{1}{3} = \frac{9}{12} - \frac{4}{12} = \frac{5}{12}$

She has $\frac{5}{12}$ lb of butter left.

4-3 Subtracting Unlike Fractions 85

Do

1. Subtract $\frac{1}{4}$ from $\frac{5}{8}$.

$\frac{1 \times 2}{4 \times 2} = \frac{?}{8}$

$\frac{5}{8} - \frac{1}{4} = \frac{5}{8} - \frac{2}{8} = \frac{3}{8}$

2. Subtract $\frac{1}{2}$ from $\frac{3}{5}$.

$\frac{3 \times 2}{5 \times 2} = \frac{?}{10}$ $\frac{1 \times 5}{2 \times 5} = \frac{?}{10}$

$\frac{3}{5} - \frac{1}{2} = \frac{6}{10} - \frac{5}{10} = \frac{1}{10}$

3. Subtract $\frac{2}{3}$ from $\frac{7}{5}$.

$\frac{7 \times 3}{5 \times 3} = \frac{?}{15}$ $\frac{2 \times 5}{3 \times 5} = \frac{?}{15}$

$\frac{7}{5} - \frac{2}{3} = \frac{21}{15} - \frac{10}{15} = \frac{11}{15}$

86 4-3 Subtracting Unlike Fractions

Think

Pose the **Think** problem and discuss Emma's question.

To estimate, students should know that $\frac{1}{3} > \frac{1}{4}$.

$\frac{3}{4} - \frac{1}{4}$ would leave $\frac{1}{2}$ lb of butter. Since $\frac{1}{3}$ is more than $\frac{1}{4}$, Emma will use more butter, and will have less than $\frac{1}{2}$ lb of butter remaining.

Students can draw a model or use equations to solve the problem. Have students share their solutions.

Learn

Have students compare their solutions from **Think** with the solution in the textbook.

Mei makes equivalent fractions using the common multiple of 12.

Once both fractions are expressed with a common denominator, we can simply subtract $\frac{4}{12}$ from $\frac{9}{12}$.

Do

❶—❹ Discuss the problems and given solutions with students. Students should give their answers in simplest form.

❶ In the fraction $\frac{5}{8}$, the denominator, 8, is a multiple of 4.

❷ 5 is not a multiple of 2. To subtract, we first need to find equivalent fractions with like denominators.

5—**6** Students can use any method to solve the problems. They should be able to work these problems independently.

Ask students questions about subsequent problems similar to the one Emma poses in **4**, "What denominators will you use and why?"

5 (f) Students should know that $1 = \frac{15}{15}$.

(g) $\frac{7}{8} - \frac{1}{4} = \frac{7}{8} - \frac{2}{8} = \frac{5}{8}$

$\frac{5}{8} - \frac{1}{2} = \frac{5}{8} - \frac{4}{8} = \frac{1}{8}$

They could also first find equivalent fractions for all three numbers with common denominators:

$\frac{7}{8} - \frac{2}{8} - \frac{4}{8} = \frac{1}{8}$

Exercise 3 • page 79

87

4 Subtract $\frac{5}{6}$ from $\frac{8}{9}$. Express the answer in simplest form.

$\frac{8}{9} - \frac{5}{6} = \frac{1}{18}$

Which common denominator will I use?

$\frac{8 \times 6}{9 \times 6} = \frac{48}{54}$ $\frac{5 \times 9}{6 \times 9} = \frac{45}{54}$

$\frac{8 \times 2}{9 \times 2} = \frac{16}{18}$ $\frac{5 \times 3}{6 \times 3} = \frac{15}{18}$

5 Subtract. Express each answer in simplest form.

(a) $\frac{4}{5} - \frac{2}{3}$ $\frac{2}{15}$

(b) $\frac{5}{6} - \frac{3}{10}$ $\frac{8}{15}$

(c) $\frac{4}{7} - \frac{1}{2}$ $\frac{1}{14}$

(d) $\frac{5}{2} - \frac{5}{8}$ $1\frac{7}{8}$

(e) $\frac{5}{4} - \frac{7}{8}$ $\frac{3}{8}$

(f) $1 - \frac{9}{15}$ $\frac{2}{5}$

(g) $\frac{7}{8} - \frac{1}{4} - \frac{1}{2}$ $\frac{1}{8}$

(h) $1 - \frac{1}{2} - \frac{1}{3} - \frac{1}{6}$ 0

6 Franco had 2 lb of flour. He used $\frac{3}{4}$ lb to make bread and $\frac{2}{5}$ lb to make muffins. How many pounds of flour does he have left?

$2 - \frac{3}{4} - \frac{2}{5} = 2 - \frac{15}{20} - \frac{8}{20} = \frac{7}{20}$ $\frac{17}{20}$ lb

Exercise 3 • page 79

Objective

- Practice adding and subtracting fractions.

After students complete the **Practice** in the textbook, have them continue to practice adding and subtracting fractions with activities from the chapter.

4. Compare problems: (a) vs (b) and (c) vs (d). The numbers and signs are the same. The only difference is the parentheses, which changes the answers.

Activity

▲ Greatest and Least

Materials: Number Cards (BLM) 0–9, multiple sets

The game works best with 2 – 4 players. Deal 5 cards to each player. In each round, players use 4 of the cards in their hand to create a proper fraction expression.

The goal in each round alternates. In Round 1, players try to make two fractions that result in the greatest answer. In Round 2, players make the expression that results in the least answer.

Sample play:

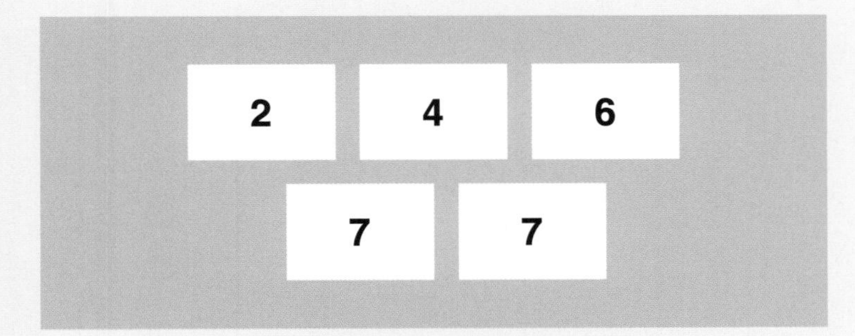

Greatest answer:

$\frac{6}{7} + \frac{4}{7} = \frac{10}{7} = 1\frac{3}{7}$

Least answer:

$\frac{4}{7} - \frac{2}{6} = \frac{24}{42} - \frac{14}{42} = \frac{10}{42} = \frac{5}{21}$

Exercise 4 • page 82

1. Divide. Express each answer in simplest form.

(a) $25 \div 7$ $3\frac{4}{7}$ (b) $32 \div 6$ $5\frac{1}{3}$

(c) $45 \div 10$ $4\frac{1}{2}$ (d) $93 \div 13$ $7\frac{2}{13}$

(e) $460 \div 6$ $76\frac{2}{3}$ (f) $1{,}000 \div 80$ $12\frac{1}{2}$

2. Express each fraction as a whole number or mixed number in simplest form.

(a) $\frac{20}{4}$ 5 (b) $\frac{21}{14}$ $1\frac{1}{2}$

(c) $\frac{40}{6}$ $6\frac{2}{3}$ (d) $\frac{18}{4}$ $4\frac{1}{2}$

(e) $\frac{97}{8}$ $12\frac{1}{8}$ (f) $\frac{570}{12}$ $47\frac{1}{2}$

3. Add or subtract. Express each answer in simplest form.

(a) $\frac{3}{8} + \frac{1}{6}$ $\frac{13}{24}$ (b) $\frac{5}{9} + \frac{3}{4}$ $1\frac{11}{36}$

(c) $\frac{4}{5} + \frac{7}{10}$ $1\frac{1}{2}$ (d) $\frac{5}{6} - \frac{5}{10}$ $\frac{1}{3}$

(e) $\frac{7}{8} - \frac{5}{6}$ $\frac{1}{24}$ (f) $\frac{3}{4} - \frac{3}{5}$ $\frac{3}{20}$

(g) $\frac{7}{10} + \frac{3}{4}$ $1\frac{9}{20}$ (h) $\frac{7}{8} - \frac{2}{5}$ $\frac{19}{40}$

4. Find the values. Express each answer in simplest form.

(a) $\frac{5}{6} - \frac{2}{3} - \frac{1}{9}$ $\frac{1}{18}$

(b) $\frac{5}{6} - (\frac{2}{3} - \frac{1}{9})$ $\frac{5}{18}$

(c) $\frac{9}{10} - \frac{1}{5} + \frac{1}{2}$ $1\frac{1}{5}$

(d) $\frac{9}{10} - (\frac{1}{5} + \frac{1}{2})$ $\frac{1}{5}$

5. A 25 m long rope is cut into 4 equal pieces. How long is each piece in meters?
$25 \div 4 = 6\frac{1}{4}$ $6\frac{1}{4}$ m

6. A baker has 38 kg of flour. He wants to put all of the flour equally into 5 tins. How many kilograms of flour should he put in each tin?
$38 \div 5 = 7\frac{3}{5}$ $7\frac{3}{5}$ kg

7. A building is 112 ft tall. It is 12 times as tall as a fire truck. How tall is the fire truck in feet?
$112 \div 12 = 9\frac{1}{3}$ $9\frac{1}{3}$ ft

8. Charlotte spent $\frac{2}{5}$ of her money on a book, $\frac{1}{4}$ of her money on a notebook, and $\frac{1}{10}$ of her money on a pen. What fraction of her money did she spend altogether?
$\frac{2}{5} + \frac{1}{4} + \frac{1}{10} = \frac{3}{4}$ $\frac{3}{4}$

9. Theodore spent $\frac{1}{3}$ of his money on a coat, $\frac{1}{4}$ of his money on shoes, and $\frac{1}{6}$ of his money on a shirt. What fraction of his money does he have left?
$1 - (\frac{1}{3} + \frac{1}{4} + \frac{1}{6}) = 1 - \frac{9}{12} = \frac{3}{12} = \frac{1}{4}$ $\frac{1}{4}$

Exercise 4 • page 82

Objective

- Add a mixed number and a fraction with unlike denominators.

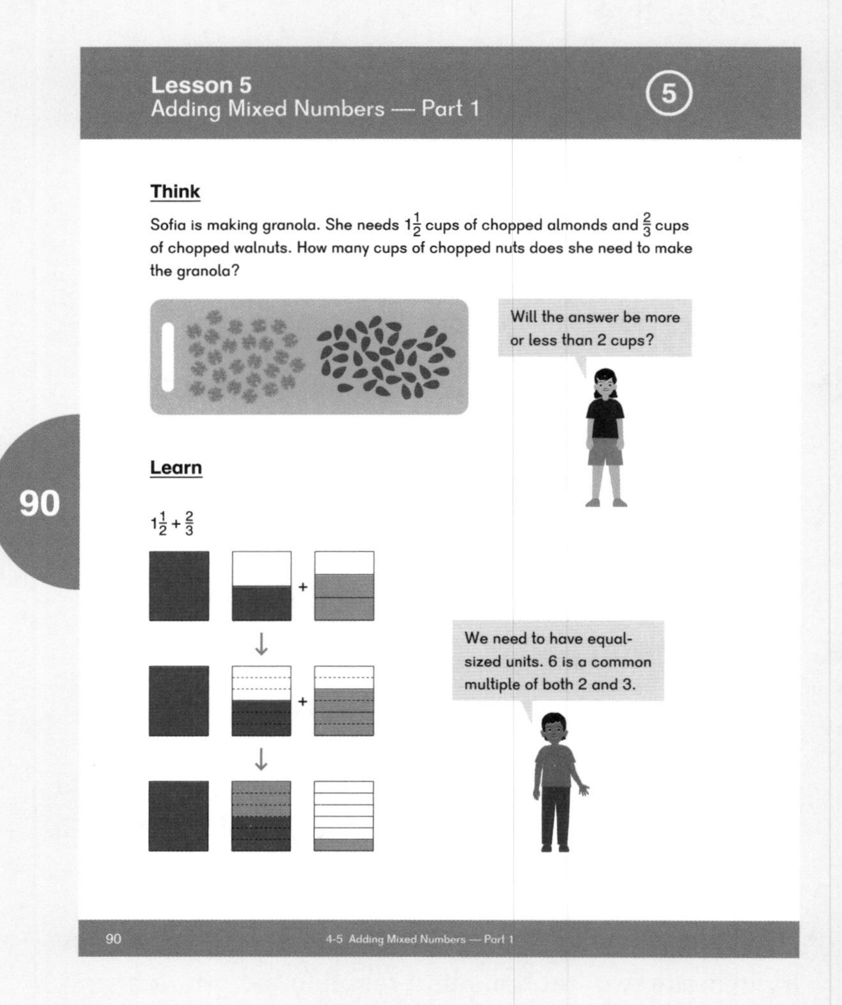

Think

Pose the **Think** problem. Discuss Mei's question. Students should see that $\frac{2}{3}$ is greater than $\frac{1}{2}$ so there will be more than 2 cups in all.

If needed, ask students:

- "What do you recall about adding mixed numbers?"
- "What common denominator could you use?"

Have students share how they solved the problem.

Learn

Have students compare their solutions from **Think** with the ones shown in the textbook. Three possible methods are shown.

Method 1

The fractional parts of the mixed number are converted to equivalent fractions with a denominator of 6.

Method 2

Dion makes a whole with part of the $\frac{4}{6}$ and has $\frac{1}{6}$ remaining. Students can recall adding to make the next ten, hundred, tenths, etc. Here, they make the next whole.

This method does not require the regrouping of the whole number of $1\frac{7}{6}$ in Method 1.

Method 3

The mixed number can be converted to an improper fraction first, and then both fractions can be expressed as equivalent fractions with a denominator of 6. The answer is then simplified.

Discuss the three methods with students. Ask them which method they prefer and why.

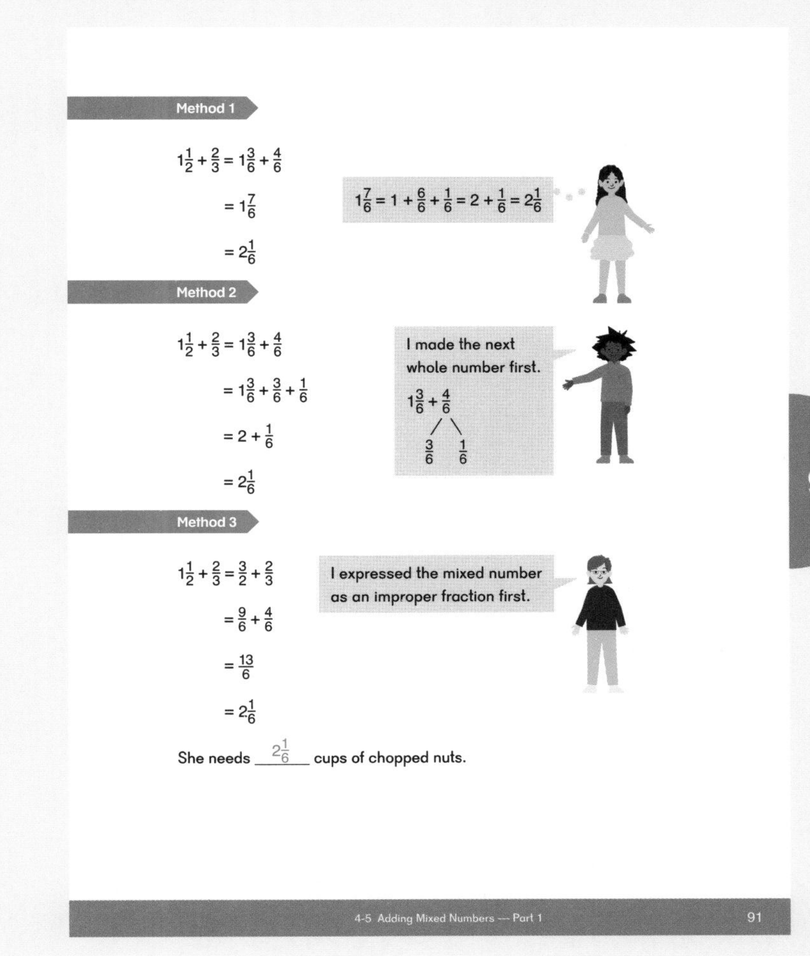

Method 1

$1\frac{1}{2} + \frac{2}{3} = 1\frac{3}{6} + \frac{4}{6}$

$= 1\frac{7}{6}$

$= 2\frac{1}{6}$

$1\frac{7}{6} = 1 + \frac{6}{6} + \frac{1}{6} = 2 + \frac{1}{6} = 2\frac{1}{6}$

Method 2

$1\frac{1}{2} + \frac{2}{3} = 1\frac{3}{6} + \frac{4}{6}$

$= 1\frac{3}{6} + \frac{3}{6} + \frac{1}{6}$

$= 2 + \frac{1}{6}$

$= 2\frac{1}{6}$

I made the next whole number first.

$1\frac{3}{6} + \frac{4}{6}$

$\frac{3}{6}$ $\frac{1}{6}$

Method 3

$1\frac{1}{2} + \frac{2}{3} = \frac{3}{2} + \frac{2}{3}$

$= \frac{9}{6} + \frac{4}{6}$

$= \frac{13}{6}$

$= 2\frac{1}{6}$

I expressed the mixed number as an improper fraction first.

She needs $2\frac{1}{6}$ cups of chopped nuts.

4-5 Adding Mixed Numbers — Part 1 91

Do

❶–❹ Discuss the problems and given solutions with students. Students should give their answers in simplest form.

❶ Mei uses Method 3 from **Learn**. She converts $1\frac{1}{3}$ into an improper fraction first, and then finds a common denominator. This method is more likely to be used when the whole number part is 1.

❷ Alex uses Method 1 from **Learn**. He converts $\frac{1}{3}$ and $\frac{4}{5}$ to fractions with a denominator of 15: $3 + \frac{5}{15} + \frac{12}{15}$ to get $3\frac{17}{15}$. Then he simplifies the sum.

❸ Ask students to identify which method is shown. They should see that it is similar to ❷ and uses Method 1 from **Learn**.

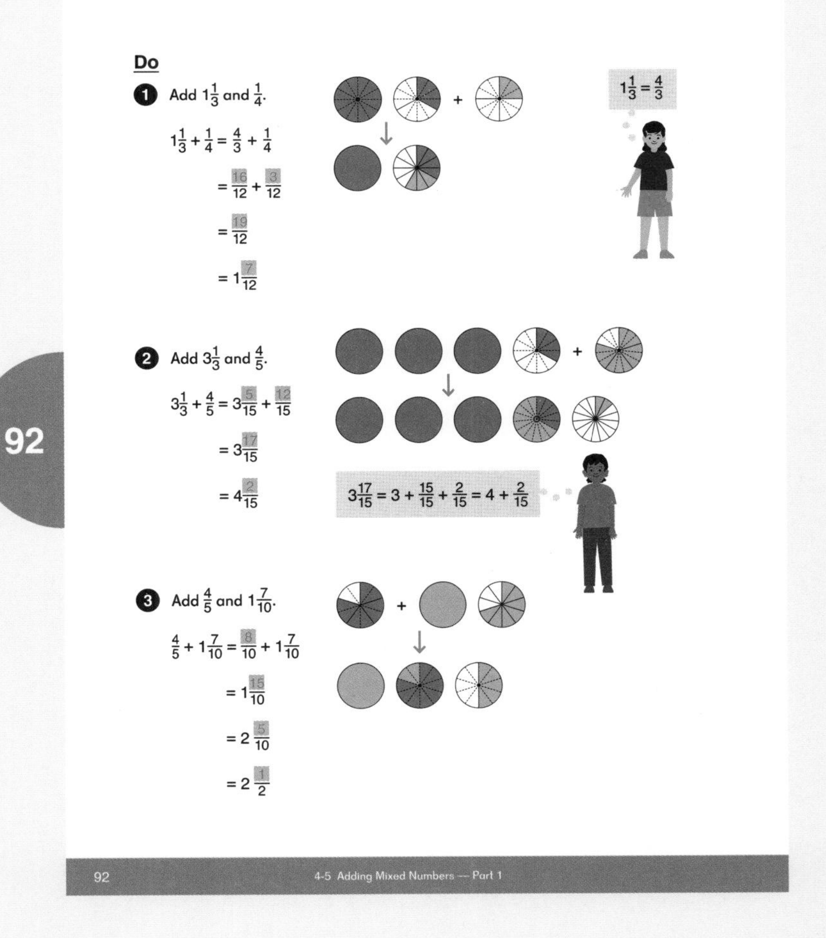

Do

❶ Add $1\frac{1}{3}$ and $\frac{1}{4}$.

$1\frac{1}{3} + \frac{1}{4} = \frac{4}{3} + \frac{1}{4}$

$= \frac{16}{12} + \frac{3}{12}$

$= \frac{19}{12}$

$= 1\frac{7}{12}$

$1\frac{1}{3} = \frac{4}{3}$

❷ Add $3\frac{1}{3}$ and $\frac{4}{5}$.

$3\frac{1}{3} + \frac{4}{5} = 3\frac{5}{15} + \frac{12}{15}$

$= 3\frac{17}{15}$

$= 4\frac{2}{15}$

$3\frac{17}{15} = 3 + \frac{15}{15} + \frac{2}{15} = 4 + \frac{2}{15}$

❸ Add $\frac{4}{5}$ and $1\frac{7}{10}$.

$\frac{4}{5} + 1\frac{7}{10} = \frac{8}{10} + 1\frac{7}{10}$

$= 1\frac{15}{10}$

$= 2\frac{5}{10}$

$= 2\frac{1}{2}$

92 4-5 Adding Mixed Numbers — Part 1

4 After converting $\frac{3}{4}$ to $\frac{6}{8}$, Sofia uses Method 2 from **Learn**. She needs $\frac{2}{8}$ to add to $\frac{6}{8}$ to make the next whole. This idea is shown with the number line.

5 Students should be able to solve the problems independently. Have them share which method they used from **Learn** to solve some of these problems.

Activity

▲ Closest to 7

Materials: Closest to 7 Cards (BLM)

Shuffle the cards and deal five to each player.

Players select two of their cards and add the numbers together. The player whose sum is closest to 7 earns a point.

For example:

In this example, Alex is closer to 7 than Mei is. He earns 1 point. Players draw two new cards for the next round to replace the two that were played. The first player to earn 5 points is the winner.

Exercise 5 • page 85

4 Add $1\frac{3}{4}$ and $\frac{5}{8}$.

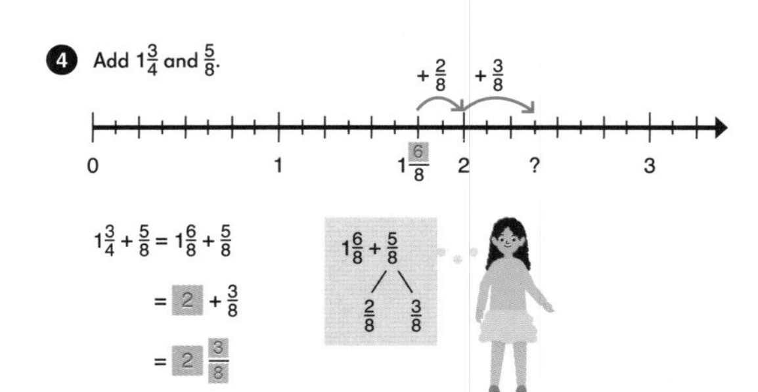

5 Add. Express the answer in simplest form.

(a) $4\frac{1}{8} + \frac{3}{8}$ $4\frac{1}{2}$

(b) $1\frac{1}{4} + \frac{1}{2}$ $1\frac{3}{4}$

(c) $8\frac{3}{4} + \frac{3}{10}$ $9\frac{1}{20}$

(d) $6\frac{4}{5} + \frac{1}{4}$ $7\frac{1}{20}$

(e) $\frac{3}{9} + 4\frac{1}{2}$ $4\frac{5}{6}$

(f) $\frac{3}{4} + 7\frac{5}{6}$ $8\frac{7}{12}$

(g) $\frac{1}{7} + \frac{1}{3} + 9\frac{2}{3}$ $10\frac{1}{7}$

(h) $2\frac{5}{9} + \frac{1}{3} + \frac{1}{2}$ $3\frac{7}{18}$

6 Hazel used $2\frac{1}{2}$ cups of water, $\frac{1}{3}$ cup of orange juice, and $\frac{1}{4}$ cup of lemon juice to make a refreshing drink. How many cups of liquid did she use altogether?

$2\frac{1}{2} + \frac{1}{3} + \frac{1}{4} = 3\frac{1}{12}$ $3\frac{1}{12}$ cups

Exercise 5 • page 85

Objective

- Add mixed numbers with unlike denominators.

Think

Pose the **Think** problem and discuss Dion's estimate. $\frac{2}{3}$ is more than $\frac{1}{2}$ so $1\frac{1}{2} + 1\frac{2}{3}$ will be more than 3 cups in all.

Have students share how they solved the problem.

Learn

Have students compare their solutions from **Think** with the ones shown in the textbook.

Method 1

The whole number part of the second mixed number is added to the first mixed number.

The fractional parts of the mixed numbers are then converted into equivalent fractions with a common denominator of 6. The fractions can be added using any of the methods from the previous lesson and the sum simplified.

Method 2

After finding equivalent fractions with a common denominator, the numbers are separated into their whole number and fractional parts, which can be added in any order. Add the whole numbers together and then add the fractional parts together.

This method is very similar to Method 1. The whole number parts and the fractional parts are added together first.

Method 3

Sofia converts both mixed numbers to improper fractions first and then expresses them with the common denominator of 6.

She can add $\frac{9}{6} + \frac{10}{6}$, and then simplify her answer: $\frac{19}{6} = 3\frac{1}{6}$.

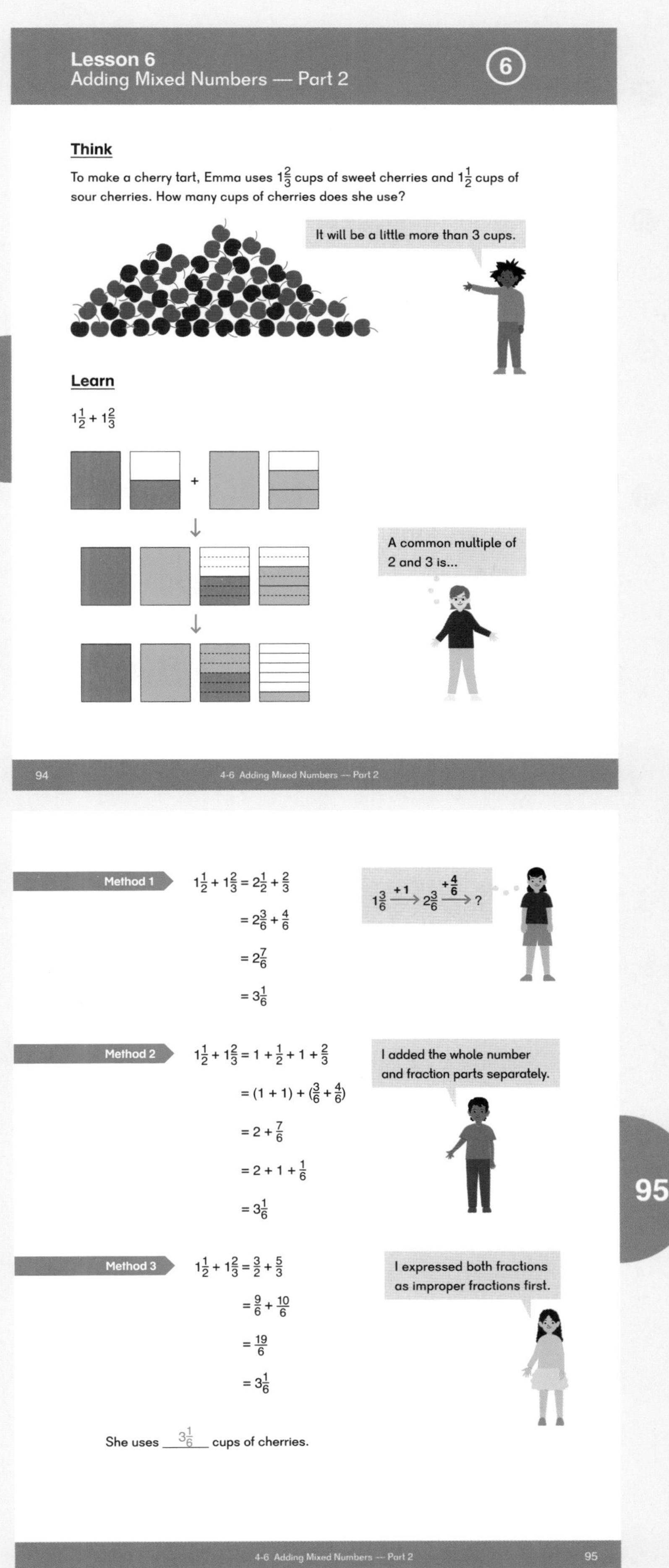

94

Lesson 6
Adding Mixed Numbers — Part 2 (6)

Think

To make a cherry tart, Emma uses $1\frac{2}{3}$ cups of sweet cherries and $1\frac{1}{2}$ cups of sour cherries. How many cups of cherries does she use?

Learn

$1\frac{1}{2} + 1\frac{2}{3}$

Method 1

$$1\frac{1}{2} + 1\frac{2}{3} = 2\frac{1}{2} + \frac{2}{3} = 2\frac{3}{6} + \frac{4}{6} = 2\frac{7}{6} = 3\frac{1}{6}$$

Method 2

$$1\frac{1}{2} + 1\frac{2}{3} = 1 + \frac{1}{2} + 1 + \frac{2}{3} = (1 + 1) + (\frac{3}{6} + \frac{4}{6}) = 2 + \frac{7}{6} = 2 + 1 + \frac{1}{6} = 3\frac{1}{6}$$

95

Method 3

$$1\frac{1}{2} + 1\frac{2}{3} = \frac{3}{2} + \frac{5}{3} = \frac{9}{6} + \frac{10}{6} = \frac{19}{6} = 3\frac{1}{6}$$

She uses $3\frac{1}{6}$ cups of cherries.

Do

❶–❸ Discuss the problems and given solutions with students. Students should give their answers in simplest form.

❶ Using Method 1 from **Learn**, add the whole numbers first: $2\frac{1}{4} + 1 = 3\frac{1}{4}$. Then find common denominators and add the fractional parts.

❷ Add the whole numbers first: $1\frac{1}{4} + 1 = 2\frac{1}{4}$. Then add the fractional parts.

$$2\frac{3}{12} + \frac{10}{12} = 2\frac{13}{12} = 3\frac{1}{12}$$

❸ Emma uses Method 2 from **Learn**. She adds the whole numbers together and the fractional parts together, then simplifies the sum.

96

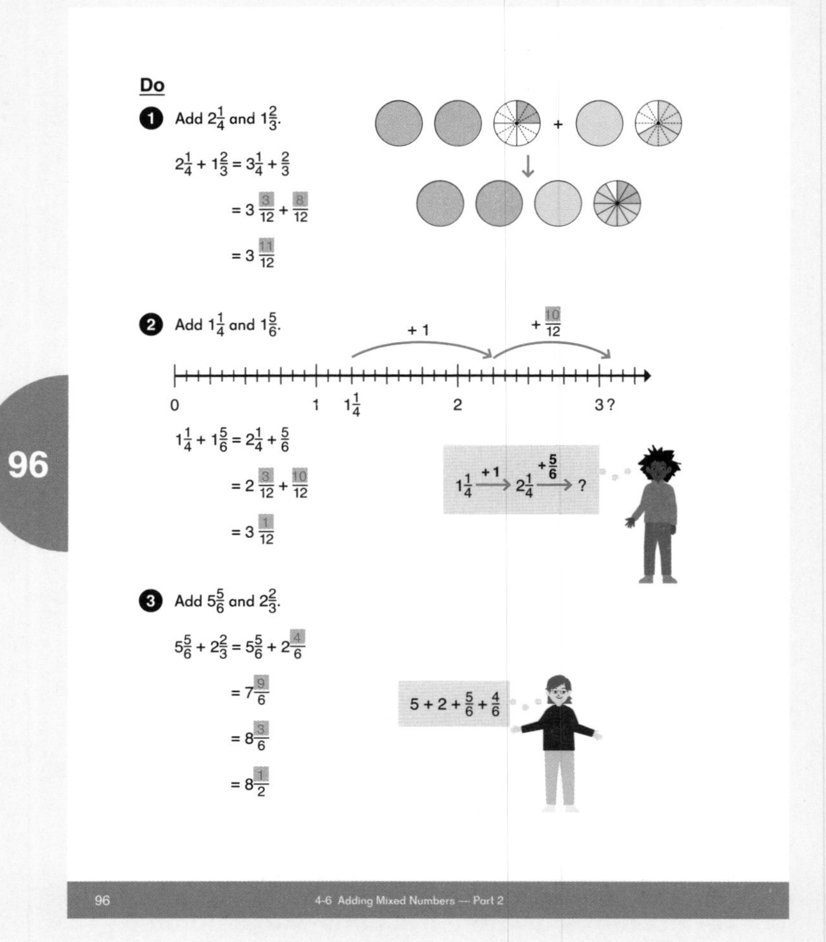
Do

❶ Add $2\frac{1}{4}$ and $1\frac{2}{3}$.

$2\frac{1}{4} + 1\frac{2}{3} = 3\frac{1}{4} + \frac{2}{3}$

$= 3\frac{3}{12} + \frac{8}{12}$

$= 3\frac{11}{12}$

❷ Add $1\frac{1}{4}$ and $1\frac{5}{6}$.

$1\frac{1}{4} + 1\frac{5}{6} = 2\frac{1}{4} + \frac{5}{6}$

$= 2\frac{3}{12} + \frac{10}{12}$

$= 3\frac{1}{12}$

❸ Add $5\frac{5}{6}$ and $2\frac{2}{3}$.

$5\frac{5}{6} + 2\frac{2}{3} = 5\frac{5}{6} + 2\frac{4}{6}$

$= 7\frac{9}{6}$

$= 8\frac{3}{6}$

$= 8\frac{1}{2}$

96 4-6 Adding Mixed Numbers — Part 2

❹ Students should be able to solve the problems independently. Have them share which methods from **Learn** they used to solve some of these problems.

Activity

▲ Greatest Sum

Materials: Number Cards (BLM) 0–9 or 10-sided die, Greatest Sum (BLM) in a dry erase sleeve

Play with the entire class. Each player has a Greatest Sum (BLM) gameboard.

The teacher draws a number card and shows it to the students. Each player chooses an empty box in which to write the number before the next card is drawn by the teacher.

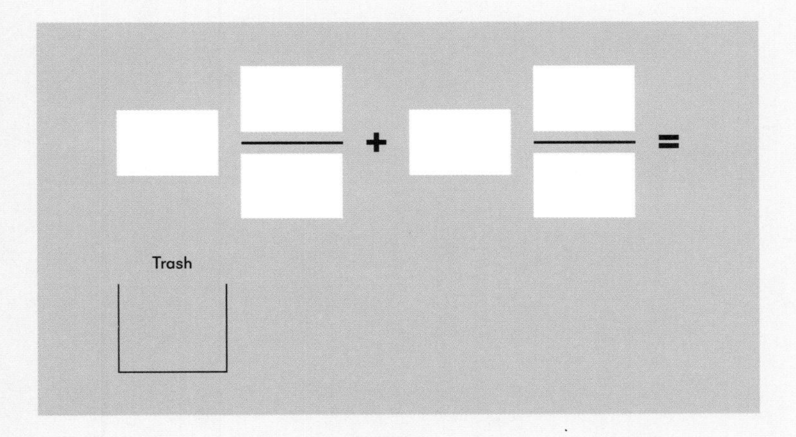

Once the number has been written, it must stay in that place.

At any point in the round, players may write one digit in the box labeled "Trash." When 7 cards have been drawn, the players add their mixed numbers together. The players with the greatest sums are the winners.

Modifications:

- Play for the least sum.
- Play in groups of up to 4 players: Players take turns drawing number cards and writing each digit in different places on their gameboards.

❹ Add. Express each answer in simplest form.

(a) $5\frac{7}{12} + 2$ $7\frac{7}{12}$ (b) $3\frac{1}{8} + 1\frac{3}{8}$ $4\frac{1}{2}$

(c) $3\frac{1}{3} + 3\frac{6}{9}$ 7 (d) $6\frac{1}{4} + 4\frac{3}{10}$ $10\frac{11}{20}$

(e) $1\frac{4}{5} + 2\frac{1}{3}$ $4\frac{2}{15}$ (f) $5\frac{1}{2} + 3\frac{5}{6}$ $9\frac{1}{3}$

(g) $6\frac{5}{6} + 5\frac{7}{10}$ $12\frac{8}{15}$ (h) $7\frac{3}{10} + 2\frac{2}{3}$ $9\frac{29}{30}$

(i) $1\frac{1}{2} + 3\frac{1}{4} + 2\frac{1}{2}$ $7\frac{1}{4}$ (j) $5\frac{5}{6} + 3\frac{4}{9} + 2\frac{2}{3}$ $11\frac{17}{18}$

❺

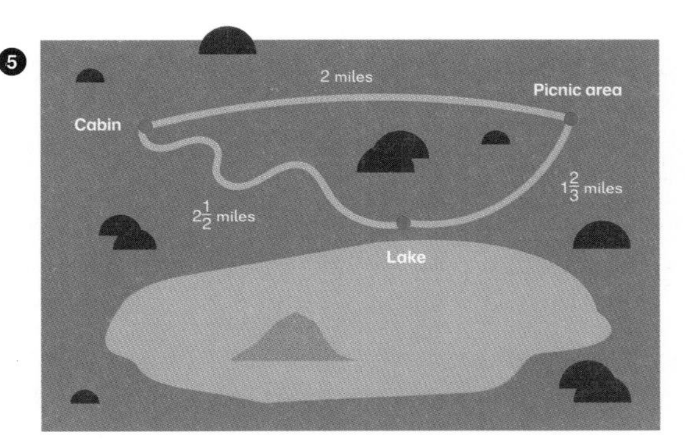

Emma and her dad walked from the cabin to the lake. After that, they walked to the picnic area, then took the shortest route back to the cabin. How far did they walk?

$2\frac{1}{2} + 1\frac{2}{3} + 2 = 6\frac{1}{6}$; $6\frac{1}{6}$ miles

Exercise 6 • page 87

97

Exercise 6 • page 87

Objective

- Subtract a fraction from a mixed number or whole number.

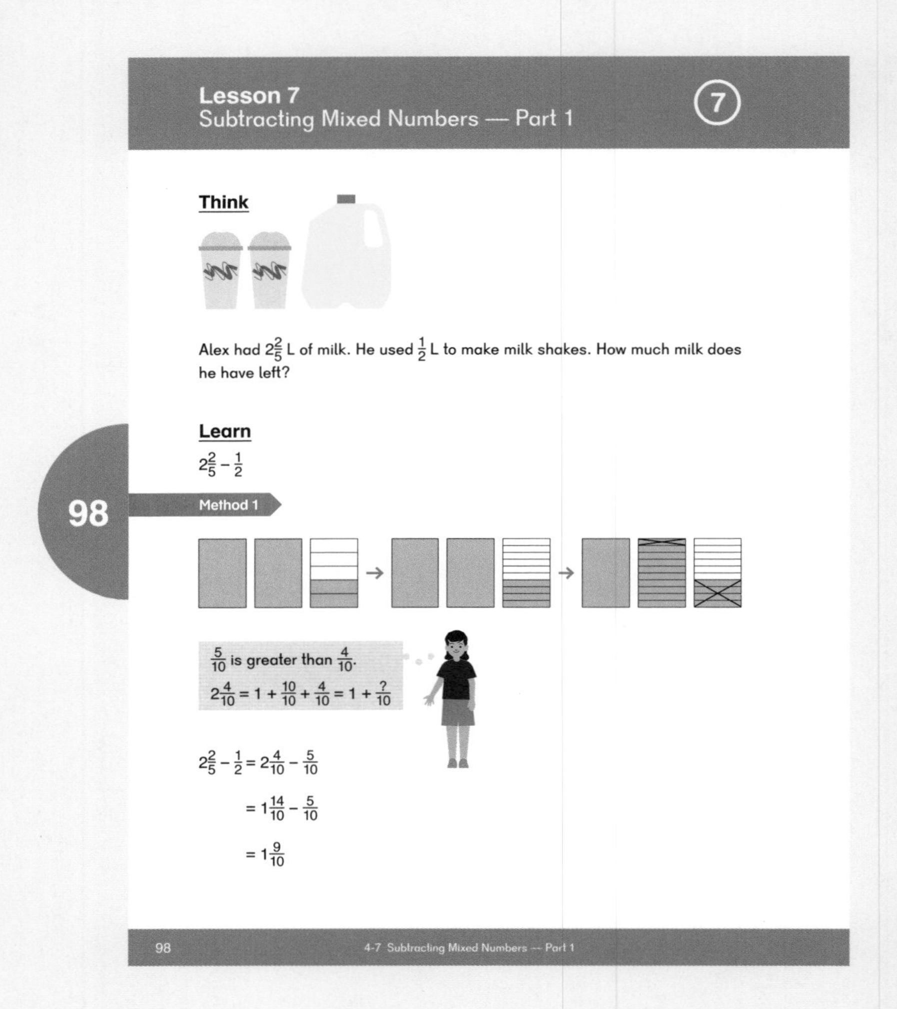

98

Lesson 7
Subtracting Mixed Numbers — Part 1

7

Think

Alex had $2\frac{2}{5}$ L of milk. He used $\frac{1}{2}$ L to make milk shakes. How much milk does he have left?

Learn

$2\frac{2}{5} - \frac{1}{2}$

Method 1

$\frac{5}{10}$ is greater than $\frac{4}{10}$.

$2\frac{4}{10} = 1 + \frac{10}{10} + \frac{4}{10} = 1 + \frac{?}{10}$

$2\frac{2}{5} - \frac{1}{2} = 2\frac{4}{10} - \frac{5}{10}$

$= 1\frac{14}{10} - \frac{5}{10}$

$= 1\frac{9}{10}$

98 4-7 Subtracting Mixed Numbers — Part 1

Think

Pose the **Think** problem and have students estimate the answer. Since $\frac{1}{2} > \frac{2}{5}$, they should estimate that there will be less than 2 cups of milk left.

Have students share how they solved the problem.

Learn

Have students compare their solutions from **Think** with the ones shown in the textbook. As in the prior lessons, three different methods are shown.

Method 1

Find equivalent fractions with a common denominator first: $2\frac{4}{10}$ and $\frac{5}{10}$.

Discuss Mei's calculations. She sees that $\frac{5}{10}$ is greater than $\frac{4}{10}$. She needs more tenths to subtract. Ask students what she needs to regroup to subtract.

Method 2

Alex subtracts from the whole number first:

$$2\frac{2}{5} - \frac{1}{2} = 2 - \frac{1}{2} + \frac{2}{5} = 1\frac{1}{2} + \frac{2}{5}$$

(number bond: $2\frac{2}{5}$ → $\frac{2}{5}$ and 2)

Alex then finds equivalent fractions with a common denominator: $1\frac{5}{10} + \frac{4}{10}$.

Method 3

Sofia converts the mixed number into an improper fraction first, then she finds equivalent fractions with a common denominator:

$2 + \frac{2}{5} = \frac{10}{5} + \frac{2}{5} = \frac{12}{5} = \frac{24}{10}$

The answer $\frac{19}{10}$ is simplified to $1\frac{9}{10}$.

Ask students why one method may be more efficient than another. Sofia's method, for example, may not be efficient if the numerators are large.

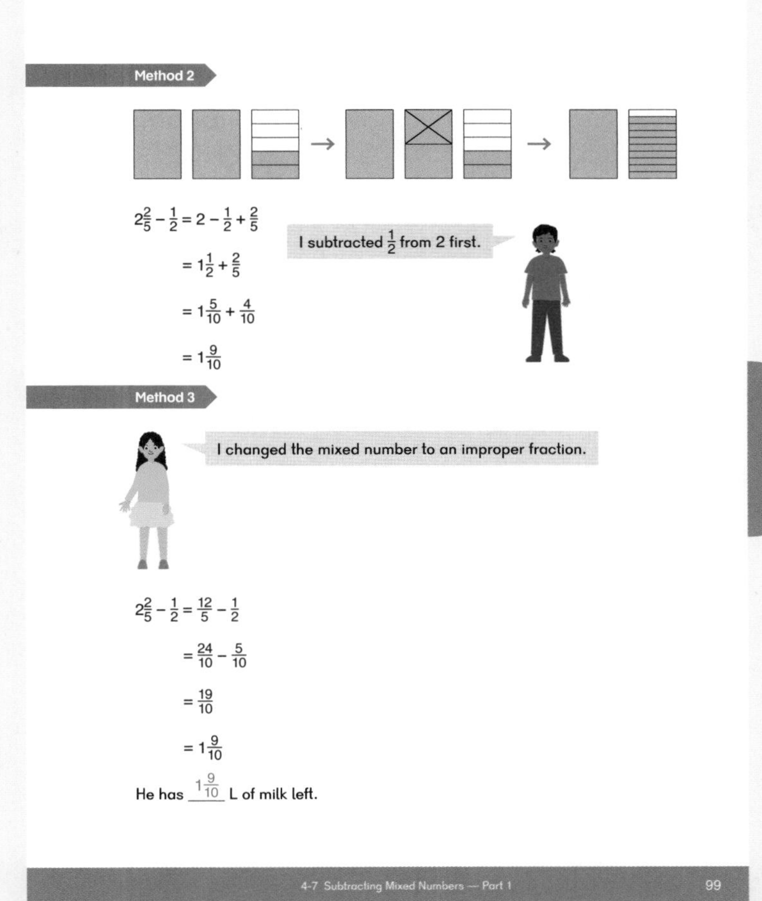

99

Do

1—**4** Discuss the problems and given solutions with students. Students should give their answers in simplest form.

1 The steps show Method 1 from **Learn**. First students express the fractions as equivalent fractions with common denominators, then they subtract.

2 Method 1 from **Learn** is used for this problem also. The number subtracted is greater than the fractional part of the mixed number. Regroup 1 whole as $\frac{10}{10}$ and then subtract.

3 Method 2 from **Learn** is used in this problem. First subtract $\frac{5}{6}$ from 2.

$$2\frac{1}{3} - \frac{5}{6} = 2 - \frac{5}{6} + \frac{1}{3} = 1\frac{1}{6} + \frac{1}{3} = 1\frac{1}{2}$$

($2\frac{1}{3}$ split into $\frac{1}{3}$ and 2)

4 Using Method 3 from **Learn**, express the mixed number as an improper fraction first. Then find a common denominator and subtract.

5 Students should be able to solve the problems independently. Have them share which method they used to solve some of these problems.

Exercise 7 • page 90

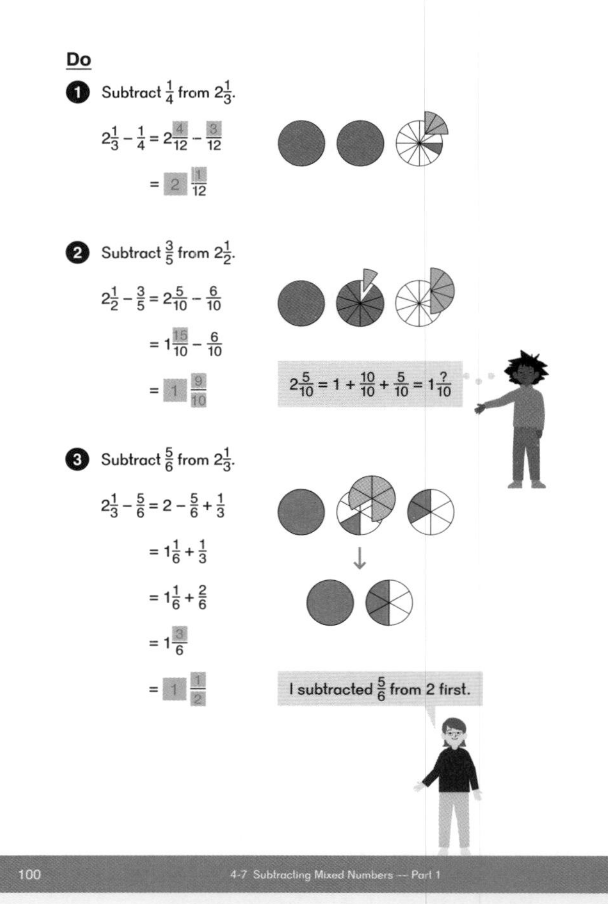

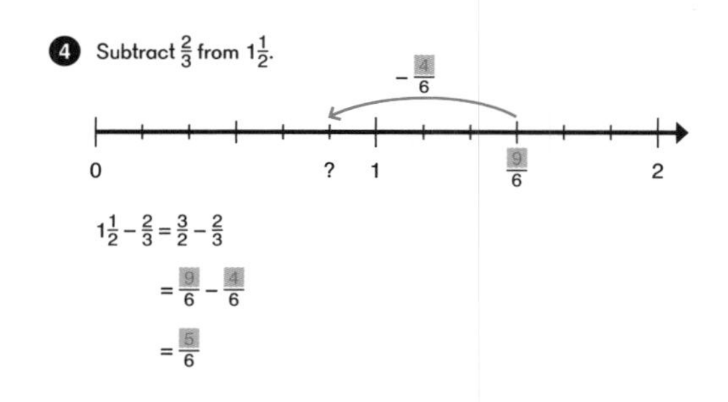

5 Subtract. Express each answer in simplest form.

(a) $5 - \frac{4}{5}$ $4\frac{1}{5}$ (b) $3\frac{5}{7} - \frac{3}{7}$ $3\frac{2}{7}$

(c) $2\frac{1}{4} - \frac{3}{8}$ $1\frac{7}{8}$ (d) $5\frac{1}{2} - \frac{1}{3}$ $5\frac{1}{6}$

(e) $8\frac{1}{5} - \frac{3}{4}$ $7\frac{9}{20}$ (f) $7\frac{3}{8} - \frac{7}{10}$ $6\frac{27}{40}$

(g) $6\frac{1}{6} - \frac{3}{10}$ $5\frac{13}{15}$ (h) $3 - \frac{1}{2} - \frac{4}{5}$ $1\frac{7}{10}$

6 Dion wants to run 5 miles this week. He ran $\frac{4}{5}$ miles on Monday and $\frac{9}{10}$ miles on Tuesday. How many more miles does he need to run?

$5 - \frac{4}{5} - \frac{9}{10} = 3\frac{3}{10}$

$3\frac{3}{10}$ miles

101

Exercise 7 • page 90

4-7 Subtracting Mixed Numbers — Part 1 101

Lesson 8 Subtracting Mixed Numbers — Part 2

Objective

- Subtract a mixed number from a mixed number or whole number.

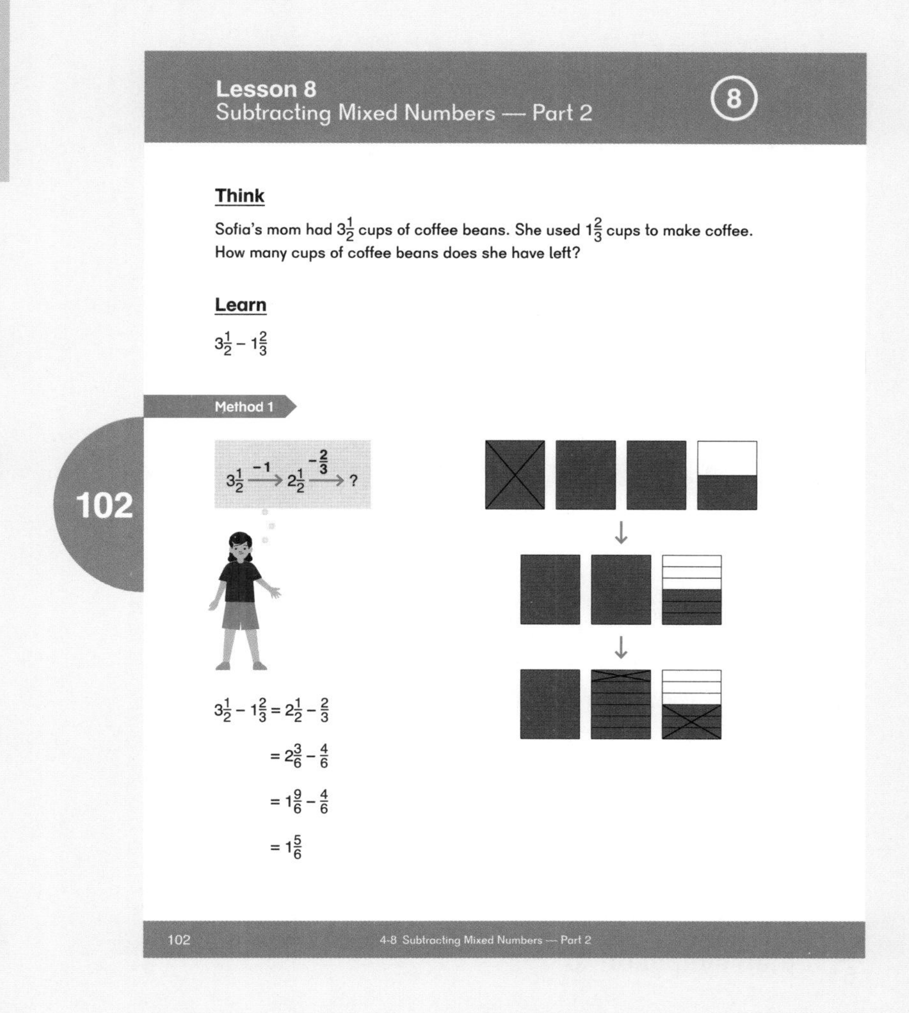
Lesson 8
Subtracting Mixed Numbers — Part 2
8

Think

Sofia's mom had $3\frac{1}{2}$ cups of coffee beans. She used $1\frac{2}{3}$ cups to make coffee. How many cups of coffee beans does she have left?

Learn

$3\frac{1}{2} - 1\frac{2}{3}$

Method 1

$3\frac{1}{2} \xrightarrow{-1} 2\frac{1}{2} \xrightarrow{-\frac{2}{3}} ?$

$3\frac{1}{2} - 1\frac{2}{3} = 2\frac{1}{2} - \frac{2}{3}$

$= 2\frac{3}{6} - \frac{4}{6}$

$= 1\frac{9}{6} - \frac{4}{6}$

$= 1\frac{5}{6}$

102 4-8 Subtracting Mixed Numbers — Part 2

Think

Pose the **Think** problem and have students estimate the difference first.

Since $\frac{2}{3} > \frac{1}{2}$, they should estimate that $3\frac{1}{2} - 1\frac{2}{3}$ will be less than 2.

Have students share how they solved the problem.

Learn

Have students compare their solutions from **Think** with the ones shown in the textbook.

Method 1

Mei subtracts the whole number first and then the fractional part.

She finds the equivalent fractions, $2\frac{3}{6}$ and $\frac{4}{6}$, and sees that $\frac{4}{6}$ is greater than $\frac{3}{6}$. She regroups 1 whole as $\frac{6}{6}$.

Mei can now subtract the fractions.

Any of the methods for subtracting a fraction from a mixed number learned in the previous lesson can be used after subtracting the whole number. For example, Sofia thinks:

$$2\frac{3}{6} - \frac{4}{6} = 2 - \frac{4}{6} + \frac{3}{6} = 1\frac{2}{6} + \frac{3}{6}$$

($2\frac{3}{6}$ split into $\frac{3}{6}$ and 2)

Method 2

Dion finds equivalent fractions with common denominators first, then he changes both mixed numbers to improper fractions.

$3\frac{3}{6} = \frac{18}{6} + \frac{3}{6} = \frac{21}{6}$

$1\frac{4}{6} = \frac{6}{6} + \frac{4}{6} = \frac{10}{6}$

$\frac{21}{6} - \frac{10}{6} = \frac{11}{6}$

$\frac{11}{6}$ is then simplified to $1\frac{5}{6}$.

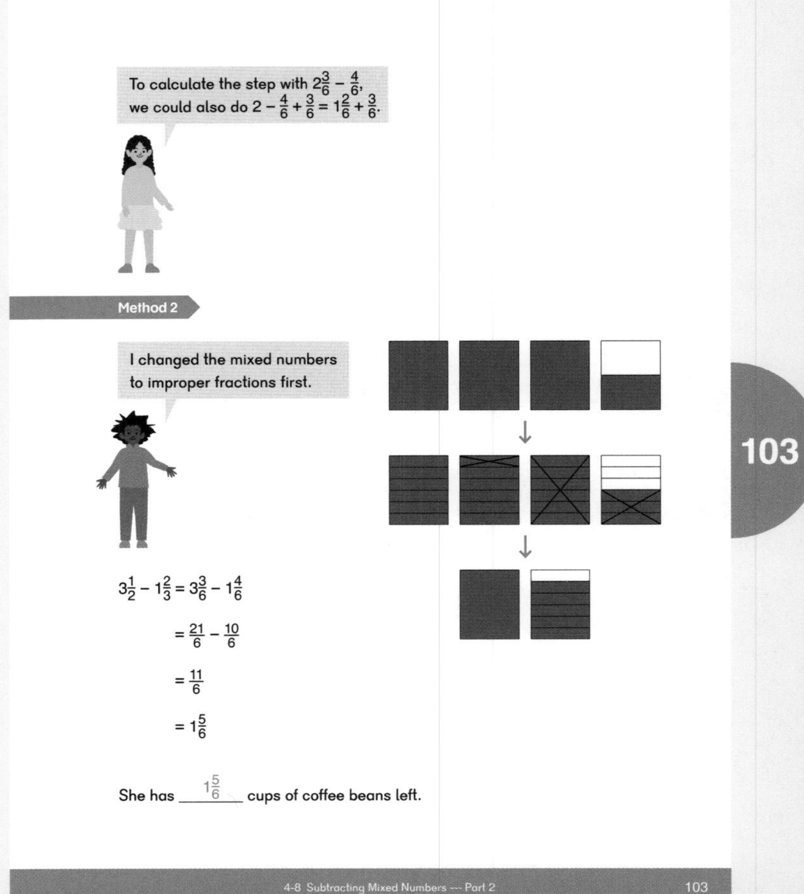

Do

❶–❹ Discuss the problems and given solutions with students. Students should give their answers in simplest form.

❶ Subtract the whole number first, find common denominators, and then subtract the fraction.

❷ Emma also subtracts the whole numbers first. Then she converts the mixed numbers to improper fractions: $1\frac{4}{12}$ to $\frac{16}{12}$.

❸ Mei converts the mixed numbers to improper fractions first, and then she subtracts.

❹ Subtract the whole numbers first: $9 - 4$ to get $5\frac{1}{10} - \frac{5}{6}$.

Ask students, "What does Alex need to regroup to subtract?" (He regroups $5\frac{3}{30}$ as $4\frac{33}{30}$ so he can subtract the fraction.)

❺ Students should be able to solve the problems independently. Have them share which method they used to solve some of the problems.

Exercise 8 • page 92

104

Do

❶ Subtract $2\frac{1}{5}$ from $4\frac{1}{2}$.

$4\frac{1}{2} - 2\frac{1}{5} = 2\frac{1}{2} - \frac{1}{5}$

$= 2\frac{5}{10} - \frac{2}{10}$

$= 2\frac{3}{10}$

❷ Subtract $1\frac{3}{4}$ from $2\frac{1}{3}$.

$-\frac{9}{12}$ -1

0 $\frac{7}{12}$ 1 2 $2\frac{1}{3}$ 3

$2\frac{1}{3} - 1\frac{3}{4} = 1\frac{1}{3} - \frac{3}{4}$

$= 1\frac{4}{12} - \frac{9}{12}$

$= \frac{16}{12} - \frac{9}{12}$

$= \frac{7}{12}$

I subtracted the whole number first.

❸ Subtract $1\frac{2}{3}$ from $2\frac{1}{2}$.

$2\frac{1}{2} - 1\frac{2}{3} = \frac{5}{2} - \frac{5}{3} = \frac{15}{6} - \frac{10}{6} = \frac{5}{6}$

I changed the mixed numbers to improper fractions first.

❹ $9\frac{1}{10} - 4\frac{5}{6} = 5\frac{1}{10} - \frac{5}{6}$

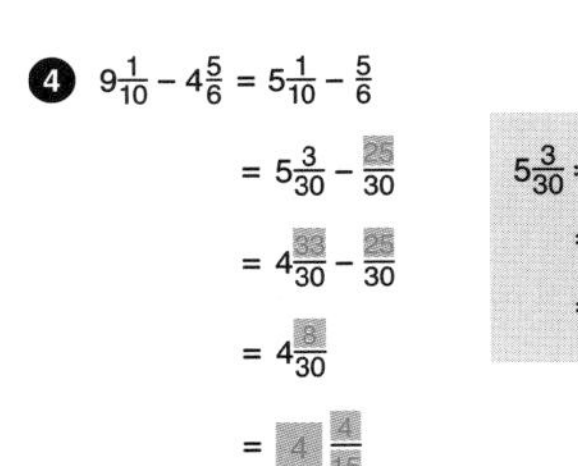

$= 5\frac{3}{30} - \frac{25}{30}$

$= 4\frac{33}{30} - \frac{25}{30}$

$= 4\frac{8}{30}$

$= 4\frac{4}{15}$

$5\frac{3}{30} = 4 + 1\frac{3}{30}$

$= 4 + \frac{30}{30} + \frac{3}{30}$

$= 4\frac{33}{30}$

❺ Subtract. Express each answer in simplest form.

(a) $5\frac{7}{8} - 2\frac{1}{4}$ $3\frac{5}{8}$

(b) $7\frac{1}{2} - 3\frac{3}{10}$ $4\frac{1}{5}$

(c) $2\frac{5}{6} - 1\frac{1}{4}$ $1\frac{7}{12}$

(d) $2\frac{1}{3} - 1\frac{1}{5}$ $1\frac{2}{15}$

(e) $8\frac{1}{4} - \frac{7}{10}$ $7\frac{11}{20}$

(f) $9\frac{1}{6} - 2\frac{5}{9}$ $6\frac{11}{18}$

(g) $7 - \frac{1}{3} - 3\frac{4}{5}$ $2\frac{13}{15}$

(h) $8\frac{3}{8} - 1\frac{3}{10} - \frac{3}{4}$ $6\frac{13}{40}$

❻ Mei had $5\frac{1}{2}$ m of ribbon. She used $1\frac{4}{5}$ m to tie cake boxes and $\frac{3}{4}$ m for a balloon. How many meters of ribbon does she have left?

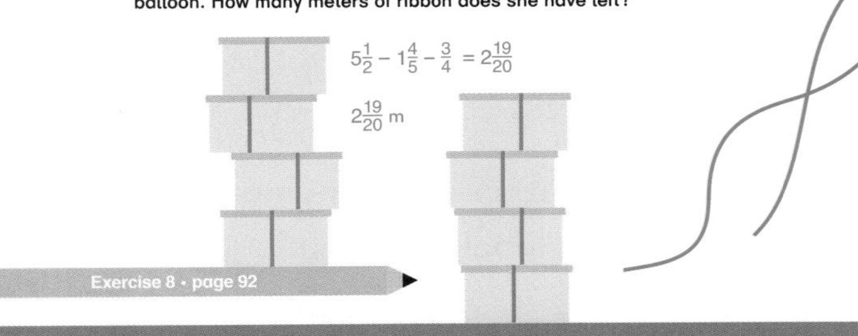

$5\frac{1}{2} - 1\frac{4}{5} - \frac{3}{4} = 2\frac{19}{20}$

$2\frac{19}{20}$ m

Exercise 8 • page 92

105

Objective

- Practice adding and subtracting mixed numbers.

After students complete the **Practice** in the textbook, have them continue to practice adding and subtracting fractions with activities from the chapter.

Activity

▲ Smallest Difference

Materials: Number Cards (BLM) 1 – 9, Smallest Difference (BLM) in a dry erase sleeve

Play with the same rules as the game in Lesson 6, except, now students are trying to make the smallest difference. If they do not have enough to subtract from, they are out of the round.

Play with entire class:

Each player has a Smallest Difference (BLM) gameboard.

The teacher draws a number card and shows it to the students. Each player chooses an empty box in which to write the number before the next card is drawn by the teacher.

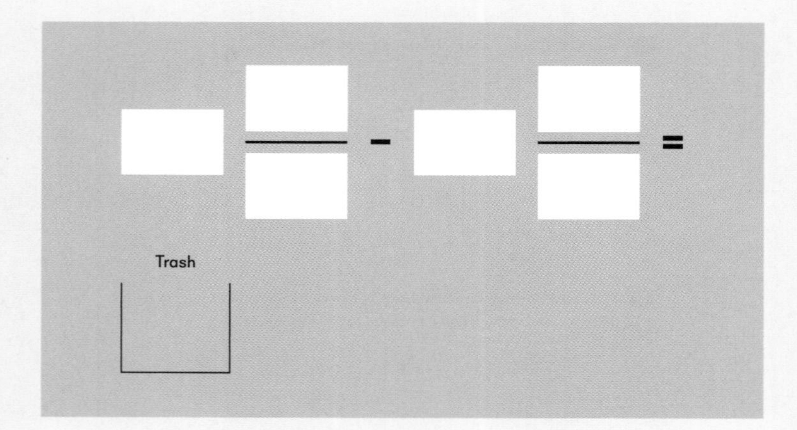

At any point in the round, players may write one number in the box labeled "Trash."

106

Lesson 9
Practice B

P 9

1. Add or subtract. Express each answer in simplest form.

(a) $1\frac{3}{4} + \frac{4}{5}$ $2\frac{11}{20}$

(b) $\frac{1}{5} + 2\frac{3}{10}$ $2\frac{1}{2}$

(c) $4\frac{5}{9} + 2\frac{1}{3}$ $6\frac{8}{9}$

(d) $1\frac{3}{8} - \frac{1}{2}$ $\frac{7}{8}$

(e) $3\frac{2}{3} - 1\frac{3}{7}$ $2\frac{5}{21}$

(f) $6\frac{3}{10} - 4\frac{5}{6}$ $1\frac{7}{15}$

(g) $6\frac{5}{6} + 3\frac{3}{8}$ $10\frac{5}{24}$

(h) $9\frac{3}{4} - 3\frac{8}{9}$ $5\frac{31}{36}$

2. Find the values. Express each answer in simplest form.

(a) $2\frac{1}{2} + \frac{3}{4} - \frac{5}{8}$ $2\frac{5}{8}$

(b) $1\frac{1}{2} - \frac{2}{3} + 5\frac{5}{6}$ $6\frac{2}{3}$

(c) $2\frac{2}{3} - (4\frac{1}{2} - 1\frac{5}{6})$ 0

(d) $2\frac{1}{4} - (\frac{3}{4} + \frac{3}{10})$ $1\frac{1}{5}$

(e) $12 - (4\frac{1}{2} - 1\frac{3}{8}) - 3\frac{1}{4}$ $5\frac{5}{8}$

(f) $(6\frac{1}{3} - 1\frac{3}{4}) + (6\frac{1}{3} - 1\frac{3}{4})$ $9\frac{1}{6}$

3. Shanice had a 2 L bottle of water. She drank $1\frac{2}{3}$ L of water. How much water does she have left?

$2 - 1\frac{2}{3} = \frac{1}{3}$ $\frac{1}{3}$ L

4. Rope A is $8\frac{3}{5}$ m long. Rope B is $5\frac{3}{10}$ m long. How much longer is Rope A than Rope B?

$8\frac{3}{5} - 5\frac{3}{10} = 3\frac{3}{10}$ $3\frac{3}{10}$ m

106 4-9 Practice B

When seven cards have been drawn, the players subtract their mixed numbers. The players with the smallest differences are the winners.

Modifications:

- Play for the greatest difference.
- Play in groups of up to 4 players: Players take turns drawing number cards and writing each digit in different places on their gameboards.

9 Encourage students to draw a picture if needed. They can see that there are 16 intervals (spaces) between 17 fence posts, so we divide by 16. Ask students to draw 3 posts and count the intervals, then 4 posts, and then 5 posts. By then, they should see the pattern that there is always 1 less interval than post.

Exercise 9 • page 94

Brain Works

★ Expression Trees

Have students create expression trees using mixed numbers or fractions when possible. They can switch with a partner, who writes out the expression shown and evaluates the expression.

Examples:

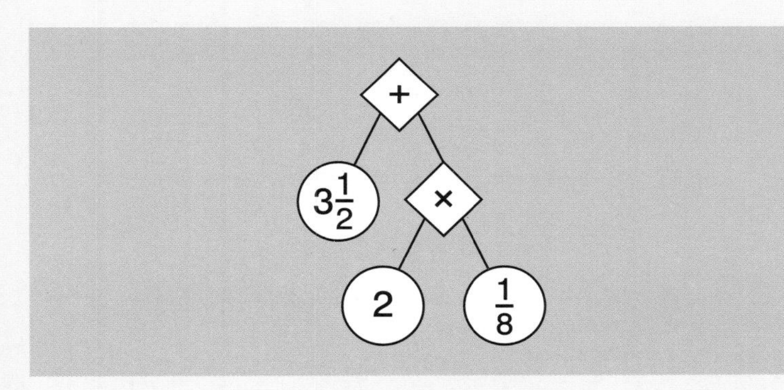

The expression is: $3\frac{1}{2} + (2 \times \frac{1}{8})$

$3\frac{1}{2} + (2 \times \frac{1}{8}) = 3\frac{1}{2} + \frac{2}{8} = 3\frac{3}{4}$

5 Sara is walking from her house to the library. The library is $1\frac{1}{2}$ miles from her house. She has already walked $\frac{3}{8}$ miles. How much farther does she have to go?

$1\frac{1}{2} - \frac{3}{8} = 1\frac{1}{8}$ $1\frac{1}{8}$ miles

6 Parker ran $2\frac{3}{5}$ miles on Friday, $3\frac{1}{2}$ miles on Saturday, and $2\frac{1}{10}$ miles on Sunday. How far did he run over the three days?

$2\frac{3}{5} + 3\frac{1}{2} + 2\frac{1}{10} = 8\frac{1}{5}$ $8\frac{1}{5}$ miles

7 Madison spent $2\frac{2}{3}$ hours working on a project on Friday and $2\frac{1}{2}$ hours working on Saturday. She finished the project on Sunday. If the project took $6\frac{3}{4}$ hours, how many hours did she spend working on Sunday?

$6\frac{3}{4} - 2\frac{2}{3} - 2\frac{1}{2} = 1\frac{7}{12}$ $1\frac{7}{12}$ hours

8 Wyatt has 16 L of orange juice and 12 L of peach juice. He poured all of the juice into 5 pitchers. Each pitcher has an equal amount of each kind of juice. How many liters of juice are in each pitcher?

$\frac{16}{5} + \frac{12}{5} = 5\frac{3}{5}$ $5\frac{3}{5}$ L

9

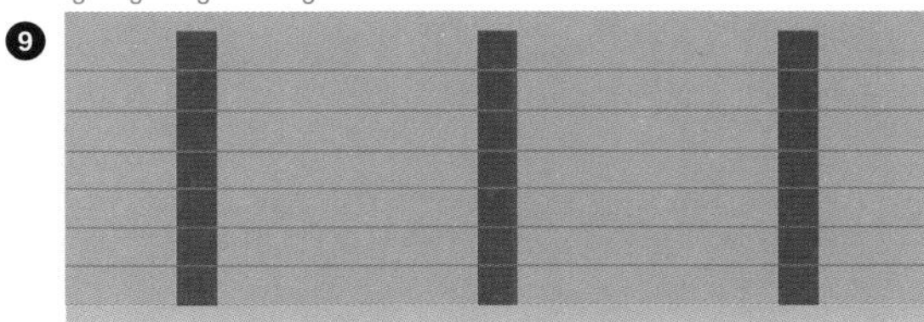

Dennis built a wire fence 168 feet long. He used 17 fence posts and spaced them equally. There is one fence post at each end of the fence. How many feet apart was each fence post?

$\frac{168}{16} = 10\frac{8}{16} = 10\frac{1}{2}$ $10\frac{1}{2}$

Exercise 9 • page 94

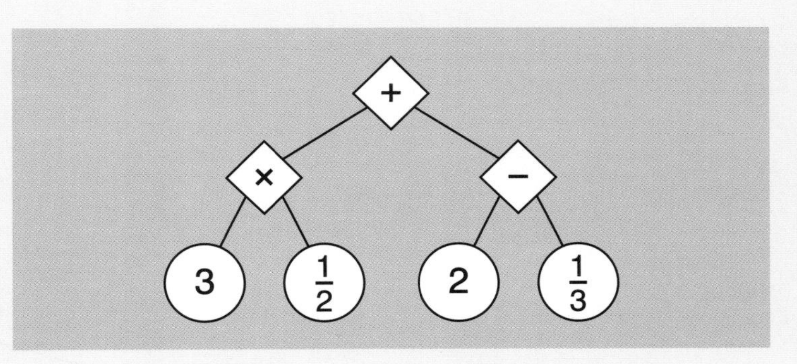

The expression is: $(3 \times \frac{1}{2}) + (2 - \frac{1}{3})$

$(3 \times \frac{1}{2}) + (2 - \frac{1}{3}) = \frac{3}{2} + 1\frac{2}{3}$

$= 1\frac{1}{2} + 1\frac{2}{3}$

$= 2\frac{3}{6} + \frac{4}{6}$

$= 3\frac{1}{6}$

Objective

- Review content from Chapters 1–4.

Use the cumulative review to practice and reinforce content and skills from the first four chapters.

1 (b) 673,895,245: 70,000,000

98,576,056: 70,000

667,300,006: 7,000,000

97,203,450: 7,000,000

700,003,000: 700,000,000

(c) 673,895,245: six hundred seventy-three thousand, eight hundred ninety-five, two hundred forty-five

98,576,056: ninety-eight million, five hundred seventy-six thousand, fifty-six

667,300,006: six hundred sixty-seven million, three hundred thousand, six

97,203,450: ninety-seven million, two hundred three thousand, four hundred fifty

700,003,000: seven hundred million, three thousand

108

Review 1

R 1

1 673,895,245 | 98,576,056 | 667,300,006 | 97,203,450 | 700,003,000

(a) Put the numbers in order from least to greatest.
97,203,450; 98,576,056; 667,300,006; 673,895,245; 700,003,000

(b) What is the value of the digit 7 in each of the numbers?
(answers in tg)

(c) Write each of the numbers in words.
(answers in tg)

2 Find the values. Use mental calculation.

(a) 2,055 × 100
205,500

(b) 9,850 ÷ 10
985

(c) 850,000 ÷ 1,000
850

(d) 4,000 × 7,000
28,000,000

(e) 6,400 ÷ 80
80

(f) 15,000 × 40
600,000

(g) 32,000 ÷ 200
160

(h) 270 × 3,000
810,000

(i) 99 × 25
2,475

(j) 6,400 × 500
3,200,000

(k) 320 × 49
15,680

(l) 998 × 12
11,976

3 Find the values.

(a) 750 + 200 × 500
100,750

(b) 300 × (30 – 5)
7,500

(c) 900 – 15 ÷ 3 × 2
890

(d) 640 ÷ (264 – 256)
80

(e) 85 × 30 – 56 ÷ 7 + 30
2,572

(f) 9 × (12 – 45 ÷ 5) + 18 – 2 × 5
35

4 Divide. Express each answer as a mixed number in simplest form.

(a) 5 ÷ 4
$1\frac{1}{4}$

(b) 24 ÷ 7
$3\frac{3}{7}$

(c) 52 ÷ 12
$4\frac{1}{3}$

(d) 140 ÷ 40
$3\frac{1}{2}$

5 Express each fraction as a whole number or mixed number in simplest form.

(a) $\frac{25}{6}$ $4\frac{1}{6}$

(b) $\frac{48}{18}$ $2\frac{2}{3}$

(c) $\frac{300}{200}$ $1\frac{1}{2}$

(d) $\frac{360}{90}$ 4

6 Estimate and then find the actual values, expressed in simplest form.
Estimates may vary.

(a) 98 × 654
64,092

(b) 86 × 243
20,898

(c) 6,263 × 47
294,361

(d) 81 × 21 × 15
25,515

(e) 86 ÷ 23
$3\frac{17}{23}$

(f) 287 ÷ 59
$4\frac{51}{59}$

(g) 4,864 ÷ 36
$135\frac{1}{9}$

(h) 34,845 ÷ 15
2,323

(i) 24,321 ÷ 75
$324\frac{7}{25}$

109

7 Find the values. Express each answer in simplest form.

(a) $\frac{7}{8} - \frac{3}{5}$ $\frac{11}{40}$

(b) $\frac{5}{9} + \frac{5}{6}$ $1\frac{7}{18}$

(c) $\frac{9}{4} - \frac{3}{2} - \frac{1}{3}$ $\frac{5}{12}$

(d) $\frac{1}{2} + \frac{3}{7} + \frac{2}{3}$ $1\frac{25}{42}$

(e) $\frac{5}{6} + 4\frac{1}{3}$ $5\frac{1}{6}$

(f) $5\frac{2}{3} - \frac{1}{5}$ $5\frac{7}{15}$

(g) $5\frac{1}{5} - 4\frac{1}{7}$ $1\frac{2}{35}$

(h) $6\frac{3}{5} - 3\frac{7}{8}$ $2\frac{29}{40}$

(i) $5\frac{3}{4} - (1\frac{1}{2} + 2\frac{1}{6})$ $2\frac{1}{12}$

(j) $(4\frac{1}{3} - 1\frac{1}{2}) + (\frac{9}{2} - 3\frac{1}{4})$ $4\frac{1}{12}$

8

11

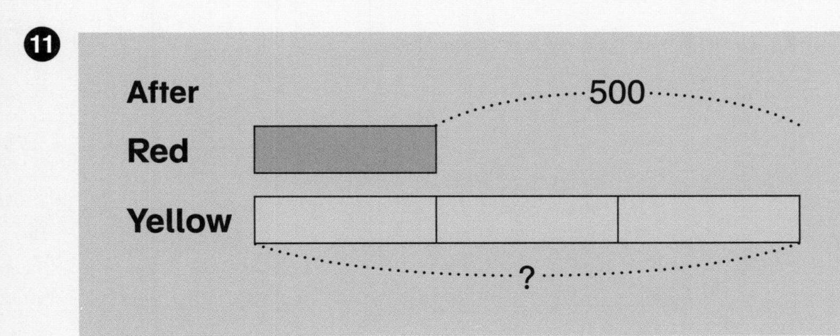

Exercise 10 • page 97

110

8 Liam and Pekelo together have $8,500. Liam has $750 more than Pekelo. How much money does each person have?

8,500 – 750 = 7,750
7,750 ÷ 2 = 3,875
3,875 + 750 = 4,625

Pekelo: $3,875
Liam: $4,625

9 Grapefruits are sold at 4 for $5. After buying 20 grapefruits, Selena had $18 left. How much money did she have at first?

20 ÷ 4 × 5 + 18 = 43
$43

10 2 watermelons and 3 cantaloupes cost $35. 4 watermelons and 3 cantaloupes cost $55. How much does one cantaloupe cost?

1 watermelon: (55 – 35) ÷2 = 10;
1 cantaloupe: 35 – (2 × 10) ÷ 3 = 5; $5

11 Dana had an equal number of red beads and yellow beads. After using 500 red beads to make necklaces, she had 3 times as many yellow beads as red beads. How many yellow beads does she have?

500 ÷ 2 × 3 = 750; 750

12 32 lb of quinoa is put equally into 12 bags. How many pounds of quinoa are in each bag? $32 \div 12 = \frac{32}{12} = \frac{16}{6} = 2\frac{4}{6} = 2\frac{2}{3}$

$2\frac{2}{3}$ lb

13 A bag has $3\frac{1}{2}$ lb of flour. After using some of it to make bread there was $\frac{3}{8}$ lb of flour left. How many pounds of flour were used?

$3\frac{1}{2} - \frac{3}{8} = 3\frac{1}{8}$; $3\frac{1}{8}$ lb

14 On Monday, Jason ran $3\frac{1}{2}$ miles in the morning and $1\frac{3}{4}$ miles in the afternoon. On Tuesday, he ran $\frac{7}{8}$ miles in the morning and $4\frac{1}{3}$ miles in the afternoon. On which day did he run farther? How much farther?

Monday: $3\frac{1}{2} + 1\frac{3}{4} = 5\frac{1}{4} = 5\frac{6}{24}$

Tuesday: $\frac{7}{8} + 4\frac{1}{3} = 5\frac{5}{24}$

$5\frac{6}{24} > 5\frac{5}{24}$; $5\frac{6}{24} - 5\frac{5}{24} = \frac{1}{24}$

Jason ran $\frac{1}{24}$ mile farther on Monday.

Exercise 10 • page 97

110 Review 1

Chapter 4 Addition and Subtraction of Fractions

Exercise 1

Basics

1. (a) Divide 2 by 5.

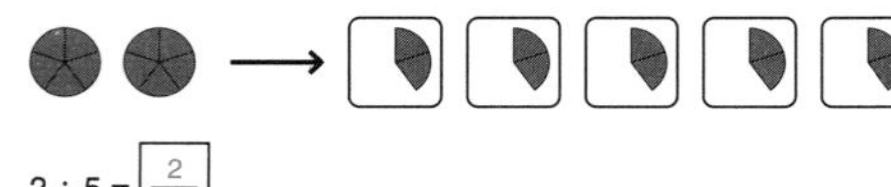

$2 \div 5 = \frac{2}{5}$

(b) Divide 37 by 5.

37 ÷ 5 is 7 with a remainder of 2.

Divide the remainder by 5: $2 \div 5 = \frac{2}{5}$

$37 \div 5 = 7 + \frac{2}{5} = 7\frac{2}{5}$

(c) Divide 762 by 5. Express the answer as a mixed number.

$762 \div 5 = 152\frac{2}{5}$

2. Express $\frac{15}{2}$ as a mixed number in simplest form.

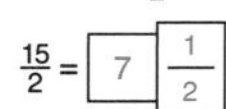

$\frac{15}{2} = 7\frac{1}{2}$

3. Express $\frac{63}{4}$ as a mixed number in simplest form.

$\frac{63}{4} = 63 \div 4 = 15\frac{3}{4}$

4. Express $\frac{146}{12}$ as a mixed number in simplest form.

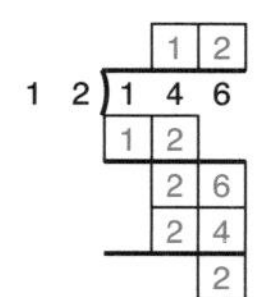

(a) $\frac{146}{12} = 146 \div 12 = 12\frac{2}{12} = 12\frac{1}{6}$

(b) Simplify $\frac{146}{12}$ and then express it as a mixed number.

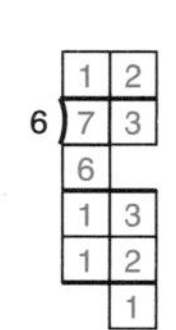

$\frac{146}{12} = \frac{73}{6} = 73 \div 6 = 12\frac{1}{6}$

5. $140 \div 21 = 20 \div 3 = 6\frac{2}{3}$

Practice

6. Express each fraction as a mixed number in simplest form.

(a) $\frac{99}{5}$ $19\frac{4}{5}$

(b) $\frac{250}{6}$ $41\frac{2}{3}$

(c) $\frac{119}{14}$ $8\frac{1}{2}$

(d) $\frac{740}{15}$ $49\frac{1}{3}$

7. Divide. Express each answer as a mixed number in simplest form.

(a) $35 \div 4$ $8\frac{3}{4}$

(b) $930 \div 8$ $116\frac{1}{4}$

(c) $260 \div 25$ $10\frac{2}{5}$

(d) $4,900 \div 90$ $54\frac{4}{9}$

8. How many pounds is 100 ounces?

$100 \div 16 = 6\frac{1}{4}$

$6\frac{1}{4}$ lb

Exercise 2

Basics

1 Add $\frac{1}{3}$ and $\frac{2}{5}$.

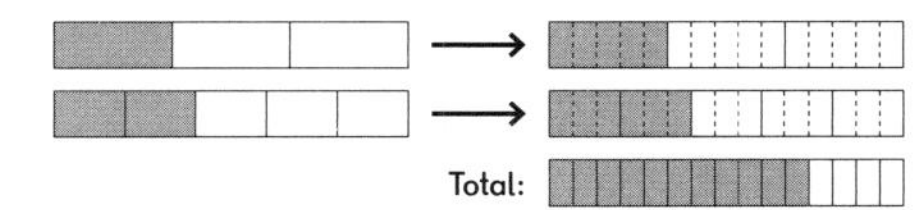

$\frac{1}{3}+\frac{2}{5}=\frac{5}{15}+\boxed{\frac{6}{15}}=\boxed{\frac{11}{15}}$

2 Add $\frac{3}{8}$ and $\frac{1}{6}$.

(a) $8 \times 6 = 48$. 48 is a common multiple of 8 and 6.

$\frac{3}{8}+\frac{1}{6}=\frac{3\times 6}{8\times 6}+\frac{1\times 8}{6\times 8}=\boxed{\frac{18}{48}}+\boxed{\frac{8}{48}}=\boxed{\frac{26}{48}}=\boxed{\frac{13}{24}}$

(b) The least common multiple of 8 and 6 is 24.

$\frac{3}{8}+\frac{1}{6}=\frac{3\times 3}{8\times 3}+\frac{1\times 4}{6\times 4}=\boxed{\frac{9}{24}}+\boxed{\frac{4}{24}}=\boxed{\frac{13}{24}}$

3 Add $\frac{3}{7}$ and $\frac{2}{3}$.

$\frac{3}{7}+\frac{2}{3}=\boxed{\frac{9}{21}}+\boxed{\frac{14}{21}}=\boxed{\frac{23}{21}}=\boxed{1}\boxed{\frac{2}{21}}$

Practice

4 Add. Express each answer in simplest form.

(a) $\frac{3}{4}+\frac{3}{20}$ $\frac{9}{10}$

(b) $\frac{1}{6}+\frac{3}{10}$ $\frac{7}{15}$

(c) $\frac{1}{6}+\frac{4}{15}$ $\frac{13}{30}$

(d) $\frac{5}{12}+\frac{3}{4}$ $1\frac{1}{6}$

(e) $\frac{6}{7}+\frac{1}{2}$ $1\frac{5}{14}$

(f) $\frac{5}{6}+\frac{8}{9}$ $1\frac{13}{18}$

(g) $\frac{1}{2}+\frac{2}{5}+\frac{1}{3}$ $1\frac{7}{30}$

(h) $\frac{3}{4}+\frac{5}{6}+\frac{2}{3}$ $2\frac{1}{4}$

5 Jaiden practiced the violin for $\frac{2}{3}$ h on Monday, $\frac{5}{6}$ h on Tuesday, and $\frac{3}{4}$ h each on Wednesday and Thursday. How long did he practice the violin altogether?

$\frac{2}{3}+\frac{5}{6}+\frac{3}{4}+\frac{3}{4}=\frac{8}{12}+\frac{10}{12}+\frac{9}{12}+\frac{9}{12}=\frac{36}{12}=3$

3 h

Challenge

6 Complete each problem using the given digits. Fractions should all be less than 1 and in simplest form.

(a) 1, 2, 5, 9

$\boxed{\frac{1}{2}}+\boxed{\frac{2}{5}}=\boxed{\frac{9}{10}}$

(b) 1, 2, 2, 5, 10

$\boxed{\frac{1}{2}}+\boxed{\frac{2}{5}}=\boxed{\frac{9}{10}}$

(c) 1, 7, 8, 12, 24

$\boxed{\frac{7}{24}}+\boxed{\frac{1}{8}}=\boxed{\frac{5}{12}}$

Exercise 3

Basics

1 Subtract $\frac{1}{4}$ from $\frac{5}{6}$.

$\frac{5}{6} - \frac{1}{4} = \frac{10}{12} - \boxed{\frac{3}{12}} = \boxed{\frac{7}{12}}$

2 Subtract $\frac{7}{10}$ from $\frac{5}{6}$.

(a) 6 × 10 = 60. 60 is a common multiple of 6 and 10.

$\frac{5}{6} - \frac{7}{10} = \frac{5 \times 10}{6 \times 10} - \frac{7 \times 6}{10 \times 6} = \boxed{\frac{50}{60}} - \boxed{\frac{42}{60}} = \boxed{\frac{8}{60}} = \boxed{\frac{2}{15}}$

(b) The least common multiple of 6 and 10 is 30.

$\frac{5}{6} - \frac{7}{10} = \frac{5 \times 5}{6 \times 5} - \frac{7 \times 3}{10 \times 3} = \boxed{\frac{25}{30}} - \boxed{\frac{21}{30}} = \boxed{\frac{4}{30}} = \boxed{\frac{2}{15}}$

3 Subtract $\frac{5}{16}$ from 1.

$1 - \frac{5}{16} = \boxed{\frac{16}{16}} - \frac{5}{16} = \boxed{\frac{11}{16}}$

Practice

4 Subtract. Express each answer in simplest form.

(a) $\frac{3}{5} - \frac{3}{15}$ $\frac{6}{15}$

(b) $\frac{3}{4} - \frac{5}{12}$ $\frac{1}{3}$

(c) $\frac{1}{2} - \frac{3}{7}$ $\frac{1}{14}$

(d) $\frac{7}{12} - \frac{3}{8}$ $\frac{5}{24}$

(e) $\frac{1}{6} - \frac{1}{10}$ $\frac{1}{15}$

(f) $1 - \frac{6}{21}$ $\frac{5}{7}$

(g) $1 - \frac{2}{5} - \frac{1}{3}$ $\frac{4}{15}$

(h) $\frac{7}{8} - \frac{1}{6} - \frac{2}{3}$ $\frac{1}{24}$

5 Louis bought $\frac{3}{4}$ kg of flour. He used $\frac{3}{10}$ kg to bake bread. How many kilograms of flour does he have left?

$\frac{3}{4} - \frac{3}{10} = \frac{30}{40} - \frac{12}{40} = \frac{18}{40} = \frac{9}{20}$

$\frac{9}{20}$ kg

Challenge

6 Study the following examples.

$\frac{1}{2} - \frac{1}{3} = \frac{1 \times 3}{2 \times 3} - \frac{1 \times 2}{3 \times 2} = \frac{3 - 2}{2 \times 3} = \frac{1}{6}$

$\frac{1}{3} - \frac{1}{4} = \frac{1 \times 4}{3 \times 4} - \frac{1 \times 3}{4 \times 3} = \frac{4 - 3}{3 \times 4} = \frac{1}{12}$

$\frac{1}{4} - \frac{1}{5} = \frac{1 \times 5}{4 \times 5} - \frac{1 \times 4}{5 \times 4} = \frac{5 - 4}{4 \times 5} = \frac{1}{20}$

Use a quick method to find the following values.

(a) $\frac{1}{9} - \frac{1}{10}$

$\frac{10 - 9}{9 \times 10} = \frac{1}{90}$

(b) $\frac{1}{99} - \frac{1}{100}$

$\frac{100 - 99}{99 \times 100} = \frac{1}{9,900}$

(c) $\frac{1}{19} - \frac{1}{20}$

$\frac{20 - 19}{19 \times 20} = \frac{1}{380}$

Exercise 4 • pages 82–84

Exercise 4

Check

1. Express each fraction as a mixed number in simplest form.

   (a) $\frac{26}{6}$ $4\frac{1}{3}$
   (b) $\frac{50}{8}$ $6\frac{1}{4}$
   (c) $\frac{455}{25}$ $18\frac{1}{5}$
   (d) $\frac{1,220}{100}$ $12\frac{1}{5}$

2. Divide. Express each answer as a mixed number in simplest form.

   (a) $98 \div 3$ $32\frac{2}{3}$
   (b) $100 \div 80$ $1\frac{1}{4}$
   (c) $500 \div 6$ $83\frac{1}{3}$
   (d) $155 \div 15$ $10\frac{1}{3}$

3. Find the values. Express each answer in simplest form.

   (a) $\frac{2}{3}+\frac{1}{8}$ $\frac{19}{24}$
   (b) $\frac{7}{15}+\frac{5}{6}$ $1\frac{3}{10}$
   (c) $\frac{9}{10}-\frac{2}{3}$ $\frac{7}{30}$
   (d) $\frac{11}{12}-\frac{5}{9}$ $\frac{13}{36}$
   (e) $\frac{9}{10}-(\frac{1}{3}+\frac{1}{2})$ $\frac{1}{15}$
   (f) $\frac{9}{10}-\frac{1}{3}+\frac{1}{2}$ $1\frac{1}{15}$
   (g) $\frac{2}{5}-(\frac{2}{5}-\frac{1}{3})$ $\frac{1}{3}$
   (h) $\frac{9}{14}+\frac{2}{3}-\frac{1}{7}$ $1\frac{1}{6}$

4. $\frac{1}{5}$ of a pole is painted green, $\frac{1}{3}$ of it is painted yellow, and $\frac{1}{6}$ of it is painted blue. The rest of it is painted red. What fraction of the pole is painted red?

   $1-\frac{1}{5}-\frac{1}{3}-\frac{1}{6}=\frac{30}{30}-\frac{6}{30}-\frac{10}{30}-\frac{5}{30}=\frac{9}{30}=\frac{3}{10}$

   $\frac{3}{10}$

5. Elena had 12 kg of flour. She used $\frac{1}{2}$ kg for bread, $\frac{1}{3}$ kg for rolls, and $\frac{1}{6}$ kg for cake. She then divided the rest of the flour into 5 containers. How much flour is in each container?

   $\frac{1}{2}+\frac{1}{3}+\frac{1}{6}=\frac{6}{12}+\frac{4}{12}+\frac{2}{12}=1$
   $12-1=11$
   $\frac{11}{5}=2\frac{1}{5}$
   $2\frac{1}{5}$ kg

Challenge

6. Find the value.

   $\frac{1}{2}-\frac{1}{3}+\frac{1}{3}-\frac{1}{4}+\frac{1}{4}-\frac{1}{5}+\frac{1}{5}-\frac{1}{6}+\frac{1}{6}-\frac{1}{7}$ $\frac{5}{14}$

Exercise 5 • pages 85–86

Exercise 5

Basics

1. Fill in the blanks for each problem. Each problem uses a different strategy to add the given numbers.

(a) $8\frac{2}{3} + \frac{3}{4} = 8\frac{8}{12} + \frac{9}{12}$

$= 8\frac{17}{12}$

$= 9\frac{5}{12}$

(b) $5\frac{1}{2} + \frac{5}{8} = 5\frac{4}{8} + \frac{5}{8}$

$= 5\frac{4}{8} + \frac{4}{8} + \frac{1}{8}$

$= 6\frac{1}{8}$

(c) $1\frac{1}{3} + \frac{3}{5} = \frac{4}{3} + \frac{3}{5}$

$= \frac{20}{15} + \frac{9}{15}$

$= \frac{29}{15}$

$= 1\frac{14}{15}$

Practice

2. Add. Use any method. Express each answer in simplest form.

(a) $4\frac{4}{9} + \frac{5}{9}$ 5

(b) $6\frac{5}{12} + \frac{11}{12}$ $7\frac{1}{3}$

(c) $3\frac{7}{8} + \frac{3}{4}$ $4\frac{5}{8}$

(d) $\frac{2}{5} + 8\frac{1}{4}$ $8\frac{13}{20}$

(e) $\frac{5}{9} + 4\frac{1}{2}$ $5\frac{1}{18}$

(f) $9\frac{5}{8} + \frac{2}{3}$ $10\frac{7}{24}$

(g) $\frac{3}{4} + \frac{1}{2} + 1\frac{5}{8}$ $2\frac{7}{8}$

(h) $\frac{1}{3} + 3\frac{1}{6} + \frac{3}{4}$ $4\frac{1}{4}$

Exercise 6

Basics

1 Fill in the blanks for each problem.

(a) $3\frac{7}{12} + 4\frac{2}{3} = 7\frac{7}{12} + \frac{2}{3}$

$= 7\frac{7}{12} + \boxed{\frac{8}{12}}$

$= 7\boxed{\frac{15}{12}}$

$= \boxed{8}\boxed{\frac{3}{12}}$

$= \boxed{8}\boxed{\frac{1}{4}}$

(b) $1\frac{1}{2} + 2\frac{4}{5} = \boxed{\frac{3}{2}} + \boxed{\frac{14}{5}}$

$= \boxed{\frac{15}{10}} + \boxed{\frac{28}{10}}$

$= \boxed{\frac{43}{10}}$

$= \boxed{4}\boxed{\frac{3}{10}}$

Practice

2 Add. Use any method. Express each answer in simplest form.

(a) $4\frac{3}{8} + 2\frac{5}{8}$ 7

(b) $4\frac{5}{7} + 4\frac{3}{7}$ $9\frac{1}{7}$

(c) $1\frac{1}{6} + 9\frac{7}{12}$ $10\frac{3}{4}$

(d) $3\frac{9}{11} + 2\frac{1}{2}$ $6\frac{7}{22}$

(e) $3\frac{9}{10} + 3\frac{5}{6}$ $7\frac{11}{15}$

(f) $12\frac{5}{6} + 7\frac{3}{8}$ $20\frac{5}{24}$

(g) $2\frac{1}{3} + \frac{3}{5} + 3\frac{2}{5}$ $6\frac{1}{3}$

(h) $2\frac{1}{2} + 3\frac{1}{3} + 4\frac{1}{4} + 5\frac{1}{5} + 6\frac{1}{6}$ $21\frac{9}{20}$

3 Last week, Calli bought $3\frac{3}{4}$ m of cloth. This week, she bought $1\frac{1}{5}$ m more cloth than what she bought last week. How many meters of cloth did she buy altogether?

$3\frac{3}{4} + 3\frac{3}{4} + 1\frac{1}{5} = 8\frac{7}{10}$

$8\frac{7}{10}$ m

Challenge

4 Use each of the digits 0 to 9 once to form two mixed numbers with a sum of 100.

This is one possible solution:

$29\frac{1}{3} + 70\frac{56}{84}$

Find another solution.

Some possible solutions:

$50\frac{1}{2} + 49\frac{38}{76}$

$78\frac{3}{6} + 21\frac{45}{90}$

Exercise 7 • pages 90–91

Exercise 7

Basics

1. Fill in the blanks for each problem. Each problem uses a different strategy to subtract the given numbers.

(a) $7\frac{1}{3} - \frac{3}{4} = 7\frac{4}{12} - \frac{9}{12}$

$= 6\frac{16}{12} - \frac{9}{12}$

$= 6\frac{7}{12}$

(b) $3\frac{2}{9} - \frac{2}{3} = 3 - \frac{2}{3} + \frac{2}{9}$

$= 2\frac{1}{3} + \frac{2}{9}$

$= 2\frac{3}{9} + \frac{2}{9}$

$= 2\frac{5}{9}$

(c) $2\frac{1}{4} - \frac{5}{7} = \frac{9}{4} - \frac{5}{7}$

$= \frac{63}{28} - \frac{20}{28}$

$= \frac{43}{28}$

$= 1\frac{15}{28}$

Practice

2. Subtract. Use any method. Express each answer in simplest form.

(a) $7\frac{4}{7} - \frac{5}{7}$ $6\frac{6}{7}$

(b) $6\frac{5}{6} - \frac{5}{12}$ $6\frac{5}{12}$

(c) $8\frac{5}{12} - \frac{1}{4}$ $8\frac{1}{6}$

(d) $4\frac{1}{3} - \frac{5}{6}$ $3\frac{1}{2}$

(e) $5\frac{7}{10} - \frac{5}{6}$ $4\frac{13}{15}$

(f) $9\frac{2}{15} - \frac{5}{6}$ $8\frac{3}{10}$

(g) $12 - \frac{3}{5} - \frac{1}{2}$ $10\frac{9}{10}$

(h) $8\frac{1}{3} - \frac{5}{6} - \frac{2}{9}$ $7\frac{5}{18}$

Exercise 8 • pages 92–93

Exercise 8

Basics

1. Fill in the blanks for each problem.

(a) $7\frac{7}{12} - 3\frac{3}{4} = 4\frac{7}{12} - \frac{3}{4}$

$= 4\frac{7}{12} - \frac{9}{12}$

$= 3\frac{19}{12} - \frac{9}{12}$

$= 3\frac{10}{12}$

$= 3\frac{5}{6}$

(b) $2\frac{3}{4} - 1\frac{1}{12} = \frac{11}{4} - \frac{13}{12}$

$= \frac{33}{12} - \frac{13}{12}$

$= \frac{20}{12}$

$= \frac{5}{3}$

$= 1\frac{2}{3}$

Practice

2. Subtract. Use any method. Express each answer in simplest form.

(a) $4\frac{3}{8} - 2\frac{5}{8}$ $1\frac{3}{4}$

(b) $7\frac{9}{14} - 2\frac{3}{7}$ $5\frac{3}{14}$

(c) $9\frac{3}{8} - 6\frac{7}{12}$ $2\frac{19}{24}$

(d) $2\frac{2}{9} - 1\frac{2}{3}$ $\frac{5}{9}$

(e) $6\frac{5}{6} - 3\frac{3}{10}$ $3\frac{8}{15}$

(f) $12\frac{3}{9} - 7\frac{5}{6}$ $4\frac{1}{2}$

(g) $12\frac{1}{3} - 3 - 2\frac{3}{5}$ $6\frac{11}{15}$

(h) $7\frac{1}{4} - 2\frac{1}{5} - 2\frac{3}{10}$ $2\frac{3}{4}$

Exercise 9 • pages 94–96

Exercise 9

Check

1. Find the values. Express each answer in simplest form.

(a) $4\frac{3}{8} - \frac{3}{4}$ $3\frac{5}{8}$

(b) $7\frac{4}{5} + \frac{4}{15}$ $8\frac{1}{15}$

(c) $9\frac{3}{8} + 2\frac{5}{12}$ $11\frac{19}{24}$

(d) $3\frac{3}{7} - 1\frac{1}{2}$ $1\frac{13}{14}$

(e) $9\frac{1}{3} - (3\frac{5}{6} - 2\frac{1}{2})$ 8

(f) $9\frac{1}{3} - 3\frac{5}{6} - 2\frac{1}{2}$ 3

2. (a) $\underline{2\frac{11}{12}} + 2\frac{1}{3} = 5\frac{1}{4}$

(b) $\underline{8\frac{2}{3}} - 3\frac{1}{2} = 5\frac{1}{6}$

3. A container has $4\frac{3}{5}$ L of water. $1\frac{7}{10}$ L is needed to fill it to full capacity. What is the capacity of the container in liters?

$4\frac{3}{5} + 1\frac{7}{10} = 6\frac{3}{10}$

$6\frac{3}{10}$ L

4. Wainani's time for running 100 m was $18\frac{1}{3}$ seconds. Taylor's time was $3\frac{4}{5}$ s less than Wainani's time. What was Taylor's time for running 100 m?

$18\frac{1}{3} - 3\frac{4}{5} = 14\frac{8}{15}$

$14\frac{8}{15}$ s

5. To make blended coffee, a barista mixed 12 lb of beans from Ecuador with 15 lb of beans from Kenya. He then divided the blend into 8 equal portions and added $1\frac{3}{4}$ lb of beans from Colombia to each bag. What is the weight of coffee in each bag?

$(12 + 15) \div 8 = 3\frac{3}{8}$
$3\frac{3}{8} + 1\frac{3}{4} = 5\frac{1}{8}$

$5\frac{1}{8}$ lb

6. A rectangle is $3\frac{1}{4}$ ft long and $2\frac{1}{3}$ ft wide. What is the perimeter in feet?

$3\frac{1}{4} + 3\frac{1}{4} + 2\frac{1}{3} + 2\frac{1}{3} = 11\frac{1}{6}$

$11\frac{1}{6}$ ft

7. A spider climbed $7\frac{1}{4}$ inches up a wall, then slid down $1\frac{1}{2}$ inches, and then climbed another $5\frac{3}{8}$ inches. How much higher did the spider end up from its starting place?

$7\frac{1}{4} - 1\frac{1}{2} + 5\frac{3}{8} = 11\frac{1}{8}$

$11\frac{1}{8}$ in

Challenge

8. Find the value.

$10\frac{1}{7} - 9\frac{1}{8} + 9\frac{1}{8} - 8\frac{1}{9} + 8\frac{1}{9} - 7\frac{1}{10} + 7\frac{1}{10} - 6\frac{1}{11} + 6\frac{1}{11} - 10\frac{1}{12}$

$\frac{5}{84}$

Exercise 10

Check

1. (a) Put commas in the correct places, then write the number in words.

   4 0 7,1 4 8,0 0 0

   four hundred seven million, one hundred forty-eight thousand

   (b) The value of the digit in the hundred millions place is 10,000 times the value of the digit in the ten thousands place.

   (c) If the digit 7 is replaced by the digit 5, the new number is 2,000,000 less than the old number.

2. What is the greatest odd number that is less than 7,000,000 + 30,000 + 20?
   7,030,019

3. A condo is sold at $589,000 when rounded to the nearest $1,000.
   What is the greatest possible price for the condo, in whole dollars?
   $589,499

4. (a) [240,000] ÷ 600 = 400

   (b) 900 × [120] = 108,000

   (c) 28,800 ÷ [72] = 400

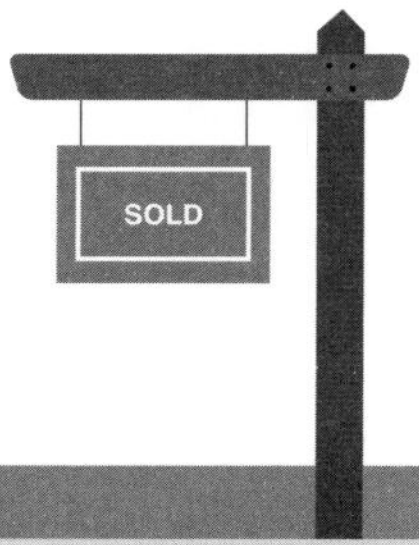

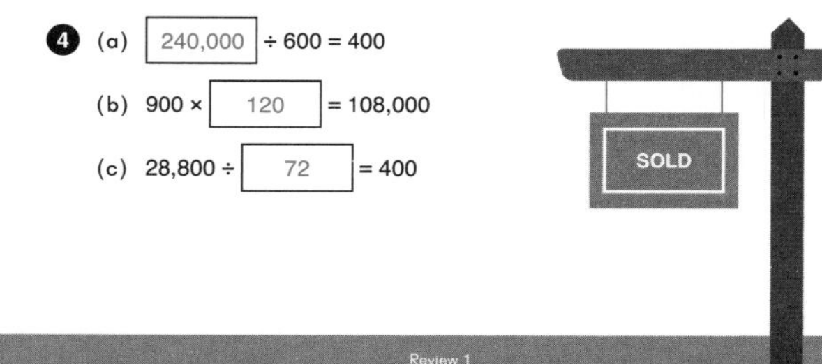

5. Find the values. Express fractions in simplest form.

   (a) 6 × (3 + 2) − 8
   22

   (b) 15 − 8 × 3 ÷ 2 + 6
   9

   (c) 2,000 ÷ (100 + 300 ÷ 15 × 20)
   4

   (d) 72 × 63 + 28 × 63
   6,300

   (e) 4,999 × 19
   94,981

   (f) (70 + 12) ÷ 12
   $6\frac{5}{6}$

   (g) 8,560 ÷ 32
   $267\frac{1}{2}$

   (h) $72 \div (7 - \frac{1}{2} - \frac{1}{3} - \frac{1}{6})$
   12

   (i) $6\frac{1}{4} - 3\frac{5}{6} + 2\frac{1}{3}$
   $4\frac{3}{4}$

   (j) $6\frac{1}{4} - (3\frac{5}{6} + 1\frac{1}{3})$
   $1\frac{1}{12}$

6. Patrick bought 12 chairs and 3 tables for $819. Each table cost 3 times as much as each chair. How much did 1 table cost?
   1 table is same cost as 3 chairs.
   3 tables is same cost as 9 chairs.
   12 + 9 = 21
   Cost of 1 chair: 819 ÷ 21 = 39
   39 × 3 = 117
   $117

7. A shopkeeper ordered 75 cans of a special brand of tea. Each can holds 50 packets of tea. Each packet costs $2, and the can costs $4. The shipping cost is $25. How much did the shopkeeper pay?
   Cost of tea: 2 × 50 × 75 = 7,500
   Cost of cans: 4 × 75 = 300
   7,500 + 300 + 25 = 7,825
   $7,825

8. A blue cable is 7 m long. It is $1\frac{4}{5}$ m longer than a yellow cable. The yellow cable is $3\frac{3}{4}$ m longer than a black cable. How long is the black cable in meters?

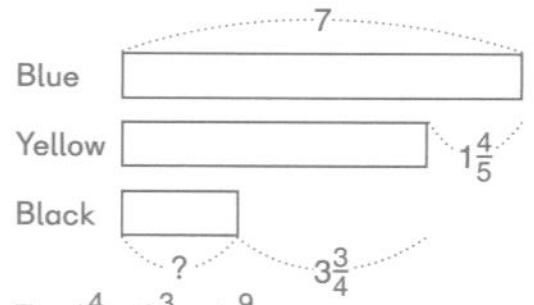

   $7 - 1\frac{4}{5} - 3\frac{3}{4} = 1\frac{9}{20}$

   $1\frac{9}{20}$ m

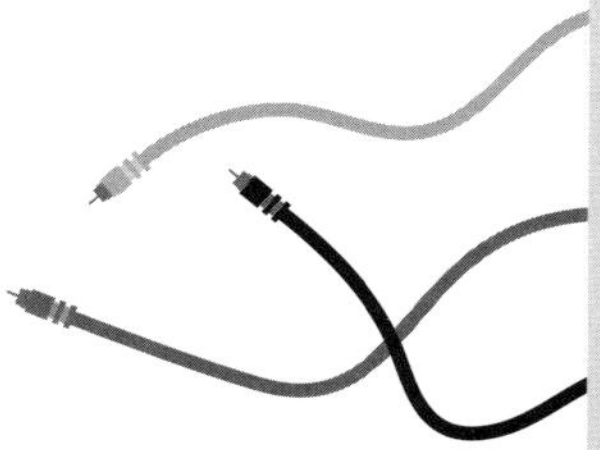

9. At first, Rita and Kim had $200 altogether. After Rita spent $62 and Kim spent $46, Kim had 3 times as much money as Rita. How much money did Kim have at first?

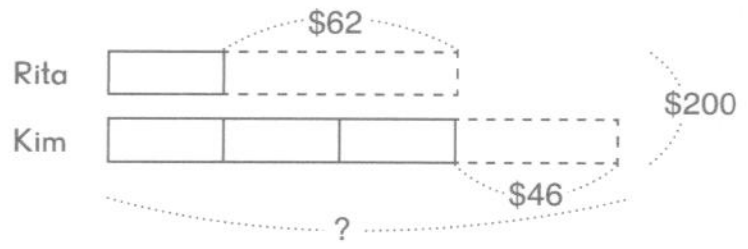

   4 units ⟶ 200 − 62 − 46 = 92
   1 unit ⟶ 92 ÷ 4 = 23
   3 × 23 + 46 = 115
   $115

10. Daniela is 11 years old. Her brother is 3 years older than she is. In how many years will their combined age be 55 years?
    Her brother will always be 3 years older.

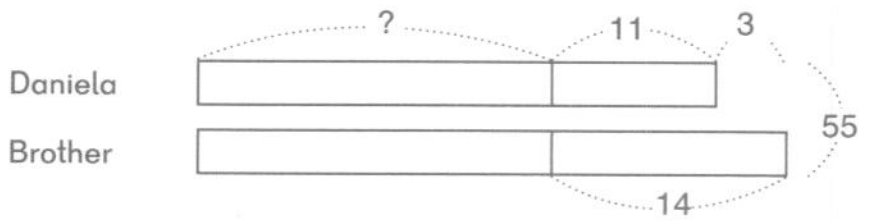

    2 units ⟶ 55 − 25 = 30
    1 unit ⟶ 30 ÷ 2 = 15
    15 years

Challenge

11 Write the greatest possible whole number that will make the following true.

$16 \times (\boxed{135} - 11) < 1,999$

2,000 ÷ 16 = 125; 125 + 11 = 136, so one less will give an answer less than 1,999.

12 Use mental calculation to find the values.

(a) 499,991 + 29,996 + 7,997 + 598 + 69
500,000 + 30,000 + 8,000 + 600 + 70 – (9 + 4 + 3 + 2 + 1)
= 538,651

(b) 3,689 – (2,489 + 899)
3,689 – 2,489 – 899 = 1,200 – 900 + 1 = 301

13 Santino has 9 bills that total $100. The bills are all 5-dollar bills, 10-dollar bills, or 20-dollar bills. How many of each kind of bill does he have?
Use educated guess and check or make a table. Student can, for example, start with nine 10-dollar bills only and convert some to 20-dollar bills and 5-dollar bills.

Three 20-dollar bills, two 10-dollar bills, and four 5-dollar bills.

14 The below expression is a way to express 26 with 5 twos, using whole numbers, fractions, and the symbols +, –, ×, ÷, and ( ).

$26 = 2 \times (\frac{22}{2} + 2)$

All the numbers from 1 to 26 can be expressed with 5 twos, except 17. Express as many numbers from 1 to 25 with 5 twos as you can. Express 17 with 6 twos.

$1 = 2 + 2 - 2 - \frac{2}{2}$

$2 = 2 + 2 + 2 - 2 - 2$

$3 = 2 + 2 - 2 + \frac{2}{2}$

$4 = 2 \times 2 \times 2 - 2 - 2$

$5 = 2 + 2 + 2 - \frac{2}{2}$

$6 = 2 + 2 + 2 + 2 - 2$

$7 = \frac{22}{2} - 2 - 2$

$8 = 2 \times 2 \times 2 + 2 - 2$

$9 = 2 \times 2 \times 2 + \frac{2}{2}$

$10 = 2 + 2 + 2 + 2 + 2$

$11 = \frac{22}{2} + 2 - 2$

$12 = 2 \times 2 \times 2 + 2 + 2$

$13 = (22 + 2 + 2) \div 2$

$14 = 2 \times 2 \times 2 \times 2 - 2$

$15 = \frac{22}{2} + 2 + 2$

$16 = (2 \times 2 + 2 + 2) \times 2$

$17 = \frac{22}{2} + (2 \times 2) + 2$

$18 = 2 \times 2 \times 2 \times 2 + 2$

$19 = 22 - 2 - \frac{2}{2}$

$20 = 22 + 2 - 2 - 2$

$21 = 22 - 2 + \frac{2}{2}$

$22 = 22 \times 2 - 22$

$23 = 22 + 2 - \frac{2}{2}$

$24 = 22 - 2 + 2 + 2$

$25 = 22 + 2 + \frac{2}{2}$

Notes

Suggested number of class periods: 11–12

	Lesson	Page	Resources	Objectives
	Chapter Opener	p. 147	TB: p. 111	Investigate multiplication of fractions.
1	Multiplying a Fraction by a Whole Number	p. 148	TB: p. 112 WB: p. 103	Understand multiplication of a fraction by a whole number as repeated addition of the fraction. Multiply a fraction by a whole number.
2	Multiplying a Whole Number by a Fraction	p. 151	TB: p. 115 WB: p. 105	Multiply a whole number by a fraction.
3	Word Problems — Part 1	p. 156	TB: p. 120 WB: p. 107	Solve multi-step word problems involving fractions.
4	Practice A	p. 160	TB: p. 124 WB: p. 111	Practice multiplying fractions. Practice solving multi-step word problems.
5	Multiplying a Fraction by a Unit Fraction	p. 162	TB: p. 126 WB: p. 115	Multiply a fraction by a unit fraction.
6	Multiplying a Fraction by a Fraction — Part 1	p. 165	TB: p. 129 WB: p. 117	Multiply a fraction by a fraction.
7	Multiplying a Fraction by a Fraction — Part 2	p. 167	TB: p. 132 WB: p. 120	Multiply a fraction by a fraction, by simplifying the calculation first.
8	Multiplying Mixed Numbers	p. 169	TB: p. 135 WB: p. 123	Multiply mixed numbers.
9	Word Problems — Part 2	p. 172	TB: p. 138 WB: p. 126	Solve multi-step word problems involving fraction of a remainder.
10	Fractions and Reciprocals	p. 175	TB: p. 142 WB: p. 130	Multiply two fractions to get a product of 1. Find the reciprocal of a fraction, a mixed number, or a whole number.
11	Practice B	p. 177	TB: p. 145 WB: p. 132	Practice multiplying fractions. Practice solving multi-step word problems.
	Workbook Solutions	p. 179		

In Dimensions Math 4A, students learned to:

- Multiply a fraction by a whole number
- Find a fraction of a set

Students will review these concepts in Lessons 1–4, then extend their understanding to multiplying fractions and mixed numbers.

Multiply a Fraction by a Whole Number

Students have learned that multiplication can be thought of as repeated addition. In other words, we are adding equal groups.

$3 \times \frac{2}{3}$ is thought of as 3 × 2 thirds = 6 thirds.

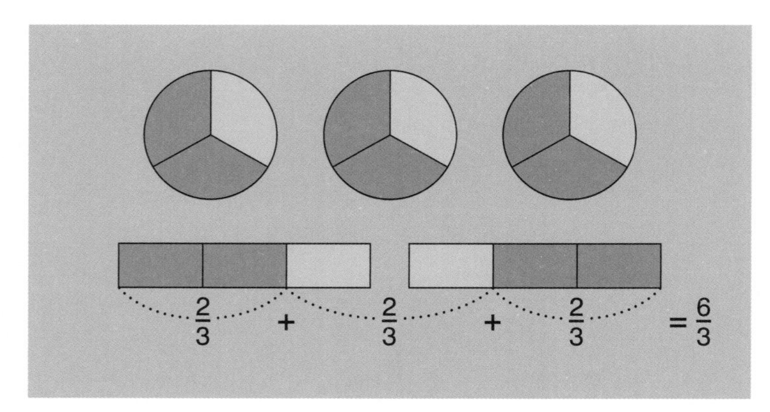

This can also be shown on a number line.

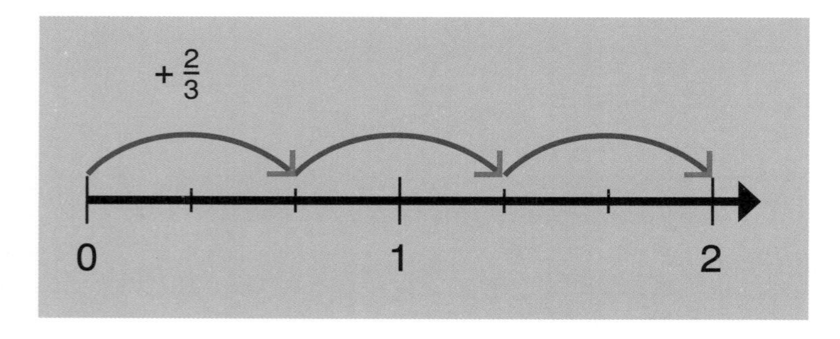

Students can see that we can find the answer by multiplying the numerator of the fraction by the whole number.

Students should give their answers in simplest form:

$3 \times \frac{2}{3} = \frac{3 \times 2}{3} = \frac{6}{3} = 2$

Students have also learned to simplify calculations:

$3 \times \frac{2}{3} = \frac{\overset{1}{\cancel{3}} \times 2}{\underset{1}{\cancel{3}}} = 2$

Multiply a Whole Number by a Fraction

In addition to repeated addition, multiplication can be thought of as scaling, where we shrink or expand a unit proportionately. Imagine a map makes a scale of 1 inch for every 6 feet. That means for a distance of 72 inches, the map shows 1 inch. $\frac{1}{72}$ × the distance = map distance.

Just as 16 is 2 times as much as 8 (16 = 2 × 8), 4 is $\frac{1}{2}$ times as much as 8 $(4 = \frac{1}{2} \times 8)$. Similarly, to find $\frac{2}{3} \times 4 = \frac{8}{3}$ means that $\frac{8}{3}$ is $\frac{2}{3}$ times as much as 4.

We can also scale fractions greater than 1. Example: $\frac{4}{3} \times 12 = 4 \times \frac{1}{3} \times 12$.

Students have solved these problems before in equation form and using the unitary method with bar models:

3 units ⟶ 12
1 unit ⟶ $\frac{12}{3}$
4 units ⟶ $4 \times \frac{12}{3}$

In Lessons 3 – 4 students practice and apply these concepts with word problems.

Multiply a Fraction by a Fraction

Students will first learn how to multiply a fraction by a unit fraction. They will shade area and bar models to understand conceptually what, for example, $\frac{1}{2}$ of $\frac{2}{3}$ means.

These area and bar models will essentially allow them to find the number that is $\frac{1}{2}$ as much as $\frac{2}{3}$.

Example: $\frac{1}{2} \times \frac{2}{3}$

Students will represent $\frac{2}{3}$ on an area model.

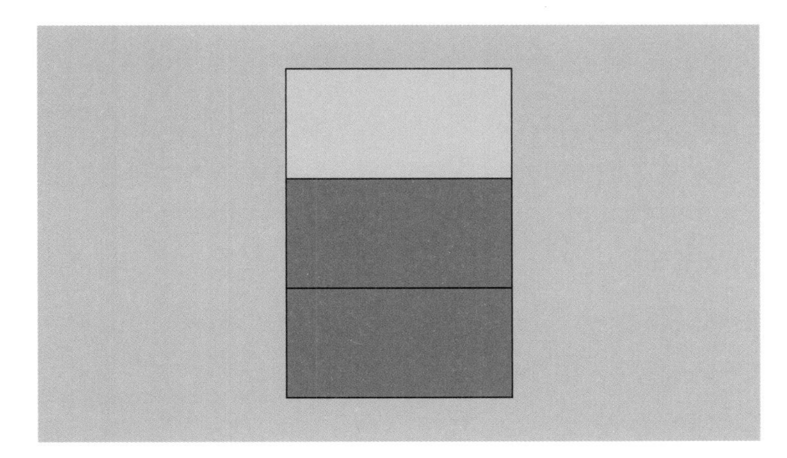

The whole is made up of 3 equal parts, and we shade 2 of those parts.

To find $\frac{1}{2}$ of this amount, we divide each part ($\frac{1}{3}$) equally into 2 units. This makes $2 \times 3 = 6$ equal units in the whole, or sixths. We then further shade half of these new units. We can see that 1×2 of the new units are shaded.

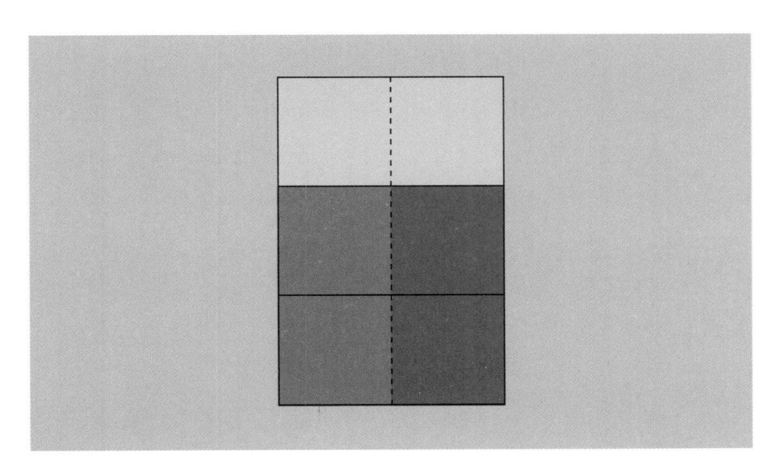

There are two shaded units of $\frac{1}{6}$, so the fraction is $\frac{2}{6}$.

From this we can see that we multiply each numerator together and each denominator together:

$\frac{1}{2} \times \frac{2}{3} = \frac{1 \times 2}{2 \times 3} = \frac{2}{6} = \frac{1}{3}$

The area model helps students to see that when we multiply by a proper fraction, the product is less than the number being multiplied (multiplicand), for example, $\frac{1}{2} \times \frac{2}{3}$ is less than $\frac{2}{3}$, and $\frac{3}{5} \times \frac{7}{8}$ is less than $\frac{7}{8}$.

$\frac{1}{2} \times \frac{2}{3}$ can also be visualized with a linear model.

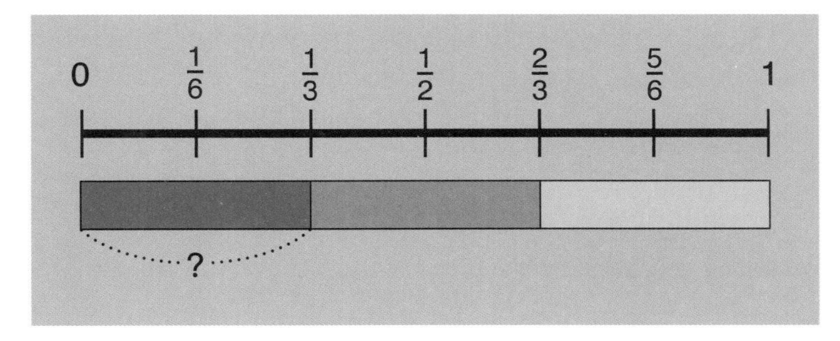

$\frac{1}{2}$ of $\frac{2}{3}$ is $\frac{2}{6}$ or $\frac{1}{3}$.

Once students have practiced multiplying by a unit fraction, they will then learn to multiply two non-unit fractions in Lesson 6. The bar model combined with a number line is particularly helpful when visualizing what happens when we multiply by an improper fraction.

Example: $\frac{3}{2} \times \frac{2}{5}$

On the linear number line, $\frac{2}{5}$ can be represented as a bar model:

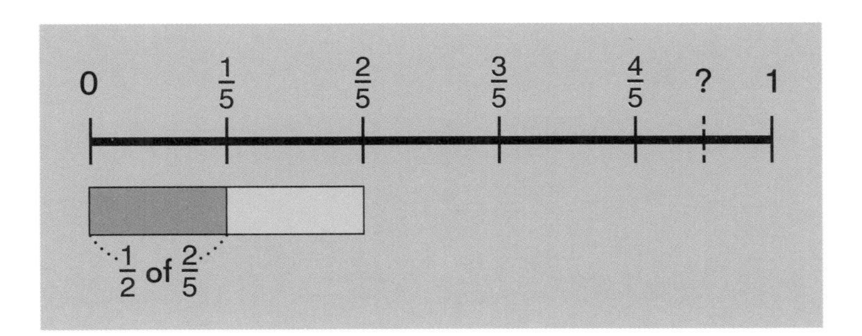

We can consider the units:

2 units $\longrightarrow \frac{2}{5}$
1 unit $\longrightarrow \frac{1}{2}$ of $\frac{2}{5}$

$\frac{3}{2}$ of $\frac{2}{5}$ can then be represented on the linear model as shown below:

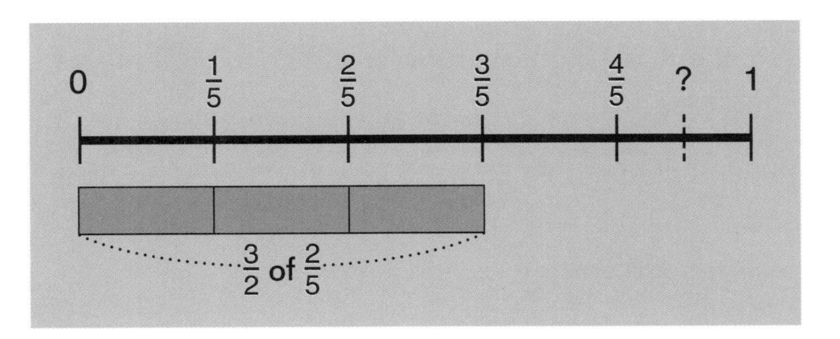

1 unit $\longrightarrow \frac{1}{2}$ of $\frac{2}{5}$
3 units $\longrightarrow 3 \times (\frac{1}{2}$ of $\frac{2}{5}) = 3 \times \frac{1}{5} = \frac{3}{5}$

When we multiply a fraction by a fraction, we multiply the numerators and the denominators.

$\frac{3 \times 2}{2 \times 5} = \frac{6}{10} = \frac{3}{5}$

After multiplying fractions, students will learn to multiply mixed numbers in Lesson 8. When multiplying mixed numbers, they will convert the mixed numbers to improper fractions and then will be able to multiply the numerators together and denominators together.

Word Problems

In Lesson 9, students will use bar models to understand and solve word problems involving multiplication of fractions.

Example: Shana walked $\frac{2}{5}$ of a mile. Farouk walked $1\frac{1}{2}$ times as far as Shana. How far did Farouk walk?

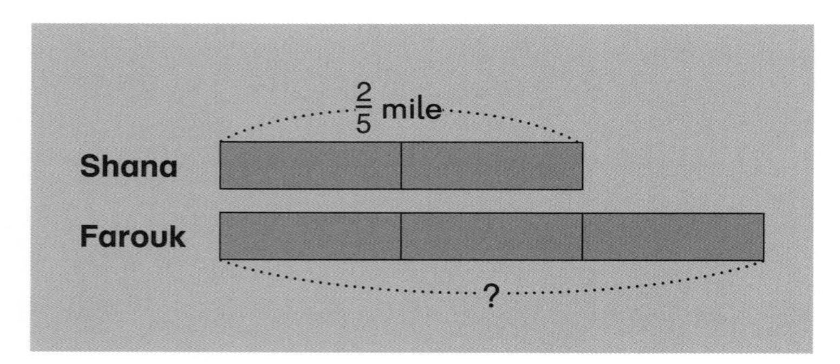

Distance Farouk walked: $1\frac{1}{2} \times \frac{2}{5} = \frac{3}{2} \times \frac{2}{5}$

We often tell students that "of" indicates we need to multiply, but this is not true of all problems and can be misleading.

In one case, $\frac{1}{6}$ of 12 potatoes is asking us to find $\frac{1}{6} \times 12$, as in $\frac{1}{6} \times 12$ potatoes = 2 potatoes. But if we say, 6 out of 12 potatoes we mean $\frac{6}{12}$, or $\frac{1}{2}$ of the set of potatoes.

Remind students to study the context of the problem, and model the problem with manipulatives or pictures rather than rely on keywords.

Reciprocals

Students are introduced to reciprocals as a precursor to division of fractions. The reciprocal of a number is the number we multiply that number by to get a product of 1.

$\frac{1}{3}$ is the reciprocal of 3 because $\frac{1}{3}$ of 3 is 1 ($\frac{1}{3} \times 3 = 1$). 3 is the reciprocal of $\frac{1}{3}$ because 3 one-thirds is 1 ($3 \times \frac{1}{3} = 1$).

Example 1: I have $\frac{1}{4}$ cup of flour. How many $\frac{1}{4}$ cups makes 1 cup?

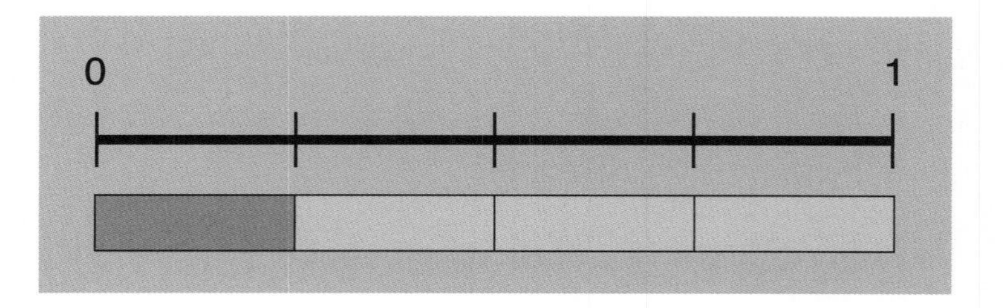

Students need to think about what they need to multiply $\frac{1}{4}$ by to get 1.

$\frac{1}{4} \times 4 = \frac{4}{4} = 1$, so 4 is the reciprocal of $\frac{1}{4}$.

Example 2: Coco's ribbon is $\frac{2}{3}$ ft long. Adam's ribbon is $1\frac{1}{2}$ times as long as Coco's ribbon. How many feet is Adam's ribbon?

2 units $\longrightarrow \frac{2}{3}$ ft

1 unit $\longrightarrow \frac{1}{2} \times \frac{2}{3}$ ft $= \frac{1}{3}$ ft

3 units $\longrightarrow 3 \times \frac{1}{3}$ ft = 1 ft

or

$1\frac{1}{2} \times \frac{2}{3} = \frac{3}{2} \times \frac{2}{3} = 1$

$\frac{3}{2}$ is the reciprocal of $\frac{2}{3}$, when $\frac{2}{3}$ is multiplied by $\frac{3}{2}$, the product becomes 1.

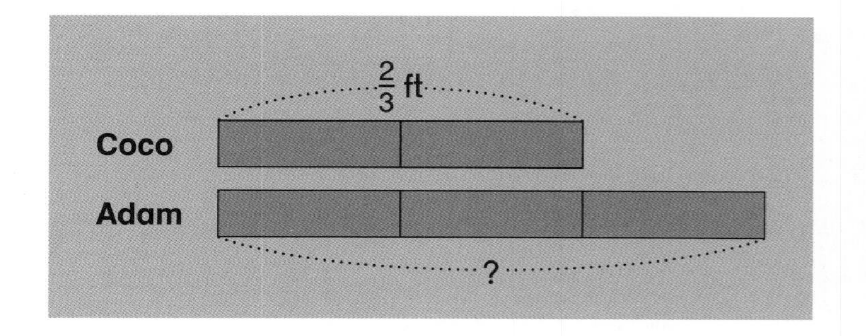

Materials

- Beans or markers
- Counters
- Fraction manipulatives
- Index cards
- Strips of paper
- Whiteboards

Blackline Masters

- Fraction Bingo Cards
- Fraction Bingo Game Board
- I Have, Who Has? Unit Fractions
- Number Cards
- Reciprocal Match Cards

Activities

Activities included in this chapter provide practice for multiplying fractions. They can be used after students complete the **Do** questions, or anytime additional practice is needed.

Notes

Objective

- Investigate multiplication of fractions.

Have students discuss the **Chapter Opener** and think about what operations they can use to solve the problems. Ask them to think about which of the problem(s) they have learned to solve previously.

This introduction can be a short discussion before beginning Lesson 1, in which students will review multiplying a fraction by a whole number.

Dion: $3 \times \frac{1}{4}$

Emma: $\frac{2}{3} \times 12$

Mei: $\frac{1}{2} \times \frac{2}{3}$

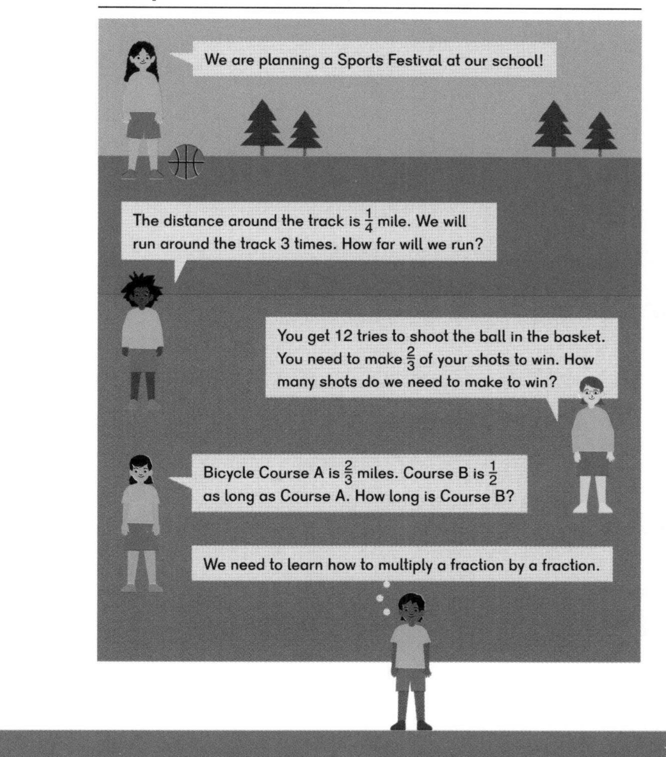

111

Lesson 1 Multiplying a Fraction by a Whole Number

Objectives

- Understand multiplication of a fraction by a whole number as repeated addition of the fraction.
- Multiply a fraction by a whole number.

Lesson Materials

- Fraction manipulatives

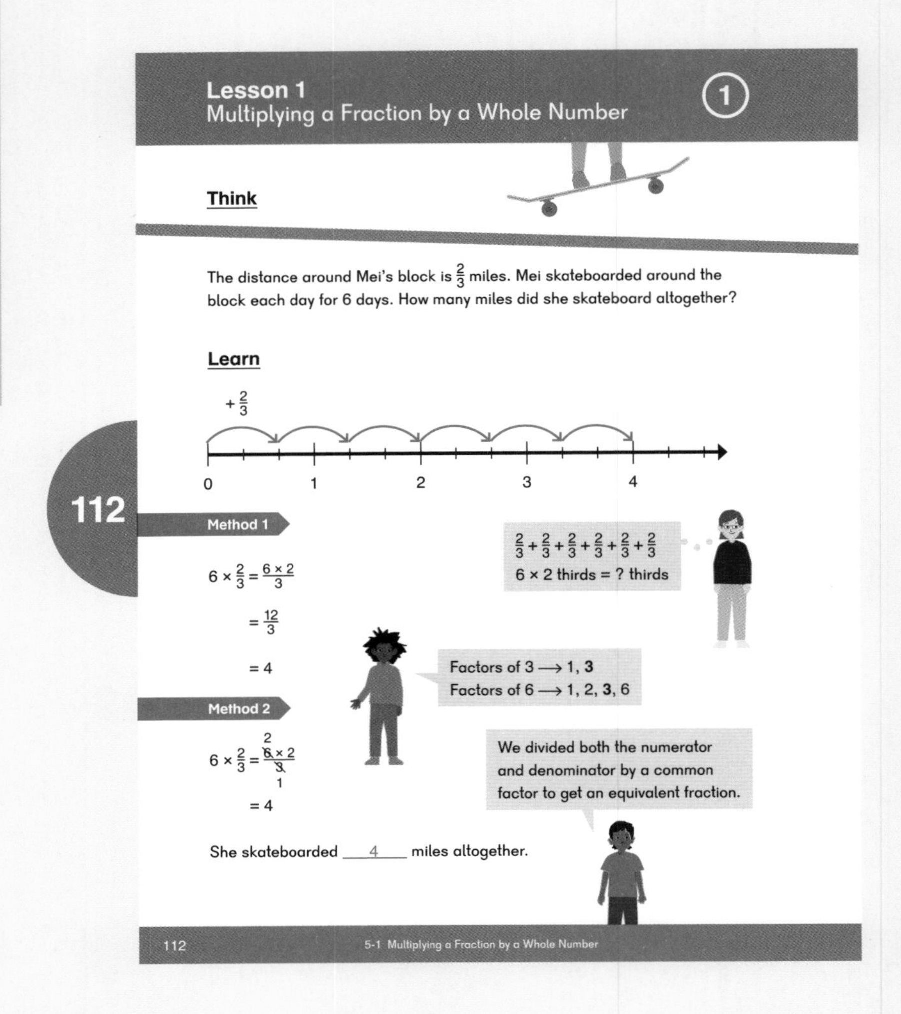

Think

Provide students with fraction manipulatives and pose the **Think** problem.

To find the distance that Mei skateboarded in all, students may:

- Use fraction manipulatives
- Draw a number line
- Draw a bar model
- Write an addition or multiplication equation

Discuss student solutions.

Learn

Discuss the two methods shown.

Method 1

By thinking of the denominator as a unit, students can relate fraction multiplication to whole number multiplication.

Ask students:

- "How many thirds of a mile did Mei skateboard?"
- "Why is Emma thinking about addition and multiplication?"
- "Why is $6 \times \frac{2}{3}$ equal to $\frac{6 \times 2}{3}$?"

In this method, the answer is calculated first, and then simplified.

Method 2

Instead of simplifying the product, we can simplify the fraction expression before computing the final answer. Dion and Alex remind students how to simplify a calculation.

Do

The methods on this page progress from pictorial to abstract to help students understand why we find the answer by multiplying the whole number by the numerator of the fraction. ❶ shows a pictorial representation. ❷ shows a number line, which is a more abstract representation. ❸ shows only the abstract expression.

❶—❹ Discuss the different examples and problems with students.

❶ Sofia's comments can be related to Method 1 in **Learn**: "Two groups of three-sevenths is how many sevenths?"

❸ Ask students:

- "How many ninths are in this product?"
- "How many thirds are in this product?"

Students could also simplify the product after multiplying:

$6 \times \frac{4}{9} = \frac{24}{9} = 2\frac{6}{9} = 2\frac{2}{3}$

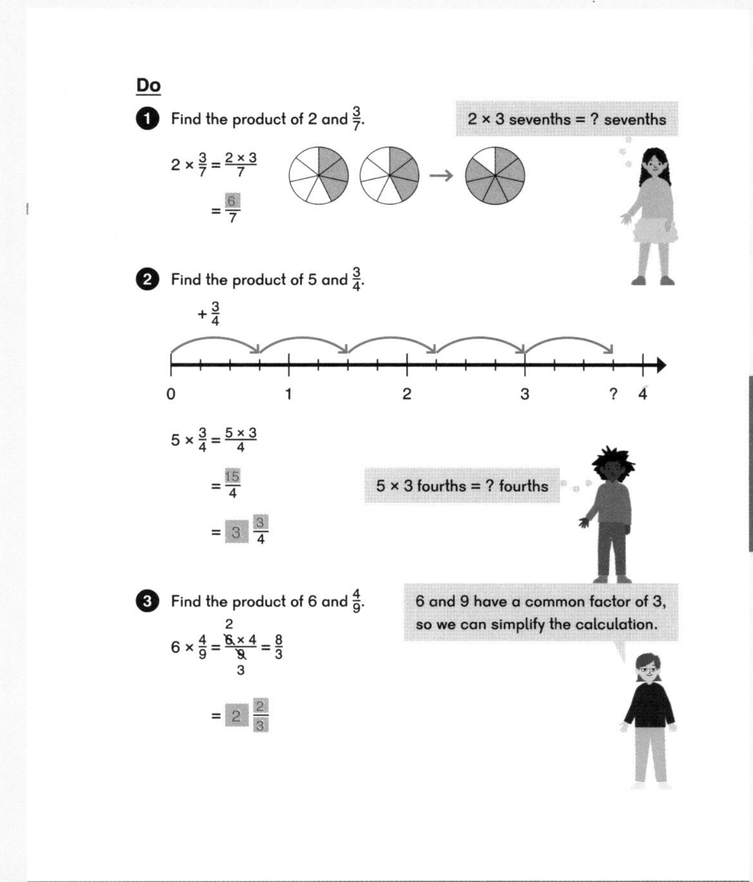

❹ Alex and Sofia simplify the calculation using different factors. Students may also simplify the product instead of the calculation:

$\frac{40}{12} = 3\frac{4}{12} = 3\frac{1}{3}$

❺—❽ Students should be able to solve these problems independently. Have them share their methods and solutions.

❽ If students need a tip for a context for their word problems, measurement quantities can be a good suggestion, for example:

- To wrap a package you need $\frac{2}{3}$ of a yard of ribbon. How many yards of ribbon are needed for seven packages?
- Seven students each win $\frac{2}{3}$ lb of candy. How many pounds of candy did they win in all?

114

❹ Find the product of 8 and $\frac{5}{12}$.

$8 \times \frac{5}{12} = \frac{\overset{2}{\cancel{8}} \times 5}{\underset{3}{\cancel{12}}} = \frac{10}{3} = 3\frac{1}{3}$

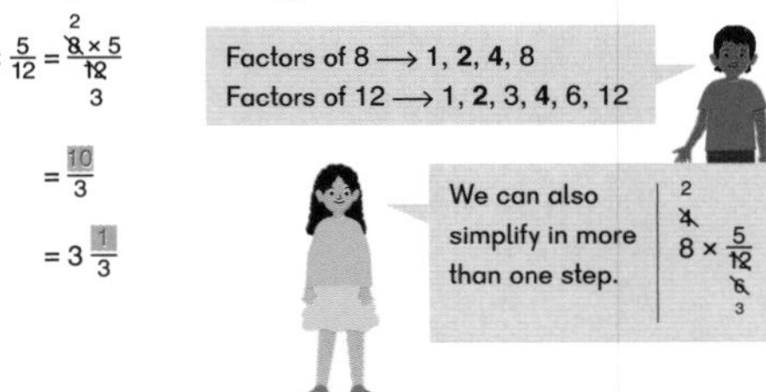

❺ Find the values. Express each answer in simplest form.

(a) $4 \times \frac{2}{9}$ $\frac{8}{9}$ (b) $5 \times \frac{3}{7}$ $2\frac{1}{7}$ (c) $6 \times \frac{3}{8}$ $2\frac{1}{4}$

(d) $9 \times \frac{5}{9}$ 5 (e) $5 \times \frac{2}{3}$ $3\frac{1}{3}$ (f) $20 \times \frac{3}{8}$ $7\frac{1}{2}$

(g) $6 \times \frac{7}{10}$ $4\frac{1}{5}$ (h) $6 \times \frac{5}{24}$ $1\frac{1}{4}$ (i) $50 \times \frac{3}{100}$ $1\frac{1}{2}$

❻ The distance around a track is $\frac{2}{5}$ km. A race was 3 laps around the track. How long was the race in kilometers?
$3 \times \frac{2}{5} = \frac{6}{5} = 1\frac{1}{5}$; $1\frac{1}{5}$ km

❼ $\frac{9}{10}$ gallons of water flows from a running faucet every minute. How many gallons of water will flow from the faucet in 30 minutes?
$30 \times \frac{9}{10} = 27$; 27 gallons

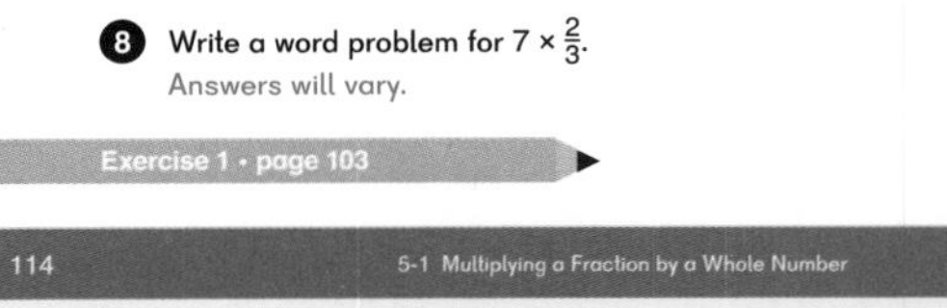

❽ Write a word problem for $7 \times \frac{2}{3}$.
Answers will vary.

Exercise 1 • page 103

114 5-1 Multiplying a Fraction by a Whole Number

Activity

▲ Greatest Product

Materials: Number Cards (BLM) 1–9, multiple sets

Players are dealt 3 cards in each round.

Players then make a proper fraction with the numbers from two of the three cards. They multiply that fraction by the number on the remaining card.

The player with the greatest product scores 1 point.

Sample play:

Player 1

Possible plays:
$5 \times \frac{2}{9}$ or $2 \times \frac{5}{9} = \frac{10}{9} = 1\frac{1}{9}$

$9 \times \frac{2}{5} = \frac{18}{5} = 3\frac{3}{5}$

He chooses $9 \times \frac{2}{5}$.

Player 2

4	1	9

Possible plays:
$4 \times \frac{1}{9}$ or $1 \times \frac{4}{9} = \frac{4}{9}$

$9 \times \frac{1}{4} = \frac{9}{4} = 2\frac{1}{4}$

She chooses $9 \times \frac{1}{4}$.

Player 1 has the greatest product, $3\frac{3}{5}$. He scores a point for the round.

The first player to 5 points is the winner.

Exercise 1 • page 103

Objective

- Multiply a whole number by a fraction.

Lesson Materials

- Counters, 20 per student or pair of students

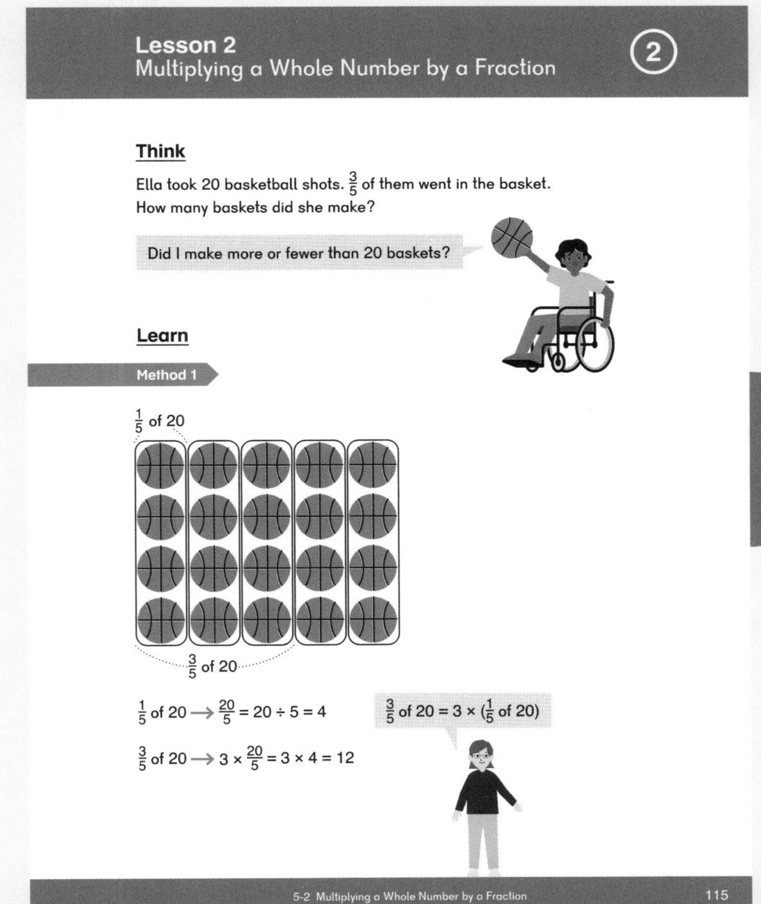
Lesson 2
Multiplying a Whole Number by a Fraction

2

Think

Ella took 20 basketball shots. $\frac{3}{5}$ of them went in the basket.
How many baskets did she make?

Learn

Method 1

$\frac{1}{5}$ of 20 $\longrightarrow \frac{20}{5} = 20 \div 5 = 4$

$\frac{3}{5}$ of 20 $\longrightarrow 3 \times \frac{20}{5} = 3 \times 4 = 12$

5-2 Multiplying a Whole Number by a Fraction 115

Think

Provide students with counters and pose the **Think** problem.

The 20 counters can represent the 20 shots at the basket that Ella took.

Ask students if the answer will be greater or less than 20 and why. They should see that we are finding a fractional part of 20, so the product will be less than 20.

Discuss student solutions.

Learn

Discuss the three methods which progress from concrete to more abstract.

Method 1

Ask students:

- "Why are the basketballs grouped into 5 groups?" (We are finding how many are in $\frac{1}{5}$ of them first.)
- "How many basketballs are in each group?" (4)
- "How many basketballs are in 3 of the groups?" (12)

To find $\frac{3}{5}$ of 20, first find $\frac{1}{5}$ of 20.

$\frac{1}{5}$ of the 20 basketballs represent 4 shots. Find 3 fifths of 20 by multiplying the previous answer by 3.

Method 2

Mei uses a bar model and relates the problem to units. She sees $\frac{3}{5}$ as 3 units of the bar model. By figuring out what 1 unit is, she can compute the answer for 3 units.

Method 3

Since $\frac{3}{5} \times 20 = 20 \times \frac{3}{5}$, we can just use the computation for multiplying a whole number by a fraction, as learned in Lesson 1.

Alex simplifies before calculating.

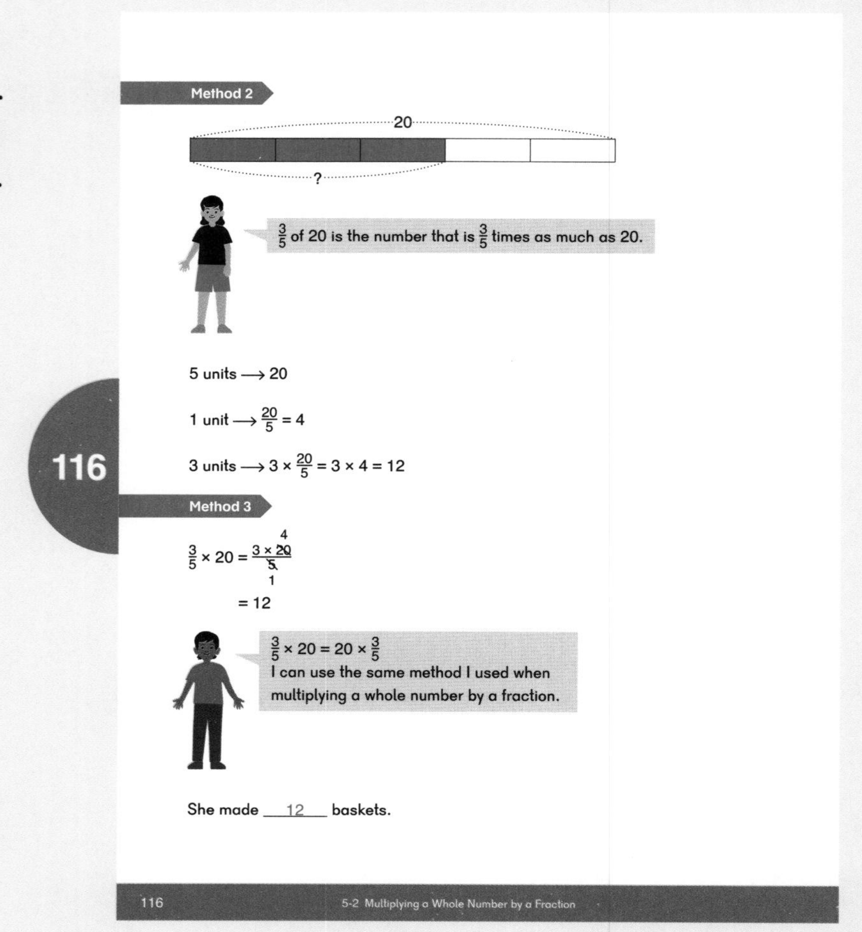

Do

❶–❻ Discuss the given models and problems with students.

❶ Similar to Method 1 in **Think**, if $\frac{1}{3}$ of 9 is 3, $\frac{2}{3}$ is twice as many, or $2 \times (9 \div 3)$.

❷ Ask students why they cannot simplify this problem before calculating. (There are no common factors of 10 and 3 to divide the numerator and denominator.) This problem results in a product with a mixed number.

❸ Students may need to think about the circles before they are divided into fourths. If we divide each whole into fourths, then we can rearrange all 24 fourths into 4 groups of 6 fourths.

The wholes are divided into fourths to help students see the 3×6, or 18 fourths in the answer. In the next two problems, students will be multiplying the whole number by the numerator of the fraction. This is the second method for finding the answer.

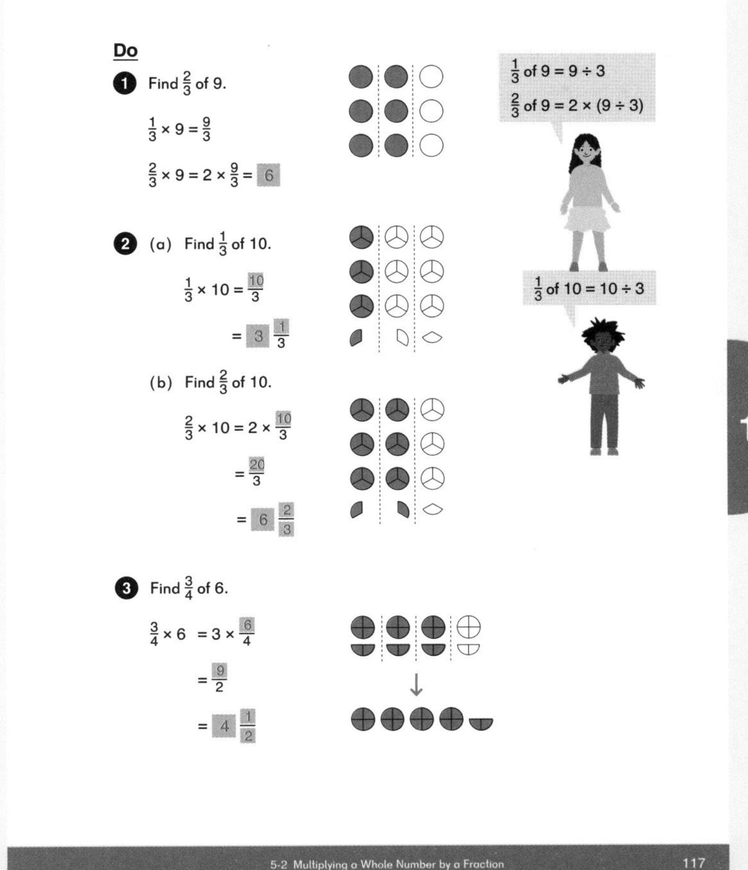

Do

❶ Find $\frac{2}{3}$ of 9.

$\frac{1}{3} \times 9 = \frac{9}{3}$

$\frac{2}{3} \times 9 = 2 \times \frac{9}{3} = 6$

$\frac{1}{3}$ of $9 = 9 \div 3$

$\frac{2}{3}$ of $9 = 2 \times (9 \div 3)$

❷ (a) Find $\frac{1}{3}$ of 10.

$\frac{1}{3} \times 10 = \frac{10}{3}$

$= 3\frac{1}{3}$

$\frac{1}{3}$ of $10 = 10 \div 3$

(b) Find $\frac{2}{3}$ of 10.

$\frac{2}{3} \times 10 = 2 \times \frac{10}{3}$

$= \frac{20}{3}$

$= 6\frac{2}{3}$

❸ Find $\frac{3}{4}$ of 6.

$\frac{3}{4} \times 6 = 3 \times \frac{6}{4}$

$= \frac{9}{2}$

$= 4\frac{1}{2}$

5-2 Multiplying a Whole Number by a Fraction 117

117

❹—❻ For each question, discuss how the expression has been simplified.

❹ Discuss Emma's estimate. Students should realize that any time the fraction is less than 1, the product will be less than the number being multiplied.

❺ The answer to Alex's question is that any time the fraction is greater than 1 (i.e. $\frac{4}{3}$), the product of the improper fraction and the whole number will be greater than the number being multiplied. In this case, greater than 12.

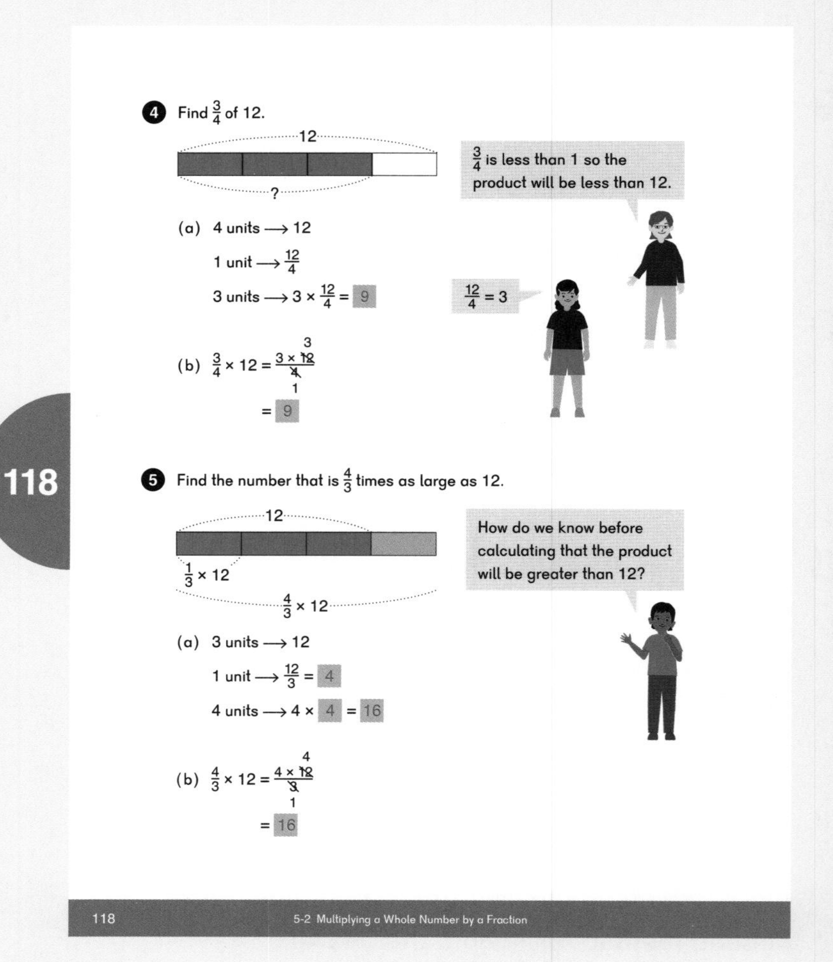

❹ Find $\frac{3}{4}$ of 12.

(a) 4 units ⟶ 12

1 unit ⟶ $\frac{12}{4}$

3 units ⟶ $3 \times \frac{12}{4} = 9$

(b) $\frac{3}{4} \times 12 = \frac{3 \times \overset{3}{\cancel{12}}}{\underset{1}{\cancel{4}}}$

$= 9$

❺ Find the number that is $\frac{4}{3}$ times as large as 12.

(a) 3 units ⟶ 12

1 unit ⟶ $\frac{12}{3} = 4$

4 units ⟶ $4 \times 4 = 16$

(b) $\frac{4}{3} \times 12 = \frac{4 \times \overset{4}{\cancel{12}}}{\underset{1}{\cancel{3}}}$

$= 16$

118 5-2 Multiplying a Whole Number by a Fraction

6 Discuss Sofia's question.

Students can visually verify the answers to the methods in both (a) and (b) on the number line.

7—**8** Have students practice estimating if the product will be less than or greater than the whole number being multiplied. They should be able to solve these problems independently.

Activity

▲ Fraction Bingo 24

Materials: Fraction Bingo Cards (BLM), Fraction Bingo Game Board (BLM), beans or markers to cover bingo numbers

Have students fill in their game boards with the numbers listed. They may choose what numbers to include.

To call a number, turn over a Fraction Bingo Card and call the fraction on it. Students multiply the fraction on the card by 24 and cover the product on the game board.

For example, if the caller says:

- $\frac{1}{3} \times 24$: Students cover 8 on their game boards.
- $\frac{4}{6} \times 24$: Students cover 16 on their game boards.

The first person to get 4 in a row wins.

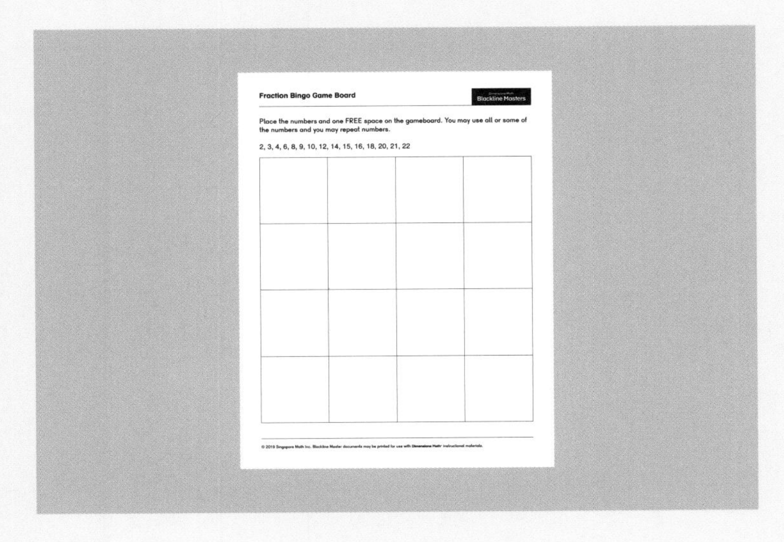

Fraction Bingo Game Board

Blackline Masters

Place the numbers and one FREE space on the gameboard. You may use all or some of the numbers and you may repeat numbers.

2, 3, 4, 6, 8, 9, 10, 12, 14, 15, 16, 18, 20, 21, 22

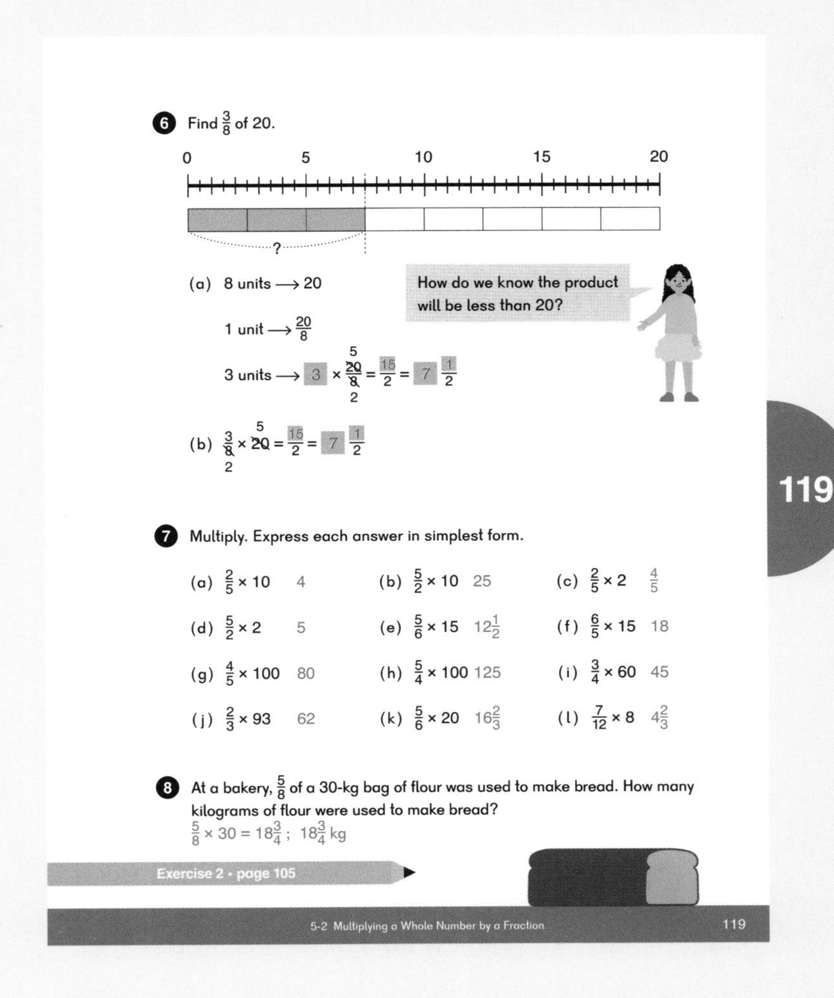

6 Find $\frac{3}{8}$ of 20.

(a) 8 units ⟶ 20

1 unit ⟶ $\frac{20}{8}$

3 units ⟶ $3 \times \frac{20}{8} = \frac{15}{2} = 7\frac{1}{2}$

(b) $\frac{3}{8} \times 20 = \frac{15}{2} = 7\frac{1}{2}$

7 Multiply. Express each answer in simplest form.

(a) $\frac{2}{5} \times 10$ 4 (b) $\frac{5}{2} \times 10$ 25 (c) $\frac{2}{5} \times 2$ $\frac{4}{5}$

(d) $\frac{5}{2} \times 2$ 5 (e) $\frac{5}{6} \times 15$ $12\frac{1}{2}$ (f) $\frac{6}{5} \times 15$ 18

(g) $\frac{4}{5} \times 100$ 80 (h) $\frac{5}{4} \times 100$ 125 (i) $\frac{3}{4} \times 60$ 45

(j) $\frac{2}{3} \times 93$ 62 (k) $\frac{5}{6} \times 20$ $16\frac{2}{3}$ (l) $\frac{7}{12} \times 8$ $4\frac{2}{3}$

8 At a bakery, $\frac{5}{8}$ of a 30-kg bag of flour was used to make bread. How many kilograms of flour were used to make bread?

$\frac{5}{8} \times 30 = 18\frac{3}{4}$; $18\frac{3}{4}$ kg

Exercise 2 • page 105

5-2 Multiplying a Whole Number by a Fraction 119

119

Exercise 2 • page 105

Objective

- Solve multi-step word problems involving fractions.

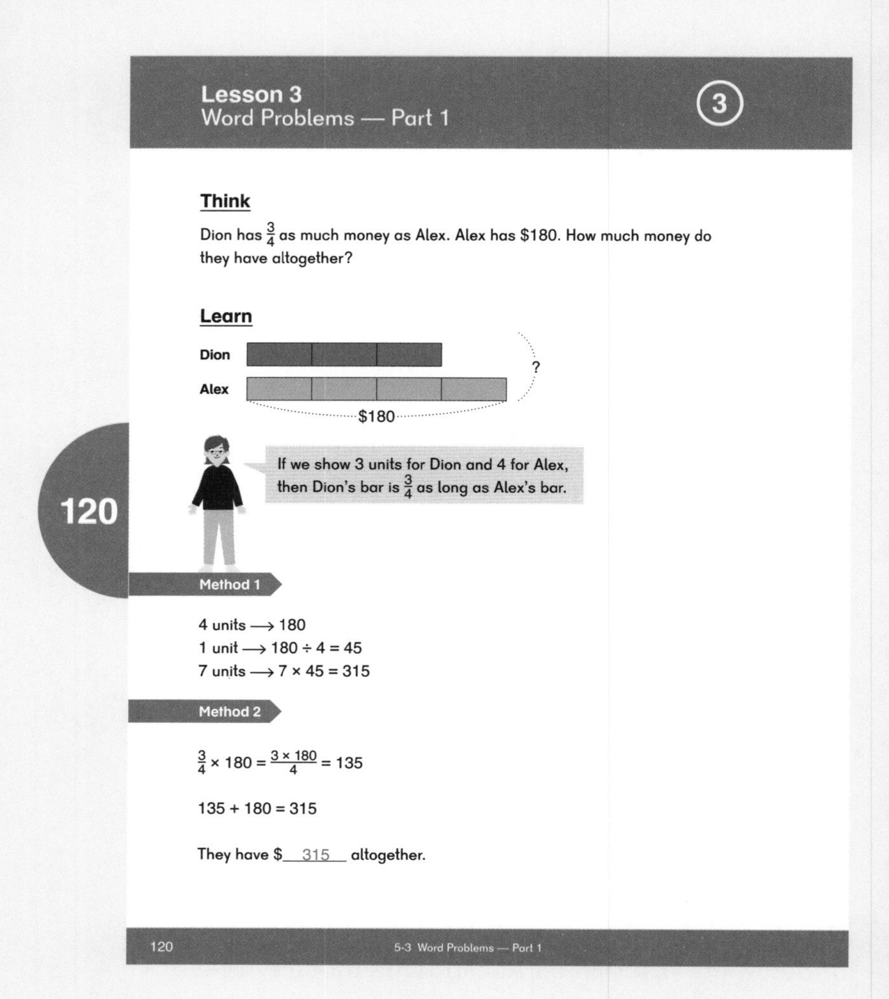

120

Lesson 3
Word Problems — Part 1

3

Think

Dion has $\frac{3}{4}$ as much money as Alex. Alex has \$180. How much money do they have altogether?

Learn

Method 1

4 units ⟶ 180
1 unit ⟶ 180 ÷ 4 = 45
7 units ⟶ 7 × 45 = 315

Method 2

$\frac{3}{4} \times 180 = \frac{3 \times 180}{4} = 135$

135 + 180 = 315

They have \$ 315 altogether.

120 5-3 Word Problems — Part 1

Think

Pose the **Think** problem and have students draw a model or write an equation to solve the problem.

If students finish quickly, challenge them to find other methods to solve the problem.

Compare and discuss student solutions.

Learn

Have students compare the two methods shown in **Learn** with their solutions from **Think**. Discuss the bar model.

Method 1

Students can use units. If they find the value of one unit, they multiply by 7 to find the value of all seven units, which is the amount of money Dion and Alex have in all. This can also be written with fractions:

1 unit ⟶ $\frac{180}{4}$
7 units ⟶ $7 \times \frac{180}{4}$

Method 2

When comparing the quantities, Alex's amount is the whole. We are comparing Dion's amount to Alex's amount. If Dion's bar represents $\frac{3}{4}$ the length of Alex's bar, then we can find Dion's amount of money by multiplying $\frac{3}{4} \times 180$.

To find the total amount, add Dion's and Alex's amounts together.

Do

❶–❻ Students should study the bar models in each problem and show the calculation steps in their solutions.

❶ Ask students how Dion and Mei are thinking about the problem:

- "Dion is finding the value of 1 part first. What fraction of the whole is this? What does this part represent?" ($\frac{1}{5}$, $\frac{1}{5}$ of 120)
- "How is Mei's computation or method different?" (Mei is finding the fraction that are adults, then simply multiplying that by the whole number.)

Students might also have solved this problem by:

$\frac{3}{5} \times 120 = 72$ (children)
$120 - 72 = 48$ (adults)

Ask students to compare this method with Mei's method.

❷ Ask students:

- "How many parts are in the whole?" (8)
- "Why isn't Alex thinking about finding the whole?" (He only needs to find the fraction of the money spent on the volleyball.)

Alternate solution:

5 units $\longrightarrow$ 60
1 unit $\longrightarrow \frac{1}{5} \times 60 = 12$
3 units $\longrightarrow 3 \times 12 = 36$

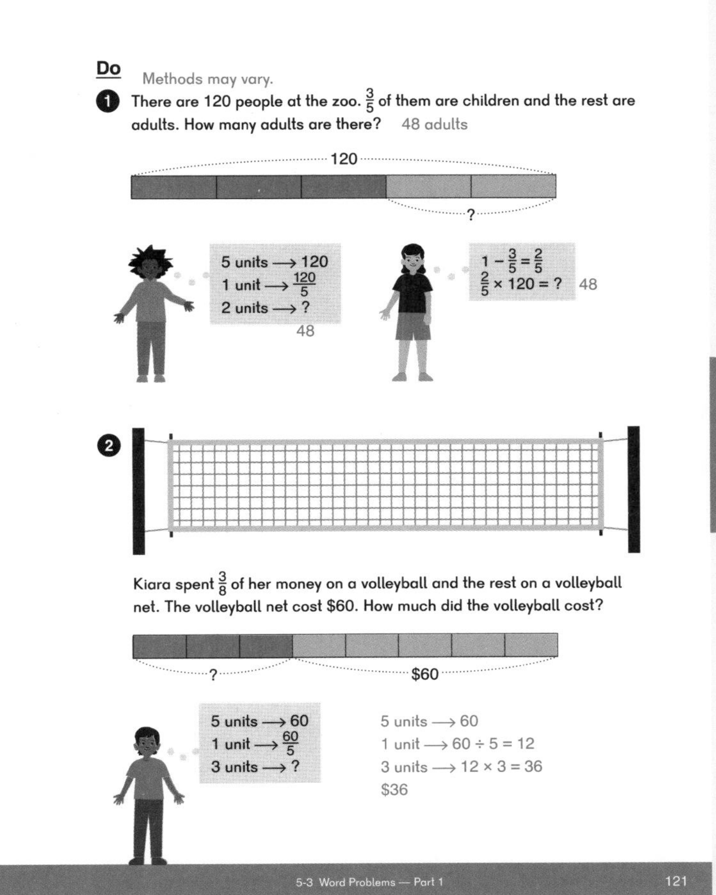

Do

Methods may vary.

❶ There are 120 people at the zoo. $\frac{3}{5}$ of them are children and the rest are adults. How many adults are there? 48 adults

❷ Kiara spent $\frac{3}{8}$ of her money on a volleyball and the rest on a volleyball net. The volleyball net cost \$60. How much did the volleyball cost?

3 – 4 As the models are all given, students should be able to work these problems independently.

3 Students may also find the value of 1 unit, then find the number of large-breed dogs and small-breed dogs, and then subtract from the whole:

Large-breed dogs ⟶ $4 \times 23 = 92$
Small-breed dogs ⟶ $7 \times 23 = 161$
Difference ⟶ $161 - 92 = 69$

This solution requires more steps and computations than the one given in the answer overlay.

Help students see that if they find the value of 1 unit, they can simply multiply by 3 to find the 3 units of the difference.

4 If we consider the number of students in the fencing club as 1 unit, then we can represent the number of students in the chess club with 2 units.

If the number of students in the fencing club is $\frac{1}{5}$ the number in the cooking club, then the cooking club must be 5 units.

There are 42 more students or 3 units more in the cooking club than the chess club, so the value of 3 units is 42 students. Once we know the value of 3 units, we can find the value of 1 unit and then 2 units, which is the number of students in the chess club.

122

3

There are 253 dogs at a dog show. There are $\frac{4}{7}$ as many large-breed dogs as small-breed dogs. How many more small-breed dogs are there than large-breed dogs?

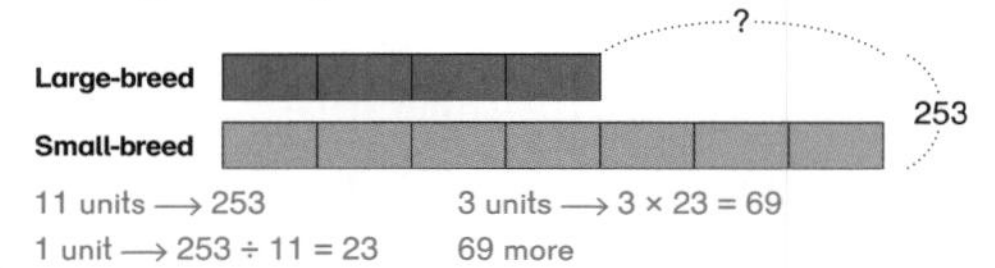

11 units ⟶ 253
1 unit ⟶ $253 \div 11 = 23$
3 units ⟶ $3 \times 23 = 69$
69 more

4 Twice as many students are in the chess club as in the fencing club. The number of students in the fencing club is $\frac{1}{5}$ the number of students in the cooking club. There are 42 more students in the cooking club than in the chess club. How many students are in the chess club?

3 units ⟶ 42
1 unit ⟶ $42 \div 3 = 14$
2 units ⟶ $2 \times 14 = 28$
28 students

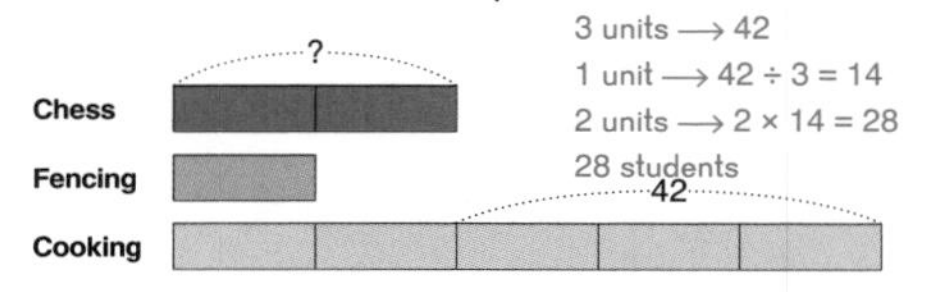

122 5-3 Word Problems — Part 1

❺ Since the problem states that $\frac{2}{5}$ of the apples in Crate A are equal to $\frac{1}{4}$ of the apples in Crate B, we know that one of the Crate B units is the same length as 2 Crate A units.

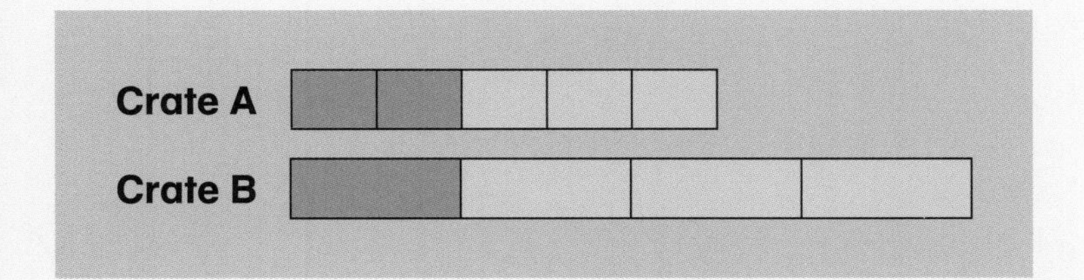

From the model in the textbook, we see that if we divide each Crate B unit in half, we have 13 equal-sized units.

13 units ⟶ 156
1 unit ⟶ 156 ÷ 13 = 12
Crate A: 5 units ⟶ 5 × 12 = 60
Crate B: 8 units ⟶ 8 × 12 = 96
Crate A: 60 apples
Crate B: 96 apples

❻ Since Aki and Cora have the same number of stickers in the end, the After bar model is shown first in the textbook. We can then work the problems backwards to find the number of stickers Cora had at first.

Before, Aki had $\frac{1}{3}$ more stickers. After, she has $\frac{2}{3}$ of the amount she started with. We can divide Aki's After bar in half to show 2 units, and then add a third unit that is the same length to show the Before amount.

Note that if students were drawing the bar model, they would not know if Cora's bar in the Before model was greater or less than Aki's bar in the Before model. They can estimate and modify when drawing the models themselves.

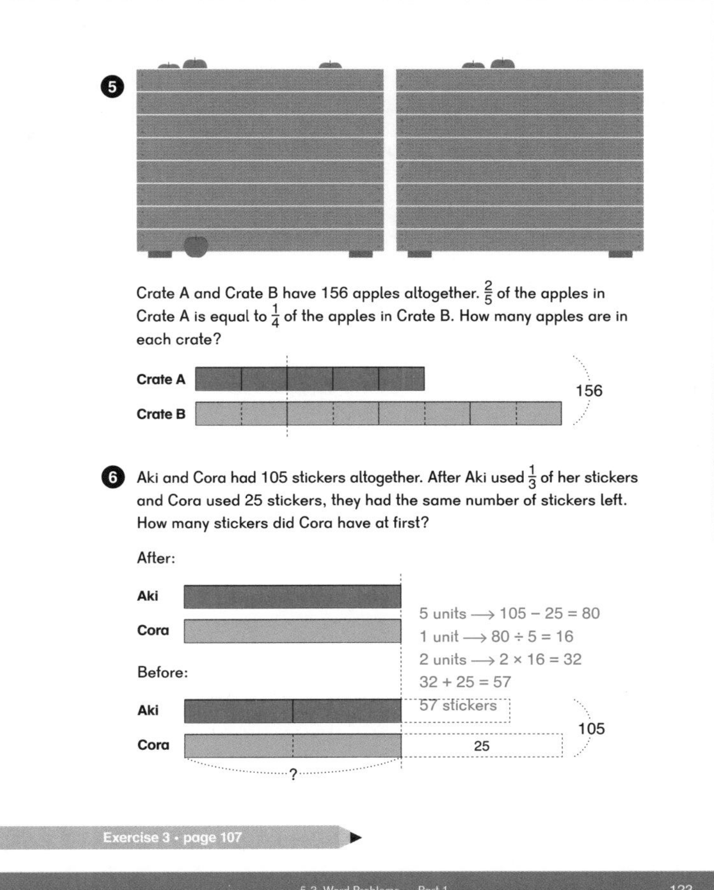

123

Exercise 3 • page 107

Objectives

- Practice multiplying fractions.
- Practice solving multi-step word problems.

After students complete the **Practice** in the textbook, have them continue to practice multiplying fractions by playing games from the chapter as needed.

❷—❿ Encourage students to draw bar models when needed. They should show the steps in their solutions.

Ask questions such as:

- "What do you need to find? What information is given in the problem?"
- "What type of model should we draw?"
- "Do the quantities change? What type of bar model could you use?"
- "What would the units represent?"

124

Lesson 4
Practice A

P ④

❶ Find the product. Express each answer in simplest form.

(a) $5 \times \frac{2}{3}$ $3\frac{1}{3}$

(b) $7 \times \frac{3}{5}$ $4\frac{1}{5}$

(c) $4 \times \frac{3}{8}$ $1\frac{1}{2}$

(d) $\frac{5}{7} \times 100$ $71\frac{3}{7}$

(e) $\frac{7}{9} \times 18$ 14

(f) $\frac{3}{4} \times 70$ $52\frac{1}{2}$

(g) $\frac{11}{12} \times 24$ 22

(h) $\frac{5}{14} \times 42$ 15

(i) $\frac{3}{4} \times 75$ $56\frac{1}{4}$

(j) $450 \times \frac{3}{5}$ 270

(k) $\frac{1}{3} + \frac{1}{4} \times 12$ $3\frac{1}{3}$

(l) $(\frac{1}{2} \times 23) + (\frac{1}{2} \times 17)$ 20

❷ There are 40 people at a concert recital. $\frac{3}{5}$ of them are adults and the rest are children. How many children are at the recital?
$\frac{2}{5} \times 40 = 16$
16 children

❸ Ximena makes \$320 a week working part time. Each week she saves $\frac{1}{4}$ of her money. How much money will she save in 4 weeks?
$\frac{1}{4} \times 4 \times 320 = 320$; \$320

❹ Fadiya spends $\frac{3}{7}$ of her monthly income on rent. Her rent is \$1,500 a month. What is her monthly income?
3 units ⟶ 1,500
1 unit ⟶ 1,500 ÷ 3 = 500
7 units ⟶ 7 × 500 = 3,500
\$3,500

❺ Oliver had \$250. He spent $\frac{3}{5}$ of it on a suit and \$75 on shoes. How much money does he have left?
$250 - (\frac{3}{5} \times 250 + 75) = 25$
\$25

124 5-4 Practice A

❺

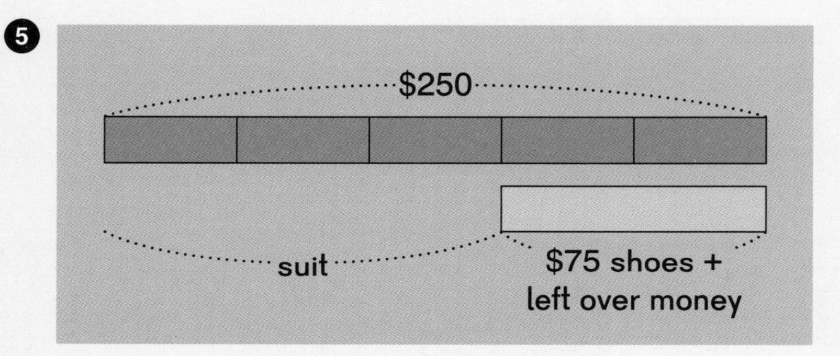

5 units ⟶ \$250
1 unit ⟶ $\frac{\$250}{5}$ = \$50
2 units ⟶ 2 × \$50 = \$100
Amount of money left: \$100 – \$75 = \$25

Alternative solution:

$(1 - \frac{3}{5}) \times \$250 = \$100$
\$100 – \$75 = \$25
\$25 left

8

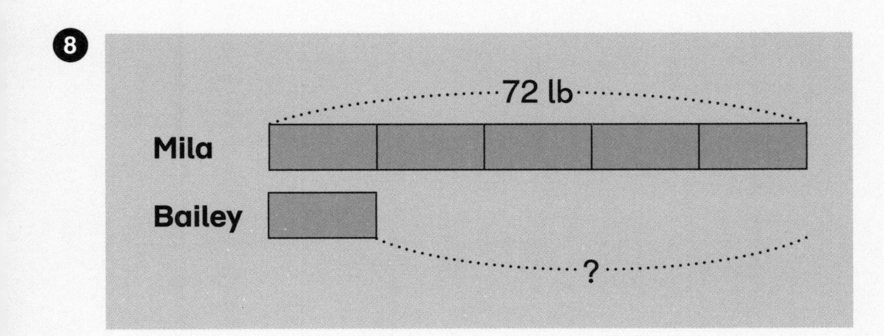

5 units $\longrightarrow$ 72 lb
1 unit $\longrightarrow \frac{72}{5}$ lb
4 units $\longrightarrow 4 \times \frac{72}{5}$ lb $= 57\frac{3}{5}$ lb more

9

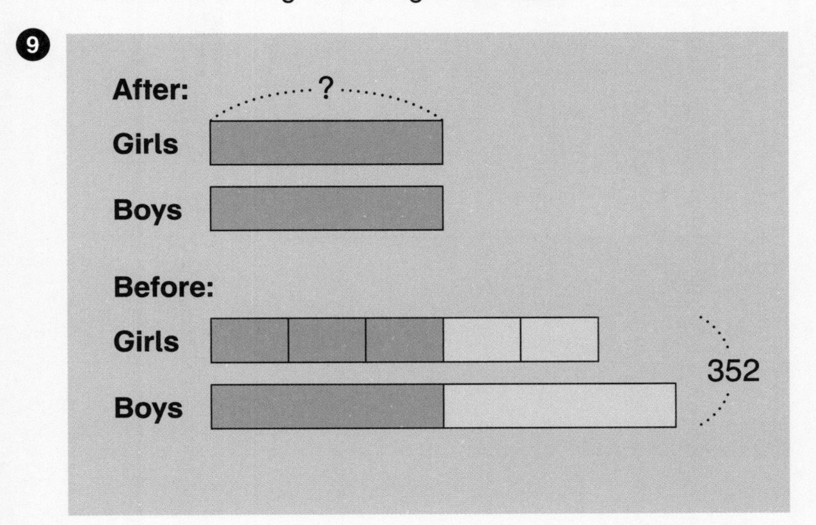

10

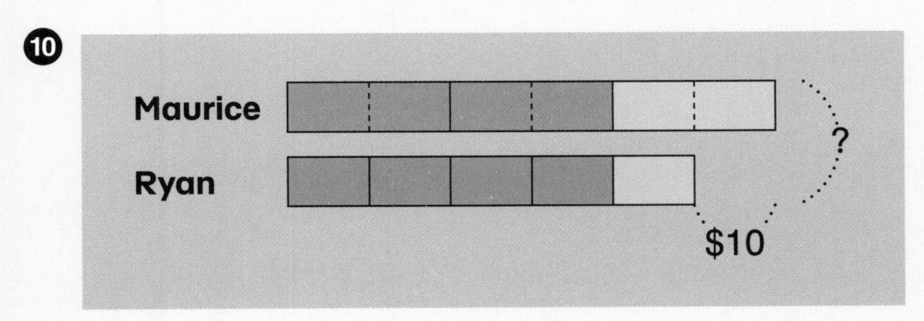

Exercise 4 • page 111

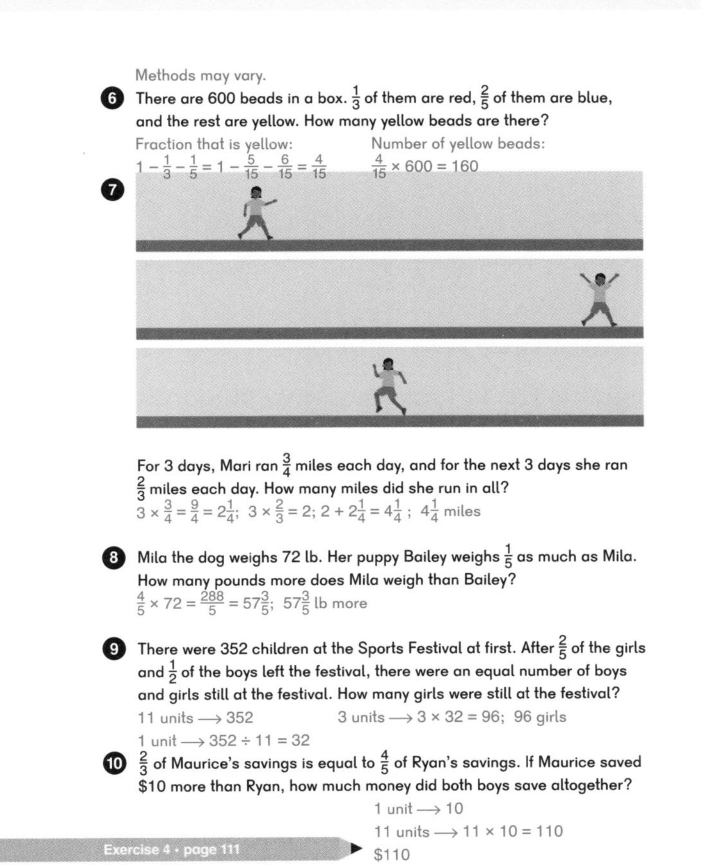

Methods may vary.

6 There are 600 beads in a box. $\frac{1}{3}$ of them are red, $\frac{2}{5}$ of them are blue, and the rest are yellow. How many yellow beads are there?

Fraction that is yellow: $1 - \frac{1}{3} - \frac{1}{5} = 1 - \frac{5}{15} - \frac{6}{15} = \frac{4}{15}$

Number of yellow beads: $\frac{4}{15} \times 600 = 160$

7 For 3 days, Mari ran $\frac{3}{4}$ miles each day, and for the next 3 days she ran $\frac{2}{3}$ miles each day. How many miles did she run in all?

$3 \times \frac{3}{4} = \frac{9}{4} = 2\frac{1}{4}$; $3 \times \frac{2}{3} = 2$; $2 + 2\frac{1}{4} = 4\frac{1}{4}$; $4\frac{1}{4}$ miles

8 Mila the dog weighs 72 lb. Her puppy Bailey weighs $\frac{1}{5}$ as much as Mila. How many pounds more does Mila weigh than Bailey?

$\frac{4}{5} \times 72 = \frac{288}{5} = 57\frac{3}{5}$; $57\frac{3}{5}$ lb more

9 There were 352 children at the Sports Festival at first. After $\frac{2}{5}$ of the girls and $\frac{1}{2}$ of the boys left the festival, there were an equal number of boys and girls still at the festival. How many girls were still at the festival?

11 units $\longrightarrow$ 352
1 unit $\longrightarrow 352 \div 11 = 32$
3 units $\longrightarrow 3 \times 32 = 96$; 96 girls

10 $\frac{2}{3}$ of Maurice's savings is equal to $\frac{4}{5}$ of Ryan's savings. If Maurice saved $10 more than Ryan, how much money did both boys save altogether?

1 unit $\longrightarrow$ 10
11 units $\longrightarrow 11 \times 10 = 110$
$110

Exercise 4 • page 111

5-4 Practice A 125

Objective

- Multiply a fraction by a unit fraction.

Lesson Materials

- Index cards

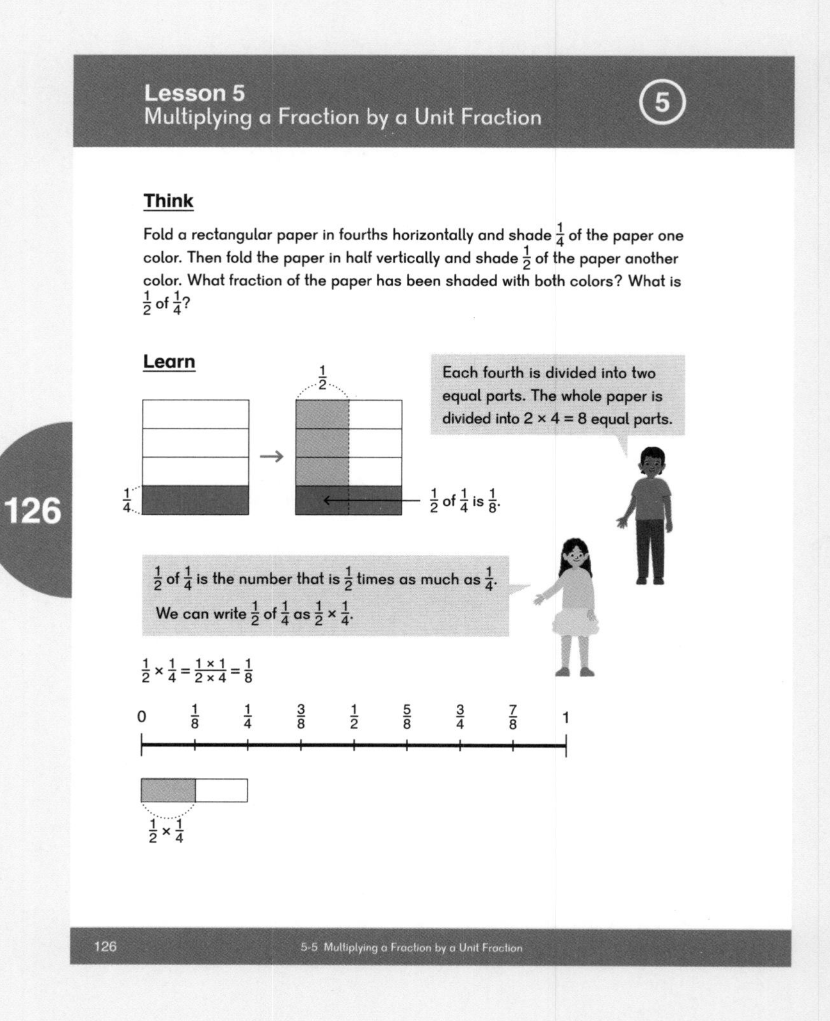

Think

Discuss the **Think** task and have students fold and shade the index cards as directed.

Ask students the **Think** questions.

Learn

Have students discuss the **Learn** examples. Their folded paper should look similar to the one in the textbook.

Ask students to count the total parts and the part that is shaded with both colors. They should see that 1 part of a total of 8 parts is double shaded.

They can label that double shaded part with the fraction of the whole, $\frac{1}{8}$.

Alex points out that when students folded the paper in fourths (by 4) and then in half (by 2), they made 2 × 4 parts which relates to the denominators of $\frac{1}{2}$ and $\frac{1}{4}$.

The total number of parts in the model is therefore the product of the denominators.

The total number of double shaded parts is the product of the numerators. We can multiply the numerators together to get the number of parts, and the denominators together to get the total parts.

Ask students about the number line model. They should see that half of $\frac{1}{4}$ is $\frac{1}{8}$.

Sofia ties the area model and the number line model together to point out that $\frac{1}{2}$ of $\frac{1}{4}$ is the same as multiplying $\frac{1}{2} \times \frac{1}{4}$.

Do

❶–❹ Discuss the problems and given models with students.

❶ Ask students how (a) and (b) are different. Students that need additional help can draw the two models and shade in $\frac{1}{3}$ and $\frac{1}{4}$ on each as they did in **Learn**.

In (a), first $\frac{1}{4}$ of the whole is shaded light green. Ask students, "How do we find $\frac{1}{3}$ of $\frac{1}{4}$?" $\frac{1}{3}$ of that $\frac{1}{4}$ is shaded with the dark green.

In (b), first $\frac{1}{3}$ is shaded light green. Ask students, "How do we find $\frac{1}{4}$ of $\frac{1}{3}$?" $\frac{1}{4}$ of $\frac{1}{3}$ is shaded with the dark green. Students should know that they get the same answer even if the order of the factors is switched.

❷ Encourage students to label the model if needed.

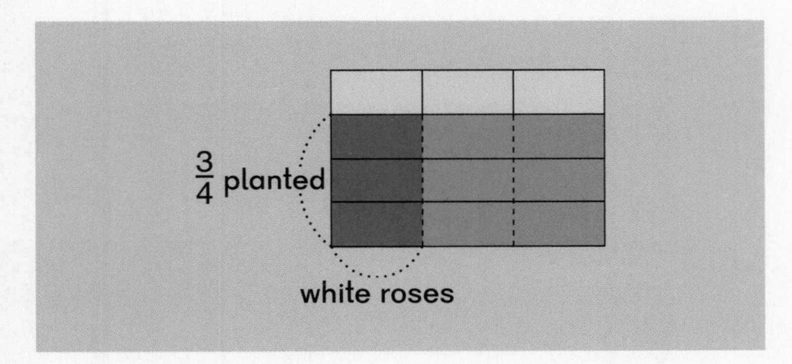

Mei points out that we find the same answer whether we show fourths using horizontal lines or vertical lines.

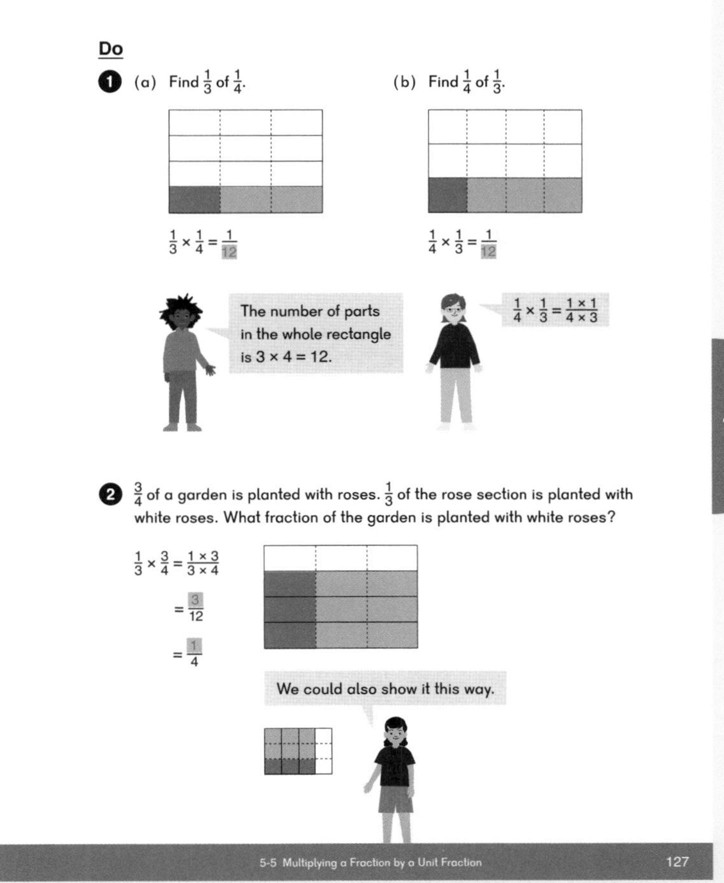

Do

❶ (a) Find $\frac{1}{3}$ of $\frac{1}{4}$.

$\frac{1}{3} \times \frac{1}{4} = \frac{1}{12}$

(b) Find $\frac{1}{4}$ of $\frac{1}{3}$.

$\frac{1}{4} \times \frac{1}{3} = \frac{1}{12}$

The number of parts in the whole rectangle is 3 × 4 = 12.

$\frac{1}{4} \times \frac{1}{3} = \frac{1 \times 1}{4 \times 3}$

❷ $\frac{3}{4}$ of a garden is planted with roses. $\frac{1}{3}$ of the rose section is planted with white roses. What fraction of the garden is planted with white roses?

$\frac{1}{3} \times \frac{3}{4} = \frac{1 \times 3}{3 \times 4}$

$= \frac{3}{12}$

$= \frac{1}{4}$

We could also show it this way.

5-5 Multiplying a Fraction by a Unit Fraction 127

127

3 In both examples, 1 whole is represented and the solid vertical lines indicate thirds.

Ask students to describe the relationship between problems (a) and (b). (We can use the answer from (a) to find the answer to (b) because $\frac{2}{3}$ is $2 \times \frac{1}{3}$.)

4 The bar model shows $\frac{3}{5}$, and the final product, $\frac{1}{6}$ of the $\frac{3}{5}$, is colored red.

5 Most students should be able to solve these problems without drawing number lines and bar models.

Activity

▲ I Have, Who Has?

Materials: I Have, Who Has? Unit Fractions (BLM)

Class play:

Pass out one card to each student. If there are extras, some students can have more than one card.

Encourage students to find the product for the expression on their card so that they are prepared to answer. Tell students that some of the products will need to be simplified.

The student with the Start card begins. They read their card: "I have $\frac{1}{4}$. Who has $\frac{1}{3} \times \frac{2}{5}$?" The player with the card $\frac{2}{15}$ reads their card: "I have $\frac{2}{15}$, who has (next expression)?"

Play continues until the game loops back to the original card.

Partner or small group play:

Have students work together to put the cards in order beginning with the Start card.

Start: I have $\frac{1}{4}$

Who has $\frac{1}{3} \times \frac{2}{5}$?

3 (a) Find $\frac{1}{2}$ of $\frac{1}{3}$.

$\frac{1}{2} \times \frac{1}{3} = \frac{1 \times 1}{2 \times 3} = \frac{1}{6}$

(b) Find $\frac{1}{2}$ of $\frac{2}{3}$.

$\frac{1}{2} \times \frac{2}{3} = \frac{1 \times 2}{2 \times 3} = \frac{2}{6} = \frac{1}{3}$

$\frac{1}{2}$ of 2 thirds = ? third

4 Alex had $\frac{3}{5}$ L of water. He drank $\frac{1}{6}$ of the water. How much water did he drink in liters?

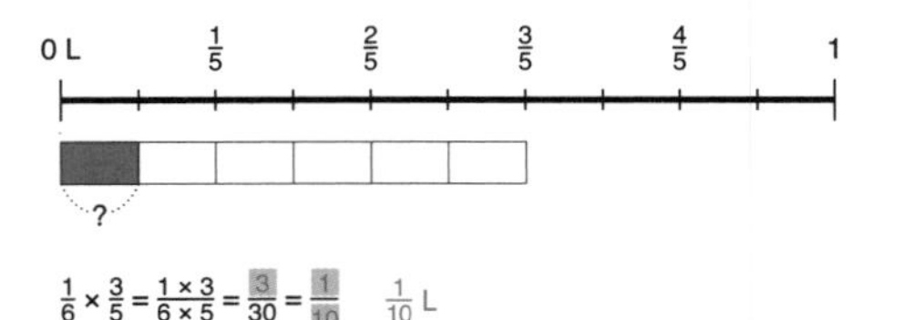

$\frac{1}{6} \times \frac{3}{5} = \frac{1 \times 3}{6 \times 5} = \frac{3}{30} = \frac{1}{10}$ $\frac{1}{10}$ L

5 Find the values. Express each answer in simplest form.

(a) $\frac{1}{2} \times \frac{1}{5}$ $\frac{1}{10}$ (b) $\frac{1}{2} \times \frac{4}{5}$ $\frac{2}{5}$ (c) $\frac{1}{6} \times \frac{1}{3}$ $\frac{1}{18}$

(d) $\frac{1}{6} \times \frac{2}{3}$ $\frac{1}{9}$ (e) $\frac{1}{3} \times \frac{1}{10}$ $\frac{1}{30}$ (f) $\frac{1}{3} \times \frac{9}{10}$ $\frac{3}{10}$

(g) $\frac{1}{4} \times \frac{4}{7}$ $\frac{1}{7}$ (h) $\frac{1}{5} \times \frac{5}{8}$ $\frac{1}{8}$ (i) $\frac{1}{3} \times \frac{5}{12}$ $\frac{5}{36}$

Exercise 5 • page 115

Exercise 5 • page 115

Lesson 6 Multiplying a Fraction by a Fraction — Part 1

Objective

- Multiply a fraction by a fraction.

Lesson Materials

- Index cards

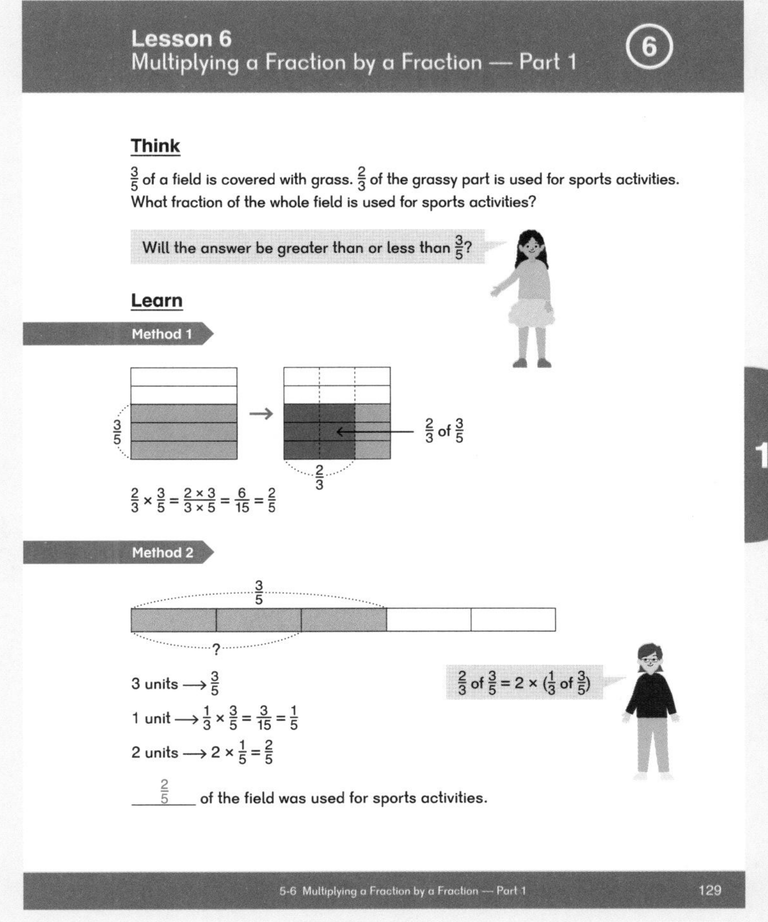

Lesson 6
Multiplying a Fraction by a Fraction — Part 1 6

Think

$\frac{3}{5}$ of a field is covered with grass. $\frac{2}{3}$ of the grassy part is used for sports activities. What fraction of the whole field is used for sports activities?

Will the answer be greater than or less than $\frac{3}{5}$?

Learn

Method 1

$\frac{3}{5}$ → $\frac{2}{3}$ of $\frac{3}{5}$, $\frac{2}{3}$

$\frac{2}{3} \times \frac{3}{5} = \frac{2 \times 3}{3 \times 5} = \frac{6}{15} = \frac{2}{5}$

Method 2

$\frac{3}{5}$?

3 units $\longrightarrow \frac{3}{5}$

1 unit $\longrightarrow \frac{1}{3} \times \frac{3}{5} = \frac{3}{15} = \frac{1}{5}$

2 units $\longrightarrow 2 \times \frac{1}{5} = \frac{2}{5}$

$\frac{2}{3}$ of $\frac{3}{5} = 2 \times (\frac{1}{3}$ of $\frac{3}{5})$

$\frac{2}{5}$ of the field was used for sports activities.

5-6 Multiplying a Fraction by a Fraction — Part 1 129

129

Think

Provide students with index cards and pose the **Think** problem.

Have students estimate as Sofia asks. Students should see that if they are multiplying $\frac{3}{5}$ by a proper fraction ($\frac{2}{3}$) then the product will be less than the number being multiplied ($\frac{3}{5}$).

Before calculating, have students either use the index cards or draw models similar to the ones covered in the previous lesson.

Discuss student solutions.

Learn

Have students discuss the **Learn** examples and compare their methods from **Think** with the ones in the textbook.

Method 1

Ask students what the first model shows.

There are 3 × 5 total parts. The total number of parts in the model is therefore the product of the denominators.

The total number of double shaded parts, 2 × 3, is the product of the numerators. Just as with unit fractions, we can multiply the numerators together to get the number of parts, and the denominators together to get the total parts.

Method 2

Ask students:

- “What does the bar represent?” (1 whole)
- “What does the yellow part of the bar represent?” ($\frac{3}{5}$ of the field)
- “What fractions does each unit represent?” ($\frac{1}{5}$)
- “How do we find $\frac{2}{3}$ of $\frac{3}{5}$?” (Count 2 of the 3 yellow units.)

In both methods, students should see that we can multiply numerators and denominators to find the final product.

Do

❶–❹ Discuss the problems and given models with students.

Ask students:

- "How many total parts are there in the model?"
- "How many parts are the darker shade?"

❸ Two ways of solving the problem are shown, one with an area model and one with a bar model.

In (b), students can relate using units to the expressions with fractions.

In this model, the whole bar is 1. We can think of Dion's equation as 3 copies of $\frac{1}{4}$ of $\frac{4}{5}$.

❹ In this bar model, the whole is $\frac{3}{5}$. Have students discuss Emma's question. They should know that $\frac{3}{2}$ is an improper fraction. The product will be greater than 1 times as many, or greater than $\frac{3}{5}$.

Mei uses steps similar to Dion's in ❸:

$3 \times (\frac{1}{2} \times \frac{3}{5}) = 3 \times \frac{3}{10} = \frac{9}{10}$

❺ Most students should be able to solve these problems without drawing any models.

❻ Sample model:

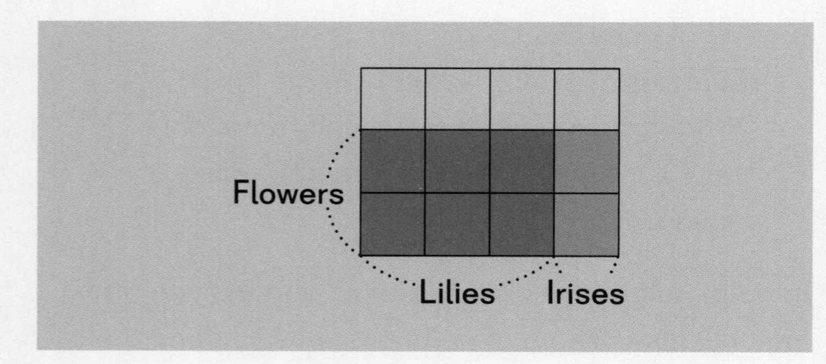

Exercise 6 • page 117

130

Do

❶ Find $\frac{2}{5}$ of $\frac{2}{3}$.

$\frac{2}{5} \times \frac{2}{3} = \frac{2 \times 2}{5 \times 3}$

$= \frac{4}{15}$

❷ Find $\frac{3}{5}$ of $\frac{5}{6}$.

$\frac{3}{5} \times \frac{5}{6} = \frac{3 \times 5}{5 \times 6}$

$= \frac{15}{30}$

$= \frac{1}{2}$

❸ Find the value of $\frac{3}{4} \times \frac{4}{5}$.

(a) $\frac{3}{4} \times \frac{4}{5} = \frac{3 \times 4}{4 \times 5}$

$= \frac{12}{20}$

$= \frac{3}{5}$

(b) 4 units $\longrightarrow \frac{4}{5}$

1 unit $\longrightarrow \frac{1}{4} \times \frac{4}{5} = \frac{4}{20} = \frac{1}{5}$

3 units $\longrightarrow 3 \times \frac{1}{5} = \frac{3}{5}$

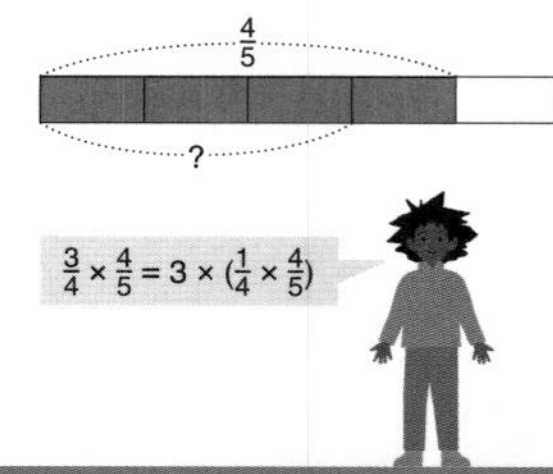

❹ Find the value of $\frac{3}{2} \times \frac{3}{5}$.

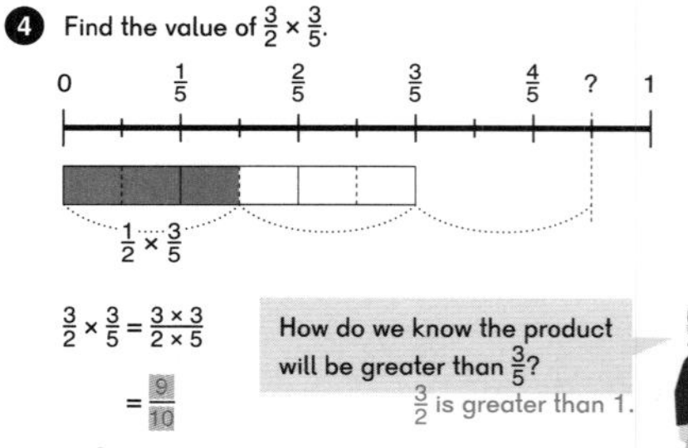

$\frac{3}{2} \times \frac{3}{5} = \frac{3 \times 3}{2 \times 5}$

$= \frac{9}{10}$

How do we know the product will be greater than $\frac{3}{5}$?

$\frac{3}{2}$ is greater than 1.

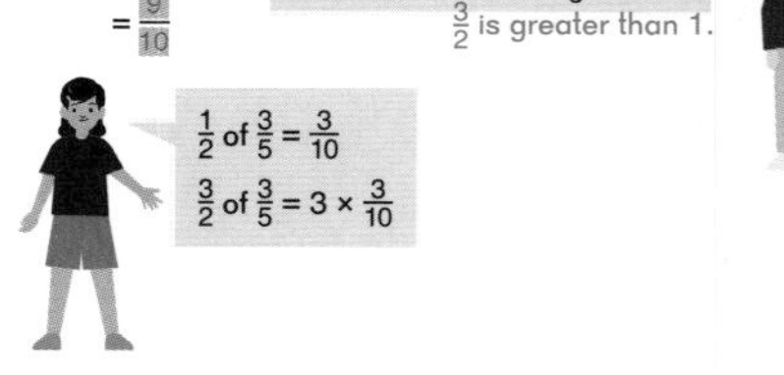

❺ Find the values. Express each answer in simplest form.

(a) $\frac{1}{3} \times \frac{1}{7}$ $\frac{1}{21}$ (b) $\frac{1}{2} \times \frac{5}{6}$ $\frac{5}{12}$ (c) $\frac{4}{5} \times \frac{5}{6}$ $\frac{2}{3}$

(d) $\frac{4}{9} \times \frac{2}{3}$ $\frac{8}{27}$ (e) $\frac{4}{3} \times \frac{4}{5}$ $1\frac{1}{15}$ (f) $\frac{3}{2} \times \frac{7}{5}$ $2\frac{1}{10}$

❻ $\frac{2}{3}$ of a garden is planted with flowers. $\frac{3}{4}$ of the flower section is planted with lilies and the rest is planted with irises.

(a) What fraction of the garden is planted with lilies?
$\frac{3}{4} \times \frac{2}{3} = \frac{1}{2}$; $\frac{1}{2}$ of the garden

(b) What fraction of the garden is planted with irises?
$(1 - \frac{3}{4}) \times \frac{2}{3} = \frac{1}{4} \times \frac{2}{3} = \frac{1}{6}$; $\frac{1}{6}$ of the garden

Exercise 6 • page 117

Objective

- Multiply a fraction by a fraction, by simplifying the calculation first.

Lesson Materials

- Strips of paper about 1 ft long

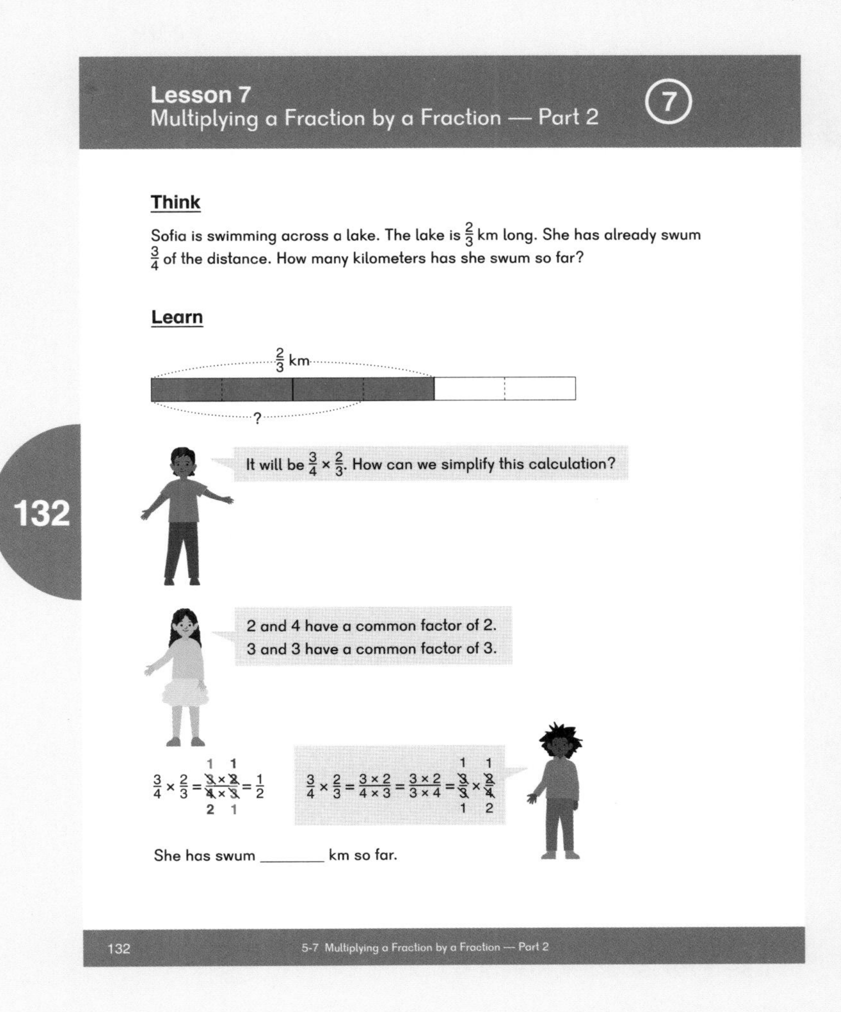

Lesson 7
Multiplying a Fraction by a Fraction — Part 2 (7)

Think

Sofia is swimming across a lake. The lake is $\frac{2}{3}$ km long. She has already swum $\frac{3}{4}$ of the distance. How many kilometers has she swum so far?

Learn

$\frac{2}{3}$ km

?

It will be $\frac{3}{4} \times \frac{2}{3}$. How can we simplify this calculation?

2 and 4 have a common factor of 2.
3 and 3 have a common factor of 3.

$\frac{3}{4} \times \frac{2}{3} = \frac{\cancel{3}^{1} \times \cancel{2}^{1}}{\cancel{4}_{2} \times \cancel{3}_{1}} = \frac{1}{2}$

$\frac{3}{4} \times \frac{2}{3} = \frac{3 \times 2}{4 \times 3} = \frac{3 \times 2}{3 \times 4} = \frac{\cancel{3}^{1}}{\cancel{3}_{1}} \times \frac{\cancel{2}^{1}}{\cancel{4}_{2}}$

She has swum _______ km so far.

132 5-7 Multiplying a Fraction by a Fraction — Part 2

132

Think

Provide students with strips of paper and pose the **Think** problem. Have them use the paper to show how to solve the problem.

Learn

Have students compare their paper strips or models with the bar model shown in **Learn**.

Alex challenges students to simplify the calculation before solving.

Dion knows that he can multiply in any order.
He can rewrite $\frac{3}{4} \times \frac{2}{3}$ as $\frac{3}{3} \times \frac{2}{4}$ and simplify to $1 \times \frac{1}{2}$.

Do

❶–❹ Discuss the problems and given models with students. The friends help by listing the common factors.

If students struggle, show them the following steps.

❷ $\frac{4 \times 5}{5 \times 6} = \frac{5 \times 4}{5 \times 6} = 1 \times \frac{4}{6} = \frac{4}{6} = \frac{2}{3}$

❸ $\frac{8 \times 3}{9 \times 10} = \frac{3 \times 8}{9 \times 10} = \frac{3}{9} \times \frac{8}{10} = \frac{1}{3} \times \frac{4}{5} = \frac{4}{15}$

❹ $\frac{5 \times 9}{12 \times 10} = \frac{9 \times 5}{12 \times 10} = \frac{9}{12} \times \frac{5}{10} = \frac{3}{4} \times \frac{1}{2} = \frac{3}{8}$

❺–❼ Students should be able to work these problems independently.

❼ Sample solutions:

$\frac{9}{10}$ of the kids in the class wear glasses. $\frac{2}{3}$ of the kids wearing glasses are boys. What fraction of the students in the class are boys that wear glasses?

$\frac{9}{10}$ of the playground is grass. $\frac{2}{3}$ of the grass is used for soccer fields. What fraction of the playground is used for soccer fields?

The track is $\frac{9}{10}$ of a mile long. I walked $\frac{2}{3}$ of the way around the track. How far have I already walked?

Exercise 7 • page 120

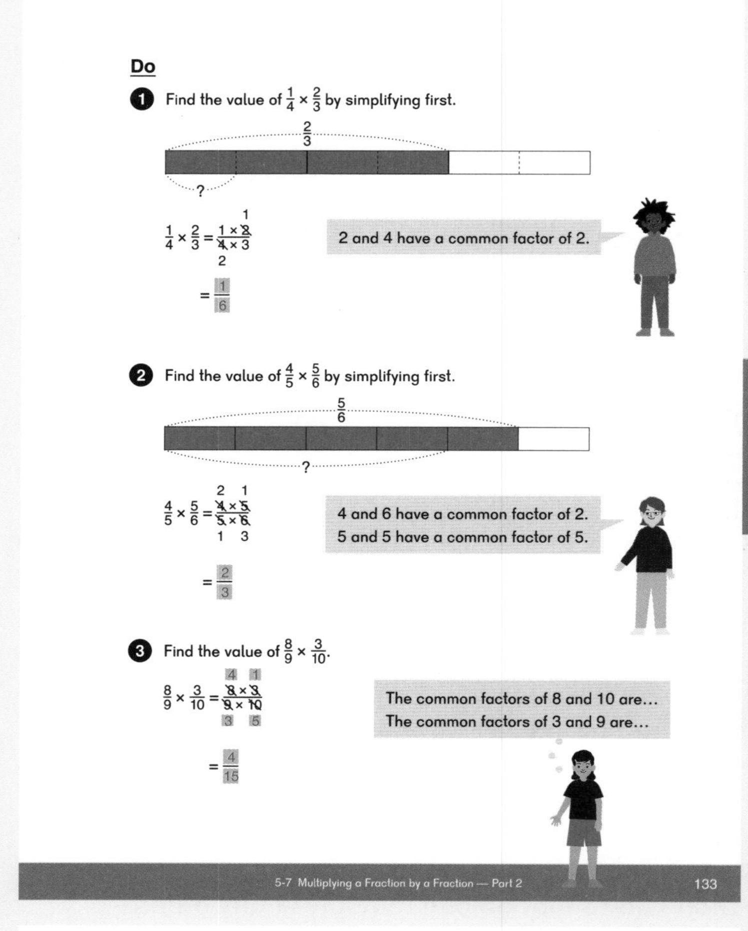

Do

❶ Find the value of $\frac{1}{4} \times \frac{2}{3}$ by simplifying first.

$\frac{1}{4} \times \frac{2}{3} = \frac{1 \times \cancel{2}^{1}}{\cancel{4}_{2} \times 3} = \frac{1}{6}$

❷ Find the value of $\frac{4}{5} \times \frac{5}{6}$ by simplifying first.

$\frac{4}{5} \times \frac{5}{6} = \frac{\cancel{4}^{2} \times \cancel{5}^{1}}{\cancel{5}_{1} \times \cancel{6}_{3}} = \frac{2}{3}$

❸ Find the value of $\frac{8}{9} \times \frac{3}{10}$.

$\frac{8}{9} \times \frac{3}{10} = \frac{\cancel{8}^{4} \times \cancel{3}^{1}}{\cancel{9}_{3} \times \cancel{10}_{5}} = \frac{4}{15}$

❹ Find the value of $\frac{5}{12} \times \frac{9}{10}$.

$\frac{\cancel{5}^{1}}{\cancel{12}_{4}} \times \frac{\cancel{9}^{3}}{\cancel{10}_{2}} = \frac{3}{8}$

❺ Find the value by simplifying first.

(a) $\frac{1}{4} \times \frac{6}{7}$ $\frac{3}{14}$

(b) $\frac{4}{9} \times \frac{1}{12}$ $\frac{1}{27}$

(c) $\frac{3}{15} \times \frac{5}{8}$ $\frac{1}{8}$

(d) $\frac{4}{9} \times \frac{3}{8}$ $\frac{1}{6}$

(e) $\frac{3}{2} \times \frac{4}{9}$ $\frac{2}{3}$

(f) $\frac{5}{6} \times \frac{4}{15}$ $\frac{2}{9}$

(g) $\frac{9}{10} \times \frac{10}{9}$ 1

(h) $\frac{15}{4} \times \frac{8}{3}$ 10

❻ Sharif ran $\frac{6}{10}$ km. Tyler ran $\frac{5}{4}$ as far as Sharif did. How many kilometers did Tyler run?

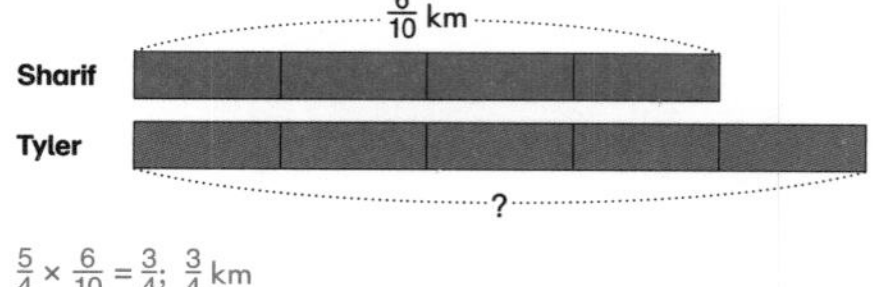

$\frac{5}{4} \times \frac{6}{10} = \frac{3}{4}$; $\frac{3}{4}$ km

❼ Write a word problem for $\frac{2}{3} \times \frac{9}{10}$.
Answers will vary.

Exercise 7 • page 120

Objective

- Multiply mixed numbers.

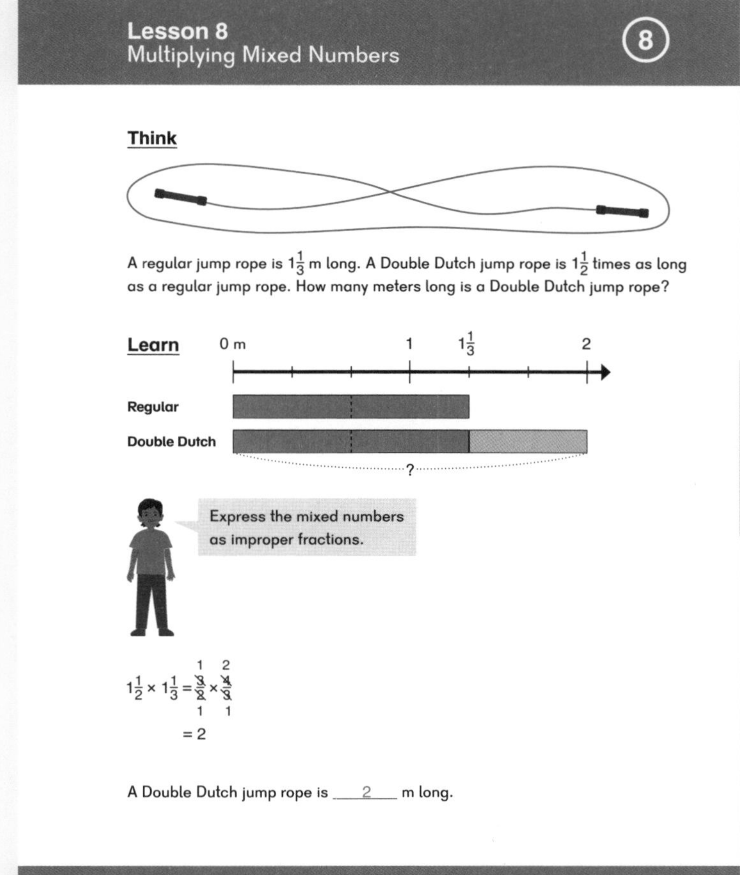

Think

Pose the **Think** problem and ask students to draw bar models to help them solve the problem.

Ask students:

- "How is this problem different from the ones in the previous lesson?" (It has mixed numbers.)
- "What have you already learned to multiply?" (Fractions)
- "Do you think the product will be greater or less than $1\frac{1}{3}$? Why?" (It will be greater than $1\frac{1}{3}$ because we are multiplying $1\frac{1}{3}$ by a number greater than 1.)

Compare and discuss student solutions.

Learn

Have students compare their models with the bar model shown in **Learn**.

Discuss the model and number line.

We could also find the length of the Double Dutch jump rope using units. In the method below, students should see they need to find 3 half-units which are each $\frac{2}{3}$. They can multiply 3 by $\frac{2}{3}$.

1 unit $\longrightarrow 1\frac{1}{3} = \frac{4}{3}$ m

$\frac{1}{2}$ unit $\longrightarrow \frac{1}{2} \times \frac{4}{3} = \frac{2}{3}$ m

$1\frac{1}{2}$ units $\longrightarrow 3 \times \frac{2}{3} = \frac{6}{3}$ or 2 m

At this point, most students should be simplifying the calculation as shown in **Learn**.

Do

❶–❹ For each question, discuss the calculations shown to find the product.

❶ Since $1\frac{1}{2} = 1 + \frac{1}{2}$, students may also see $3 \times 1 + 3 \times \frac{1}{2} = 3 + \frac{3}{2} = 4\frac{1}{2}$.

❷ Ask students:

- "What does the bar represent?" ($1\frac{1}{2}$)
- "How many parts is it divided into?" (3)
- "What is the value of each unit?" ($\frac{1}{2}$)

The bar model shows that $\frac{1}{3}$ of the bar lines up with $\frac{1}{2}$ on the number line, which is the same as the answer obtained from the calculation.

136

Do

❶ Find the value of $3 \times 1\frac{1}{2}$.

$3 \times 1\frac{1}{2} = 3 \times \frac{3}{2}$

$= \frac{3 \times 3}{2}$

$= \frac{9}{2}$

$= 4\frac{1}{2}$

❷ Find the value of $\frac{1}{3} \times 1\frac{1}{2}$. Express the answer in simplest form.

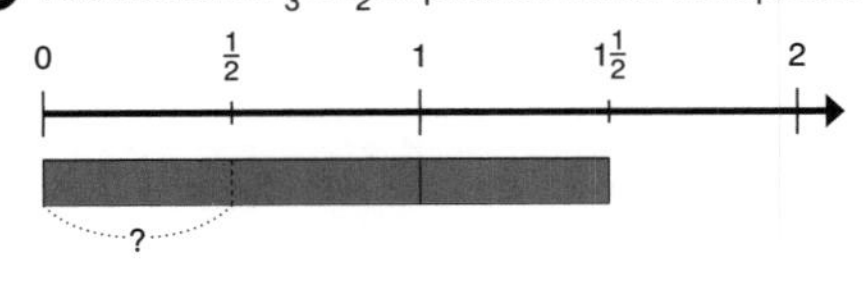

$\frac{1}{3} \times 1\frac{1}{2} = \frac{1}{3} \times \frac{3}{2}$

$= \frac{1}{2}$

❹ Similar to the **Think** problem, students should see that both mixed numbers will need to be expressed as improper fractions before multiplying.

❺ Have students share their methods for solving some of the problems.

Activity

▲ Greatest Product

Materials: Number Cards (BLM) 1–9

Deal each player 5 number cards. Players arrange their cards into a mixed number and a fraction and then multiply the numbers.

The player with the greatest product gets a point. The first player to 5 points is the winner.

Example:

$8\frac{4}{5} \times \frac{1}{6} = 1\frac{7}{15}$

Exercise 8 • page 123

137

❸ Find the value of $1\frac{1}{6} \times \frac{3}{5}$. Express the answer in simplest form.

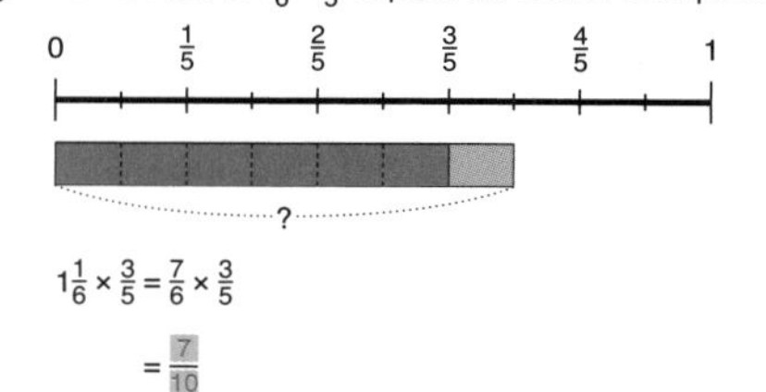

$1\frac{1}{6} \times \frac{3}{5} = \frac{7}{6} \times \frac{3}{5}$

$= \frac{7}{10}$

❹ Find the product of $1\frac{3}{4}$ and $2\frac{1}{3}$.

$1\frac{3}{4} \times 2\frac{1}{3} = \frac{7}{4} \times \frac{7}{3} = \frac{49}{12} = 4\frac{1}{12}$

❺ Find the values. Express each answer in simplest form.

(a) $7 \times 2\frac{5}{8}$ $18\frac{3}{8}$

(b) $5\frac{1}{4} \times 6$ $31\frac{1}{2}$

(c) $\frac{3}{5} \times 1\frac{1}{9}$ $\frac{2}{3}$

(d) $4\frac{2}{3} \times \frac{5}{7}$ $3\frac{1}{3}$

(e) $1\frac{2}{5} \times \frac{7}{8}$ $1\frac{9}{40}$

(f) $2\frac{1}{4} \times 1\frac{3}{5}$ $3\frac{3}{5}$

❻ The students in Class 5A ate $3\frac{1}{2}$ pizzas. The students in Class 5B ate $\frac{3}{4}$ as much pizza as Class 5A. How many pizzas did Class 5B eat?
$\frac{3}{4} \times 3\frac{1}{2} = 2\frac{5}{8}$; $2\frac{5}{8}$ pizzas

❼ Write a word problem for $3\frac{2}{3} \times \frac{3}{4}$.
Answers will vary.

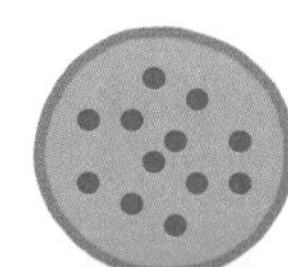

Exercise 8 • page 123

Lesson 9 Word Problems — Part 2

Objective

- Solve multi-step word problems involving fraction of a remainder.

Think

Pose the **Think** problem and have students draw a model and/or write equations to solve the problem. Discuss student solutions.

Learn

Discuss the bar model.

Ask students:

- "What does the top bar represent?" (The whole, or the total amount of money she had, which is \$300.)
- "Why is it divided into fifths?" (To show the $\frac{2}{5}$ spent on shoes.)
- "Why is the amount remaining after Sofia buys soccer shoes redrawn as a new bar below?" (It makes it easier to show the remainder divided into fourths.)

Have students compare the methods shown in **Learn** with their solutions from **Think**. Discuss the different methods.

In addition to the four methods shown, students may also have solved the problem using units:

5 larger units ⟶ 300
1 larger unit ⟶ 300 ÷ 5 = 60
3 larger units ⟶ 3 × 60 = 180
4 smaller units ⟶ 180
1 smaller unit ⟶ 180 ÷ 4 = 45
3 smaller units ⟶ 3 × 45 (or 180 – 45) = 135

This is similar to Method 3, but shows intermediate steps and uses division instead of multiplication of a fraction by a whole number.

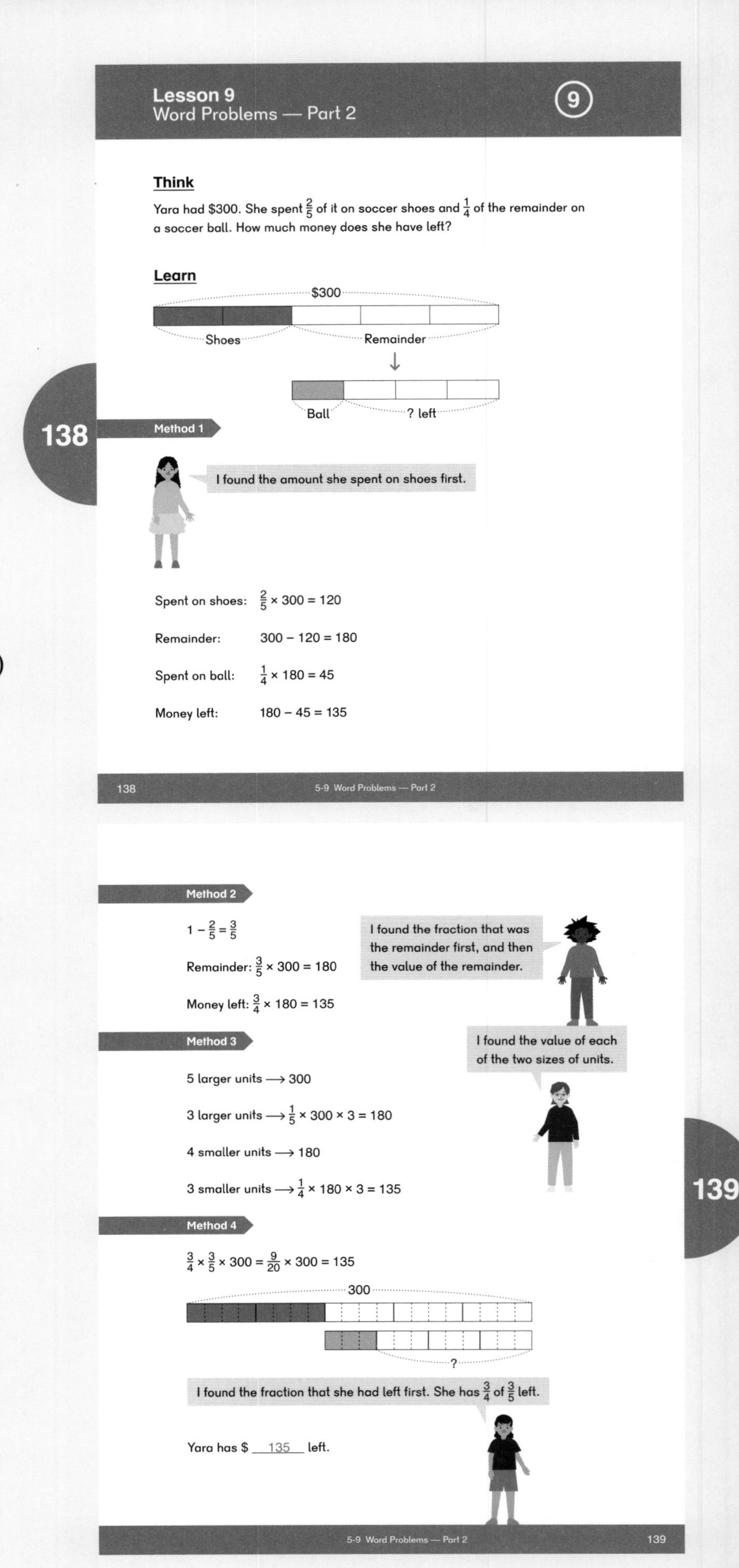

138

Lesson 9
Word Problems — Part 2 (9)

Think

Yara had \$300. She spent $\frac{2}{5}$ of it on soccer shoes and $\frac{1}{4}$ of the remainder on a soccer ball. How much money does she have left?

Learn

Method 1

Spent on shoes: $\frac{2}{5} \times 300 = 120$

Remainder: $300 - 120 = 180$

Spent on ball: $\frac{1}{4} \times 180 = 45$

Money left: $180 - 45 = 135$

138 5-9 Word Problems — Part 2

Method 2

$1 - \frac{2}{5} = \frac{3}{5}$

Remainder: $\frac{3}{5} \times 300 = 180$

Money left: $\frac{3}{4} \times 180 = 135$

Method 3

5 larger units ⟶ 300

3 larger units ⟶ $\frac{1}{5} \times 300 \times 3 = 180$

4 smaller units ⟶ 180

3 smaller units ⟶ $\frac{1}{4} \times 180 \times 3 = 135$

139

Method 4

$\frac{3}{4} \times \frac{3}{5} \times 300 = \frac{9}{20} \times 300 = 135$

Yara has \$ 135 left.

5-9 Word Problems — Part 2 139

Do

❶–❹ As the models are given, students should be able to work these problems independently. Any method from the **Learn** is an acceptable solution. The answer overlay shows one solution for each problem.

❶–❷ The total amounts in each problem are given. Students can calculate as in **Learn**.

❸ We are given the final amount and need to work backwards to find the money Asimah had at first.

140

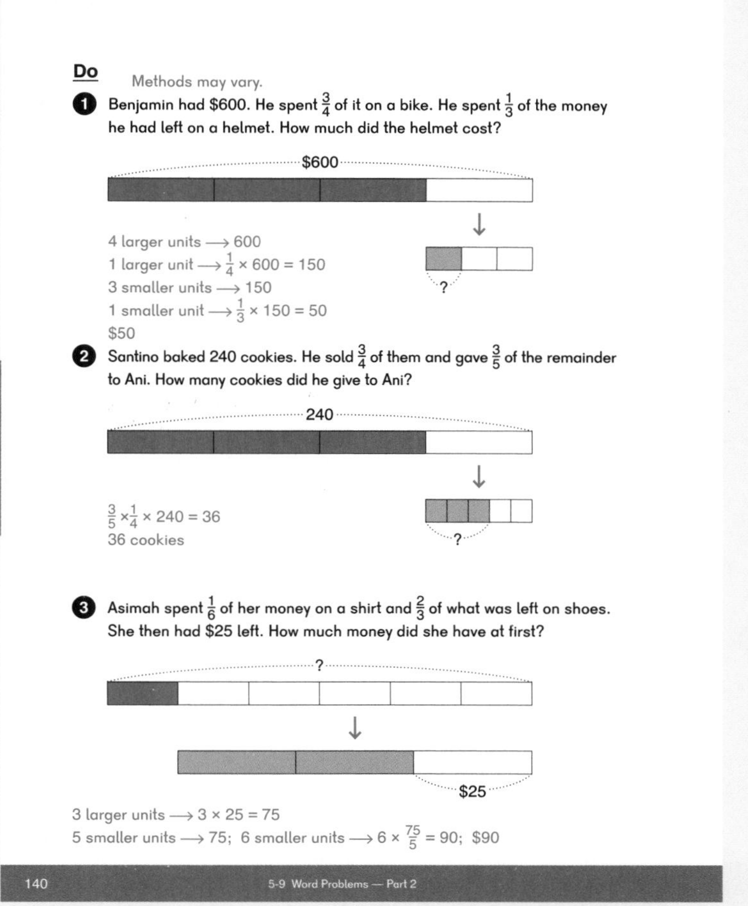

Do Methods may vary.

❶ Benjamin had \$600. He spent $\frac{3}{4}$ of it on a bike. He spent $\frac{1}{3}$ of the money he had left on a helmet. How much did the helmet cost?

4 larger units ⟶ 600
1 larger unit ⟶ $\frac{1}{4} \times 600 = 150$
3 smaller units ⟶ 150
1 smaller unit ⟶ $\frac{1}{3} \times 150 = 50$
\$50

❷ Santino baked 240 cookies. He sold $\frac{3}{4}$ of them and gave $\frac{3}{5}$ of the remainder to Ani. How many cookies did he give to Ani?

$\frac{3}{5} \times \frac{1}{4} \times 240 = 36$
36 cookies

❸ Asimah spent $\frac{1}{6}$ of her money on a shirt and $\frac{2}{3}$ of what was left on shoes. She then had \$25 left. How much money did she have at first?

3 larger units ⟶ $3 \times 25 = 75$
5 smaller units ⟶ 75; 6 smaller units ⟶ $6 \times \frac{75}{5} = 90$; \$90

❹ Questions to ask students, as needed:

- "What do the red units in the first bar represent?" ($\frac{3}{5}$ of Sofia's stickers.)
- "Why is one of the red units divided in half?" (Sofia gives half of the $\frac{3}{5}$ to Dion. That is $1\frac{1}{2}$ red units.)
- "What does the second bar represent?" (Dion's stickers.)
- "Why is the second bar divided into 3 units?" (Dion gives Emma $\frac{1}{3}$ of his stickers and has 48 left.)

❺–❻ Students should draw bar models to help them see the steps to solve each problem if needed.

❺

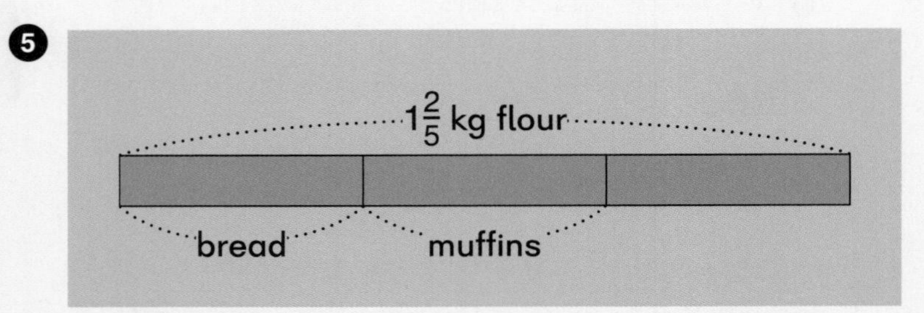

❻

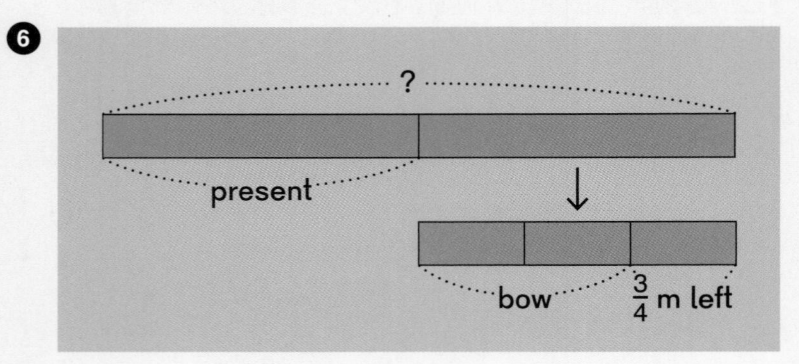

Exercise 9 • page 126

❹ Sofia had some stickers. She used $\frac{2}{5}$ of them and gave $\frac{1}{2}$ of the remainder to Dion. Then, Dion gave $\frac{1}{3}$ of his stickers to Emma. Now Dion has 48 stickers left. How many stickers did Sofia have at first?

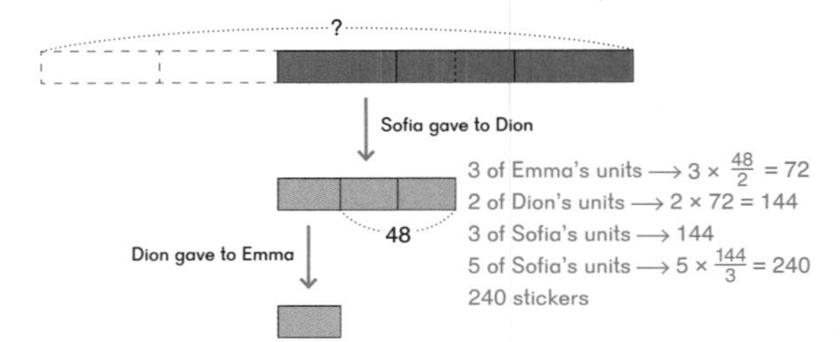

❺

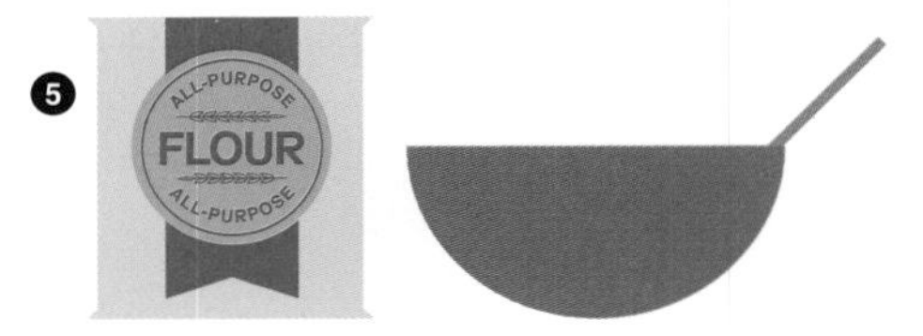

Jeremy had $1\frac{2}{5}$ kg of flour. He used $\frac{1}{3}$ of the flour to make bread and $\frac{1}{2}$ of the remaining flour to make muffins. How much flour did he use to make muffins? 1 unit ⟶ $\frac{1}{3} \times 1\frac{2}{5} = \frac{7}{15}$

$\frac{7}{15}$ kg

❻ Misha used $\frac{1}{2}$ of a roll of ribbon to wrap a present and $\frac{2}{3}$ of the rest of the roll to make a bow. If she had $\frac{3}{4}$ m of ribbon left, how long was the ribbon to start with?

3 smaller units ⟶ $3 \times \frac{3}{4} = \frac{9}{4}$

1 larger unit ⟶ $\frac{9}{4}$

2 larger units ⟶ $2 \times \frac{9}{4} = \frac{9}{2} = 4\frac{1}{2}$

$4\frac{1}{2}$ m

Exercise 9 • page 126

5-9 Word Problems — Part 2 141

141

Objectives

- Multiply two fractions to get a product of 1.
- Find the reciprocal of a fraction, a mixed number, or a whole number.

Lesson Materials

- Strips of paper about 1 ft long, 2 per student or pair of students

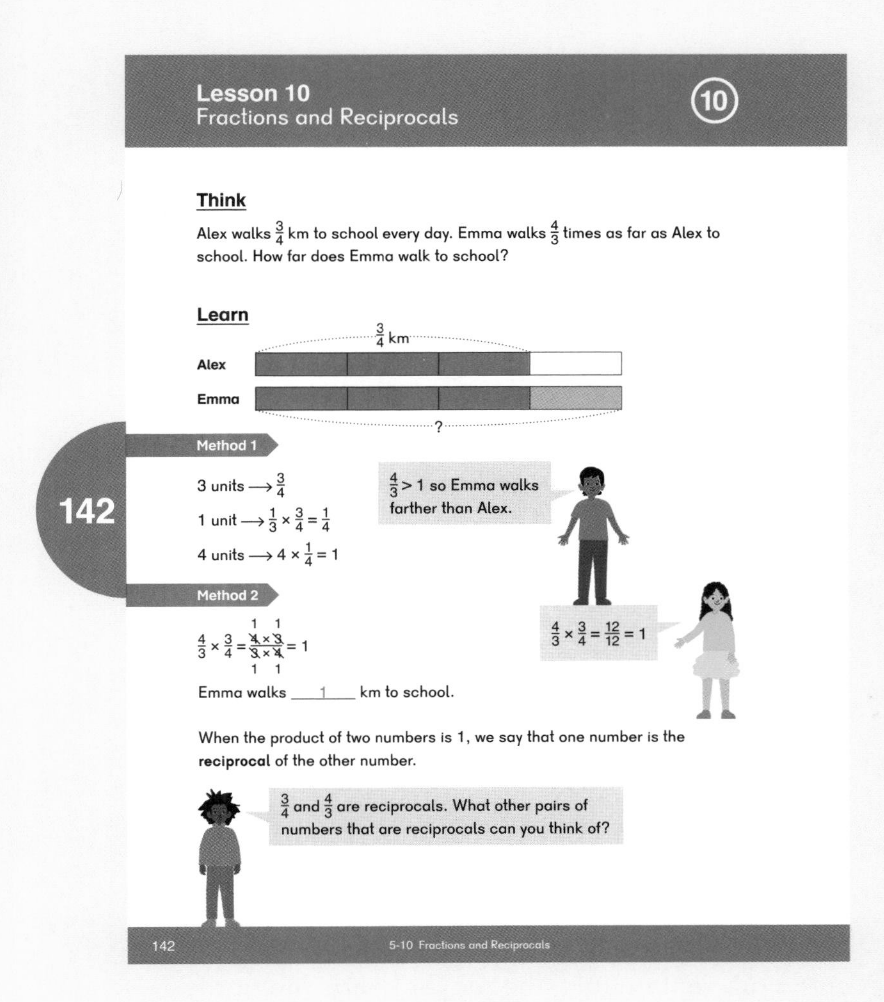

142

Lesson 10
Fractions and Reciprocals

Think

Alex walks $\frac{3}{4}$ km to school every day. Emma walks $\frac{4}{3}$ times as far as Alex to school. How far does Emma walk to school?

Learn

3 units $\longrightarrow \frac{3}{4}$

1 unit $\longrightarrow \frac{1}{3} \times \frac{3}{4} = \frac{1}{4}$

4 units $\longrightarrow 4 \times \frac{1}{4} = 1$

$\frac{4}{3} \times \frac{3}{4} = \frac{\overset{1}{\cancel{4}} \times \overset{1}{\cancel{3}}}{\underset{1}{\cancel{3}} \times \underset{1}{\cancel{4}}} = 1$

Emma walks __1__ km to school.

When the product of two numbers is 1, we say that one number is the **reciprocal** of the other number.

142 5-10 Fractions and Reciprocals

Think

Provide students with 2 strips of paper each and pose the **Think** problem. Students can use the paper strips or draw a model to solve the problem.

Learn

Have students compare their paper strips or models with the bar model shown in **Learn**.

Method 1

The distance Alex walks is in red. The red bar is divided into 3 parts so that we can find $\frac{4}{3}$ of those parts to find how far Emma walks.

If Alex walks $\frac{3}{4}$ km, then Emma walks $\frac{4}{4}$ km, or 1 km.

Method 2

Discuss what happens when the shortcut method of simplifying the computation is applied to this problem.

If needed, remind students that they have learned that we can multiply in any order:

$$\frac{4 \times 3}{3 \times 4} = \frac{4 \times 3}{4 \times 3} = 1 \times 1$$

Introduce the term “reciprocals.” Have students find other reciprocals as Dion asks. Ask students what they notice about reciprocals. They should notice that the reciprocal of any fraction is the number that inverts the numerator and denominator of the fraction. The reciprocal of a whole number, for example 4, can also be thought of this way because $4 = \frac{4}{1}$.

Do

❶—❷ Discuss the problems and given models with students.

❶ Ask students about Emma's and Mei's comments. Ask, "How do we know a fraction with a denominator of 1 is equal to the same whole number? i.e. $\frac{4}{1} = 4$, $\frac{5}{1} = 5$?" (4 ones = 4 and 5 ones = 5)

❷ Students should see that to find the reciprocal, the mixed number is expressed as an improper fraction.

❸—❻ Students should be able to work these problems independently.

Activity

▲ Reciprocal Memory

Materials: Reciprocal Match Cards (BLM)

Shuffle the cards and lay them facedown in an array. On each turn, players turn two cards faceup. If the cards are reciprocals, the player keeps the cards and plays again.

If the cards are not reciprocals, they are turned facedown and the player's turn is over.

The player with the most cards at the end of the game is the winner.

Sample play:

$1\frac{1}{2}$	$\frac{2}{3}$

Exercise 10 • page 130 ▶

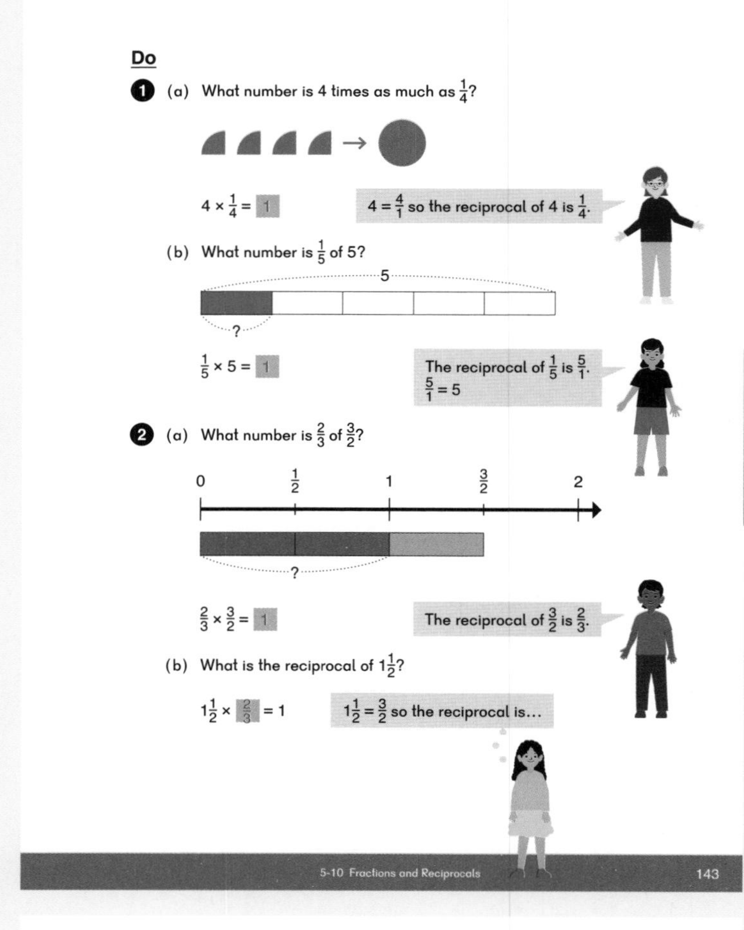

Do

❶ (a) What number is 4 times as much as $\frac{1}{4}$?

$4 \times \frac{1}{4} = 1$

(b) What number is $\frac{1}{5}$ of 5?

$\frac{1}{5} \times 5 = 1$

❷ (a) What number is $\frac{2}{3}$ of $\frac{3}{2}$?

$\frac{2}{3} \times \frac{3}{2} = 1$

(b) What is the reciprocal of $1\frac{1}{2}$?

$1\frac{1}{2} \times \frac{2}{3} = 1$

144

❸ Find pairs of numbers that have a product of 1.

$\frac{4}{7}$ 2 $\frac{3}{8}$ $\frac{7}{4}$ $\frac{8}{5}$ $3\frac{2}{7}$ $\frac{8}{3}$ $\frac{5}{8}$ $\frac{7}{23}$ $\frac{1}{2}$

$\frac{4}{7}$ and $\frac{7}{4}$, 2 and $\frac{1}{2}$, $\frac{3}{8}$ and $\frac{8}{3}$, $\frac{8}{5}$ and $\frac{5}{8}$, $3\frac{2}{7}$ and $\frac{7}{23}$

❹ Find the reciprocal of each number.

(a) $\frac{8}{11}$ $1\frac{3}{8}$ or $\frac{11}{8}$ (b) $\frac{1}{5}$ 5

(c) 6 $\frac{1}{6}$ (d) $\frac{9}{5}$ $\frac{5}{9}$

(e) $2\frac{1}{10}$ $\frac{10}{21}$ (f) $5\frac{3}{4}$ $\frac{4}{23}$

❺ Find the missing numbers.

(a) $\frac{4}{9} \times \frac{9}{4} = 1$ (b) $1\frac{1}{2} \times \frac{2}{3} = 1$

(c) $\frac{1}{3} \times \frac{1}{2} \times 6 = 1$ (d) $4 \times \frac{1}{4} = 1$

(e) $\frac{1}{8} \times 8 = 1$ (f) $\frac{3}{5} \times \frac{2}{7} \times \frac{35}{6} = 1$

❻ What is the reciprocal of 1?

The reciprocal of 1 is 1. $1 \times 1 = 1$

❼ Does 0 have a reciprocal? Explain why or why not.

No. The product of 0 and any number is 0; it is not possible to get a product of 1 when a number is multiplied by 0.

Exercise 10 • page 130 ▶

Objectives

- Practice multiplying fractions
- Practice solving multi-step word problems.

After students complete the **Practice** in the textbook, have them continue to practice multiplying fractions using the activities from the chapter.

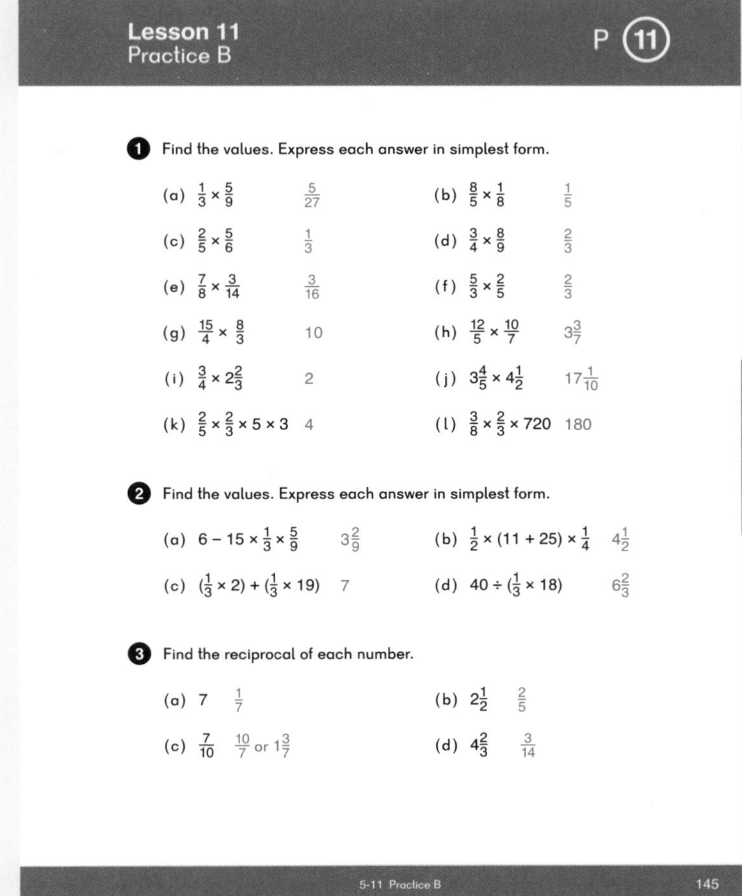

Lesson 11
Practice B

P 11

1. Find the values. Express each answer in simplest form.

(a) $\frac{1}{3} \times \frac{5}{9}$ $\frac{5}{27}$

(b) $\frac{8}{5} \times \frac{1}{8}$ $\frac{1}{5}$

(c) $\frac{2}{5} \times \frac{5}{6}$ $\frac{1}{3}$

(d) $\frac{3}{4} \times \frac{8}{9}$ $\frac{2}{3}$

(e) $\frac{7}{8} \times \frac{3}{14}$ $\frac{3}{16}$

(f) $\frac{5}{3} \times \frac{2}{5}$ $\frac{2}{3}$

(g) $\frac{15}{4} \times \frac{8}{3}$ 10

(h) $\frac{12}{5} \times \frac{10}{7}$ $3\frac{3}{7}$

(i) $\frac{3}{4} \times 2\frac{2}{3}$ 2

(j) $3\frac{4}{5} \times 4\frac{1}{2}$ $17\frac{1}{10}$

(k) $\frac{2}{5} \times \frac{2}{3} \times 5 \times 3$ 4

(l) $\frac{3}{8} \times \frac{2}{3} \times 720$ 180

2. Find the values. Express each answer in simplest form.

(a) $6 - 15 \times \frac{1}{3} \times \frac{5}{9}$ $3\frac{2}{9}$

(b) $\frac{1}{2} \times (11 + 25) \times \frac{1}{4}$ $4\frac{1}{2}$

(c) $(\frac{1}{3} \times 2) + (\frac{1}{3} \times 19)$ 7

(d) $40 \div (\frac{1}{3} \times 18)$ $6\frac{2}{3}$

3. Find the reciprocal of each number.

(a) 7 $\frac{1}{7}$

(b) $2\frac{1}{2}$ $\frac{2}{5}$

(c) $\frac{7}{10}$ $\frac{10}{7}$ or $1\frac{3}{7}$

(d) $4\frac{2}{3}$ $\frac{3}{14}$

5-11 Practice B 145

145

4

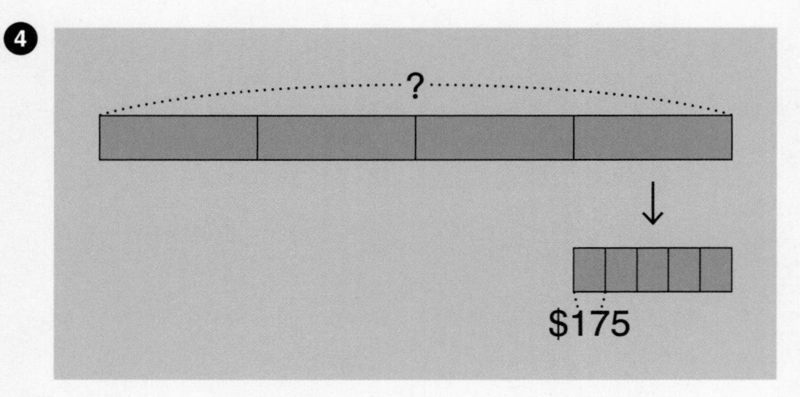

6

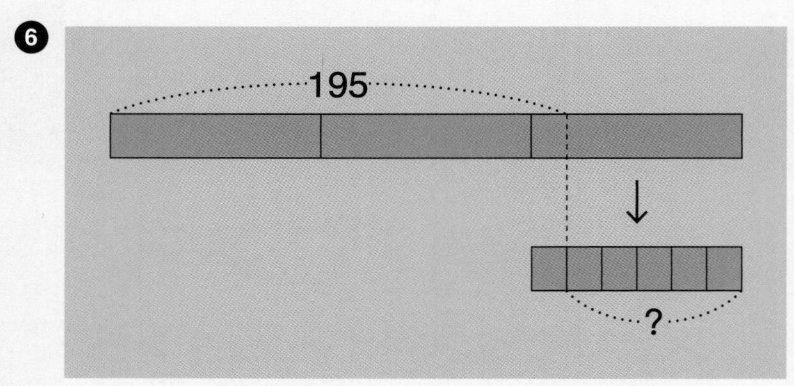

7

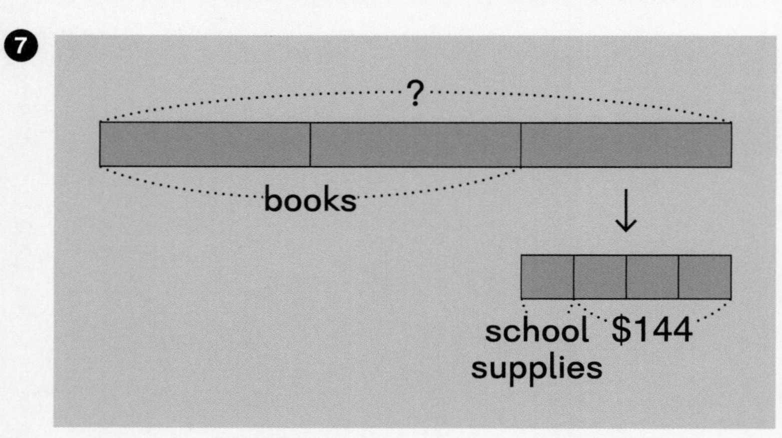

Exercise 11 • page 132

146

4. Justin earned some money cutting lawns. He saved $\frac{3}{4}$ of it and gave the rest equally to 5 charities. Each charity received \$175. How much money did Justin earn cutting lawns? 1 smaller unit $\longrightarrow$ 175
   5 smaller units $\longrightarrow 5 \times 175 = 875$; 1 larger unit $\longrightarrow$ 875
   4 larger units $\longrightarrow 4 \times 875 = 3{,}500$; \$3,500
5. A baker had some flour in a container. After using 12 lb to bake pita bread and $\frac{1}{3}$ of the remainder to bake naan bread, he had 12 lb left. How much flour was in the container?
   Naan: $\frac{1}{2} \times 12 = 6$
   Container: $12 + 6 + 12 = 30$; 30 lb
6. A fruit vendor sold $\frac{2}{3}$ of his apples in the morning and $\frac{1}{6}$ of his remaining apples in the afternoon. He sold 195 apples altogether. How many apples did he have left?
   $195 = (6 \times 2 + 1)$ small units = 13 small units
   1 small unit $= 195 \div 13 = 15$; 5 small units $= 5 \times 15 = 75$, 75 apples.
7. Michelle spent $\frac{2}{3}$ of her money on books and $\frac{1}{4}$ of the remainder on school supplies. She had \$144 left. How much money did she have at first?
   1 smaller unit $\longrightarrow \frac{1}{3} \times 144 = 48$; 4 smaller units $\longrightarrow 4 \times 48 = 192$
   1 larger unit $\longrightarrow$ 192; 3 larger units $\longrightarrow 3 \times 192 = 576$; \$576
8. Kalama's mother made $2\frac{3}{5}$ L of lemonade. Kalama drank $\frac{1}{2}$ of the lemonade. How many liters of lemonade were left?
   $\frac{1}{2} \times 2\frac{3}{5} = 1\frac{3}{10}$; $1\frac{3}{10}$ L
9. Rope A is $5\frac{3}{5}$ m long. Rope B is $1\frac{2}{3}$ times as long as Rope A. Rope C is $1\frac{3}{7}$ times as long as Rope A. How long are the three ropes altogether in meters?
   $5\frac{3}{5} + (1\frac{2}{3} \times 5\frac{3}{5}) + (1\frac{3}{7} \times 5\frac{3}{5}) = 5\frac{3}{5} + 9\frac{1}{3} + 8 = 22\frac{14}{15}$
   $22\frac{14}{15}$ m
10. Tomas had a board that was $3\frac{1}{5}$ m long. He sawed off $1\frac{3}{5}$ m of the board and used $\frac{1}{3}$ of the remaining board for a ramp. How long was the ramp in meters?
   Remaining board: $3\frac{1}{5} - 1\frac{3}{5} = 1\frac{3}{5}$; Ramp: $\frac{1}{3} \times 1\frac{3}{5} = \frac{8}{15}$; $\frac{8}{15}$ m

Exercise 11 • page 132

146 5-11 Practice B

Brain Works

★ Ages

Callie's age is $\frac{3}{8}$ of Luke's age. Sara is $\frac{3}{4}$ as old as Callie. If Luke turned 24 years old today, how old is Sara?

If it is November now, in which month is Sara's birthday?

Callie $\longrightarrow \frac{3}{8} \times 24 = 9$ years old

Sara $\longrightarrow \frac{3}{4} \times 9 = \frac{27}{4} = 6\frac{3}{4}$

$\frac{3}{4} \times 12$ months = 9 months

9 months from November is August.

Sara's birthday is in August.

Exercise 1 • pages 103–104

Chapter 5 Multiplication of Fractions

Exercise 1

Basics

1. Find the value of 4 groups of $\frac{7}{10}$.

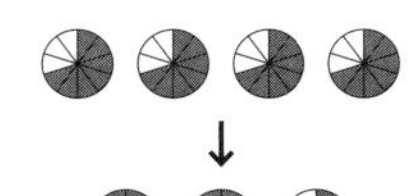

$4 \times \frac{7}{10} = \frac{\overset{2}{\cancel{4}} \times 7}{\underset{5}{\cancel{10}}}$

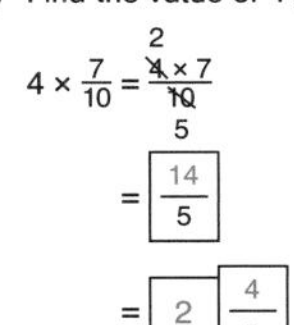

$= \frac{14}{5}$

$= 2\frac{4}{5}$

2. Find the product of 6 and $\frac{5}{9}$.

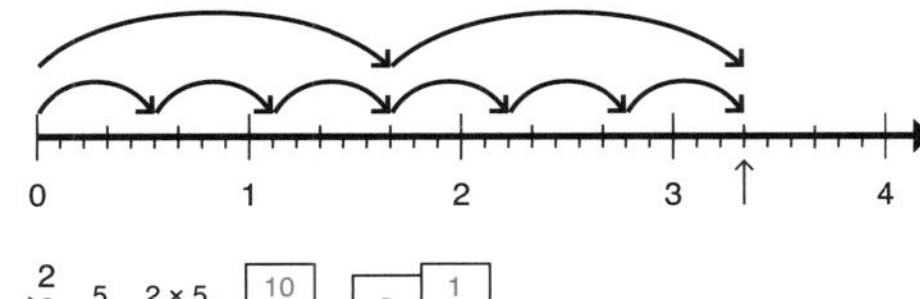

$\overset{2}{\cancel{6}} \times \frac{5}{\underset{3}{\cancel{9}}} = \frac{2 \times 5}{3} = \frac{10}{3} = 3\frac{1}{3}$

3. $25 \times \frac{5}{8} = \frac{125}{8} = 15\frac{5}{8}$

4. $16 \times \frac{5}{6} = \frac{40}{3} = 13\frac{1}{3}$

Practice

5. Multiply. Express each answer in simplest form.

(a) $15 \times \frac{2}{5}$ 6

(b) $24 \times \frac{3}{4}$ 18

(c) $13 \times \frac{3}{7}$ $5\frac{4}{7}$

(d) $10 \times \frac{3}{8}$ $3\frac{3}{4}$

(e) $8 \times \frac{3}{10}$ $2\frac{2}{5}$

(f) $20 \times \frac{5}{6}$ $16\frac{2}{3}$

(g) $8 \times \frac{7}{20}$ $2\frac{4}{5}$

(h) $15 \times \frac{5}{12}$ $6\frac{1}{4}$

6. A paper clip is $\frac{7}{8}$ in long. How long are 12 paper clips placed in a row end to end?

$12 \times \frac{7}{8} = 10\frac{1}{2}$

$10\frac{1}{2}$ in

Exercise 2 • pages 105–106

Exercise 2

Basics

1. Find $\frac{3}{8}$ of 24.

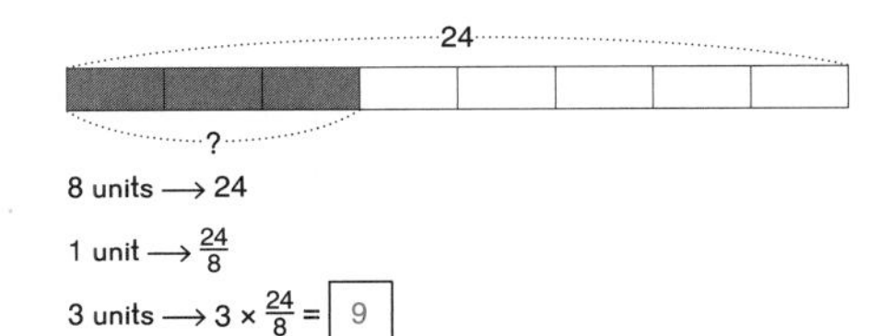

8 units ⟶ 24

1 unit ⟶ $\frac{24}{8}$

3 units ⟶ $3 \times \frac{24}{8} = 9$

2. Find $\frac{7}{10}$ of 4.

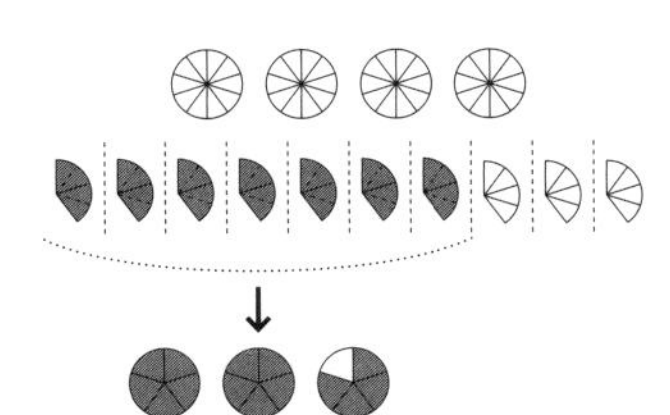

$\frac{7}{10} \times 4 = 7 \times \frac{\overset{2}{\cancel{4}}}{\underset{5}{\cancel{10}}}$

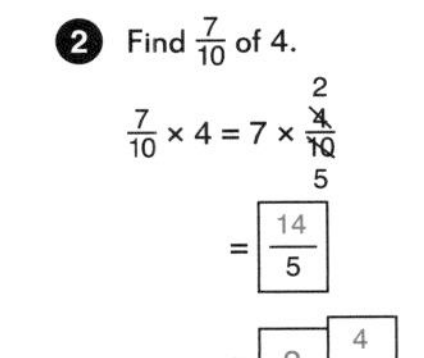

$= \frac{14}{5}$

$= 2\frac{4}{5}$

3. Find $\frac{5}{9}$ of 6.

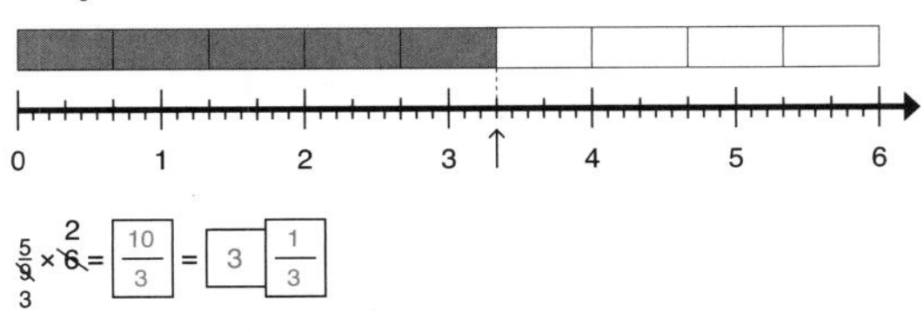

$\frac{5}{\underset{3}{\cancel{9}}} \times \overset{2}{\cancel{6}} = \frac{10}{3} = 3\frac{1}{3}$

Practice

4. Multiply. Express each answer in simplest form.

(a) $\frac{1}{9} \times 180$ 20

(b) $\frac{3}{8} \times 56$ 21

(c) $\frac{3}{10} \times 120$ 36

(d) $\frac{5}{9} \times 3$ $1\frac{2}{3}$

(e) $\frac{3}{4} \times 30$ $22\frac{1}{2}$

(f) $\frac{7}{8} \times 20$ $17\frac{1}{2}$

(g) $\frac{3}{7} \times 18$ $7\frac{5}{7}$

(h) $\frac{7}{10} \times 15$ $10\frac{1}{2}$

5. Stanley used $\frac{3}{4}$ of the cement in a 94-pound bag of cement. How many pounds of cement did he use?

$\frac{3}{4} \times 94 = 70\frac{1}{2}$

$70\frac{1}{2}$ lb

CEMENT
94 LB

Exercise 3

Basics

1 $\frac{2}{5}$ of the pens in a box are blue. $\frac{1}{2}$ of them are black. The rest of them are red. There are 36 more blue pens than red pens. How many pens are there altogether?

$\frac{2}{5} = \frac{4}{10}$ $\frac{1}{2} = \frac{5}{10}$

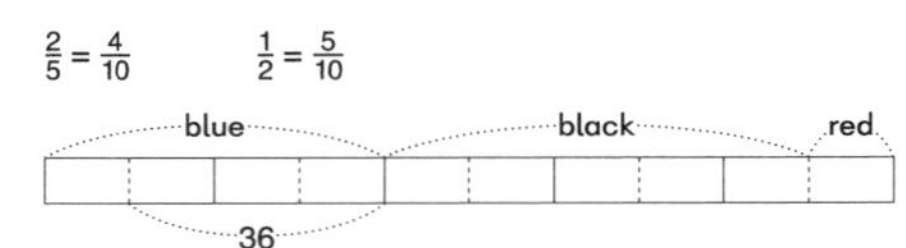

3 units ⟶ 36

1 unit ⟶ $\frac{36}{3} = 12$

10 units ⟶ $10 \times 12 = 120$

120 pens

2 $\frac{1}{2}$ of Aurora's savings is equal to $\frac{2}{3}$ of Hazel's savings. After Hazel saved another $45, they both had the same amount of money. How much money did Aurora save?

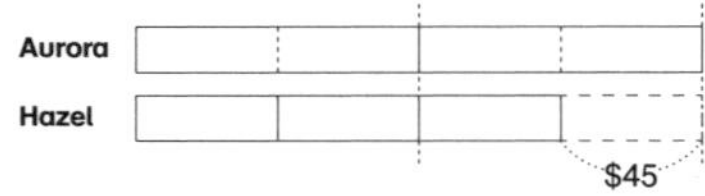

1 unit ⟶ 45

4 units ⟶ $4 \times 45 = 180$

$180

3 Jody had $\frac{2}{3}$ as many action figures as Aiden. After Aiden gave $\frac{1}{2}$ of his action figures to Jody, Jody had 21 action figures. How many action figures did Jody have at first?

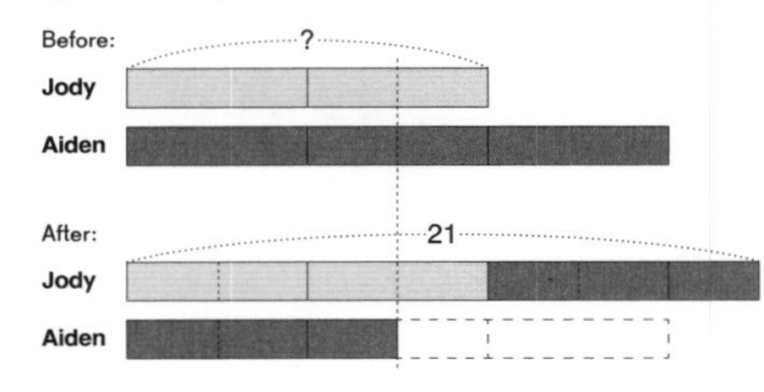

7 units ⟶ 21

1 unit ⟶ $\frac{21}{7} = 3$

4 units ⟶ $4 \times 3 = 12$

12 action figures

Practice

4 Sarah spent $\frac{2}{5}$ of her money on a keyboard. If the keyboard cost $240, how much money did she have at first?

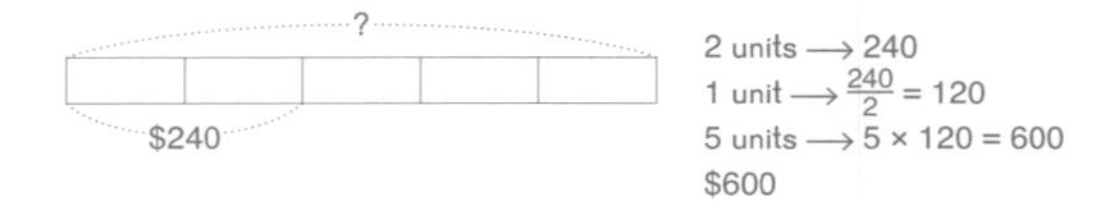

2 units ⟶ 240

1 unit ⟶ $\frac{240}{2} = 120$

5 units ⟶ $5 \times 120 = 600$

$600

5 There were 10 lb of flour in a bag. Alberto used $\frac{2}{5}$ of the flour for bread and $\frac{1}{4}$ of the flour for pancakes. How many pounds of flour are left?

$1 - \frac{2}{5} - \frac{1}{4} = \frac{7}{20}$

$\frac{7}{20} \times 10 = 3\frac{1}{2}$

$3\frac{1}{2}$ lb

6 Malik has $\frac{5}{8}$ as much money as Emilio. Altogether, they have $195. How much money does Emilio have?

Malik

Emilio

$195

$\frac{8}{13} \times 195 = 120$

$120

7 Amalie had $472 in savings. She spent $105 on hiking boots and some more money on hiking poles. She has $\frac{5}{8}$ of her savings left. How much did she spend on the hiking poles?

$\frac{3}{8} \times 472 = 177$

$177 - 105 = 72$

$72

8 A baker made 3 kinds of bagels. $\frac{3}{8}$ of them were plain bagels and $\frac{1}{5}$ of them were cheese bagels. The rest were sesame seed bagels. There were 28 fewer cheese bagels than plain bagels. How many sesame seed bagels were there?

$\frac{3}{8} = \frac{15}{40}$ $\frac{1}{5} = \frac{8}{40}$

40 units total

15 units plain bagels, 8 units cheese bagels.

$40 - 15 - 8 = 17$

17 units sesame seed bagels.

$15 - 8 = 7$

7 more units plain than cheese.

7 units ⟶ 28

1 unit ⟶ $\frac{28}{7} = 4$

17 units ⟶ $4 \times 17 = 68$

68 sesame seed bagels

Students may be able to realize from the common denominator that there are 40 units, and not have to draw the bar model.

9 $\frac{1}{4}$ of Clara's savings is equal to $\frac{2}{3}$ of Maria's savings. Clara saved $80 more than Maria. How much did Maria save?

Clara

Maria

?

$80

5 units ⟶ 80

1 unit ⟶ $\frac{80}{5} = 16$

3 units ⟶ $3 \times 16 = 48$

$48

Exercise 4

Check

1. Find the values. Express each answer in simplest form.

(a) $35 \times \frac{3}{5}$ — 21

(b) $\frac{3}{8} \times 120$ — 45

(c) $\frac{2}{3} \times 16$ — $10\frac{2}{3}$

(d) $8 \times \frac{7}{12}$ — $4\frac{2}{3}$

(e) $36 \times \frac{3}{8}$ — $13\frac{1}{2}$

(f) $\frac{5}{9} \times 33$ — $18\frac{1}{3}$

(g) $8\frac{1}{3} + 7 \times \frac{1}{6}$ — $9\frac{1}{2}$

(h) $(1\frac{1}{2} - \frac{3}{4}) \times 2$ — $1\frac{1}{2}$

(i) $8 \times \frac{1}{3} - 6 \times \frac{1}{3}$ — $\frac{2}{3}$

(j) $\frac{4}{5} \times 6 + \frac{1}{2} \times 3$ — $6\frac{3}{10}$

2. Jacob charged \$35 a day for pet sitting. In June, he had 3 clients. He worked for the first client for $\frac{1}{5}$ of the days in the month, and for the other two clients for $\frac{3}{10}$ of the days of the month. He saved $\frac{1}{3}$ of the money he made, and spent the rest. How much money did he spend? (June has 30 days.)

$\frac{1}{5} \times 30 + 2 \times (\frac{3}{10} \times 30) = 24$
$35 \times 24 = 840$
$\frac{2}{3} \times 840 = 560$
\$560

3. There are 240 seats in a small drama theatre. $\frac{1}{4}$ of the seats are premium seats that cost \$75. The rest are regular seats that cost \$60. For one show, tickets were sold for $\frac{2}{3}$ of the premium seats and $\frac{4}{5}$ of the regular seats. How much money was received from ticket sales?

$\frac{1}{4} \times 240 = 60$; 60 premium seats
$240 - 60 = 180$; 180 regular seats
$75 \times \frac{2}{3} \times 60 = 3{,}000$
$60 \times \frac{4}{5} \times 180 = 8{,}640$
$3{,}000 + 8{,}640 = 11{,}640$
\$11,640

4. Three friends participated in a fund-raising project. Dexter collected $\frac{2}{5}$ of the total amount. Carter collected \$272 more than Jack. Jack collected \$764. How much did the three of them collect altogether?

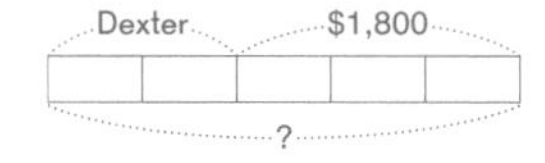

764 + 764 + 272 = 1,800; \$1,800

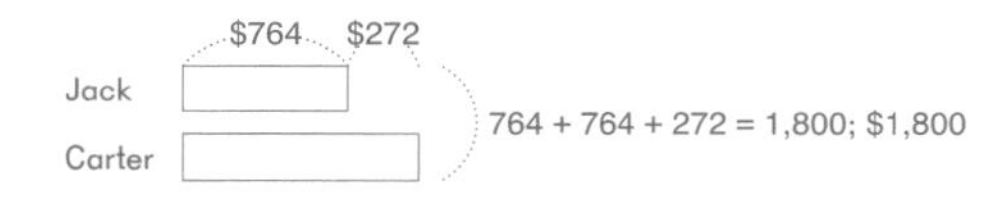

3 units ⟶ 1,800
1 unit ⟶ 1,800 ÷ 3 = 600
5 units ⟶ 5 × 600 = 3,000
\$3,000

5. There were 1,265 people at a boat show. After $\frac{1}{5}$ of the adults and $\frac{1}{3}$ of the children left, there was an equal number of children and adults at the show. How many people left the show?

$\frac{4}{5}$ of the adults and $\frac{2}{3}$ of the children are still at the show, and their numbers are equal.

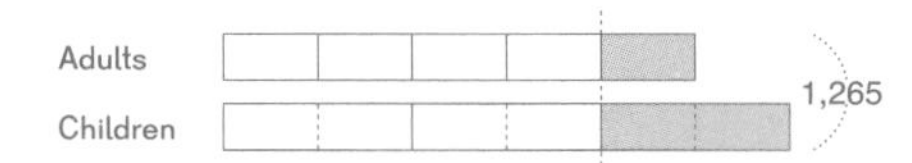

11 units ⟶ 1,265
1 unit ⟶ 1,265 ÷ 11 = 115
3 units ⟶ 3 × 115 = 345
345 people

Challenge

6. $297 \times \frac{26}{74}$ is closest to which of the following numbers?

50 | 75 | **100** | 150 | 20

Use estimation: $297 \times \frac{26}{74} \approx 300 \times \frac{25}{75} = 300 \times \frac{1}{3} = 100$

7. Kai has some new kittens. When he was asked how many he had, he said the number of kittens he had was equal to three fourths of the total number plus three fourths of a kitten. How many kittens does he have?

$\frac{3}{4}$ of a kitten is $\frac{1}{4}$ of all of his kittens.

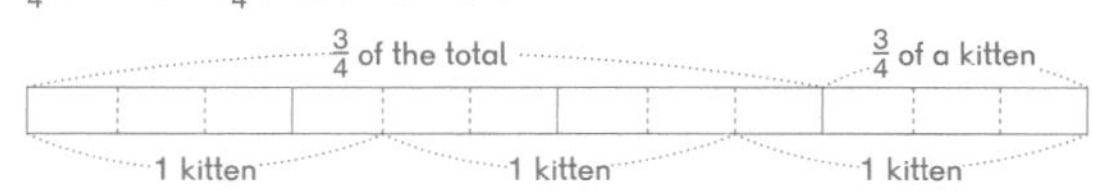

3 kittens

8. After Josie sold $\frac{1}{4}$ of the cabbages and $\frac{3}{5}$ of the cauliflowers at the market, she had the same number of cabbages as cauliflowers left. If she sold 42 more cauliflowers than cabbages, how many cabbages did she have at first?

She has the same number of each left, so $\frac{3}{4}$ of the cabbages is equal to $\frac{2}{5}$ of the cauliflowers. 3 units of cabbage = 2 units of cauliflower. Make equal units. A common multiple of 3 and 2 is 6.

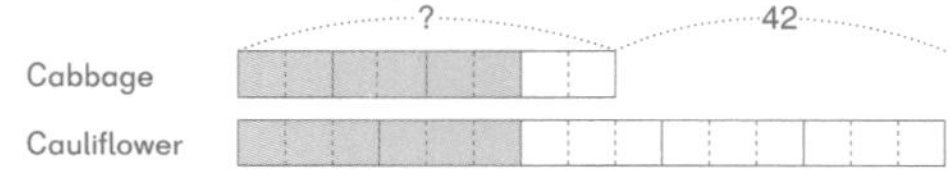

7 units ⟶ 42
1 unit ⟶ $\frac{42}{7} = 6$
8 units ⟶ 8 × 6 = 48
48 cabbages

Exercise 5

Basics

1. Shade the rectangle to show $\frac{1}{2}$ of $\frac{3}{5}$.

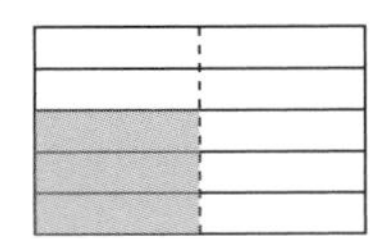

$\frac{1}{2} \times \frac{3}{5} = \frac{1 \times 3}{2 \times 5}$

$= \frac{3}{10}$

Students may shade using 2 colors overlapping, or draw diagonal lines in different directions.

2. Shade the rectangle to show $\frac{1}{6}$ of $\frac{2}{3}$.

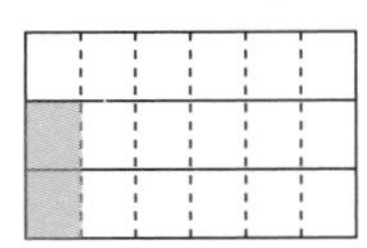

$\frac{1}{6} \times \frac{2}{3} = \frac{1 \times 2}{6 \times 3}$

$= \frac{2}{18}$

$= \frac{1}{9}$

3. Shade the bar and draw an arrow on the number line to show $\frac{1}{6}$ of $\frac{3}{4}$.

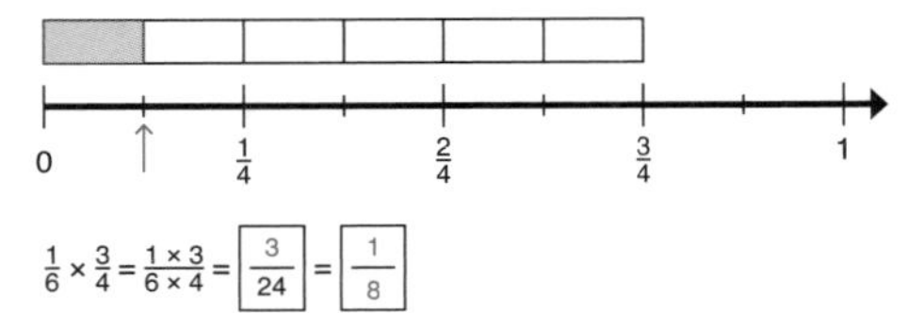

$\frac{1}{6} \times \frac{3}{4} = \frac{1 \times 3}{6 \times 4} = \frac{3}{24} = \frac{1}{8}$

Practice

4. Find the values. Express each answer in simplest form.

(a) $\frac{1}{4} \times \frac{1}{6}$ $\frac{1}{24}$

(b) $\frac{1}{3} \times \frac{3}{5}$ $\frac{1}{5}$

(c) $\frac{1}{3} \times \frac{5}{6}$ $\frac{5}{18}$

(d) $\frac{1}{2} \times \frac{6}{7}$ $\frac{3}{7}$

(e) $\frac{1}{6} \times \frac{3}{10}$ $\frac{1}{20}$

(f) $\frac{1}{12} \times \frac{3}{4}$ $\frac{1}{16}$

(g) $\frac{1}{9} \times \frac{6}{7}$ $\frac{2}{21}$

(h) $\frac{1}{9} \times \frac{72}{100}$ $\frac{2}{25}$

5. John has a garden with an area of $\frac{4}{5}$ acres. He planted herbs in $\frac{1}{8}$ of the garden. How many acres did he plant with herbs?

$\frac{1}{8} \times \frac{4}{5} = \frac{1}{10}$

$\frac{1}{10}$ acres

Exercise 6

Basics

1. Shade the rectangle to show $\frac{2}{3}$ of $\frac{4}{5}$.

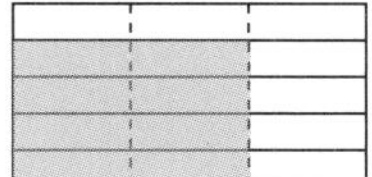

$\frac{2}{3} \times \frac{4}{5} = \frac{2 \times 4}{3 \times 5} = \frac{8}{15}$

2. Shade the rectangle to show $\frac{5}{6}$ of $\frac{2}{3}$.

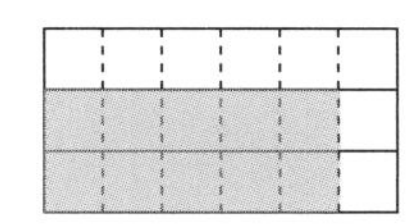

$\frac{5}{6} \times \frac{2}{3} = \frac{5 \times 2}{6 \times 3} = \frac{10}{18} = \frac{5}{9}$

3. Shade the rectangles to show $\frac{5}{6}$ of $\frac{4}{3}$.

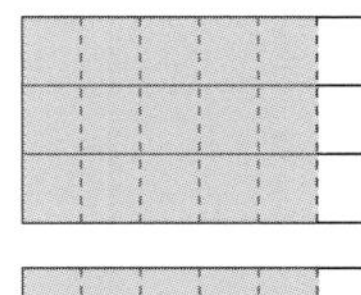

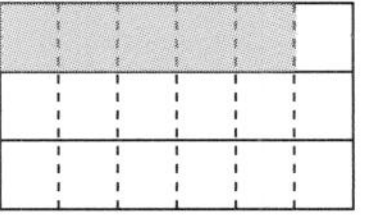

$\frac{5}{6} \times \frac{4}{3} = \frac{5 \times 4}{6 \times 3} = \frac{20}{18} = 1\frac{1}{9}$

4. Shade the bar and draw an arrow on the number line to show $\frac{5}{6}$ of $\frac{3}{4}$.

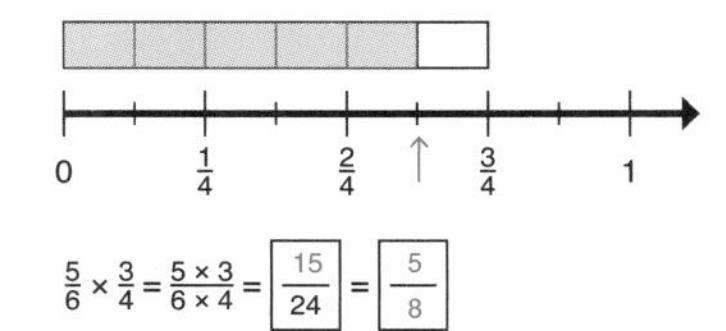

$\frac{5}{6} \times \frac{3}{4} = \frac{5 \times 3}{6 \times 4} = \frac{15}{24} = \frac{5}{8}$

5. Shade the bar and draw an arrow on the number line to show $\frac{7}{6}$ of $\frac{3}{4}$.

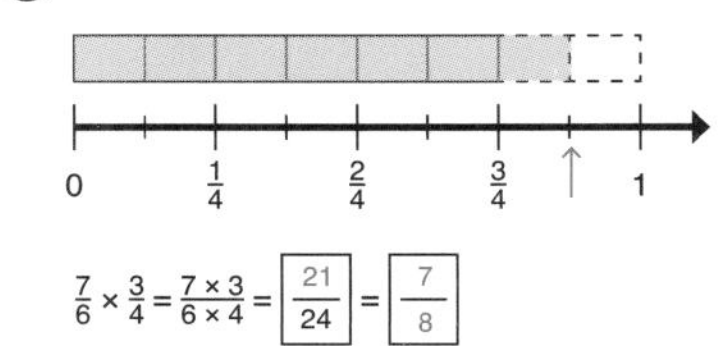

$\frac{7}{6} \times \frac{3}{4} = \frac{7 \times 3}{6 \times 4} = \frac{21}{24} = \frac{7}{8}$

6. Shade the bar and draw an arrow on the number line to show $\frac{7}{6}$ of $\frac{5}{4}$.

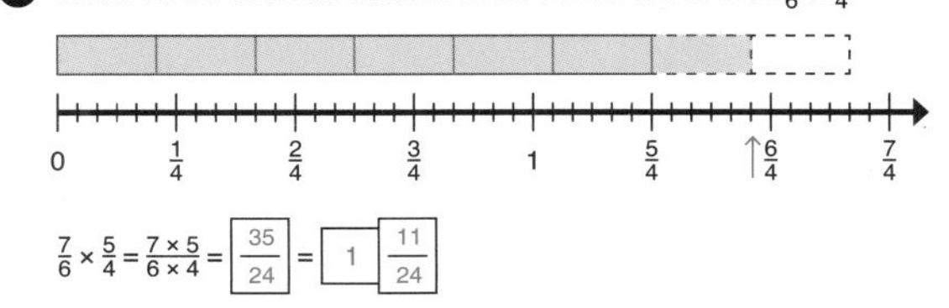

$\frac{7}{6} \times \frac{5}{4} = \frac{7 \times 5}{6 \times 4} = \frac{35}{24} = 1\frac{11}{24}$

Practice

7. Which of the following will have values greater than $\frac{2}{3}$?

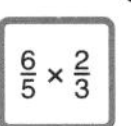 $\frac{2}{3} \times \frac{5}{6}$ $\frac{6}{5} \times \frac{2}{3}$  $\frac{5}{8} \times \frac{2}{3}$ $\frac{2}{3} \times \frac{8}{5}$ 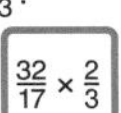 $\frac{32}{17} \times \frac{2}{3}$

8. Find the values. Express each answer in simplest form.

(a) $\frac{3}{4} \times \frac{7}{10}$ $\frac{21}{40}$

(b) $\frac{2}{3} \times \frac{4}{7}$ $\frac{8}{21}$

(c) $\frac{2}{3} \times \frac{5}{6}$ $\frac{5}{9}$

(d) $\frac{3}{4} \times \frac{8}{11}$ $\frac{6}{11}$

(e) $\frac{7}{4} \times \frac{7}{20}$ $\frac{49}{80}$

(f) $\frac{5}{6} \times \frac{3}{2}$ $1\frac{1}{4}$

(g) $\frac{3}{2} \times \frac{7}{5}$ $2\frac{1}{10}$

(h) $\frac{5}{4} \times \frac{8}{5}$ 2

Exercise 7

Basics

1. Find $\frac{5}{6}$ of $\frac{2}{3}$.

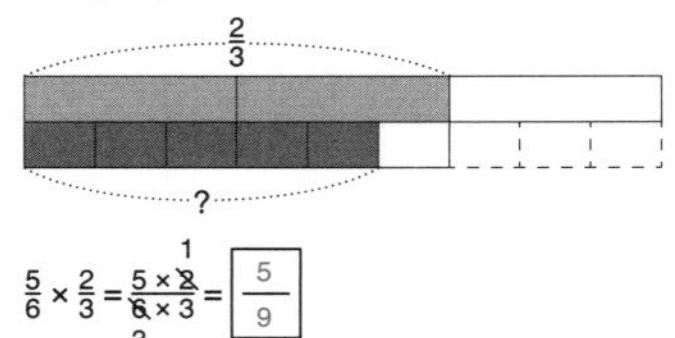

$\frac{5}{6} \times \frac{2}{3} = \frac{5 \times \cancel{2}^{1}}{\cancel{6}_{3} \times 3} = \boxed{\frac{5}{9}}$

2. Find $\frac{8}{5}$ of $\frac{5}{12}$.

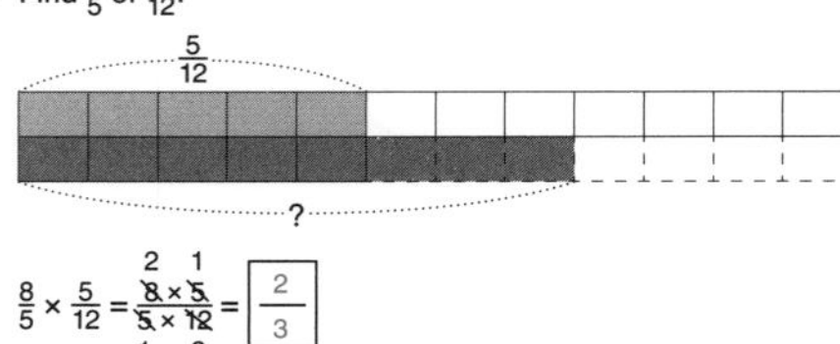

$\frac{8}{5} \times \frac{5}{12} = \frac{\cancel{8}^{2} \times \cancel{5}^{1}}{\cancel{5}_{1} \times \cancel{12}_{3}} = \boxed{\frac{2}{3}}$

3. Find the product of $\frac{5}{9}$ and $\frac{6}{7}$.

$\frac{5}{\cancel{9}_{3}} \times \frac{\cancel{6}^{2}}{7} = \boxed{\frac{10}{21}}$

4. Find the product of $\frac{12}{5}$ and $\frac{15}{8}$.

$\frac{\cancel{12}^{3}}{\cancel{5}_{1}} \times \frac{\cancel{15}^{3}}{\cancel{8}_{2}} = \boxed{\frac{9}{2}} = \boxed{4}\boxed{\frac{1}{2}}$

Practice

5. Find the values. Express each answer in simplest form.

(a) $\frac{4}{5} \times \frac{3}{14}$ $\frac{6}{35}$

(b) $\frac{2}{3} \times \frac{4}{5}$ $\frac{8}{15}$

(c) $\frac{5}{9} \times \frac{3}{10}$ $\frac{1}{6}$

(d) $\frac{3}{8} \times \frac{4}{15}$ $\frac{1}{10}$

(e) $\frac{5}{6} \times \frac{8}{15}$ $\frac{4}{9}$

(f) $\frac{8}{3} \times \frac{9}{20}$ $1\frac{1}{5}$

(g) $\frac{5}{3} \times \frac{12}{5}$ 4

(h) $\frac{105}{104} \times \frac{16}{7}$ $2\frac{4}{13}$

6. A bag of rice weighs $\frac{9}{10}$ kg. Amy used $\frac{2}{3}$ of it to make rice pudding. How many kilograms of rice did she use?

$\frac{2}{3} \times \frac{9}{10} = \frac{3}{5}$

$\frac{3}{5}$ kg

Challenge

7. $\frac{1}{3}$ and $\frac{1}{4}$ have the same product and difference:

$\frac{1}{3} \times \frac{1}{4} = \frac{1}{3} - \frac{1}{4}$

Name five other pairs of numbers that have the same product and difference.

Possible answers: $\frac{1}{2}$ and $\frac{1}{3}$, $\frac{1}{4}$ and $\frac{1}{5}$, $\frac{1}{5}$ and $\frac{1}{6}$, $\frac{1}{11}$ and $\frac{1}{12}$, $\frac{1}{100}$ and $\frac{1}{101}$

Any pair of unit fractions where one denominator is 1 more than the other denominator is a solution.

8. Fill in the blanks to make each equation true. All fractions must be less than 1 and in simplest form.

(a) $\boxed{\frac{3}{10}} \times \boxed{\frac{5}{7}} = \boxed{\frac{3}{14}}$

(b) $\boxed{\frac{5}{12}} \times \boxed{\frac{4}{15}} = \boxed{\frac{1}{9}}$

(c) $\boxed{\frac{5}{21}} \times \boxed{\frac{7}{10}} = \boxed{\frac{1}{6}}$

(d) $\boxed{\frac{8}{15}} \times \boxed{\frac{9}{10}} = \boxed{\frac{12}{25}}$

Exercise 8 • pages 123–125

Exercise 8

Basics

1. Find 4 groups of $1\frac{2}{3}$.

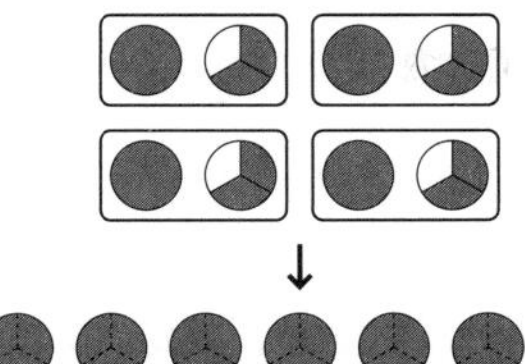

$4 \times 1\frac{2}{3} = 4 \times \frac{5}{3}$

$= \frac{20}{3}$

$= 6\frac{2}{3}$

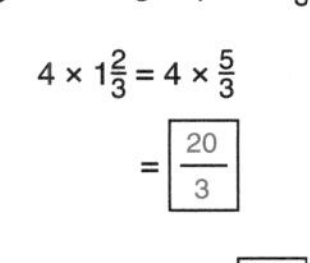

2. Shade the bar and draw an arrow on the number line to show $\frac{5}{6}$ of $1\frac{1}{4}$.

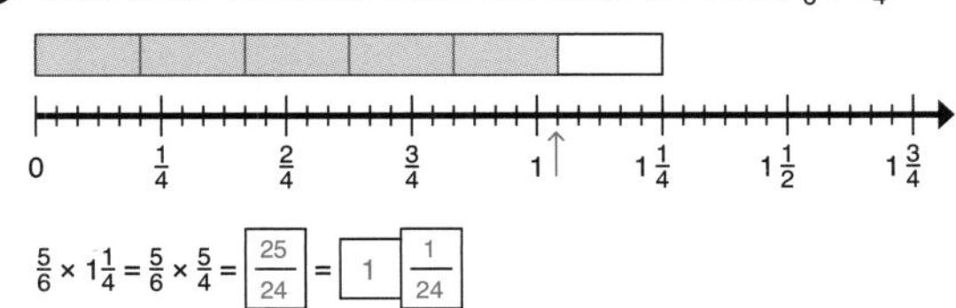

$\frac{5}{6} \times 1\frac{1}{4} = \frac{5}{6} \times \frac{5}{4} = \frac{25}{24} = 1\frac{1}{24}$

3. Shade the bar and draw an arrow on the number line to show $1\frac{1}{2}$ times as much as $1\frac{1}{3}$.

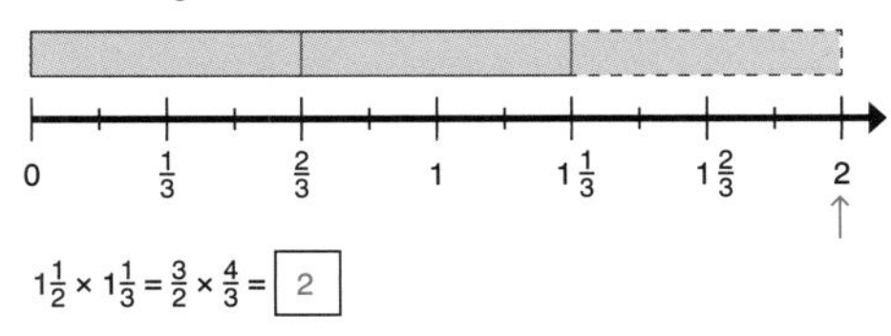

$1\frac{1}{2} \times 1\frac{1}{3} = \frac{3}{2} \times \frac{4}{3} = 2$

Practice

4. Find the values. Express each answer in simplest form.

(a) $3\frac{2}{5} \times 25$ 85

(b) $14 \times 2\frac{4}{5}$ $39\frac{1}{5}$

(c) $15 \times 2\frac{4}{9}$ $36\frac{2}{3}$

(d) $\frac{4}{5} \times 3\frac{1}{8}$ $2\frac{1}{2}$

(e) $1\frac{5}{6} \times \frac{5}{8}$ $1\frac{7}{48}$

(f) $1\frac{1}{8} \times 3\frac{5}{9}$ 4

(g) $2\frac{1}{7} \times 4\frac{1}{5}$ 9

(h) $1\frac{7}{9} \times 2\frac{1}{10}$ $3\frac{11}{15}$

5. Josh picked $4\frac{3}{4}$ pounds of strawberries. Mandy picked $1\frac{1}{3}$ times as many pounds of strawberries as Josh did. How many pounds of strawberries did they pick altogether?

$1\frac{1}{3} \times 4\frac{3}{4} = \frac{4}{3} \times \frac{19}{4} = \frac{19}{3} = 6\frac{1}{3}$

$4\frac{3}{4} + 6\frac{1}{3} = 11\frac{1}{12}$

$11\frac{1}{12}$ lb

6. 25 seeds are planted. The distance between each seed is $1\frac{3}{4}$ inches. What is the distance between the first and last seed in inches?

There are 24 intervals between the first and last seed.

$24 \times 1\frac{3}{4} = 42$

42 inches

Challenge

7. Write the digits 1, 2, or 3 in each blank space to make each equation true. All fractions must be in simplest form.

(a) $3\frac{1}{2} \times \frac{2}{3} = 2\frac{1}{3}$

(b) $1\frac{2}{3} \times 1\frac{2}{5} = 2\frac{1}{3}$

Exercise 9 • pages 126–129

Exercise 9

Basics

1 $\frac{2}{9}$ of the buttons in a bag are green.

(a) $\frac{1}{4}$ of the green buttons have two holes and the rest have 4 holes. What fraction of the buttons are green and have 4 holes?

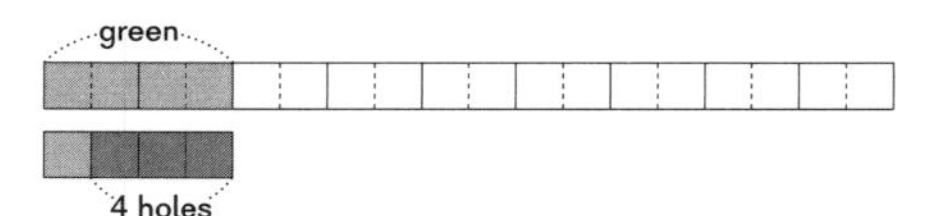

$\frac{3}{4} \times \frac{2}{9} = \frac{1}{6}$

(b) $\frac{1}{2}$ of the remaining buttons are red. The rest of the buttons are brown. What fraction of the total number of buttons are brown?

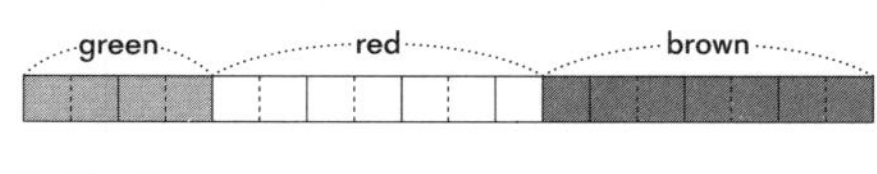

$\frac{1}{2} \times \frac{7}{9} = \frac{7}{18}$

(c) There are 14 brown buttons. How many buttons are there altogether?

7 units ⟶ 14

1 unit ⟶ 14 ÷ 7 = 2

18 units ⟶ 18 × 2 = 36

36 buttons

2 A bakery has 510 bagels. $\frac{1}{3}$ of the bagels are plain, $\frac{1}{6}$ of them are salt, $\frac{2}{5}$ of the remainder are garlic, and the rest are sesame seed. How many of the bagels are sesame seed?

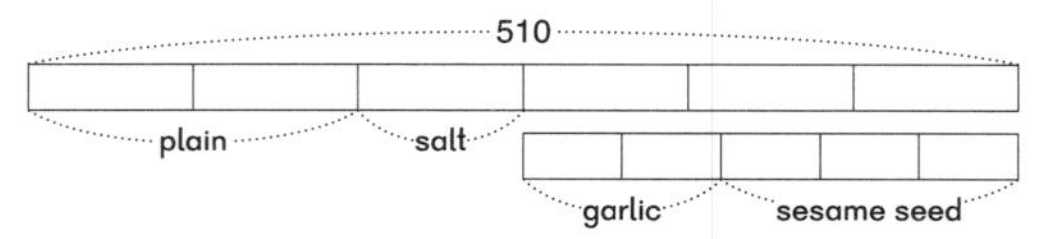

Remainder (garlic and sesame seed): $1 - (\frac{1}{3} + \frac{1}{6}) = \frac{1}{2}$

Sesame seed: $\frac{3}{5} \times \frac{1}{2} \times 510 = 153$

3 $\frac{1}{5}$ of the passengers on a ship are men. $\frac{2}{3}$ of the remainder are women, and the rest are children. There are 234 more children than men. How many of the passengers are women?

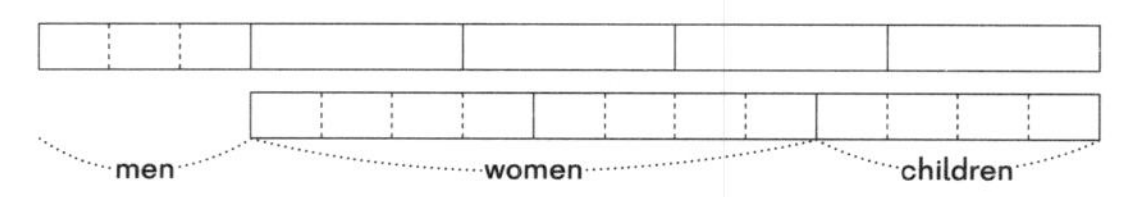

Women: $\frac{2}{3} \times \frac{4}{5} = \frac{8}{15}$

Children: $\frac{1}{3} \times \frac{4}{5} = \frac{4}{15}$

$\frac{4}{15} - \frac{1}{5} = \frac{1}{15}$

$\frac{1}{15}$ of the total ⟶ 234

$\frac{8}{15}$ of the total ⟶ 8 × 234 = 1,872

1,872 passengers

Practice

4 Patrick spent $\frac{5}{6}$ of his money on camping equipment. $\frac{2}{5}$ of what he spent was for a backpack and the rest was for a tent. He had $60 left. How much did the tent cost?

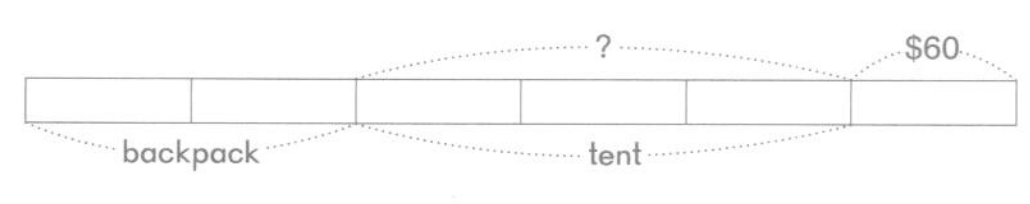

1 unit ⟶ 60
3 units ⟶ 3 × 60 = 180
$180

5 Rosa spent $\frac{1}{4}$ of her money on a camping stove and $\frac{1}{6}$ of the remainder on a water purifier. She spent $267. How much money did she have at first?

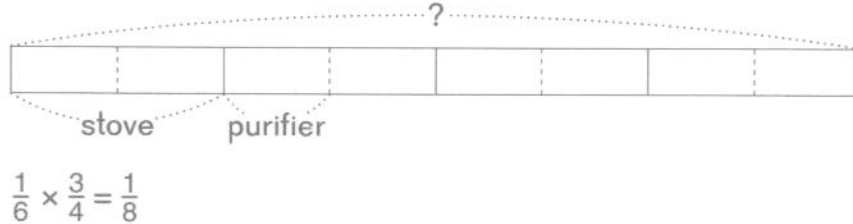

$\frac{1}{6} \times \frac{3}{4} = \frac{1}{8}$
stove + purifier = 3 out of 8 units
3 units ⟶ 267
1 unit ⟶ 267 ÷ 3 = 89
8 units ⟶ 8 × 89 = 712
$712

6 Josie sold $\frac{3}{7}$ of all the ears of corn she brought to the market in the morning and $\frac{2}{3}$ of the remaining ears of corn in the afternoon. She sold 255 ears of corn in all. She donated the leftover ears of corn to the food bank. How many ears of corn did she donate to the food bank?

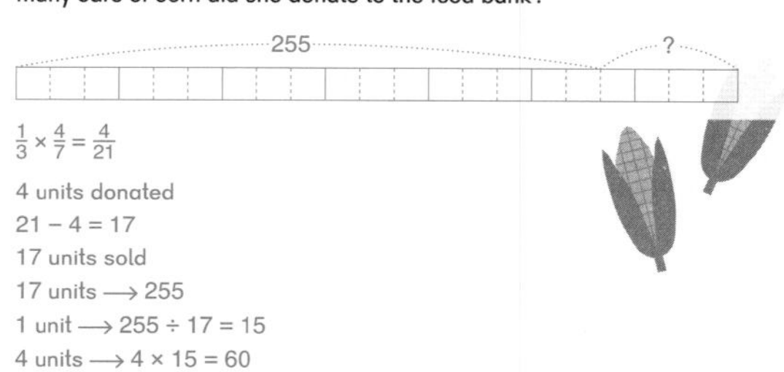

$\frac{1}{3} \times \frac{4}{7} = \frac{4}{21}$
4 units donated
21 − 4 = 17
17 units sold
17 units ⟶ 255
1 unit ⟶ 255 ÷ 17 = 15
4 units ⟶ 4 × 15 = 60
60 ears of corn

Challenge

7 Luisa had $5\frac{1}{2}$ kg of beans. On Monday, she used $\frac{1}{5}$ of the beans to make refried beans. On Tuesday, she used $\frac{1}{3}$ of the remaining beans to make enchiladas. On Wednesday, she used $\frac{5}{8}$ of the rest of the beans to make soup. How many kilograms of beans does she have left?

After Monday, $\frac{4}{5}$ of the total remain. After Tuesday, $\frac{2}{3}$ of $\frac{4}{5}$ of the total remain. After Wednesday, $\frac{3}{8}$ of $\frac{2}{3}$ of $\frac{4}{5}$ of the total remains.

$\frac{3}{8} \times \frac{2}{3} \times \frac{4}{5} \times 5\frac{1}{2} = 1\frac{1}{10}$

$1\frac{1}{10}$ kg

Exercise 10 • pages 130–131

Exercise 10

Basics

1 Find the value of 3 groups of $\frac{1}{3}$.

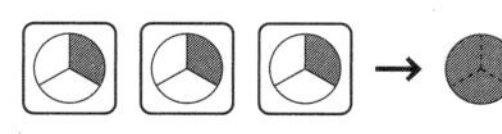

$3 \times \frac{1}{3} = \boxed{1}$

$3 \times$ $\frac{1}{3}$ = 1, so the reciprocal of 3 is $\frac{1}{3}$.

2 Shade the bar and draw an arrow on the number line to show $\frac{5}{2}$ of $\frac{2}{5}$.

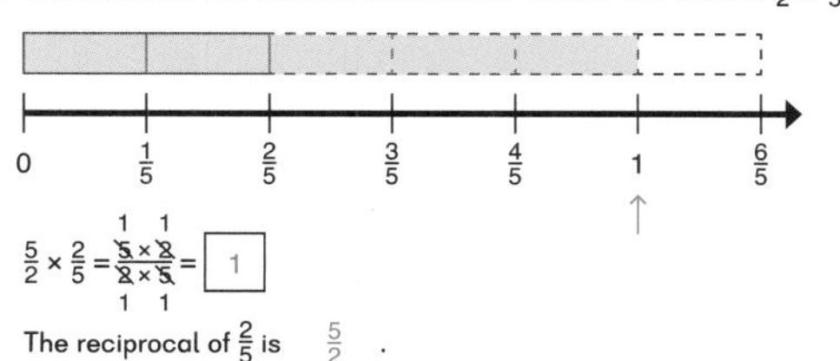

$\frac{5}{2} \times \frac{2}{5} = \frac{\cancel{5}^1 \times \cancel{2}^1}{\cancel{2}_1 \times \cancel{5}_1} = \boxed{1}$

The reciprocal of $\frac{2}{5}$ is $\frac{5}{2}$.

3 Shade the bar and draw an arrow on the number line to show $\frac{4}{7}$ of $\frac{7}{4}$.

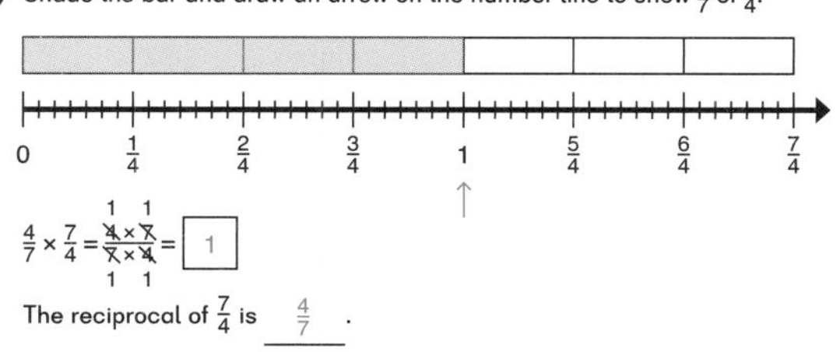

$\frac{4}{7} \times \frac{7}{4} = \frac{\cancel{4}^1 \times \cancel{7}^1}{\cancel{7}_1 \times \cancel{4}_1} = \boxed{1}$

The reciprocal of $\frac{7}{4}$ is $\frac{4}{7}$.

4 Find the reciprocal of $4\frac{1}{3}$.

$4\frac{1}{3} =$ 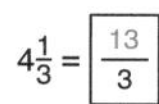 $\boxed{\frac{13}{3}}$

The reciprocal of $4\frac{1}{3}$ is $\boxed{\frac{3}{13}}$.

Practice

5 Write the reciprocal of each number. Express fractions greater than 1 as imperfect fractions.

(a) $\frac{1}{8}$ 8

(b) $\frac{7}{12}$ $\frac{12}{7}$

(c) $\frac{10}{3}$ $\frac{3}{10}$

(d) $2\frac{1}{9}$ $\frac{9}{19}$

(e) 10 $\frac{1}{10}$

(f) $2\frac{5}{8}$ $\frac{8}{21}$

6 Fill in the blanks. Express answers in simplest form.

(a) 12 $\times \frac{1}{12} = 1$

(b) $1\frac{2}{5} \times$ $\frac{5}{7}$ $= 1$

(c) $1\frac{3}{7}$ $\times \frac{7}{10} = 1$

(d) $\frac{3}{7}$ $\times 2\frac{1}{3} = 1$

(e) $\frac{1}{3} \times \frac{3}{5} \times$ 5 $= 1$

(f) $1\frac{1}{4} \times \frac{3}{5} \times$ $1\frac{1}{3}$ $= 1$

Exercise 11 • pages 132–136

Exercise 11

Check

1 Find the values. Express each answer in simplest form.

(a) $\frac{4}{9} \times \frac{1}{2}$ $\frac{2}{9}$

(b) $\frac{2}{5} \times \frac{7}{8}$ $\frac{7}{20}$

(c) $\frac{5}{6} \times \frac{6}{5}$ 1

(d) $3 \times 3\frac{5}{9}$ $10\frac{2}{3}$

(e) $1\frac{1}{6} \times 9\frac{6}{7}$ $11\frac{1}{2}$

(f) $\frac{4}{5} \times \frac{3}{8} \times 20$ 6

(g) $\frac{2}{3} + \frac{2}{5} \times \frac{1}{4}$ $\frac{23}{30}$

(h) $\frac{5}{6} \times 18 \div 4 \times \frac{1}{3}$ $1\frac{1}{4}$

(i) $\frac{2}{3} \times \frac{2}{5} + \frac{1}{3} + 28 \div 6$ $5\frac{4}{15}$

(j) $15 - (14 \times \frac{5}{6}) + \frac{3}{5} \times \frac{5}{6}$ $3\frac{5}{6}$

2 Write the reciprocal of each value. Express fractions greater than 1 as imperfect fractions.

(a) $\frac{5}{8}$ $\frac{8}{5}$

(b) $\frac{7}{5}$ $\frac{5}{7}$

(c) $2\frac{2}{11}$ $\frac{11}{24}$

(d) $5 + 3$ $\frac{1}{8}$

(e) $\frac{1}{5} \times \frac{1}{3}$ 15

(f) $\frac{1}{5} + \frac{1}{3}$ $\frac{15}{8}$

3 What is the sum of the reciprocals of $\frac{3}{5}$ and $\frac{2}{3}$?

$\frac{5}{3} + \frac{3}{2} = 3\frac{1}{6}$

4 Three identical bags of sand weigh 10 kg altogether. How many kilograms do 8 of these bags weigh?

$8 \times \frac{10}{3} = \frac{80}{3} = 26\frac{2}{3}$

$26\frac{2}{3}$ lb

5 How many $\frac{3}{4}$-cup scoops of flour will make 1 cup of flour?

$1\frac{1}{3}$ scoops

Methods may vary.

6 On Saturday, Tomas read $\frac{1}{3}$ of his book. On Sunday, he read $\frac{2}{5}$ of what was left. What fraction of his book does he still have to read?

The remainder after Saturday is $\frac{2}{3}$. After Sunday it is $\frac{3}{5}$ of that.

$\frac{3}{5} \times \frac{2}{3} = \frac{2}{5}$

$\frac{2}{5}$ of his book

7 Tania had $3\frac{3}{5}$ L of juice. She drank $\frac{1}{3}$ of it on Monday, and $\frac{2}{3}$ of the remainder on Tuesday. How many liters of juice does she have left?

Remainder from Monday: $\frac{2}{3} \times 3\frac{3}{5} = \frac{2}{3} \times \frac{18}{5} = \frac{12}{5}$

Remainder from Tuesday: $\frac{1}{3} \times \frac{12}{5} = \frac{4}{5}$

$\frac{4}{5}$ L

8 In Amy's class, $\frac{2}{3}$ of the students have pets. $\frac{3}{4}$ of the students who have pets have dogs. If 15 students have dogs, how many students are in her class?

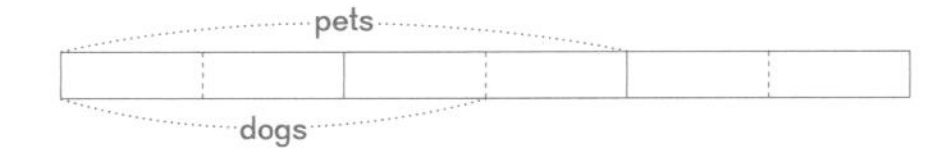

3 units ⟶ 15
6 units ⟶ 2 × 15 = 30
30 students

9 A square has sides $5\frac{1}{3}$ cm long. The rectangle below is made up of $3\frac{1}{2}$ of these squares. What is the perimeter of the figure?

$5\frac{1}{3}$ cm

One side is 1 unit. The perimeter is 9 units total.

Perimeter: $9 \times 5\frac{1}{3} = 48$

48 cm

10 Rohan bought some tiles for a kitchen floor. $\frac{3}{5}$ of the tiles were white, $\frac{1}{4}$ of the remainder were yellow, and the rest were blue. There were 60 more white tiles than blue tiles. Each tile cost $3. What was the total cost of the tiles?

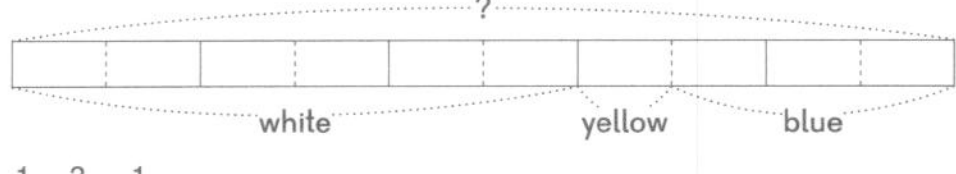

$\frac{1}{4} \times \frac{2}{5} = \frac{1}{10}$

Divide the whole bar into 10 units.
Divide each fifth in half.
There are 6 units of white and 3 units of blue.
3 units ⟶ 60
1 unit ⟶ 60 ÷ 3 = 20
10 units ⟶ 10 × 20 = 200
3 × 200 = 600
$600

Challenge

11 A tank is $\frac{2}{3}$ full. If another 3 L of water is added, it will be $\frac{7}{8}$ full. What is the capacity of the tank?

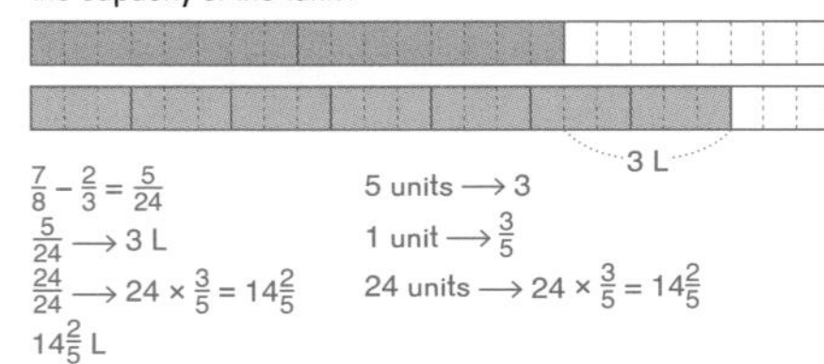

$\frac{7}{8} - \frac{2}{3} = \frac{5}{24}$

$\frac{5}{24} \longrightarrow 3$ L

$\frac{24}{24} \longrightarrow 24 \times \frac{3}{5} = 14\frac{2}{5}$

$14\frac{2}{5}$ L

5 units ⟶ 3

1 unit ⟶ $\frac{3}{5}$

24 units ⟶ $24 \times \frac{3}{5} = 14\frac{2}{5}$

12 A passenger fell asleep on a train halfway to his destination. He slept until he had half as far to go as the distance he traveled while he was asleep. What fraction of the trip was he sleeping?

$\frac{2}{3} \times \frac{1}{2} = \frac{1}{3}$

$\frac{1}{3}$ of his trip

13 A boy has as many sisters as brothers, but each sister has only half as many sisters as brothers. How many brothers and sisters are in the family?

4 brothers and 3 sisters. Students can use guess and check or logical thinking.

Suggested number of class periods: 7–8

	Lesson	Page	Resources	Objectives
	Chapter Opener	p. 193	TB: p. 147	Investigate division of fractions.
1	Dividing a Unit Fraction by a Whole Number	p. 194	TB: p. 148 WB: p. 137	Divide a unit fraction by a whole number.
2	Dividing a Fraction by a Whole Number	p. 196	TB: p. 151 WB: p. 139	Divide a fraction by a whole number.
3	Practice A	p. 200	TB: p. 155 WB: p. 141	Practice dividing a fraction by a whole number.
4	Dividing a Whole Number by a Unit Fraction	p. 201	TB: p. 156 WB: p. 143	Divide a whole number by a unit fraction.
5	Dividing a Whole Number by a Fraction	p. 204	TB: p. 159 WB: p. 146	Divide a whole number by a fraction.
6	Word Problems	p. 207	TB: p. 163 WB: p. 149	Solve multi-step problems involving division of a fraction by a whole number, or a whole number by a fraction.
7	Practice B	p. 210	TB: p. 166 WB: p. 152	Practice concepts from the chapter.
	Workbook Solutions	p. 211		

In this chapter, students deepen their understanding of fractions by learning how to divide a fraction by a whole number, and a whole number by a fraction.

When students first learned about division, they used the related multiplication fact to solve for a missing factor. For example, to find $15 \div 3$ they thought of $3 \times ? = 15$. They have also learned to use division to solve a missing factor problem. For example, $3 \times ? = 822$ can be found using division: $822 \div 3 = ?$

Similarly, if students know that $3 \times \frac{1}{6} = \frac{1}{2}$, then they know that $\frac{1}{2} \div 3 = \frac{1}{6}$. Students will learn that a problem that can be interpreted as $? \times \frac{2}{3} = 4$ (how many two-thirds are in 4?) can be solved by dividing $4 \div \frac{2}{3} = ?$ Additionally, $4 = \frac{2}{3} \times ?$ (4 is $\frac{2}{3}$ of what number?) can also be solved with division.

Dividing a Fraction by a Whole Number

Lessons 1–3 introduce and offer practice on dividing a fraction by a whole number. Students will first learn how to divide a unit fraction by a whole number. The sharing model of division is an easy way to understand dividing a fraction by a whole number. For example, $\frac{1}{3} \div 4$ means that $\frac{1}{3}$ is divided into 4 equal groups and we are finding the size of each group. Students will see that this is equal to $\frac{1}{4}$ of $\frac{1}{3}$, a problem they learned to solve in the last chapter.

Students will use different models along with number lines to help them understand fraction division concepts.

Example: $\frac{1}{3} \div 4$

We can see from a bar model and number line that dividing $\frac{1}{3}$ by 4 is the same as finding $\frac{1}{4}$ of $\frac{1}{3}$:

$\frac{1}{3} \div 4 = \frac{1}{4} \times \frac{1}{3} = \frac{1}{12}$

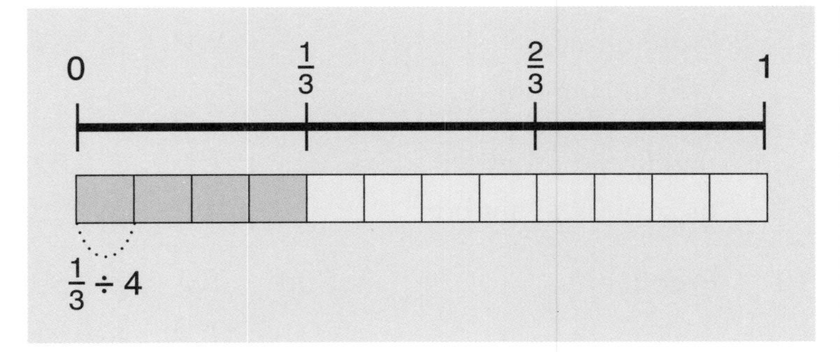

Students will then understand that dividing by 4 is the same as multiplying by the reciprocal of 4, which is $\frac{1}{4}$.

Using this knowledge, students will solve problems involving division of a fraction by a whole number by multiplying by the reciprocal.

Example: $\frac{6}{7} \div 3$

$\frac{6}{7} \div 3 = \frac{1}{3}$ of $\frac{6}{7} = \frac{1}{3} \times \frac{6}{7} = \frac{2}{7}$

Students will learn additional strategies for dividing a fraction by a whole number.

In the example above, the numerator is easily divisible by 3, and we can think of the denominator as the unit:

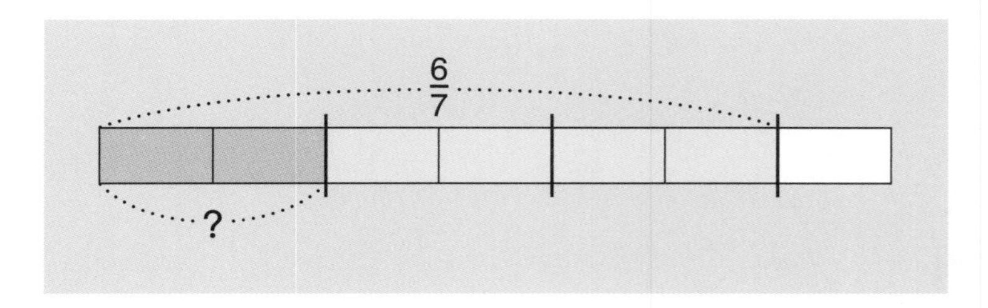

6 sevenths ÷ 3 = 2 sevenths

Students can relate this to their prior understanding of division with units. For example, 6 centimeters divided by 3 = 2 centimeters.

Another strategy is to divide the unit fraction, $\frac{1}{7}$, by 3, and then multiply by the numerator, 6:

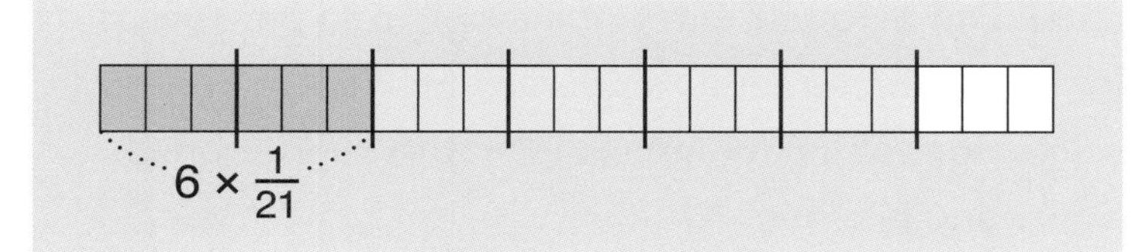

$\frac{1}{7} \div 3 = \frac{1}{7} \times \frac{1}{3} = \frac{1}{21}$

$\frac{6}{7} \div 3 = 6 \times \frac{1}{21} = \frac{6}{21} = \frac{2}{7}$

These strategies can also be used when dividing a fraction where the numerator is not a multiple of the whole number or dividend by using equivalent fractions:

$\frac{2}{3} \div 4 = \frac{4}{6} \div 4 = \frac{1}{6}$ (4 sixths ÷ 4 = 1 sixth)

$\frac{1}{5} \div 4 = \frac{1}{20}$

$\frac{3}{5} \div 4 = 3 \times \frac{1}{20} = \frac{3}{20}$

We can use this unitary approach to divide any number by 4, including an improper fraction.

$\frac{1}{3} \div 4 = \frac{1}{12}$

$\frac{4}{3} \div 4 = 4 \times \frac{1}{12} = \frac{4}{12} = \frac{1}{3}$

$\frac{7}{3} \div 4 = 7 \times \frac{1}{12} = \frac{7}{12}$

$\frac{15}{3} \div 4 = 15 \times \frac{1}{12} = \frac{15}{12} = 1\frac{1}{4}$

$\frac{50}{3} \div 4 = 50 \times \frac{1}{12} = \frac{50}{12} = 4\frac{1}{6}$

Students will see that they can also divide an improper fraction by a whole number by multiplying by the reciprocal. For example:

$\frac{15}{3} \div 4 = \frac{15}{3} \times \frac{1}{4} = \frac{15}{12} = 1\frac{1}{4}$

Dividing a Whole Number by a Fraction

Lessons 4 and 5 introduce dividing a whole number by a fraction, e.g. $3 \div \frac{1}{2}$. Students often struggle to understand the difference between, for example, dividing by $\frac{1}{2}$ and finding half of a number.

To help understand division by a fraction, students should return to their experience of understanding division as grouping rather than sharing.

First, students divide by a unit fraction.

Example: $3 \div \frac{1}{2}$

$3 \div \frac{1}{2}$ means that 3 wholes are divided into groups of size $\frac{1}{2}$. We are finding how many such groups there are:

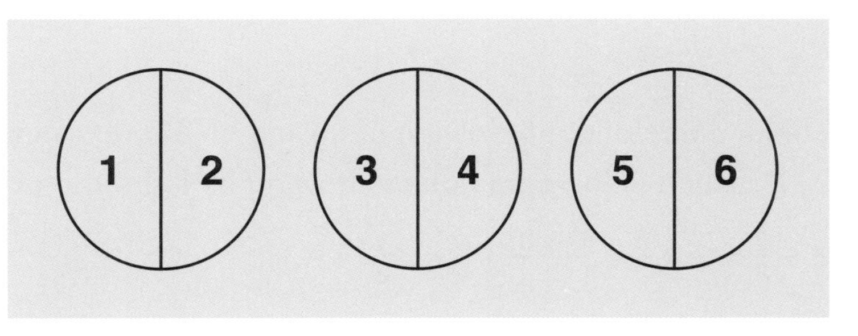

There are six $\frac{1}{2}$s in 3.

If students struggle, have them think about the problem with whole numbers: 6 ÷ 3 = ? asks us to find how many groups of 3 are in six, or ? × 3 = 6.

Students can see that to divide by $\frac{1}{2}$, we can multiply by the reciprocal of $\frac{1}{2}$, which is 2.

Using this knowledge, students will see that to divide a whole number that is not a unit fraction, we can also multiply by the reciprocal.

Example: $3 \div \frac{2}{3}$ or, "How many $\frac{2}{3}$ are in 3?"

First we can think, "How many one-thirds are in 3?"

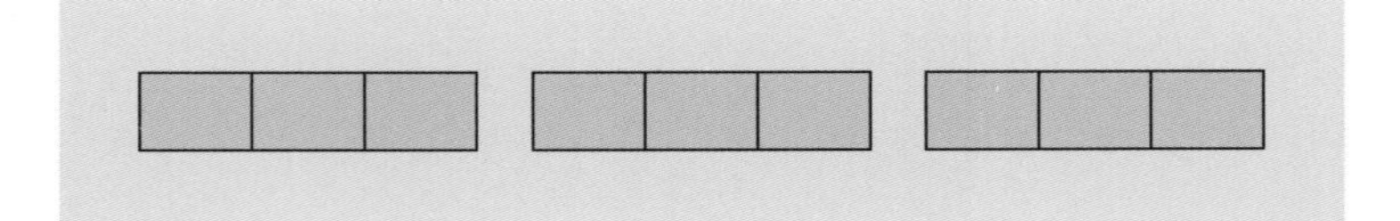

$3 \div \frac{1}{3} = 3 \times 3 = 9$

We then need to group these by 2 to find out how many groups of two $\frac{1}{3}$s are in 9.

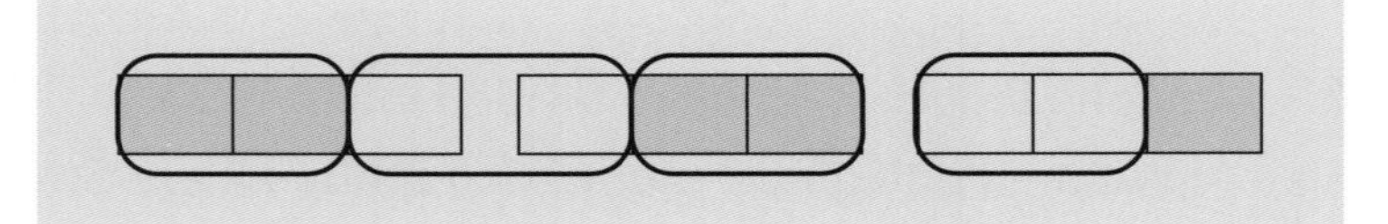

$9 \div 2 = \frac{9}{2} = 4\frac{1}{2}$

These calculations involve multiplying by 3 and dividing by 2, which is the same as multiplying by the reciprocal:

$3 \div \frac{2}{3} = 3 \times \frac{3}{2} = \frac{(3 \times 3)}{2} = \frac{9}{2} = 4\frac{1}{2}$

Students will practice these two concepts in Lessons 6 and 7 with word problems. By the end of the chapter, students should conceptually understand why we multiply by the reciprocal when dividing with fractions.

It is advised that teachers should not teach the shortcut procedure "invert and multiply" or "keep, flip, change." These shortcuts confuse students and puts their attention on procedural rules instead of understanding division with fractions in general.

Students will learn to divide a fraction by a fraction in Dimensions Math 6A.

Materials

- Counters
- Die
- Index cards
- Paper clips
- Pattern blocks
- Paper strips
- Whiteboards

Note: Many of the lessons make use of paper strips of equal length to allow students to fold, shade, partition, and cut lengths to understand division. The strips should all be about the same length and between a foot and a meter long. Students can work in groups with longer strips, or individually with shorter ones. Some suggestions:

Cut copy paper lengthwise, into 3 cm wide strips.

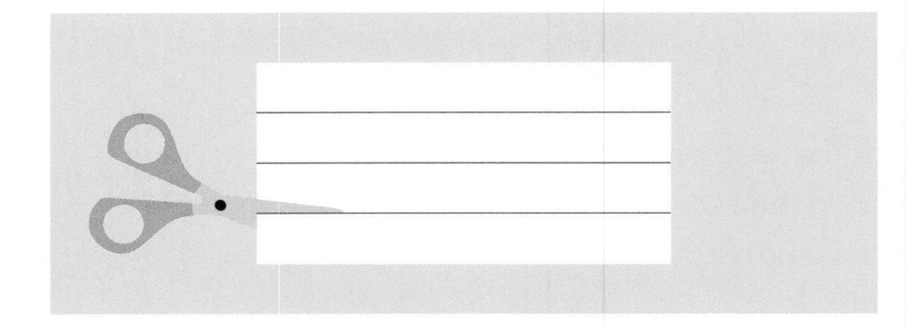

Cut equal lengths of adding tape.

Blackline Masters

- Dividing Domino Cards
- Fraction 3 in a Row
- Number Cards
- Unit Fraction 3 in a Row
- Quick Quotients

Activities

Activities included in this chapter provide practice for dividing fractions. They can be used after students complete the <u>**Do**</u> questions, or anytime additional practice is needed.

Objective

- Investigate division of fractions.

Lesson Materials

- Pattern Blocks

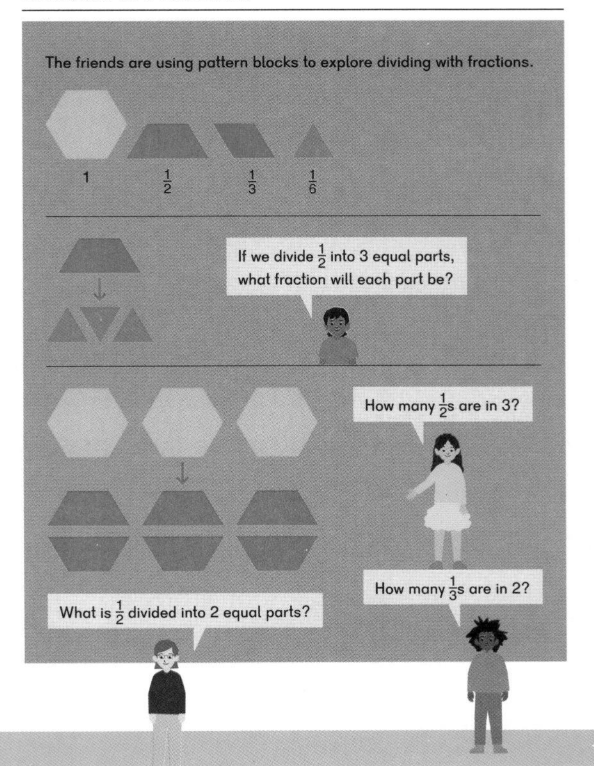

With the textbook closed, provide students with pattern blocks and tell them that the hexagon has a value of 1. Ask them what the value of the other shapes in the pattern blocks would be. For example, students should see that the trapezoid is $\frac{1}{2}$ of the value of the hexagon. Ask students questions such as the following:

- "How many sixths equal $\frac{1}{3}$? How many sixths equal $\frac{2}{3}$?"
- "Show $1\frac{1}{2}$ with pattern blocks. How many halves equal $1\frac{1}{2}$? How many sixths equal $1\frac{1}{2}$?"

Then have students ask each other similar questions. After time to explore fraction concepts, have students discuss the friends' questions on the textbook page.

Ask students:

- "Is 'How many halves are in 3?' the same as dividing 3 in half?" (No because there are 6 halves in 3, and $\frac{1}{2}$ of 3 is $1\frac{1}{2}$.)
- "What kind of equation would we write for this?"

  Alex: $\frac{1}{2} \div 3 = \frac{1}{6}$

  Sofia: $3 \div \frac{1}{2} = 6$

  Dion: $2 \div \frac{1}{3} = 6$

  Emma: $\frac{1}{2} \div 2 = \frac{1}{4}$

Using the pattern blocks, ask students to show the answers for the questions and write division expressions representing these answers.

★ To extend, have students write other equations involving division by halves, thirds, and sixths, and use the pattern blocks to find the answers.

Objective

- Divide a unit fraction by a whole number.

Lesson Materials

- Paper strips of equal length

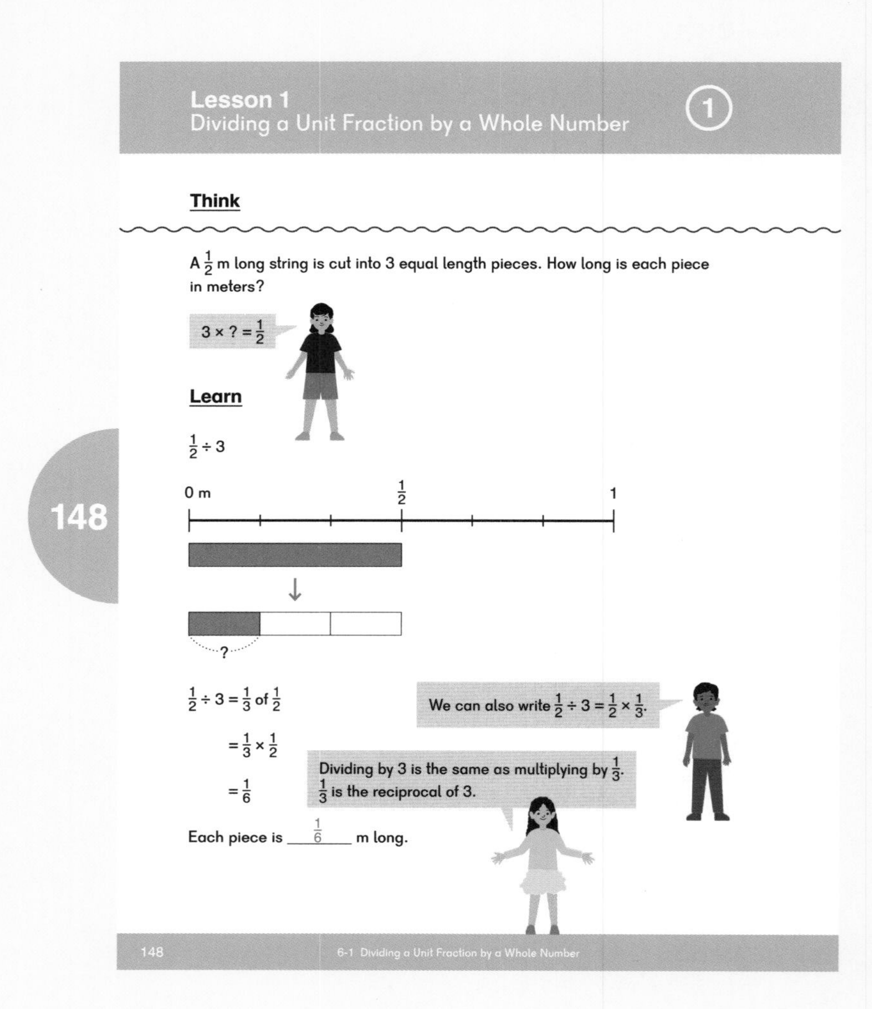

Think

Provide students with paper strips to represent the 1 m long string and pose the **Think** problem.

Ask students, "Is this problem a sharing or grouping division problem? How do you know?" (This is a sharing division problem because there are 3 equal pieces, i.e., groups.)

Discuss Mei's comment. It should prompt students to think of this as a missing factor problem.

Have students fold and shade the paper strip to show how long each piece of the string is in meters.

Learn

Discuss the number line and bar model.

The bar model first shows a length of $\frac{1}{2}$ m, then that $\frac{1}{2}$ m is divided into 3 equal parts. This makes each equal part $\frac{1}{6}$ of the 1 m.

Students can think about whole numbers when relating multiplication and division. Just as $3 \times ? = 15$ can be found with $15 \div 3 = ?$, we can also find $3 \times ? = \frac{1}{2}$ by calculating $\frac{1}{2} \div 3 = ?$

Ask students why Alex is thinking about both a division and multiplication expression. They should recall that the reciprocal of 3 is $\frac{1}{3}$.

Do

❶–❹ Discuss the different examples and problems with students. Different models for ❶ – ❸ are each shown. Students may choose to draw a model to help them solve problems as needed involving division of fractions.

❶ The whole of 1 is shown and the dividend ($\frac{1}{4}$) is shaded dark orange. When we divide $\frac{1}{4}$ by 2, each part is now $\frac{1}{8}$.

❷ The rectangle is 1 whole and is divided into fifths vertically and into fourths horizontally, creating twentieths. Each fifth is therefore divided into fourths, and one of those is $\frac{1}{20}$.

Students should see the similarity between this and how they first learned to multiply a fraction by a fraction. They should see that we can multiply by the reciprocal to find the answer. ($\frac{1}{5} \times \frac{1}{4} = \frac{1}{20}$)

❸ Ask students, "Do we get the same answer as if we multiplied by the reciprocal of 5?" Dividing a number by 5 is the same as finding one-fifth of that number.

❺–❽ Students should be able to solve these problems independently.

❻ Have students draw models as needed.

Activity

▲ Unit Fraction 3 in a Row

Materials: Unit Fraction 3 in a Row (BLM), die, counters

Players each get a Unit Fraction 3 in a Row (BLM) gameboard. On each turn, a player rolls the die and chooses a problem from that column to solve. If he solves the problem correctly, he covers the square with a counter.

The winner is the first player to mark 3 in a row, column, or diagonal.

Exercise 1 • page 137

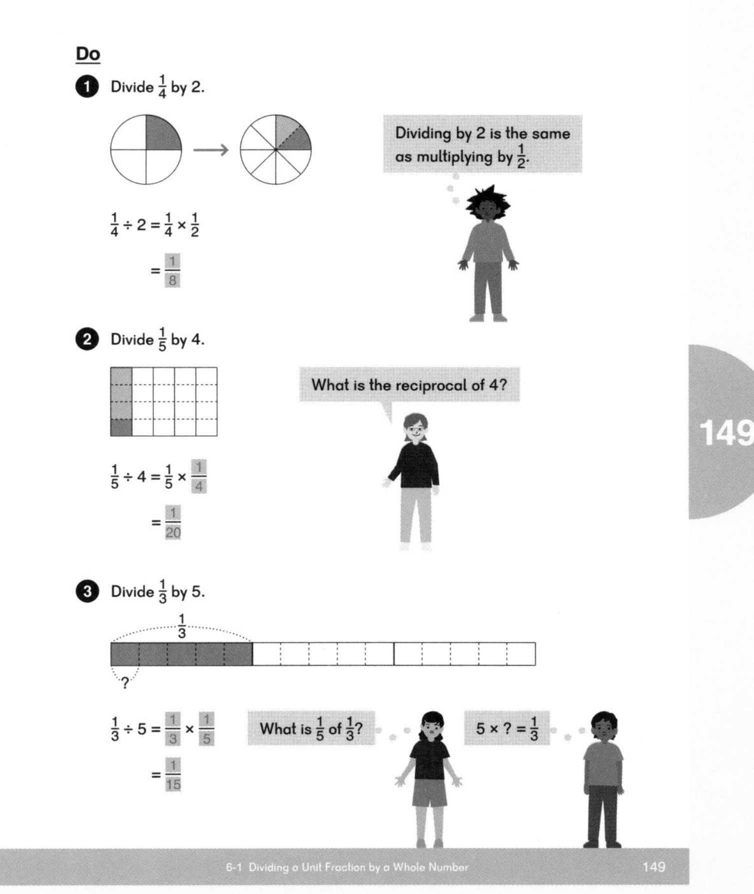

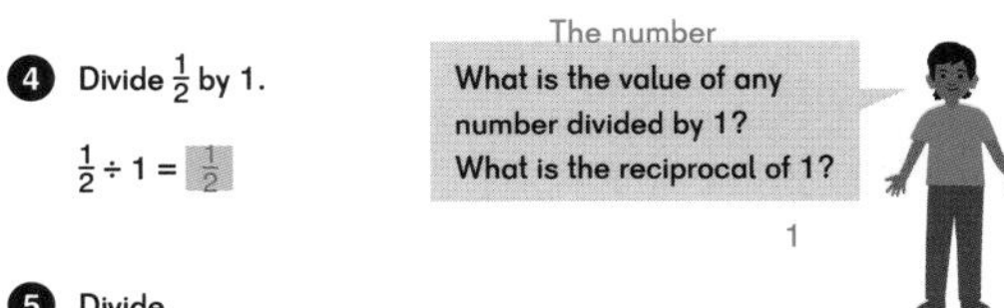

5 Divide.

(a) $\frac{1}{3} \div 7$ $\frac{1}{21}$ (b) $\frac{1}{7} \div 3$ $\frac{1}{21}$

(c) $\frac{1}{6} \div 2$ $\frac{1}{12}$ (d) $\frac{1}{2} \div 6$ $\frac{1}{12}$

(e) $\frac{1}{8} \div 5$ $\frac{1}{40}$ (f) $\frac{1}{9} \div 3$ $\frac{1}{27}$

6 (a) $\frac{1}{5} \div 2 = \frac{1}{10}$

(b) $\frac{1}{4} \div 5 = \frac{1}{20}$

(c) $\frac{1}{3} \div 2 = \frac{1}{6}$

7 $\frac{1}{5}$ L of juice is poured equally into 5 cups. How many liters of juice are in each cup?

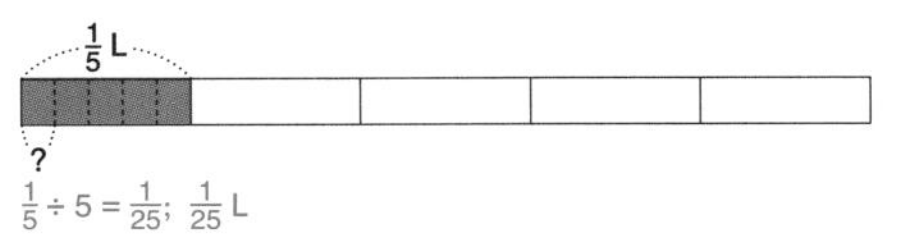

$\frac{1}{5} \div 5 = \frac{1}{25}$; $\frac{1}{25}$ L

8 Write a word problem for $\frac{1}{3} \div 2$.
Answers will vary.

Exercise 1 • page 137

Objective

- Divide a fraction by a whole number.

Lesson Materials

- Index cards
- Paper strips of equal length

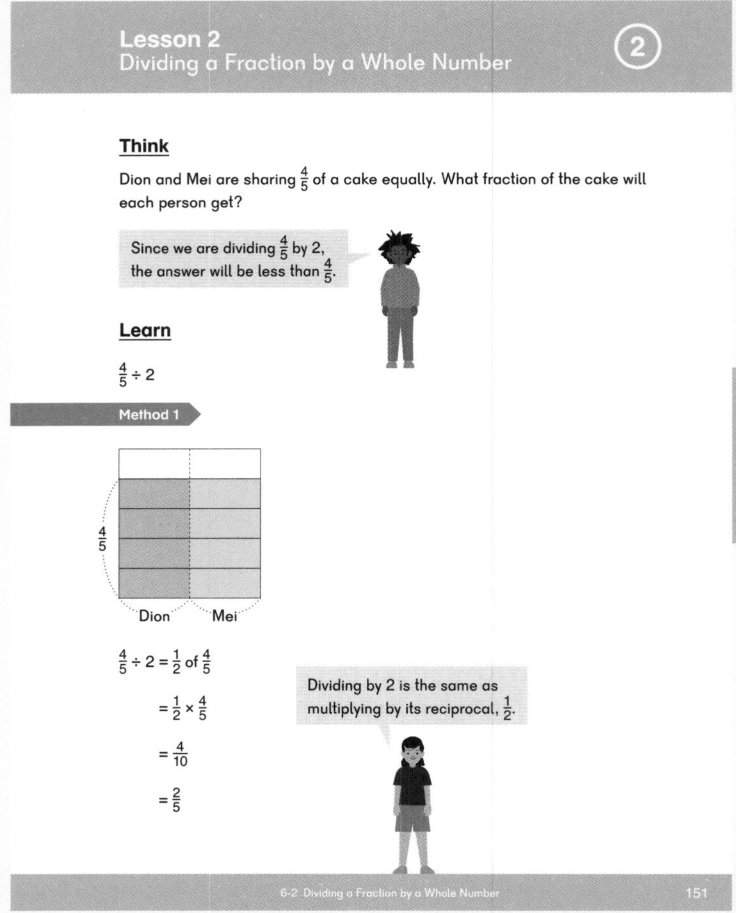
Lesson 2
Dividing a Fraction by a Whole Number
2

Think

Dion and Mei are sharing $\frac{4}{5}$ of a cake equally. What fraction of the cake will each person get?

Since we are dividing $\frac{4}{5}$ by 2, the answer will be less than $\frac{4}{5}$.

Learn

$\frac{4}{5} \div 2$

Method 1

$\frac{4}{5} \div 2 = \frac{1}{2}$ of $\frac{4}{5}$

$= \frac{1}{2} \times \frac{4}{5}$

$= \frac{4}{10}$

$= \frac{2}{5}$

Dividing by 2 is the same as multiplying by its reciprocal, $\frac{1}{2}$.

6-2 Dividing a Fraction by a Whole Number 151

151

Think

Discuss the **Think** problem and Dion's comment.

Ask students to choose an index card, paper strip, or draw a bar model to illustrate the solution to the **Think** problem.

Discuss student solutions.

Learn

Have students compare their solutions from **Think** with the ones in the textbook.

Discuss the models shown in the three methods.

Method 1

Students learned in Lesson 1 that dividing a unit fraction by a whole number is the same as multiplying that unit fraction by the whole number's reciprocal. Here, students should see that dividing $\frac{4}{5}$ by 2 is the same as multiplying $\frac{4}{5}$ by $\frac{1}{2}$.

$\frac{4}{5} \div 2 = \frac{1}{2}$ of $\frac{4}{5}$

Students already know that they can multiply in any order so they might also write:

$\frac{1}{2} \times \frac{4}{5} = \frac{4}{5} \times \frac{1}{2}$

$\frac{4}{5} \div 2 = \frac{4}{5} \times \frac{1}{2}$

Method 2

Alex uses units. Just as 4 cm ÷ 2 = 2 cm, 4 fifths ÷ 2 = 2 fifths.

Method 3

Discuss Sofia's comment. If we draw the model, $\frac{4}{5}$ of the whole is shaded orange first. Each of these shaded one-fifths is then divided by 2, or in half, represented by the light and darker orange shading.

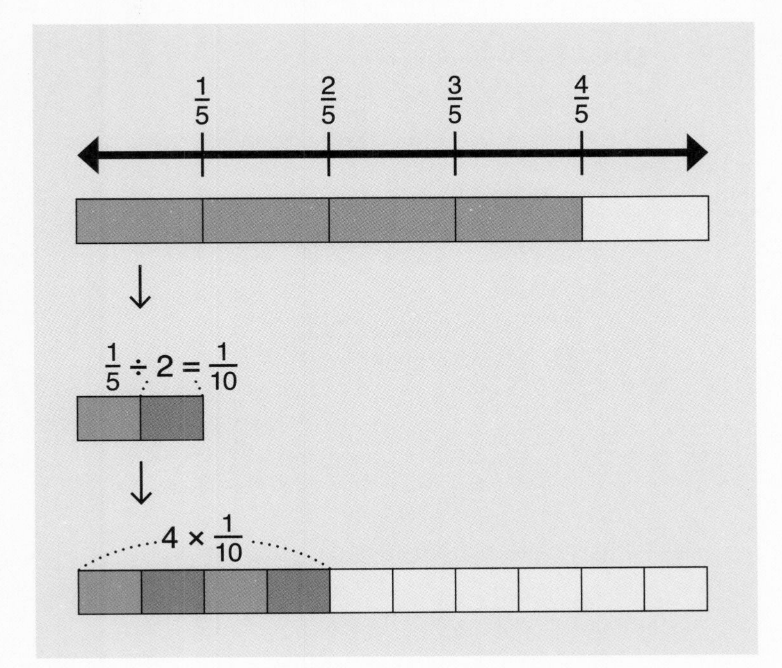

$\frac{1}{5} \div 2 = \frac{1}{10}$

$\frac{4}{5} \div 2 = 4 \times \frac{1}{10}$

When the four tenths are put together in the second bar model, we can see $4 \times \frac{1}{10}$.

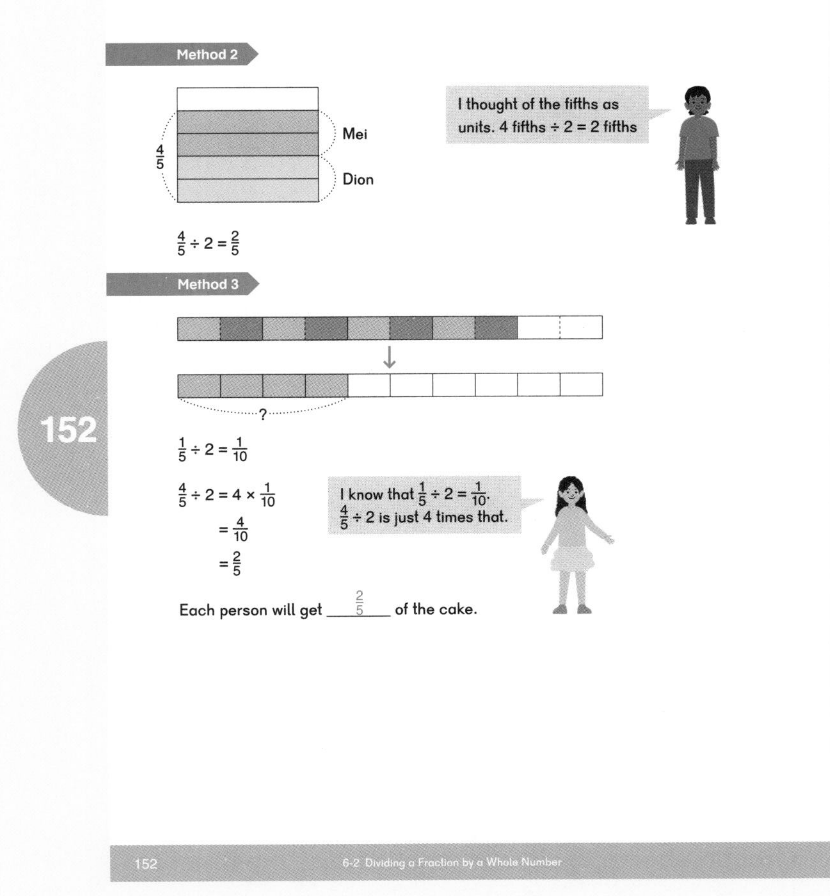

Do

❶—❹ Discuss the given models and problems with students.

❶ Dion is thinking of fourths as units. Just as 3 tens divided by 3 is 1 ten, 3 fourths divided by 3 is 1 fourth.

❷ From the model and prior knowledge, students should see that finding $\frac{6}{7}$ divided by 2 is the same as finding $\frac{1}{2}$ of $\frac{6}{7}$.

❸ (a) In the model shown, the rectangle is divided vertically into fourths and horizontally into thirds. The model is similar to what students used in the previous chapter, and will help students see why dividing by a whole number gives the same answer as multiplying by the reciprocal.

Some students may choose to simply calculate: $\frac{2}{3} \times \frac{1}{4} = \frac{2}{12}$, then simplify, or simplify before calculating.

(b) In **Learn** as well as ❶ and ❷, the numerator of the fraction being divided is a multiple of the divisor. In order to use the method of simply dividing the numerator by the divisor, Mei is finding an equivalent fraction. $\frac{4}{6} \div 4$ is easy to calculate.

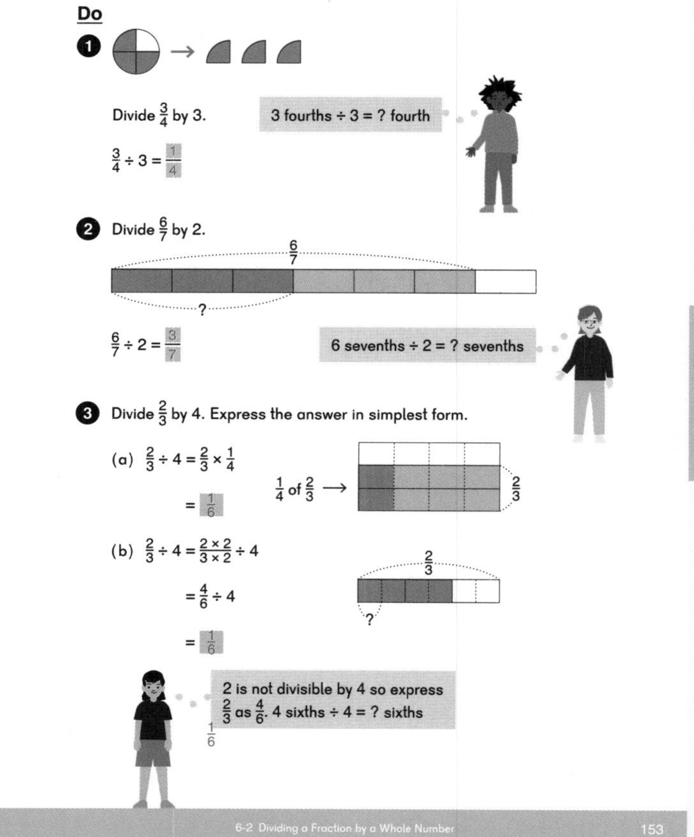

Do

❶ Divide $\frac{3}{4}$ by 3.

$\frac{3}{4} \div 3 = \frac{1}{4}$

❷ Divide $\frac{6}{7}$ by 2.

$\frac{6}{7} \div 2 = \frac{3}{7}$

❸ Divide $\frac{2}{3}$ by 4. Express the answer in simplest form.

(a) $\frac{2}{3} \div 4 = \frac{2}{3} \times \frac{1}{4}$

$= \frac{1}{6}$

(b) $\frac{2}{3} \div 4 = \frac{2 \times 2}{3 \times 2} \div 4$

$= \frac{4}{6} \div 4$

$= \frac{1}{6}$

6-2 Dividing a Fraction by a Whole Number 153

❺—❽ Most students should be able to solve these problems without drawing any models.

❺ Discuss which method students used to solve the problems.

For example:

(a) Thinking of sevenths as units, students should see that 4 one-sevenths = 4 sevenths, so it is easy to divide $\frac{4}{7}$ by 4.

(b) 7 is not divisible by 4. Many students will multiply $\frac{7}{4}$ by $\frac{1}{4}$. Some students may decide to find an equivalent fraction of $\frac{7}{4}$ in which the numerator is a multiple of 7, similar to Mei's method in ❸. For example:

$\frac{28}{16} \div 4 = \frac{7}{16}$

Activity

▲ Fraction 3 in a Row

Materials: Fraction 3 in a Row (BLM), die, counters

Players each get a Fraction 3 in a Row (BLM) gameboard. On each turn, a player rolls the die and chooses a problem from that column to solve. If he solves the problem correctly, he covers the square with a counter.

The winner is the first player to mark 3 in a row, column, or diagonal.

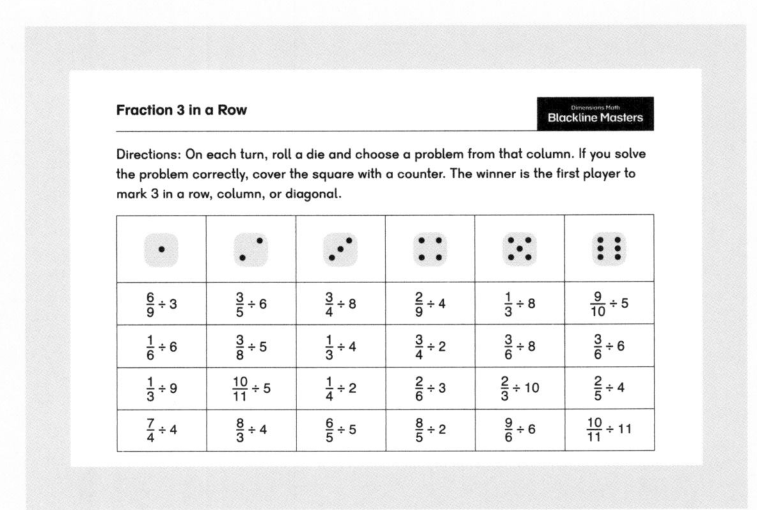

Fraction 3 in a Row — Dimensions Math Blackline Masters

Directions: On each turn, roll a die and choose a problem from that column. If you solve the problem correctly, cover the square with a counter. The winner is the first player to mark 3 in a row, column, or diagonal.

⚀	⚁	⚂	⚃	⚄	⚅
$\frac{6}{9} \div 3$	$\frac{3}{5} \div 6$	$\frac{3}{4} \div 8$	$\frac{2}{9} \div 4$	$\frac{1}{3} \div 8$	$\frac{9}{10} \div 5$
$\frac{1}{6} \div 6$	$\frac{3}{8} \div 5$	$\frac{1}{3} \div 4$	$\frac{3}{4} \div 2$	$\frac{3}{6} \div 8$	$\frac{3}{6} \div 6$
$\frac{1}{3} \div 9$	$\frac{10}{11} \div 5$	$\frac{1}{4} \div 2$	$\frac{2}{6} \div 3$	$\frac{2}{3} \div 10$	$\frac{2}{5} \div 4$
$\frac{7}{4} \div 4$	$\frac{8}{3} \div 4$	$\frac{6}{5} \div 5$	$\frac{8}{5} \div 2$	$\frac{9}{6} \div 6$	$\frac{10}{11} \div 11$

❹ A 3-m pipe weighs $\frac{9}{10}$ kg. How many kilograms does 1 m of the pipe weigh?

0 m 1 2 3

? $\frac{9}{10}$ kg

$\frac{9}{10} \div 3$

$\frac{9}{10} \div 3 = \frac{3}{10}$; $\frac{3}{10}$ kg

❺ Find the values.

(a) $\frac{4}{7} \div 4$ $\frac{1}{7}$ (b) $\frac{7}{4} \div 4$ $\frac{7}{16}$ (c) $\frac{8}{9} \div 4$ $\frac{2}{9}$

(d) $\frac{3}{5} \div 6$ $\frac{1}{10}$ (e) $\frac{2}{3} \div 10$ $\frac{1}{15}$ (f) $\frac{5}{8} \div 2$ $\frac{5}{16}$

❻ Dion wants to cut $\frac{2}{3}$ m of rope into 6 pieces of equal length. How long in meters should he cut each piece?
$\frac{2}{3} \div 6 = \frac{1}{9}$; $\frac{1}{9}$ m

❼ $\frac{9}{10}$ L of juice was poured into 6 cups. How many liters of juice are in each cup?
$\frac{9}{10} \div 6 = \frac{3}{20}$; $\frac{3}{20}$ L

❽ Write a word problem for $\frac{4}{5} \div 2$.
Answers will vary.

Exercise 2 • page 139

154

Exercise 2 • page 139

Objective

- Practice dividing a fraction by a whole number.

After students complete the **Practice** in the textbook, have them continue to practice dividing fractions by playing the games from the chapter as needed.

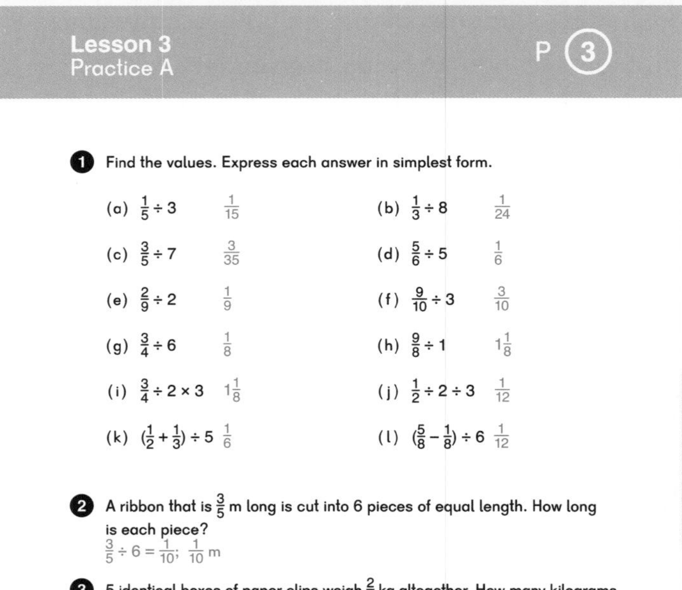

Lesson 3
Practice A

P 3

1. Find the values. Express each answer in simplest form.

(a) $\frac{1}{5} \div 3$	$\frac{1}{15}$	(b) $\frac{1}{3} \div 8$	$\frac{1}{24}$
(c) $\frac{3}{5} \div 7$	$\frac{3}{35}$	(d) $\frac{5}{6} \div 5$	$\frac{1}{6}$
(e) $\frac{2}{9} \div 2$	$\frac{1}{9}$	(f) $\frac{9}{10} \div 3$	$\frac{3}{10}$
(g) $\frac{3}{4} \div 6$	$\frac{1}{8}$	(h) $\frac{9}{8} \div 1$	$1\frac{1}{8}$
(i) $\frac{3}{4} \div 2 \times 3$	$1\frac{1}{8}$	(j) $\frac{1}{2} \div 2 \div 3$	$\frac{1}{12}$
(k) $(\frac{1}{2} + \frac{1}{3}) \div 5$	$\frac{1}{6}$	(l) $(\frac{5}{8} - \frac{1}{8}) \div 6$	$\frac{1}{12}$

2. A ribbon that is $\frac{3}{5}$ m long is cut into 6 pieces of equal length. How long is each piece?
$\frac{3}{5} \div 6 = \frac{1}{10}$; $\frac{1}{10}$ m

3. 5 identical boxes of paper clips weigh $\frac{2}{3}$ kg altogether. How many kilograms does 1 box of paper clips weigh?
$\frac{2}{3} \div 5 = \frac{2}{15}$; $\frac{2}{15}$ kg

4. $\frac{3}{4}$ lb of almonds are put equally into 6 bags. What is the weight of the almonds in each bag?
$\frac{3}{4} \div 6 = \frac{1}{8}$; $\frac{1}{8}$ lb

5. The perimeter of a square is $\frac{2}{5}$ m. What is the length of one side of the square in meters?
$\frac{2}{5} \div 4 = \frac{1}{10}$; $\frac{1}{10}$ m

Exercise 3 • page 141

155

Activity

▲ Fraction Puzzler

● + ● $= \frac{1}{4}$

★ + ★ $= \frac{6}{8}$

☾ + ☾ + ☾ $= \frac{9}{10}$

● + ★ + ☾ = ?

$\frac{1}{8} + \frac{3}{8} + \frac{3}{10} = \frac{4}{5}$

★ Students can create a similar puzzle using the symbols for a classmate to solve.

Exercise 3 • page 141

Objective

- Divide a whole number by a unit fraction.

Lesson Materials

- Paper strips of equal length

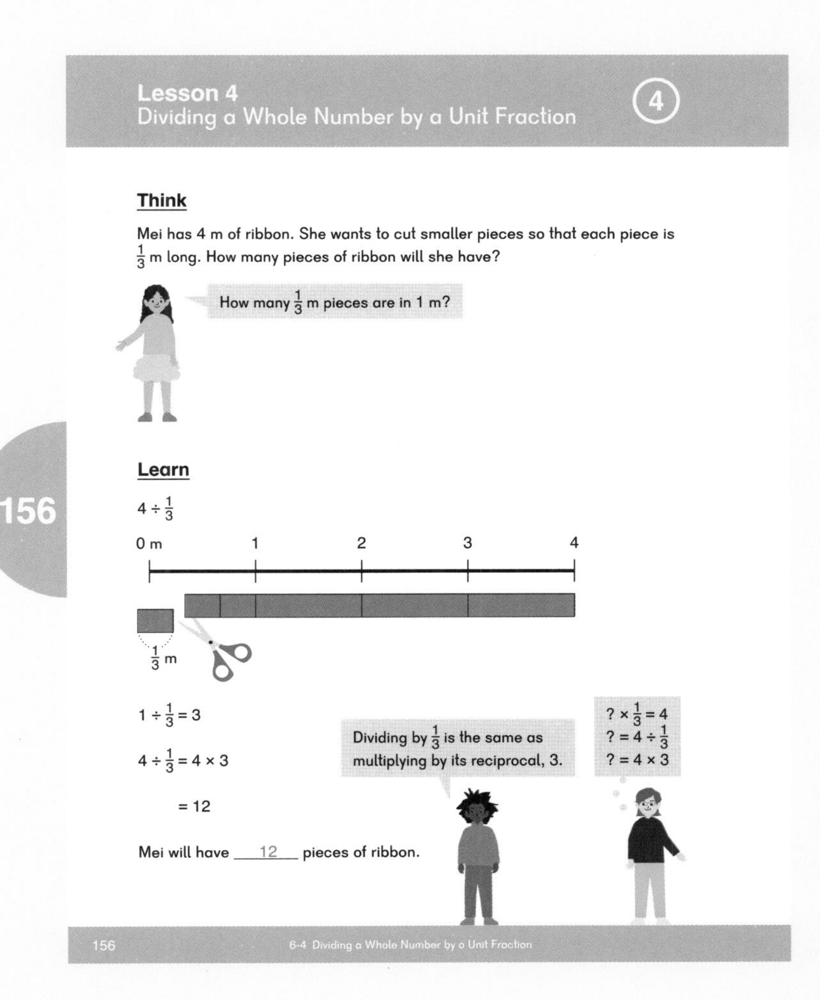

Think

Provide each student with four paper strips and pose the **Think** problem. Discuss Sofia's question.

Students can fold, shade, or cut the paper strips to find their answers.

Discuss student solutions.

Learn

Have students compare their paper strips with the bar model shown in **Learn**.

Relate this to whole number division by showing students that we can approach this as a grouping problem. We can think about grouping division with whole numbers. For example, $6 \div 2$ can be thought of as, "How many twos are in six?"

Similarly, we can think about $4 \text{ m} \div \frac{1}{3} \text{ m}$ as, "How many parts of size $\frac{1}{3}$ m are in 4 m?"

If we can find the number of $\frac{1}{3}$ m pieces in 1 m, we can multiply by 4 to find the number of $\frac{1}{3}$ m pieces in 4 m.

Discuss how the three equations Emma is thinking about to help her solve the problem are related.

Do

❶—❹ Discuss the given models and problems with students. From the models, students will further develop the connection between division of fractions and multiplying by the reciprocal.

❶ (a) $1 \div \frac{1}{4} = 1 \times 4$

(b) $3 \div \frac{1}{4} = 3 \times 4$

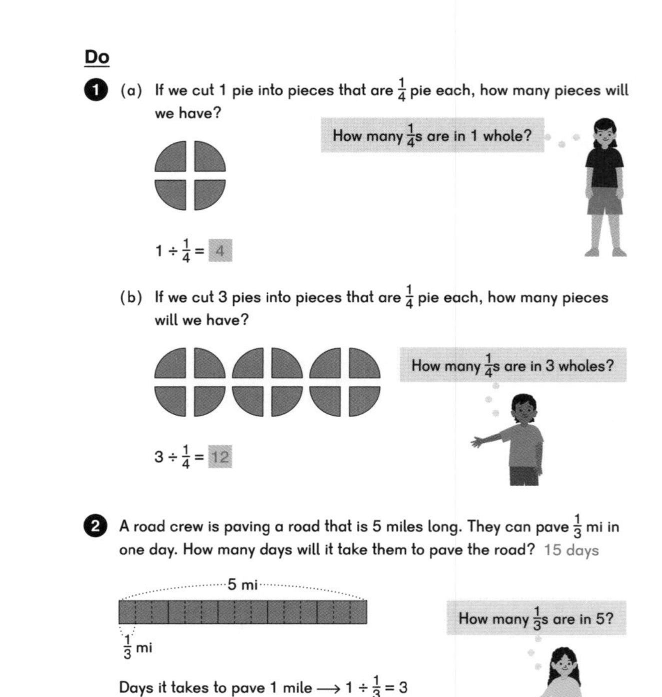

157

❸ In ❷ all of the one-thirds are drawn, while ❸ only shows the number of one-eighths in 1 L. Drawing 32 units of one-eighths would be cumbersome.

❹ If needed, ask students, “How many one-fourths are in 1 lb?”

❺—❻ Most students should be able to solve these problems without drawing any models.

Activity

▲ Quick Quotients

Materials: Quick Quotients (BLM), paper clip

In each round, players take turns spinning the spinner and filling out the boxes in the equation. When the two boxes are filled, players calculate their answers. The player with the greatest quotient wins the round.

If desired, players may keep score and declare a winner after five rounds.

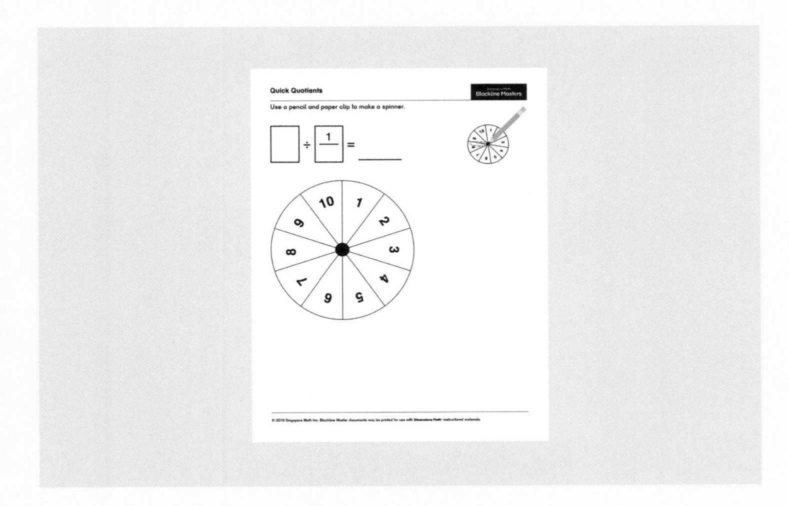
Quick Quotients

Use a pencil and paper clip to make a spinner.

$\square \div \frac{1}{\square} =$ ______

Exercise 4 • page 143

158

❸ Sofia has 4 L of water. She puts $\frac{1}{8}$ L of water in each glass. How many glasses will she need? 32 glasses

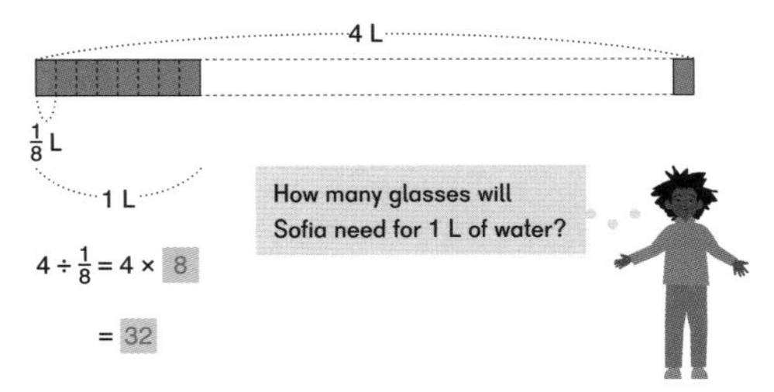

$4 \div \frac{1}{8} = 4 \times 8$

$= 32$

❹ $\frac{1}{4}$ lb of coffee costs \$2. How much does 1 lb of coffee cost?

$\frac{1}{4}$ lb ⟶ \$2

1 lb ⟶ $\$2 \div \frac{1}{4} = \$2 \times 4 = \$8$

❺ Find the values.

(a) $1 \div \frac{1}{8}$ 8

(b) $2 \div \frac{1}{3}$ 6

(c) $9 \div \frac{1}{2}$ 18

(d) $6 \div \frac{1}{5}$ 30

(e) $12 \div \frac{1}{9}$ 108

(f) $10 \div \frac{1}{10}$ 100

❻ Write a word problem for $3 \div \frac{1}{2}$.
Answers will vary.

Exercise 4 • page 143

Objective

- Divide a whole number by a fraction.

Lesson Materials

- Paper strips of equal lengths

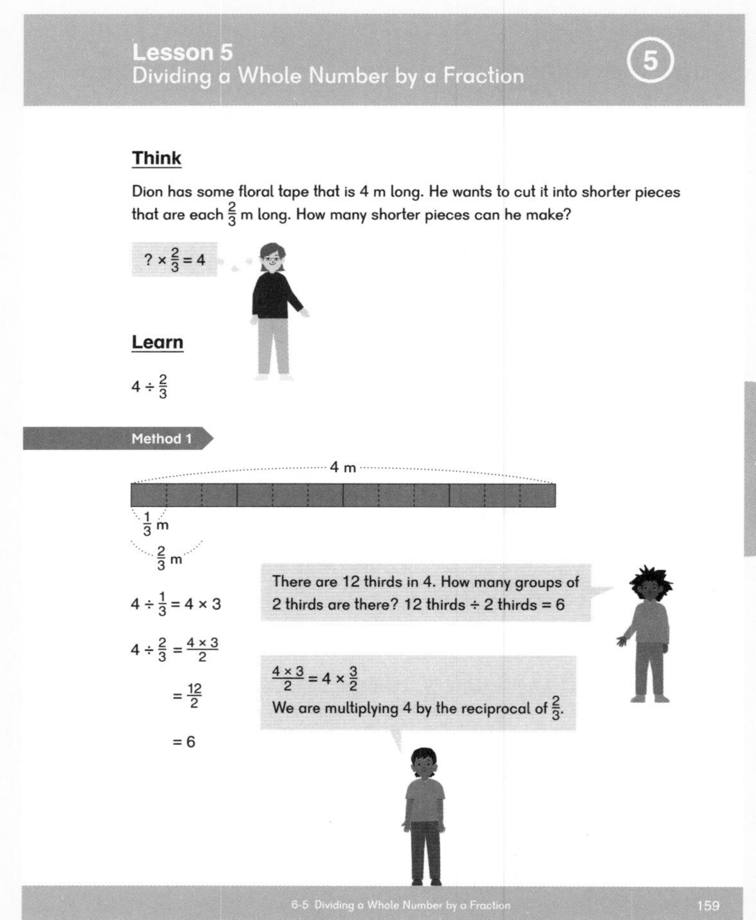

Think

Provide students with paper strips and pose the **Think** problem. Discuss Emma's equation. Ask students what is alike and what is different between this **Think** problem and the **Think** problem in Lesson 4. (They are both dividing a whole number by a fraction. In Lesson 4, they divide by a unit fraction, here they do not.)

Students can think of this as, "How many $\frac{2}{3}$ m are in 4 m?" Students can fold, shade, or cut the paper strips to find their answers.

Discuss student solutions.

Learn

Have students compare their paper strips with the models shown in **Learn**.

Method 1

Dion thinks of thirds as units. Once we find the number of thirds, we can group them by 2, to find the number of two-thirds in 4. We are multiplying 4 by 3 to get the number of thirds, then dividing that by 2 to group by two-thirds which gives the same answer as multiplying by the reciprocal.

Ask students:

- "How many total units is the 4 m divided into?" (12 total units because each meter is divided into 3 units.)
- "What fraction of a meter is each of these units?" ($\frac{1}{3}$ m)
- "How can we use this to find how many $\frac{2}{3}$ m are in the 4 m?" (12 thirds ÷ 2 thirds = 6 thirds)

Method 2

Looking at the bar model and number line, Mei sees that there is one $\frac{2}{3}$ m piece and then another half of a $\frac{2}{3}$ m piece in 1 m, or 3 halves of a $\frac{2}{3}$ m piece. Four of these pieces will be four times as many as $\frac{3}{2}$ m.

$1 \div \frac{2}{3} = \frac{3}{2}$

$4 \div \frac{2}{3} = 4 \times \frac{3}{2}$

Ask students:

- "What sized units is the 4 m divided into?" ($\frac{2}{3}$ m)
- "How many of these units are in 1 m?" ($1\frac{1}{2}$ or $\frac{3}{2}$)
- "How can we use this to find how many two-thirds are in the 4 m?" ($4 \times \frac{3}{2} = 6$)

Do

❶—❹ Discuss the problems and given models with students. Students who are confused can use fraction manipulatives to help them find the answers.

❷ First we multiply by 5 to find how many one-fifths are in 3. Then, we divide by 3 to find how many three-fifths there are in 3.

❸ Students can think:

$\frac{3}{4}$ wall $\longrightarrow$ 1 can

$\frac{1}{4}$ wall $\longrightarrow$ 1 can $\div 3 = \frac{1}{3}$ can

1 wall $\longrightarrow \frac{1}{3}$ can $\times 4 = \frac{4}{3}$ can

4 walls $\longrightarrow \frac{4}{3}$ can $\times 4 = \frac{16}{3}$ or $5\frac{1}{3}$ cans

160

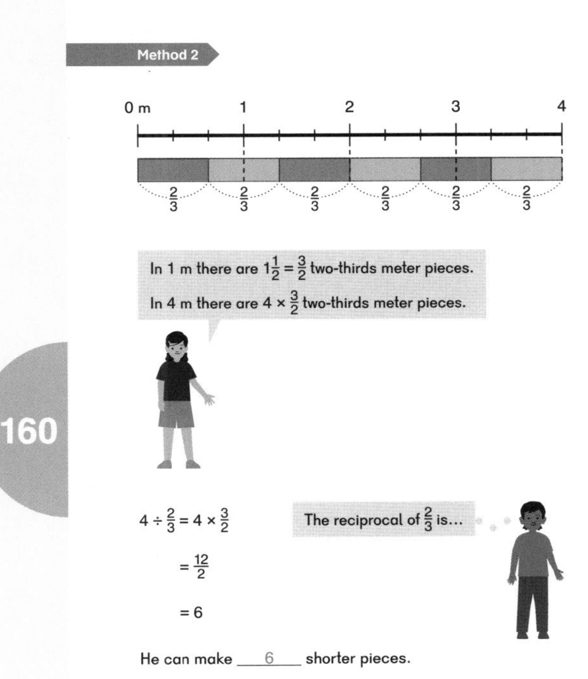

Do

❶ How many $\frac{2}{3}$s are in 2?

$2 \div \frac{2}{3} = 3$

❷ There are 3 pies. If we put $\frac{3}{5}$ of a pie on each plate, how many plates will we need?

$3 \div \frac{1}{5} = 3 \times 5$

$3 \div \frac{3}{5} = \frac{3 \times 5}{3}$

$= 5$ 5 plates

In 3 pies, there are 15 pieces that are $\frac{1}{5}$ of a pie.

161

❸ It takes one can of paint to paint $\frac{3}{4}$ of a wall. How many cans of paint will it take to paint 4 of the same sized walls?

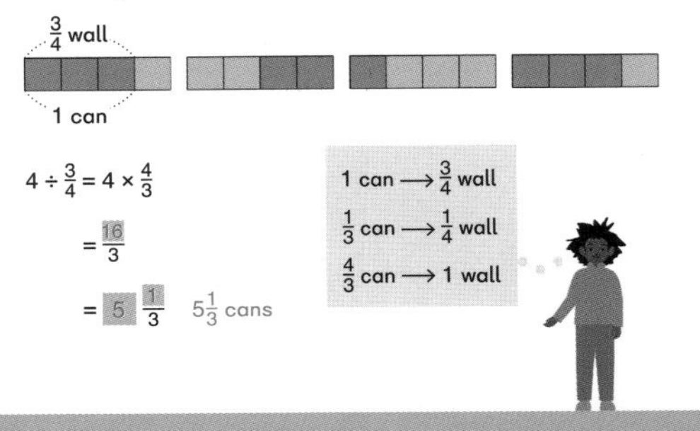

❹ Mei knows that Emma has biked part of the trail and she needs to find how long the trail is in all. She finds the value of 1 unit, the distance of $\frac{1}{3}$ of the trail, and then multiplies by 3.

Emma knows $5 = \frac{2}{3} \times ?$ is the same as $5 \div \frac{2}{3} = ?$

Students should see that Mei's solution, $3 \times \frac{5}{2}$, results in the same product as the solution found by multiplying by the reciprocal of $\frac{2}{3}$, i.e $5 \times \frac{3}{2}$.

❺–❼ Most students should be able to solve these problems without drawing any models.

Activity

▲ Greatest Quotient

Materials: Number Cards (BLM) 1–9

Deal each player three number cards. Players arrange their cards into a whole number and a proper fraction and then divide. The player with the greatest quotient gets a point. The first player to 5 points is the winner.

Example:

Player 1 has cards 5, 6, and 8:

$5 \div \frac{6}{8} = 6\frac{2}{3}$

$6 \div \frac{5}{8} = 9\frac{3}{5}$

$8 \div \frac{5}{6} = 9\frac{3}{5}$

Player 1 chooses $6 \div \frac{5}{8} = 9\frac{3}{5}$.

Player 2 has cards 7, 2, and 5:

$2 \div \frac{5}{7} = 2\frac{4}{5}$

$5 \div \frac{2}{7} = 17\frac{1}{2}$

$7 \div \frac{2}{5} = 17\frac{1}{2}$

Player 2 chooses $7 \div \frac{2}{5} = 17\frac{1}{2}$.

Player 2 is the winner of the round.

162

❹ Emma bikes 5 miles, which is $\frac{2}{3}$ of the way along the trail. How long is the trail in miles?

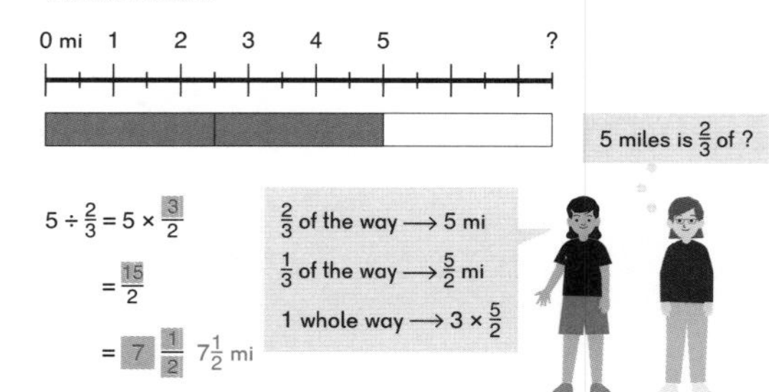

$5 \div \frac{2}{3} = 5 \times \frac{3}{2}$

$= \frac{15}{2}$

$= 7\frac{1}{2}$ $7\frac{1}{2}$ mi

$\frac{2}{3}$ of the way ⟶ 5 mi

$\frac{1}{3}$ of the way ⟶ $\frac{5}{2}$ mi

1 whole way ⟶ $3 \times \frac{5}{2}$

❺ Find the values. Express each answer in simplest form.

(a) $3 \div \frac{3}{4}$ 4 (b) $4 \div \frac{4}{5}$ 5 (c) $6 \div \frac{2}{7}$ 21

(d) $3 \div \frac{2}{3}$ $4\frac{1}{2}$ (e) $7 \div \frac{3}{4}$ $9\frac{1}{3}$ (f) $5 \div \frac{3}{8}$ $13\frac{1}{3}$

(g) $3 \div \frac{3}{2}$ 2 (h) $7 \div \frac{4}{3}$ $5\frac{1}{4}$ (i) $5 \div \frac{8}{3}$ $1\frac{7}{8}$

❻ A store manager has 8 lb of coffee. She wants to put $\frac{2}{3}$ lb of coffee in each bag. How many bags will she need?

$8 \div \frac{2}{3} = 12$; 12 bags

❼ Write a word problem for $6 \div \frac{3}{4}$.

Answers will vary.

COFFEE & CO
FRENCH ROAST

Exercise 5 • page 146

162 6-5 Dividing a Whole Number by a Fraction

Exercise 5 • page 146

Objective

- Solve multi-step problems involving division of a fraction by a whole number, or a whole number by a fraction.

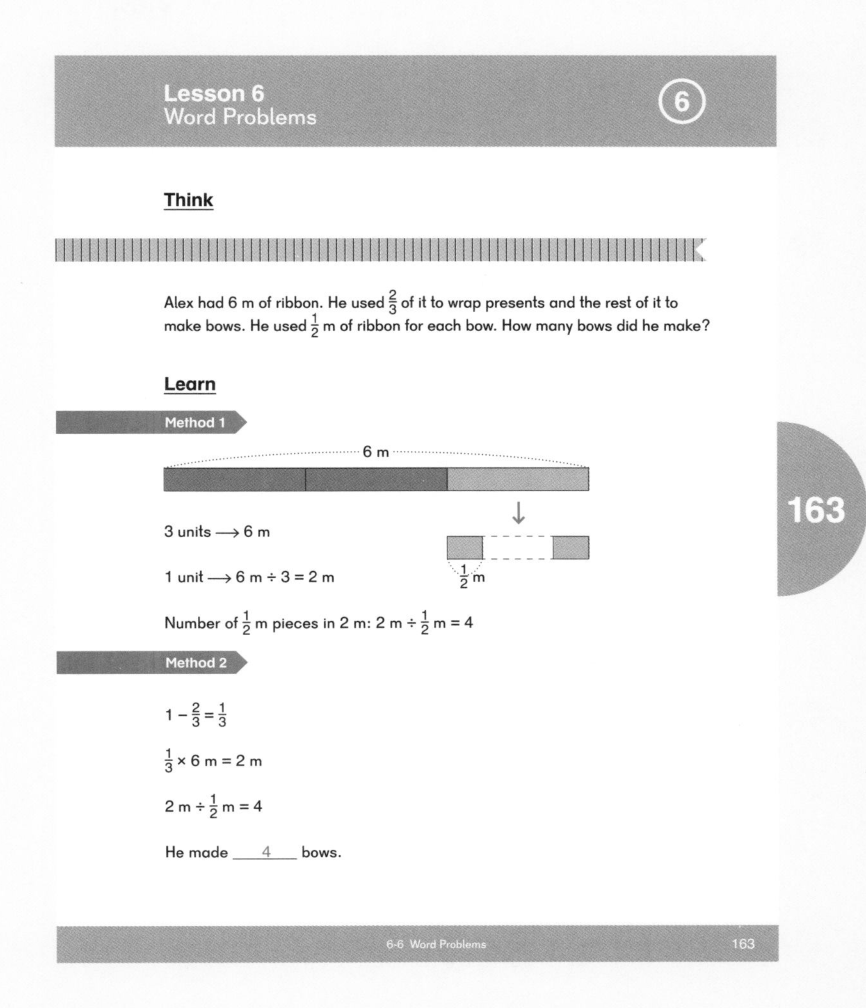

Lesson 6
Word Problems

6

Think

Alex had 6 m of ribbon. He used $\frac{2}{3}$ of it to wrap presents and the rest of it to make bows. He used $\frac{1}{2}$ m of ribbon for each bow. How many bows did he make?

Learn

Method 1

3 units ⟶ 6 m

1 unit ⟶ 6 m ÷ 3 = 2 m

Number of $\frac{1}{2}$ m pieces in 2 m: 2 m ÷ $\frac{1}{2}$ m = 4

Method 2

$1 - \frac{2}{3} = \frac{1}{3}$

$\frac{1}{3} \times 6$ m = 2 m

2 m ÷ $\frac{1}{2}$ m = 4

He made 4 bows.

6-6 Word Problems 163

163

Think

Pose the **Think** problem and have students draw a bar model to help them find how many bows Alex made.

Discuss student solutions.

Learn

Have students discuss the **Learn** examples and compare their methods from **Think** with the ones in the textbook.

Method 1

Ask students:

- “What does the first bar represent?” (6 m of ribbon.)
- “What does the dark orange part of the bar represent?” (The $\frac{2}{3}$ of the 6 m used to wrap presents.)
- “What does the light orange part of the bar represent?” ($\frac{1}{3}$ of the 6 m remaining of the ribbon that is used to make bows.)
- “How many one-halves are in 2 m?” (4)

Method 2

Ask students, “How is this method different from Method 1?” (One method is working with units in a bar model, changing fractions to parts and using division, while the other is actually calculating with fractions.)

Do

❶–❹ Discuss the problems and given models with students.

❶ The bar is first divided in half, because the farm used half of the milk to make cheese. Then, because they put half of the remaining milk into bottles, the remainder on the model is divided into half. To keep equal units, we also divide the "cheese" part of the bar model in half. We now have 4 equal units.

❷ The first bar shows eighths because the box weighs $\frac{1}{8}$ of a pound and that weight can be subtracted from the total weight to find the weight of the peanuts. 5 units of peanuts are divided into 10. To have 10 equal parts (10 bags of peanuts) the 5 units of eighths need to each be split into 2, so each orange part in the second bar is $\frac{1}{16}$. The $\frac{1}{8}$ lb shown in the first bar in light orange, is not part of the weight of the peanuts so it is white in the second bar.

$$\frac{5}{8} \div 10 = \frac{5}{8} \times \frac{1}{10} = \frac{5}{80} = \frac{1}{16}$$

164

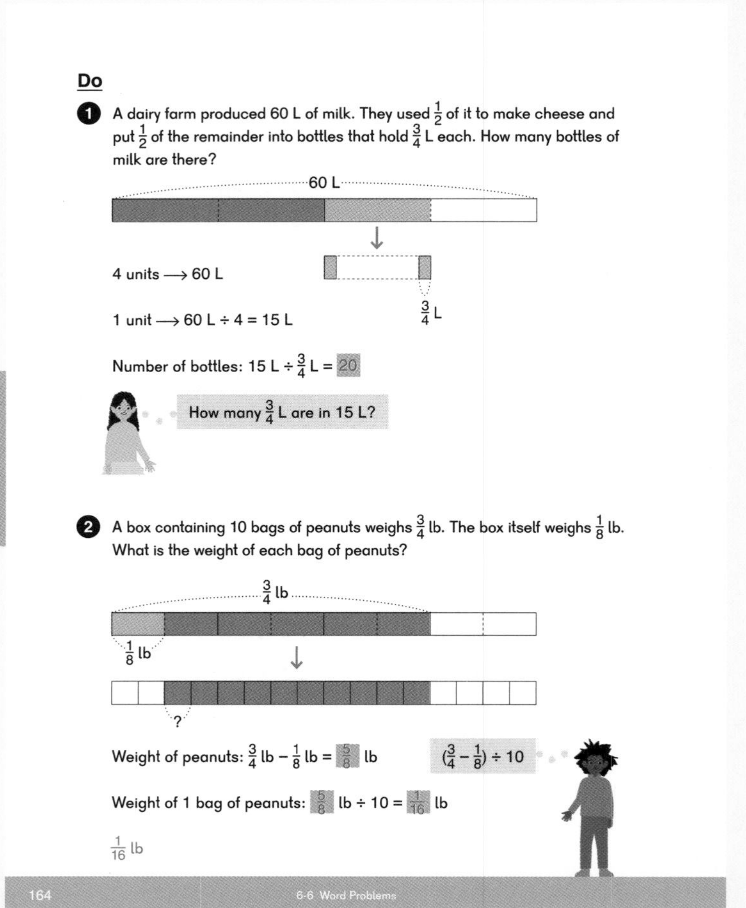

Do

❶ A dairy farm produced 60 L of milk. They used $\frac{1}{2}$ of it to make cheese and put $\frac{1}{2}$ of the remainder into bottles that hold $\frac{3}{4}$ L each. How many bottles of milk are there?

60 L

4 units ⟶ 60 L

1 unit ⟶ 60 L ÷ 4 = 15 L

$\frac{3}{4}$ L

Number of bottles: 15 L ÷ $\frac{3}{4}$ L = 20

How many $\frac{3}{4}$ L are in 15 L?

❷ A box containing 10 bags of peanuts weighs $\frac{3}{4}$ lb. The box itself weighs $\frac{1}{8}$ lb. What is the weight of each bag of peanuts?

$\frac{3}{4}$ lb

$\frac{1}{8}$ lb

?

Weight of peanuts: $\frac{3}{4}$ lb − $\frac{1}{8}$ lb = $\frac{5}{8}$ lb

$(\frac{3}{4} - \frac{1}{8}) \div 10$

Weight of 1 bag of peanuts: $\frac{5}{8}$ lb ÷ 10 = $\frac{1}{16}$ lb

$\frac{1}{16}$ lb

164 6-6 Word Problems

3 Ask students:

- "Why is the first bar divided into fifths?" (To show the $\frac{4}{5}$.)
- "Why is the second bar drawn below divided into 10 units?" (To show $\frac{4}{5} \div 2 = \frac{1}{10}$ of a kg.)

4 Ask students:

- "What does the first bar represent?" (Flower pots and $\frac{2}{3}$ m of ribbon.)
- "What does the second bar represent?" ($\frac{3}{3}$, or 1 m of ribbon.)

Exercise 6 • page 149

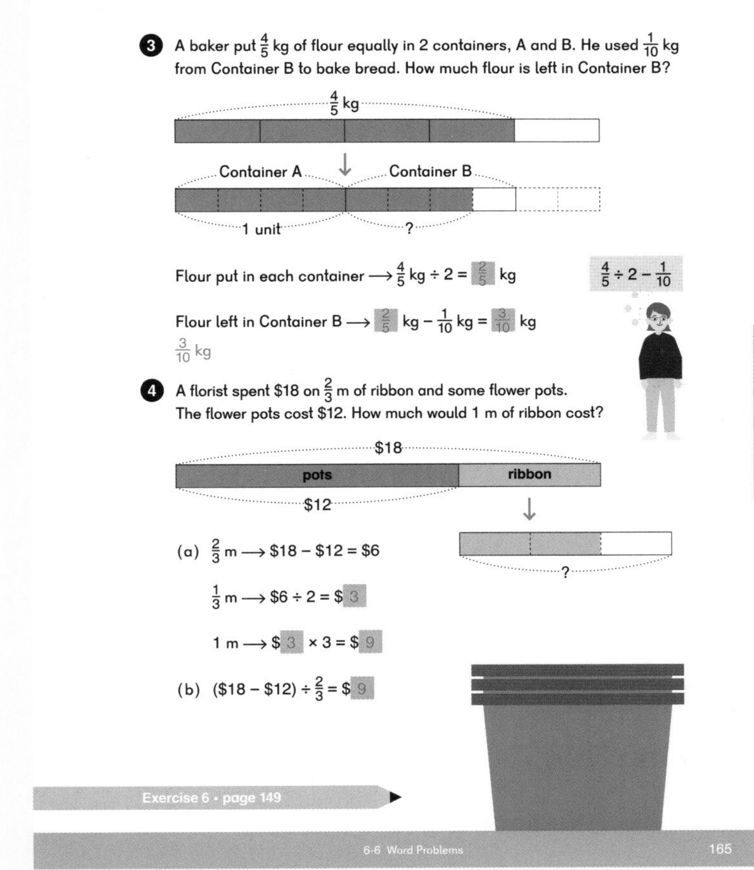

Objective

- Practice concepts from the chapter.

After students complete the **Practice** in the textbook, have them continue to practice division with fractions using the activities from the chapter.

❸ Alternate solution:

$\frac{1}{5}$ hr ⟶ 40 miles

$\frac{5}{5}$ hr ⟶ 5 × 40 miles

Exercise 7 • page 152

166

Lesson 7
Practice B P ⑦

❶ Find the values. Express each answer in simplest form.

(a) $4 \div \frac{1}{3}$	12	(b) $10 \div \frac{1}{6}$	60	(c) $6 \div \frac{6}{7}$	7
(d) $2 \div \frac{2}{5}$	5	(e) $5 \div \frac{3}{5}$	$8\frac{1}{3}$	(f) $12 \div \frac{3}{4}$	16
(g) $9 \div \frac{5}{7}$	$12\frac{3}{5}$	(h) $4 \times 2 \div \frac{1}{2}$	16	(i) $120 - 15 \div \frac{3}{5}$	95
(j) $4 \times 3 \div \frac{3}{4}$	16	(k) $8 \div (\frac{3}{4} - \frac{1}{2})$	32	(l) $(4\frac{1}{3} + \frac{4}{6}) \div \frac{5}{6}$	6

❷ A cook has 3 lb of pasta. Each pasta dish needs $\frac{1}{8}$ lb of pasta. How many pasta dishes can he make?
3 lb ÷ $\frac{1}{8}$ lb = 24; 24 pasta dishes

❸ A bullet train can travel 40 mi in $\frac{1}{5}$ h. How far can the train travel in 1 h?
40 mi ÷ $\frac{1}{5}$ = 200 mi; 200 mi

❹ A $\frac{1}{4}$ m long rope was cut into 3 equal pieces. How long is each piece of rope in meters?
$\frac{1}{4} \div 3 = \frac{1}{12}$; $\frac{1}{12}$

❺ Mary Jane had $\frac{3}{5}$ kg of apples. She ate $\frac{1}{10}$ kg and used the rest to make 5 apple pies. How many kilograms of apples did she use for each pie?
($\frac{3}{5}$ kg − $\frac{1}{10}$ kg) ÷ 5 = $\frac{1}{10}$ kg; $\frac{1}{10}$ kg

❻ A store employee had 75 lb of light roast coffee and 60 lb of dark roast coffee. She made bags of $\frac{3}{4}$ lb of coffee to sell. How many bags of each type of coffee did she make? 75 lb ÷ $\frac{3}{4}$ lb = 100; 60 lb ÷ $\frac{3}{4}$ lb = 80
100 bags of light roast; 80 bags of dark roast

Exercise 7 • page 152

166 6-7 Practice B

Brain Works

★ Dividing Dominoes

Materials: Dividing Domino Cards (BLM)

Begin with the domino card labeled "Start."

Players match a division expression on one half of the domino card with the correct solution on one half of another domino card.

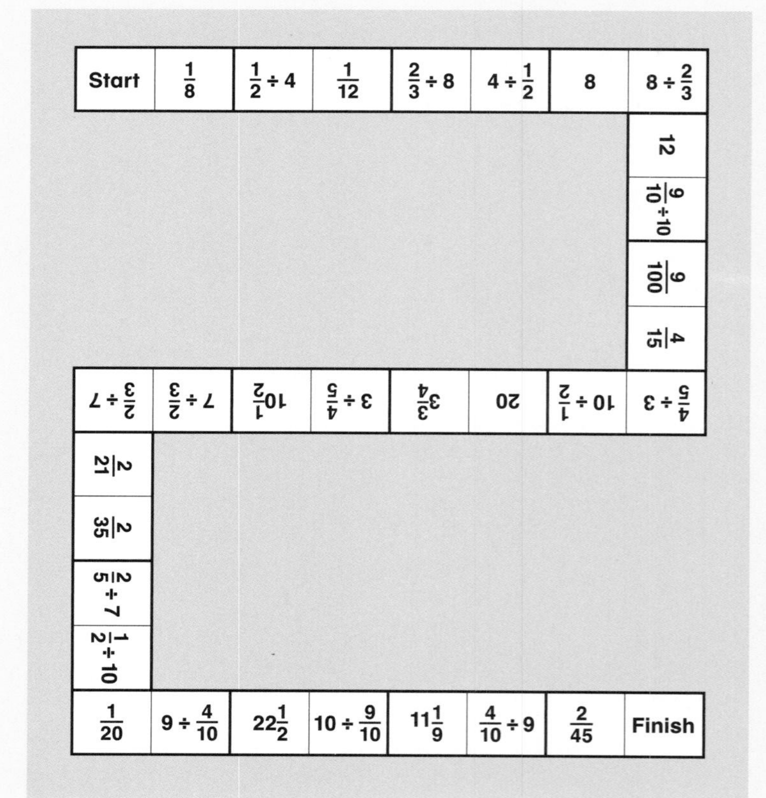

Exercise 1 • pages 137–138

Chapter 6 Division of Fractions

Exercise 1

Basics

1. Divide $\frac{1}{5}$ by 2.

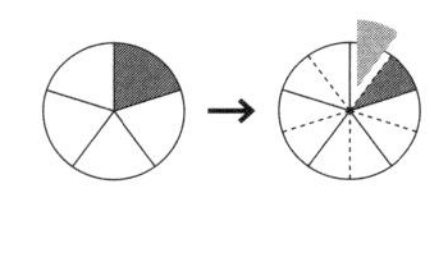

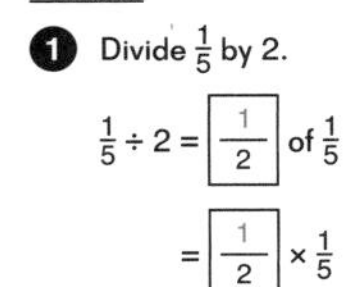

$\frac{1}{5} \div 2 = \boxed{\frac{1}{2}}$ of $\frac{1}{5}$

$= \boxed{\frac{1}{2}} \times \frac{1}{5}$

$= \boxed{\frac{1}{10}}$

2. Shade the rectangle to show $\frac{1}{2} \div 6$.

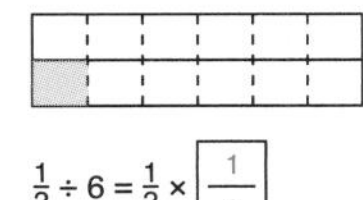

Students may instead shade using 2 colors overlapping, or draw diagonal lines in different directions.

$\frac{1}{2} \div 6 = \frac{1}{2} \times \boxed{\frac{1}{6}}$

$= \boxed{\frac{1}{12}}$

3. Shade the bar and draw an arrow on the number line to show $\frac{1}{3} \div 4$.

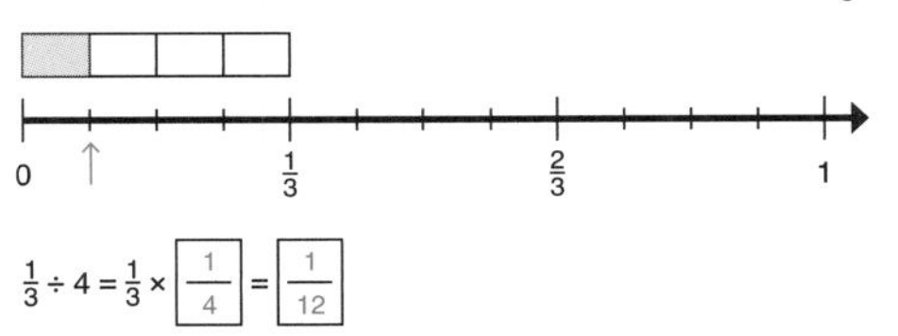

$\frac{1}{3} \div 4 = \frac{1}{3} \times \boxed{\frac{1}{4}} = \boxed{\frac{1}{12}}$

Practice

4. Divide.

(a) $\frac{1}{5} \div 5$ $\frac{1}{25}$

(b) $\frac{1}{8} \div 2$ $\frac{1}{16}$

(c) $\frac{1}{10} \div 10$ $\frac{1}{100}$

(d) $\frac{1}{15} \div 4$ $\frac{1}{60}$

5. (a) $\frac{1}{7} \div \boxed{6} = \frac{1}{42}$

(b) $\frac{1}{3} \div \boxed{6} = \frac{1}{18}$

(c) $\boxed{\frac{1}{2}} \div 25 = \frac{1}{50}$

(d) $\boxed{\frac{1}{20}} \div 5 = \frac{1}{100}$

6. 4 sheets of plywood are $\frac{1}{2}$ in thick. How thick is 1 sheet of plywood?

$\frac{1}{2} \div 4 = \frac{1}{8}$

$\frac{1}{8}$ inch

7. 5 racquetballs weigh $\frac{1}{4}$ kg. How many kilograms does 1 racquetball weigh?

$\frac{1}{4} \div 5 = \frac{1}{20}$

$\frac{1}{20}$ kg

Exercise 2 • pages 139–140

Exercise 2

Basics

1. Divide $\frac{2}{3}$ by 4.

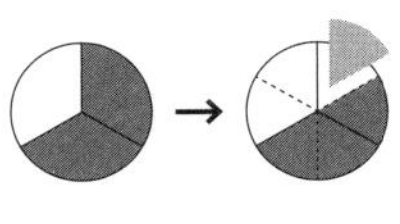

$\frac{2}{3} \div 4 = \boxed{\frac{1}{4}}$ of $\frac{2}{3}$

$= \boxed{\frac{1}{4}} \times \frac{2}{3}$

$= \boxed{\frac{1}{6}}$

2. Shade the rectangle to show $\frac{3}{4} \div 5$.

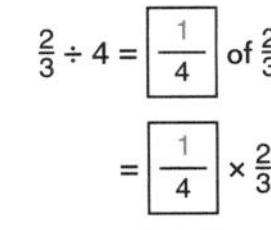

$\frac{3}{4} \div 5 = \frac{3}{4} \times \boxed{\frac{1}{5}}$

$= \boxed{\frac{3}{20}}$

3. Shade the bar and draw an arrow on the number line to show $\frac{2}{3} \div 6$.

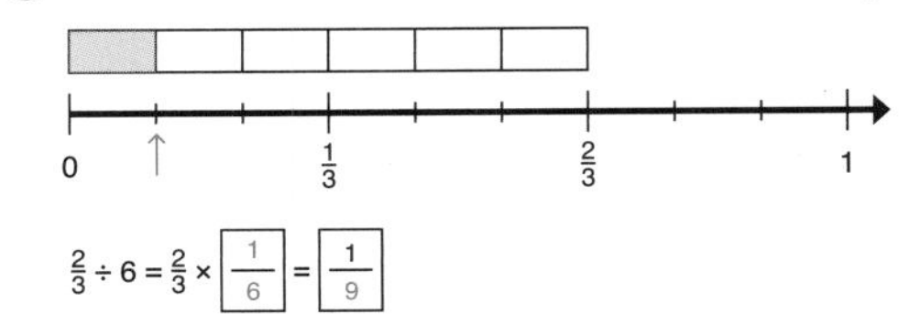

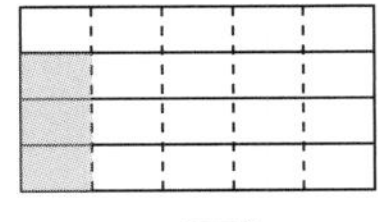

$\frac{2}{3} \div 6 = \frac{2}{3} \times \boxed{\frac{1}{6}} = \boxed{\frac{1}{9}}$

Practice

4. Divide. Express each answer in simplest form.

(a) $\frac{3}{10} \div 2$ $\frac{3}{20}$

(b) $\frac{5}{6} \div 3$ $\frac{5}{18}$

(c) $\frac{5}{8} \div 10$ $\frac{1}{16}$

(d) $\frac{6}{7} \div 9$ $\frac{2}{21}$

(e) $\frac{8}{9} \div 12$ $\frac{2}{27}$

(f) $\frac{3}{5} \div 12$ $\frac{1}{20}$

5. A regular hexagon has 6 equal sides. Its perimeter is $\frac{3}{5}$ m. How long is one side in meters?

$\frac{3}{5} \div 6 = \frac{1}{10}$

$\frac{1}{10}$ m

6. Joseph bought $\frac{9}{10}$ kg of grapes. He bought 3 times as many kilograms of grapes as Paula bought. How many kilograms of grapes did Paula buy?

$\frac{9}{10} \div 3 = \frac{3}{10}$

$\frac{3}{10}$ kg

Challenge

7. (a) $\boxed{\frac{5}{7}} \div 25 = \frac{1}{35}$

(b) $\boxed{\frac{9}{10}} \div 6 = \frac{3}{20}$

Exercise 3 • pages 141–142

Exercise 3

Check

1. Find the values. Express each answer in simplest form.

(a) $\frac{1}{6} \div 5$ $\frac{1}{30}$

(b) $\frac{8}{9} \div 4$ $\frac{2}{9}$

(c) $\frac{3}{4} \div 6$ $\frac{1}{8}$

(d) $\frac{6}{7} \div 10$ $\frac{3}{35}$

(e) $\frac{2}{3} \div 10 \times \frac{6}{7}$ $\frac{2}{35}$

(f) $(2\frac{1}{7} \times 2\frac{1}{3}) \div 5$ 1

(g) $(\frac{4}{5} - \frac{1}{2}) \div 3 \times 20$ 2

(h) $(2\frac{1}{3} - \frac{5}{6} - \frac{1}{2}) \div 6 \times \frac{3}{5}$ $\frac{1}{10}$

2. Violet used $\frac{3}{4}$ of a bag of dirt to fill 6 pots. What fraction of the bag of dirt is in each pot?

$\frac{3}{4} \div 6 = \frac{1}{8}$

$\frac{1}{8}$ of the bag

3. 8 identical blocks weigh $\frac{2}{5}$ kg. How many kilograms does 1 block weigh?

$\frac{2}{5} \div 8 = \frac{1}{20}$

$\frac{1}{20}$ kg

4. Isaiah spent $\frac{1}{3}$ of his money on a notebook and the remainder on 4 identical pencils. What fraction of his money did he spend on 1 pencil?

The remainder is $\frac{2}{3}$ of his money.

$\frac{2}{3} \div 4 = \frac{1}{6}$

$\frac{1}{6}$ of his money

Challenge

5. (a) $\frac{2}{7} \div \boxed{4} = \frac{1}{14}$

(b) $\frac{8}{15} \div \boxed{12} = \frac{2}{45}$

6. Find the values. Express each answer in simplest form.

(a) $7\frac{1}{2} \div 2$ $\frac{15}{2} \times \frac{1}{2} = 3\frac{3}{4}$

(b) $5\frac{3}{5} \div 8$ $\frac{28}{5} \times \frac{1}{8} = \frac{7}{10}$

(c) $(5 - 1\frac{4}{7}) \div 4$ $\frac{24}{7} \times \frac{1}{4} = \frac{6}{7}$

(d) $5 - 3\frac{3}{5} \div 3$ $5 - \frac{18}{5} \times \frac{1}{3} = 5 - \frac{6}{5} = 3\frac{4}{5}$

Exercise 4

Basics

1 (a) 5 is the reciprocal of $\frac{1}{5}$.

(b) How many fifths are in 2 wholes?

$2 \div \frac{1}{5} = 2 \times$ 5

= 10

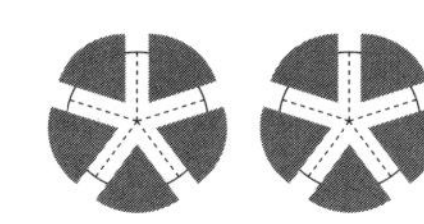

2 (a) 4 is the reciprocal of $\frac{1}{4}$.

(b) How many fourths are in 3 wholes?

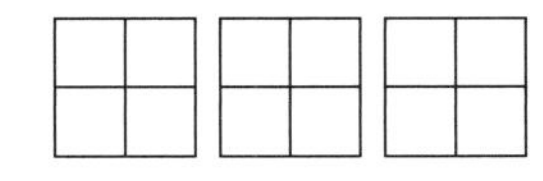

$3 \div \frac{1}{4} = 3 \times$ 4

= 12

3 How many halves are in 6?

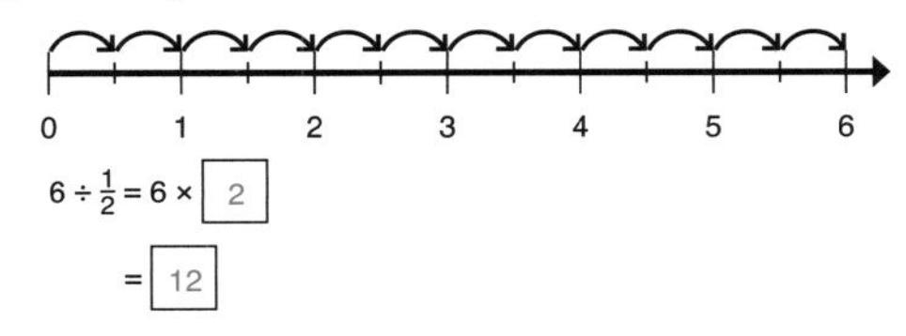

$6 \div \frac{1}{2} = 6 \times$ 2

= 12

4 Finish labeling the tick marks on the number lines to find the answers.

(a) $\frac{1}{2}$ of what is 6?

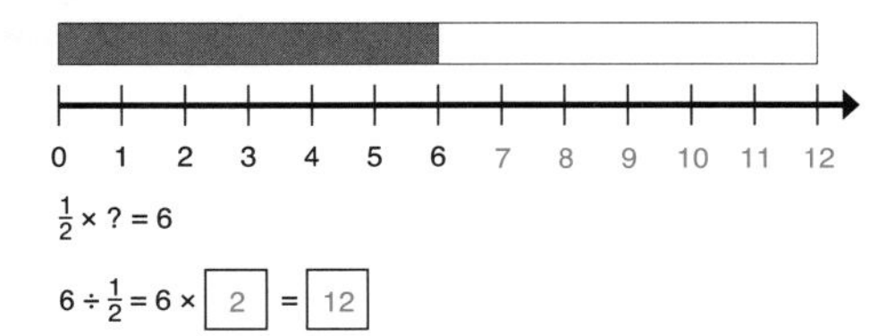

$\frac{1}{2} \times ? = 6$

$6 \div \frac{1}{2} = 6 \times$ 2 = 12

(b) 3 is $\frac{1}{3}$ of what number?

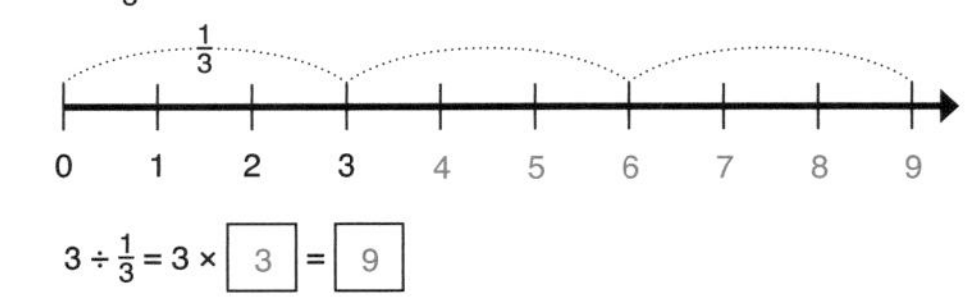

$3 \div \frac{1}{3} = 3 \times$ 3 = 9

Practice

5 Divide.

(a) $4 \div \frac{1}{5}$ 20

(b) $1 \div \frac{1}{10}$ 10

(c) $3 \div \frac{1}{12}$ 36

(d) $50 \div \frac{1}{2}$ 100

6 (a) $3 \div$ $\frac{1}{2}$ $= 6$

(b) $7 \div$ $\frac{1}{4}$ $= 28$

(c) 10 $\div \frac{1}{4} = 40$

(d) 9 $\div \frac{1}{6} = 54$

7 Each of the sides of a polygon is $\frac{1}{5}$ m long. The perimeter of the polygon is 2 m. How many sides does the polygon have?

$2 \div \frac{1}{5} = 10$

10 sides

8 $\frac{1}{12}$ of a length of rope is 5 ft. How long is the rope in feet?

$5 \div \frac{1}{12} = 5 \times 12 = 60$

60 feet

Exercise 5

Basics

1. How many $\frac{2}{5}$s are in 2 wholes?

$2 \div \frac{1}{5} = 2 \times 5$

$2 \div \frac{2}{5} = \frac{2 \times 5}{2}$

$= 2 \times \frac{5}{2}$

$= 5$

2. (a) $\frac{3}{2}$ is the reciprocal of $\frac{2}{3}$.

(b) How many $\frac{2}{3}$s are in 6?

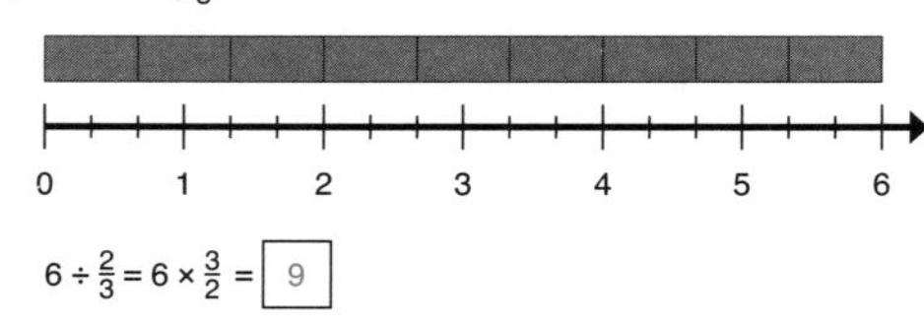

$6 \div \frac{2}{3} = 6 \times \frac{3}{2} = 9$

(c) How many $\frac{2}{3}$s are in 3?

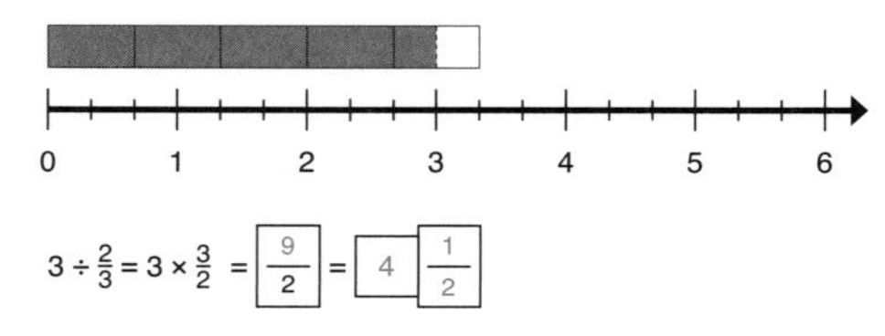

$3 \div \frac{2}{3} = 3 \times \frac{3}{2} = \frac{9}{2} = 4\frac{1}{2}$

3. (a) $\frac{5}{3}$ is the reciprocal of $\frac{3}{5}$.

(b) $\frac{3}{5}$ of what number is 3?

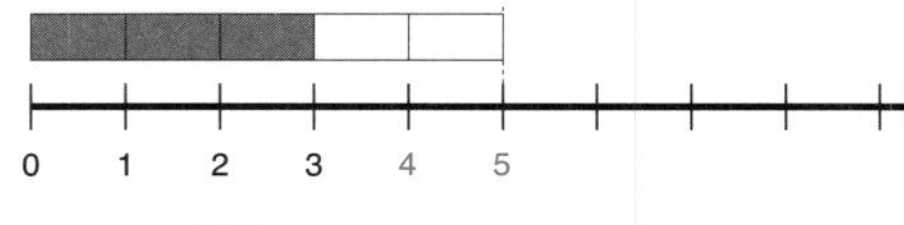

$3 \div \frac{3}{5} = 3 \times \frac{5}{3} = 5$

(c) $\frac{3}{5}$ of what number is 5?

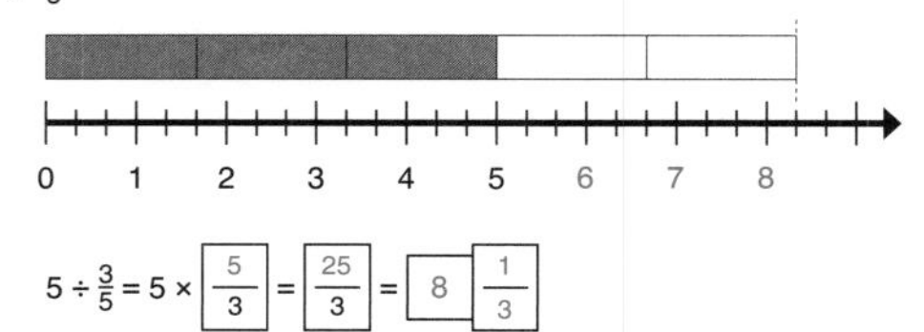

$5 \div \frac{3}{5} = 5 \times \frac{5}{3} = \frac{25}{3} = 8\frac{1}{3}$

Practice

4. Divide.

(a) $3 \div \frac{3}{10}$ 10

(b) $4 \div \frac{2}{5}$ 10

(c) $6 \div \frac{3}{7}$ 14

(d) $60 \div \frac{4}{5}$ 75

5. Divide. Express each answer in simplest form.

(a) $7 \div \frac{2}{3}$ $10\frac{1}{2}$

(b) $8 \div \frac{3}{4}$ $10\frac{2}{3}$

(c) $6 \div \frac{4}{3}$ $4\frac{1}{2}$

(d) $60 \div \frac{9}{5}$ $33\frac{1}{3}$

6. A sheet of plywood is $\frac{3}{8}$ inches thick. A stack of these sheets of plywood is 9 inches high. How many sheets of plywood are in the stack?

$9 \div \frac{3}{8} = 24$

24 sheets of plywood

7. Crushed garlic is divided into small containers to be frozen and used later. One of the containers has 5 g of crushed garlic, which is $\frac{2}{7}$ of the total amount of crushed garlic. What is the weight of the total amount of crushed garlic?

$5 \div \frac{2}{7} = \frac{35}{2} = 17\frac{1}{2}$

$17\frac{1}{2}$ g

Exercise 6 • pages 149–151

Exercise 6

Basics

1. A farmer had 100 lb of brussels sprouts. He put them into bags each holding $\frac{2}{3}$ lb to sell at the farmer's market. He then sold $\frac{3}{5}$ of the bags in the morning and $\frac{7}{10}$ of the remaining bags in the afternoon.

(a) How many bags of brussels sprouts did he have?

$100 \div \frac{2}{3} = 150$

150 bags

(b) What fraction of the brussels sprouts did he sell in the afternoon?

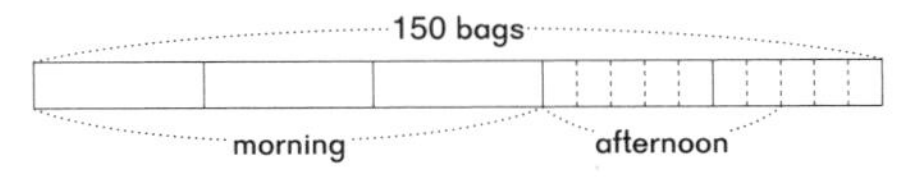

$\frac{7}{10} \times \frac{2}{5} = \frac{7}{25}$

(c) How many pounds of brussels sprouts does he have left?

$\frac{3}{10} \times \frac{2}{5} \times 150 = 18$

or

25 units $\longrightarrow$ 150

1 unit $\longrightarrow \frac{150}{25} = 6$

3 units $\longrightarrow 3 \times 6 = 18$

$18 \times \frac{2}{3} = 12$

12 lb

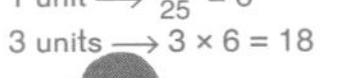

Practice Methods may vary.

2. A box with 8 bags of pretzels and a jar of mustard weighs $2\frac{1}{6}$ lb. The jar of mustard weighs $1\frac{3}{8}$ lb and the box alone weighs $\frac{1}{8}$ lb. 5 bags of pretzels were taken out. How many pounds does the box with the remaining bags and jar of mustard now weigh?

Weight of mustard and box: $1\frac{3}{8} + \frac{1}{8} = 1\frac{1}{2}$

Weight of 8 bags: $2\frac{1}{6} - 1\frac{1}{2} = \frac{2}{3}$

Weight of 1 bag: $\frac{2}{3} \div 8 = \frac{1}{12}$

Weight of 3 bags: $3 \times \frac{1}{12} = \frac{1}{4}$

Total weight: $\frac{1}{4} + 1\frac{1}{2} = 1\frac{3}{4}$

$1\frac{3}{4}$ lb

3. A farm harvested 432 lb of cherries. It sold $\frac{5}{9}$ of the cherries to stores and put $\frac{5}{8}$ of the remainder into bags holding $\frac{3}{4}$ lb, which it sold at a stand for \$4 each. How much money did the farm receive from the sales at the stand?

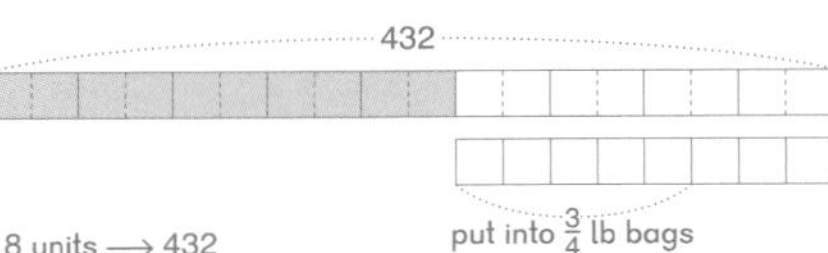

18 units $\longrightarrow$ 432

1 unit $\longrightarrow$ 24

5 units $\longrightarrow 5 \times 24 = 120$

$120 \div \frac{3}{4} = 160$

$4 \times 160 = 640$

\$640

4. Trees are going to be planted along the side of a road. One tree will be planted at the start, then another 30 trees for $\frac{3}{5}$ km total. The remaining stretch of the road will have an additional 25 trees in all planted every $\frac{1}{10}$ km.

(a) How many kilometers apart from each other will the first 31 trees be?

$\frac{3}{5} \div 30 = \frac{1}{50}$

$\frac{1}{50}$ km

(b) How long is the road in kilometers?

$\frac{1}{10} \times 25 = 2\frac{1}{2}$

$\frac{3}{5} + 2\frac{1}{2} = \frac{31}{10} = 3\frac{1}{10}$

$3\frac{1}{10}$ km

5. A store sold 12 laptops on Saturday and $\frac{2}{5}$ of its remaining laptops on Sunday. Altogether the store sold $\frac{2}{3}$ of its stock of laptops in those two days. How many laptops did it have at first?

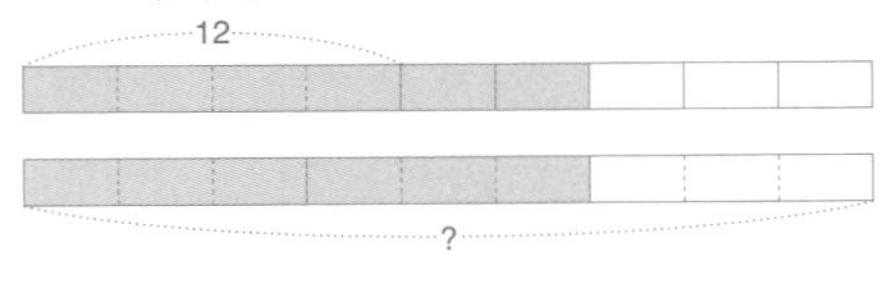

4 units $\longrightarrow$ 12

9 units $\longrightarrow \frac{12}{4} \times 9 = 27$

27 laptops

Exercise 7 • pages 152–156

Check

1. Find the values. Express each answer in simplest form.

(a) $5 \div \frac{1}{6}$ 30

(b) $7 \div \frac{1}{8}$ 56

(c) $6 \div \frac{3}{4}$ 8

(d) $12 \div \frac{2}{3}$ 18

(e) $100 \div \frac{4}{5}$ 125

(f) $5 \div \frac{5}{6}$ 6

(g) $4 \div \frac{8}{9}$ $4\frac{1}{2}$

(h) $100 \div \frac{6}{7}$ $116\frac{2}{3}$

(i) $10 \div \frac{2}{3} \times \frac{1}{2}$ $7\frac{1}{2}$

(j) $(2\frac{1}{7} \times 2\frac{1}{3}) \div \frac{7}{10}$ $7\frac{1}{7}$

(k) $35 \div \frac{2}{3} - 17 \div \frac{2}{3}$ 27

(l) $25 \div \frac{1}{2} - 25 \div \frac{2}{3}$ $12\frac{1}{2}$

Methods may vary.

2. A sheet of plywood is $\frac{3}{4}$ in thick. A stack of these sheets of plywood is 2 feet high. How many sheets of plywood are in the stack?

2 ft = 24 in
$24 \div \frac{3}{4} = 32$
32 sheets of plywood

3. Mariam is cutting 20 inches of yarn into pieces each $\frac{3}{8}$ inch long for an art project. How many $\frac{3}{8}$ inch pieces will she have?

$20 \div \frac{3}{8} = \frac{160}{3} = 53\frac{1}{3}$
53 pieces

4. One lap around a track is $\frac{1}{3}$ of a mile. Riya ran 5 miles around the track. How many laps did she run?

$5 \div \frac{1}{3} = 15$
15 laps

5. A store made 96 lb of peppermint bark for the holidays. The peppermint bark was split into $\frac{3}{8}$ lb portions and boxed. $\frac{3}{4}$ of the boxes were sold for $6 each before the holidays. The rest were sold at $\frac{2}{3}$ of the pre-holiday price. How much money did the shop receive from the sales of the peppermint bark?

$96 \div \frac{3}{8} = 256$
$\frac{3}{4} \times 256 = 192$ (sold at $6)
$256 - 192 = 64$ (sold at $\frac{2}{3}$ of $6 or $4)
$6 \times 192 + 4 \times 64 = 1{,}408$
$1,408

6. Ray used 45 bags of cement to build a patio. Each bag of cement contained 95 lb of cement. The patio is $\frac{3}{8}$ the area of a driveway that he is going to build. How many 95 lb bags of cement does he need to build the driveway?

$45 \times 95 = 4{,}275$
$4{,}275 \div \frac{3}{8} = 11{,}400$
$11{,}400 \div 95 = 120$
120 bags

Challenge

7. A tank was $\frac{1}{4}$ of the way filled of water. After 3 L of water was added, it was $\frac{7}{10}$ full. How many liters of water did it have at first?

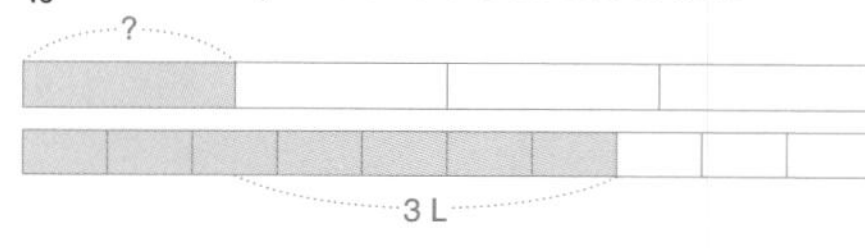

$\frac{7}{10} - \frac{1}{4} = \frac{9}{20}$
3 L is $\frac{9}{20}$ of the tank.
$3 \div \frac{9}{20} = \frac{20}{3}$
$\frac{1}{4} \times \frac{20}{3} = \frac{5}{3} = 1\frac{2}{3}$
$1\frac{2}{3}$ L

or:
$\frac{9}{20}$ of the tank $\longrightarrow$ 3 L
$\frac{1}{20}$ of the tank $\longrightarrow \frac{3}{9} = \frac{1}{3}$ L
$\frac{5}{20}$ of the tank $\longrightarrow 5 \times \frac{1}{3} = \frac{5}{3} = 1\frac{2}{3}$ L

8. A jug was $\frac{1}{4}$ full of water. After some water was added, it was $\frac{7}{10}$ full. It is now $\frac{1}{2}$ L from being full. How many liters of water were added?

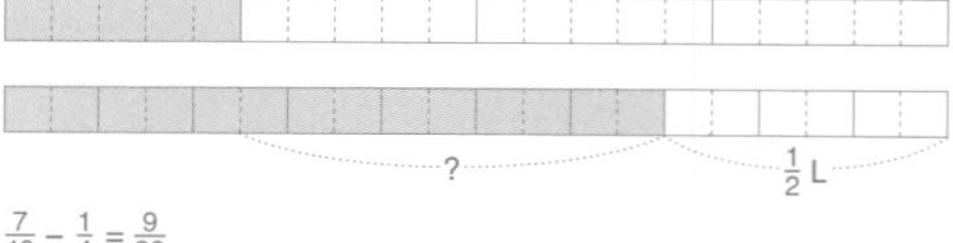

$\frac{7}{10} - \frac{1}{4} = \frac{9}{20}$

6 units $\longrightarrow \frac{1}{2}$ L
1 unit $\longrightarrow \frac{1}{2}$ L $\div 6 = \frac{1}{12}$ L
9 units $\longrightarrow 9 \times \frac{1}{12}$ L $= \frac{3}{4}$ L
$\frac{3}{4}$ L

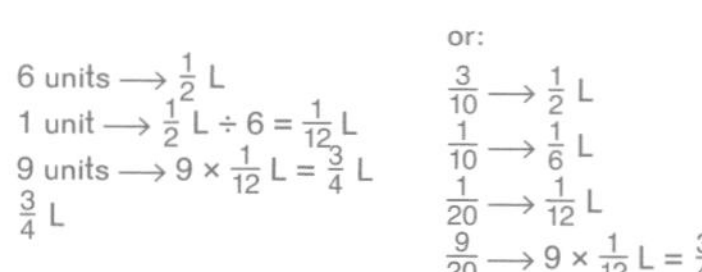

or:
$\frac{3}{10} \longrightarrow \frac{1}{2}$ L
$\frac{1}{10} \longrightarrow \frac{1}{6}$ L
$\frac{1}{20} \longrightarrow \frac{1}{12}$ L
$\frac{9}{20} \longrightarrow 9 \times \frac{1}{12}$ L $= \frac{3}{4}$ L

9. One small block is $\frac{2}{3}$ of the weight of a large block. How many of the available blocks need to be added to the right side so that it is balanced?

3 small blocks weigh the same as 2 large blocks

Draw a picture:

left side

right side

4 large blocks and 1 small block. 5 blocks in all.

10. It would take Steve 4 hours to paint a room. If Andre helps him, they can finish painting the room in 3 hours. How long would Andre take to paint the room by himself?

Steve ⟶ $\frac{1}{4}$ of the room in 1 hour

Steve and Andre ⟶ $\frac{1}{3}$ of the room in 1 hour

Andre ⟶ $\frac{1}{3} - \frac{1}{4} = \frac{1}{12}$ of the room in 1 hour

12 hours

Notes

Suggested number of class periods: 7–8

	Lesson	Page	Resources	Objectives
	Chapter Opener	p. 223	TB: p. 167	Review measurement concepts.
1	Fractions and Measurement Conversions	p. 224	TB: p. 168 WB: p. 157	Convert measurements of length, weight, liquid volume, or time involving fractions or mixed numbers from a larger unit to a smaller unit.
2	Fractions and Area	p. 227	TB: p. 172 WB: p. 160	Find the area of rectangles with fractional side lengths.
3	Practice A	p. 230	TB: p. 176 WB: p. 163	Practice concepts from Lessons 1 and 2.
4	Area of a Triangle — Part 1	p. 231	TB: p. 178 WB: p. 166	Find the area of a triangle when the height is given inside of the triangle.
5	Area of a Triangle — Part 2	p. 236	TB: p. 184 WB: p. 171	Find the area of a triangle when the height for a given base falls outside the triangle.
6	Area of Complex Figures	p. 239	TB: p. 189 WB: p. 175	Find the area of complex figures composed of rectangles and triangles.
7	Practice B	p. 243	TB: p. 193 WB: p. 180	Practice concepts from the chapter.
	Workbook Solutions	p. 245		

In Dimensions Math 4B, students learned to:

- Convert measurements from larger units to smaller units, for example, $\frac{3}{4}$ ft = $\frac{3}{4}$ × 12 in = 9 in.
- Use the formula for area of a rectangle, Area = Length × Width, to find the area of rectangles, and when given the area, find a missing side length by dividing the area by the known side length.
- Find the area of composite figures made up of rectangles.
- Identify right, equilateral, and isosceles triangles.

In this chapter, students will review measurement conversions, find the area of rectangles and rectilinear figures with side lengths given in fractions, and find the area of triangles and composite figures made up of triangles and rectangles.

Measurement Conversions

In Lesson 1, students will review converting measurements given in fractions from a larger unit to a smaller unit. For student reference, a conversion chart for common conversions is provided in Lesson 1.

Example: $2\frac{1}{2}$ lb = _____ oz

Convert the whole number and fraction separately.

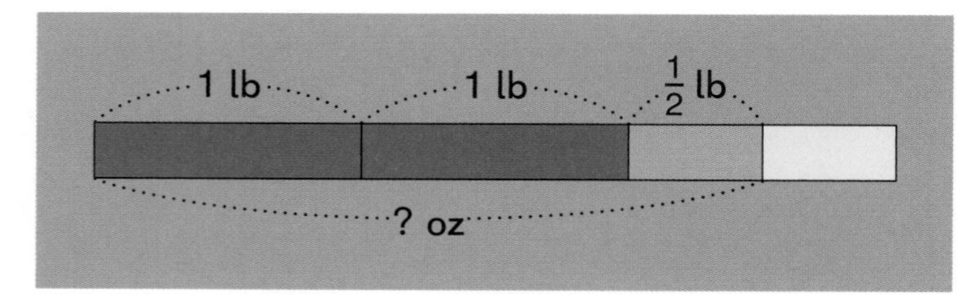

1 lb = 16 oz
2 lb = 2 × 16 oz = 32 oz
$\frac{1}{2}$ lb = $\frac{1}{2}$ × 16 oz = 8 oz
$2\frac{1}{2}$ lb = 2 lb + $\frac{1}{2}$ lb = 32 oz + 8 oz = 40 oz

Students may also choose to express the mixed number as an improper fraction and then convert to ounces.

$2\frac{1}{2}$ lb = $\frac{5}{2}$ lb
$\frac{5}{\cancel{2}_1} \times \cancel{16}^{8}$ oz = 5 × 8 oz = 40 oz

This method can be helpful in Lesson 2 when finding the areas of rectangles with fractional side measurements.

Fractions and Area

Students will apply their knowledge of area of a rectangle to find the area of composite figures with side lengths that are fractions and mixed numbers in Lesson 2.

There are two general methods used to find the areas of rectangles with side lengths that are mixed numbers.

1. Convert the mixed numbers to improper fractions and multiply.
2. Use the distributive property of multiplication, which is easily understood by using an area model.

Example:

Method 1

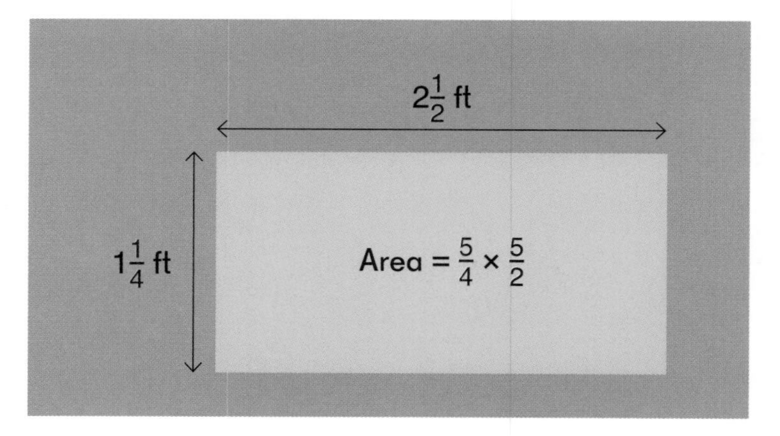

$1\frac{1}{4} \times 2\frac{1}{2} = \frac{5}{4} \times \frac{5}{2} = \frac{25}{8} = 3\frac{1}{8}$ ft^2

Method 2

A common error made by students is to multiply the whole numbers together (1 × 2), and the fractions together ($\frac{1}{4} \times \frac{1}{2}$) to get an incorrect product of $2\frac{1}{8}$.

An area model can be a helpful visual for students who make this mistake.

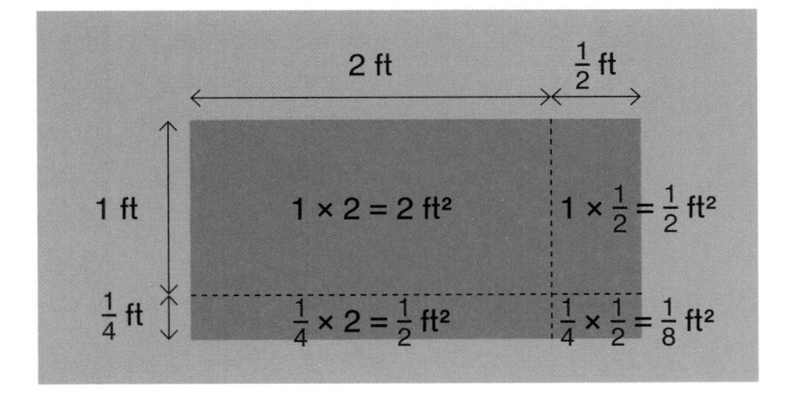

$1\frac{1}{4} \times 2\frac{1}{2} = (1 \times 2) + (1 \times \frac{1}{2}) + (\frac{1}{4} \times 2) + (\frac{1}{4} \times \frac{1}{2})$

$= 2 + \frac{1}{2} + \frac{1}{2} + \frac{1}{8} = 3\frac{1}{8}$ ft²

Applying the distributive property is more useful and less likely to result in error when only one of the sides is a mixed number. For example:

$3 \times 2\frac{1}{2} = (3 \times 2) + (3 \times \frac{1}{2})$

Students will use the same methods they learned in Grade 4 for finding the area of composite figures with whole number side lengths to find the area of composite figures with fractional side lengths.

Example:

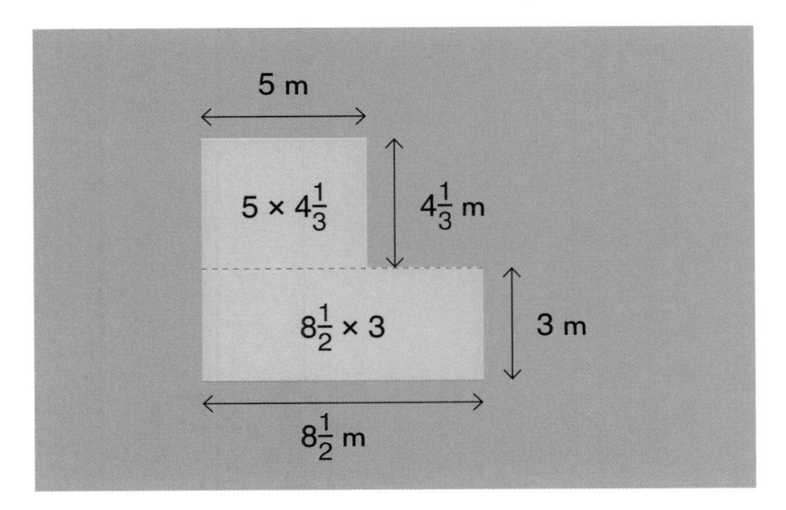

Area of top rectangle:
$5 \times 4\frac{1}{3} = 20 + \frac{5}{3} = 21\frac{2}{3}$ m²

Area of bottom rectangle:
$8\frac{1}{2} \times 3 = 24 + \frac{3}{2} = 25\frac{1}{2}$ m²

Area of the figure:
$21\frac{2}{3} + 25\frac{1}{2} = 46\frac{7}{6} = 47\frac{1}{6}$ m²

Students could also find the area by adding in a part to make a large rectangle, $7\frac{1}{3}$ m by $8\frac{1}{2}$ m, finding the area of the large rectangle, and then subtracting the area of the part they added in (a rectangle $3\frac{1}{2}$ m by $4\frac{1}{3}$ m).

Area of a Triangle

Students will apply their knowledge of finding the area of rectangles to find the area of triangles in Lessons 4–5. Students will begin with a variety of activities that show that the area of a triangle is $\frac{1}{2}$ of the area of its related rectangle. The related rectangle is one that has the same base and height as the triangle. They will learn to identify bases and corresponding heights.

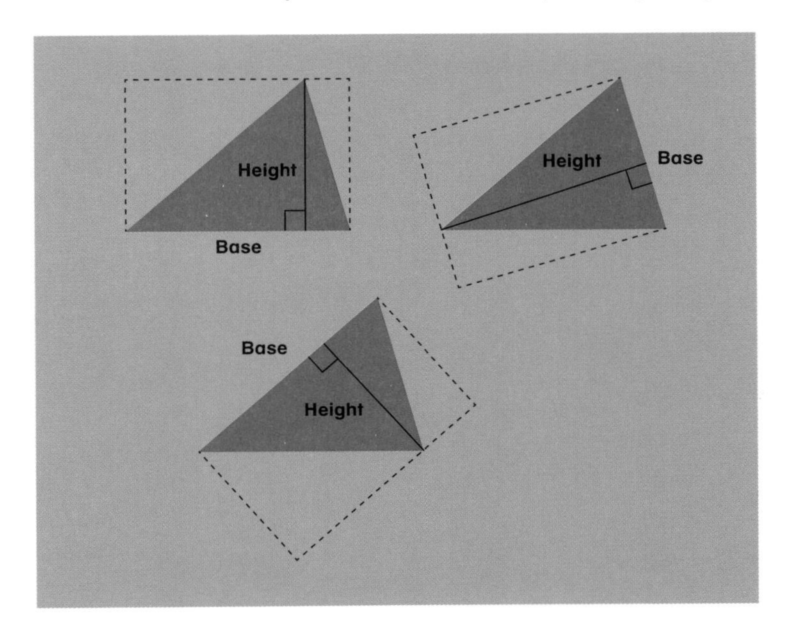

Students will then extend this knowledge to cases where the height of the triangle does not intersect its base as in examples B and C below.

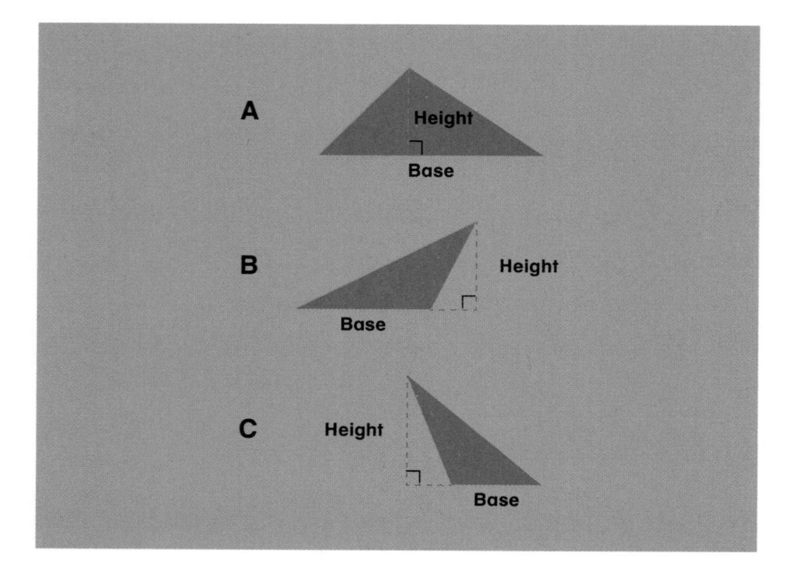

Students should be shown a variety of triangles, including obtuse scalene triangles, and learn to identify corresponding bases and heights. Have students imagine standing their triangles up on any side to find the highest point. The height is measured using a line from the opposite vertex perpendicular to the corresponding base.

Materials

- Construction paper
- Graph paper
- Measuring tape
- Measuring tools, for example: yardstick, meter stick, ruler, measuring cup, pint, quart, liter, and gallon containers, balance scale, food scale, analog clock, etc.
- Ruler
- Set square or straight edge
- Square pieces of paper
- Whiteboards

Blackline Masters

- Area of a Triangle 1
- Area of a Triangle 2
- Area of Complex Figures
- Conversion Match Cards

Activities

Fewer games and activities are included in this chapter as students will be drawing often in the **Think** and **Learn** sections. The included activities can be used after students complete the **Do** questions, or anytime additional practice is needed.

Objective

- Review measurement concepts.

Lesson Materials

- Measuring tools, for example: yardstick, meter stick, ruler, measuring cup, pint, quart, liter, and gallon containers, balance scale, food scale, analog clock, etc.

Have students read the **Chapter Opener**. They can recall and share the different units of measurement they have learned:

Inch	Kilogram	Milliliter
Foot	Ounce	Liter
Yard	Pound	Second
Mile	Fluid ounces	Minute
Centimeter	Cup	Hour
Meter	Pint	Day
Kilometer	Quart	Week
Gram	Gallon	Month

Have students discuss measurement tools. Ask students what each tool is used for and discuss the difference between length, area, volume, and the units that are used to measure each.

Students may know other units, such as, nautical mile, stone, fathom, degree Fahrenheit, dollar, cent, acre, furlong, cubit, and lightyear.

For struggling students, use the materials listed to do a review of the measurement concepts taught in prior grade levels.

Ask students to define area and perimeter: "What is alike and what is different?" (Perimeter is a linear measure of the outline of a shape. Area is the amount of space inside the outline of a shape.)

Ask students how to find the perimeter and area of a rectilinear shape.

Chapter 7

Measurement

What kinds of measurement have we learned so far?

We have learned how to measure length and find the perimeter.

We have learned how to measure capacity and liquid volume.

We have learned how to find the area of figures made from rectangles.

I wonder if we can do the same types of calculations when the measurements are fractions.

167

167

They should recall:

Perimeter = 2 × Length + 2 × Width
Area = Length × Width

If students easily recall units of measurement, continue to Lesson 1 where they will practice converting units of measurement.

Objective

- Convert measurements of length, weight, liquid volume, or time involving fractions or mixed numbers from a larger unit to a smaller unit.

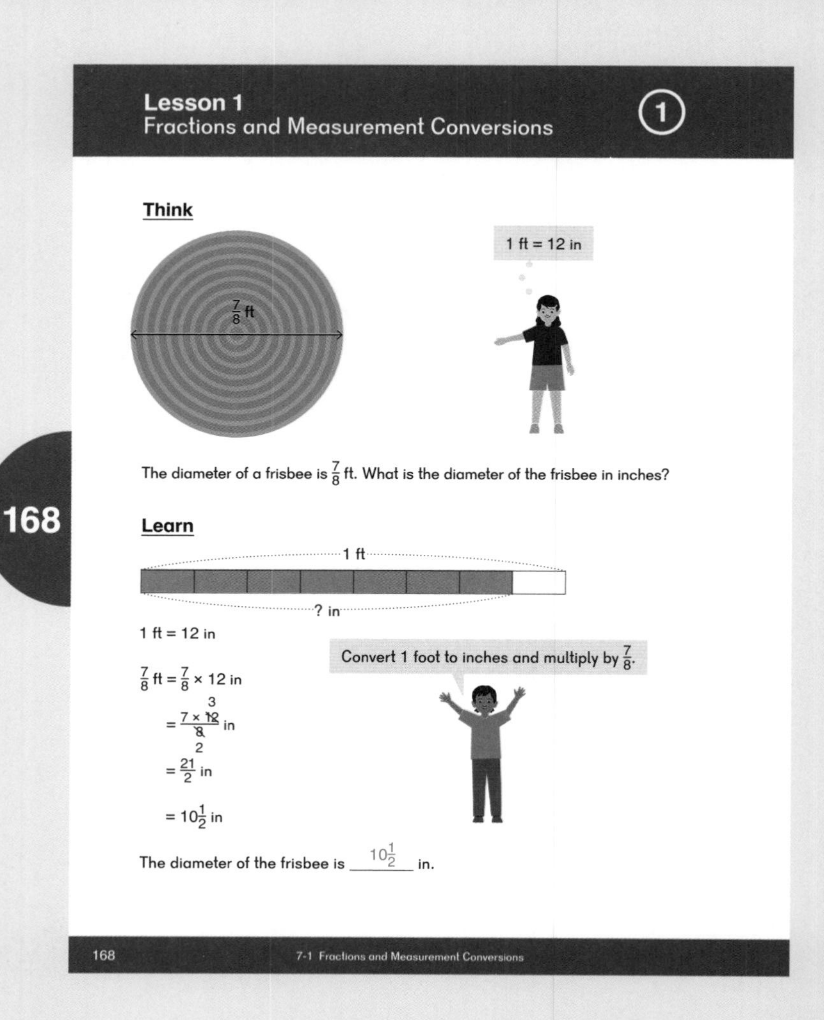

168

Lesson 1
Fractions and Measurement Conversions ①

Think

The diameter of a frisbee is $\frac{7}{8}$ ft. What is the diameter of the frisbee in inches?

Learn

1 ft = 12 in

$\frac{7}{8}$ ft $= \frac{7}{8} \times 12$ in

$= \frac{7 \times \overset{3}{\cancel{12}}}{\underset{2}{\cancel{8}}}$ in

$= \frac{21}{2}$ in

$= 10\frac{1}{2}$ in

The diameter of the frisbee is $10\frac{1}{2}$ in.

168 7-1 Fractions and Measurement Conversions

Think

Pose the **Think** problem and discuss Mei's thought. It should prompt students to recall conversion rates that they have learned. Students can draw a bar model to help them solve the problem.

Ask students:

- "Will the answer require you to multiply or divide? Why?" (Multiply. There are 12 inches in 1 foot, so there will be more inches than feet.)
- "Will the answer be greater than or less than 12 inches?" (The answer will be less than 12 inches because we are multiplying 12 by a fraction less than 1.)

Discuss student solutions.

Learn

Students should recall how to multiply a fraction by a whole number from Chapter 5.

They could also apply a unit approach if they used a bar model:

8 units $\longrightarrow$ 12 in

1 unit $\longrightarrow \frac{1}{8} \times 12 = \frac{12}{8} = \frac{3}{2}$ in

7 units $\longrightarrow 7 \times \frac{3}{2} = \frac{21}{2} = 10\frac{1}{2}$ in

Conversions that students have learned are provided in a table in the textbook for quick reference.

Do

❶–❺ Discuss the different bar models and problems with students.

Ensure students understand what they need to find in each problem. Ask if they should express the answer in smaller units or compound units. (❶, ❷, ❸, and ❺ require smaller units. ❹ requires compound units.)

Students who are struggling may also solve the problems by thinking of units as shown below. Help students see how the method shown in the textbook and the method shown below are related.

❶ 4 units ⟶ 60 min
1 unit ⟶ $\frac{60}{4}$ = 15 min
3 units ⟶ 3 × 15 = 45 min

❷ 5 units ⟶ 4 qt
1 unit ⟶ $\frac{4}{5}$ qt
4 units ⟶ $4 \times \frac{4}{5} = \frac{16}{5} = 3\frac{1}{5}$ qt

❸ & ❺ Since these questions require expressing the products in smaller units, students should understand that they must convert both the whole number part and the fraction part of each mixed number to the smaller units. Studying the bar model in ❸ should help students understand the problem.

❹ Because the question requires expressing the product in both feet and inches, students need only to convert the fractional part of the mixed number to inches.

Customary Conversions	
1 ft .... 12 in	1 lb .... 16 oz
1 yd .... 3 ft	1 day .... 24 h
1 qt .... 4 c	1 min .... 60 s
1 gal .... 4 qt	1 h .... 60 min

Metric Conversions	
1 km ..... 1,000 m	1 L ..... 1,000 mL
1 m ..... 100 cm	1 kg ..... 1,000 g
1 cm ..... 10 mm	

Do

❶ Mei played badminton for $\frac{3}{4}$ of an hour. How many minutes did she play badminton?

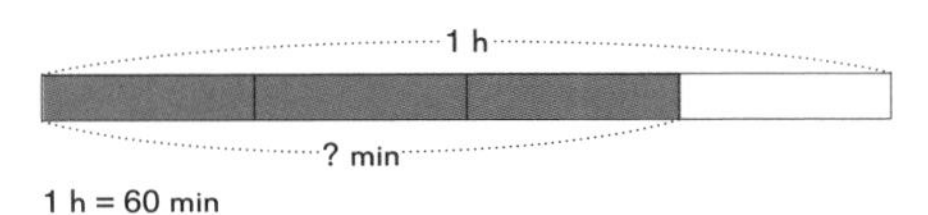

1 h = 60 min

$\frac{3}{4}$ h = $\frac{3}{4}$ × 60 min = 45 min

169

❷ A jug holds 1 gal of water. It is $\frac{4}{5}$ full. How many quarts of water are in the jug? Express the answer as a mixed number in simplest form.

1 gal

? qt

1 gal = 4 qt

$\frac{4}{5}$ gal = $\frac{4}{5}$ × 4 qt = $3\frac{1}{5}$ qt

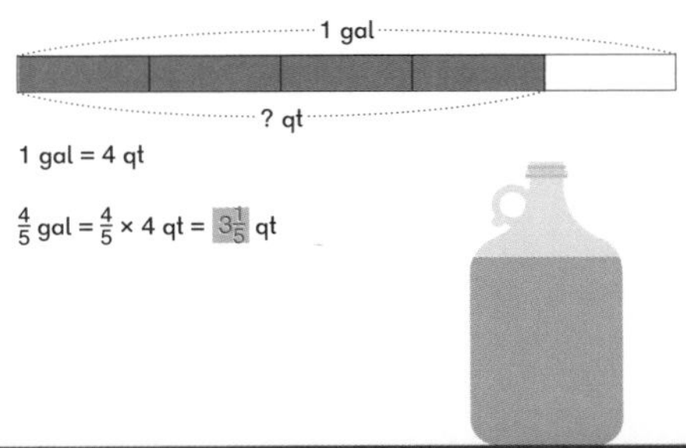

❸

A metal pipe weighs $2\frac{3}{4}$ pounds. How many ounces does the pipe weigh?

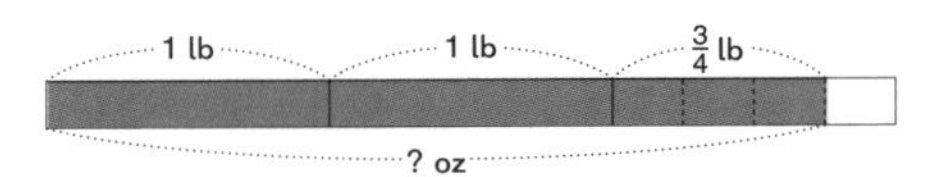

1 lb = 16 oz

2 lb = 2 × 16 oz = 32 oz

$\frac{3}{4}$ lb = $\frac{3}{4}$ × 16 oz = 12 oz

$2\frac{3}{4}$ lb = 32 oz + 12 oz = 44 oz

170

❹ A tennis racket is $2\frac{1}{3}$ ft long. How long is the tennis racket in feet and inches?

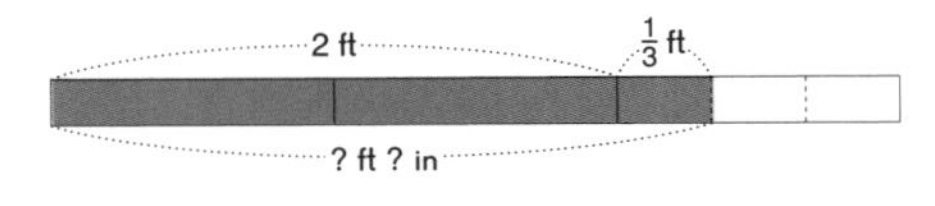

1 ft = 12 in

$\frac{1}{3}$ ft = $\frac{1}{3}$ × 12 in = 4 in

$2\frac{1}{3}$ ft = 2 ft 4 in

❺ Ask students how what Sofia is thinking is related to the steps of the calculation shown on the left. (Once we find the number of grams in 3 kg and $\frac{1}{2}$ kg, we can add the grams together.)

❻—❼ Students should be able to solve these problems independently. Students can use the conversion charts on textbook page 169 for reference.

❼ Ask students how the problems in each row are related. They should see that the first column has students converting just the fractional parts to the smaller units as in ❹. The second column has students converting the same mixed number measurement to smaller units as in ❺.

If necessary, walk students through some of the problems in ❼, using the strategy shown in ❺.

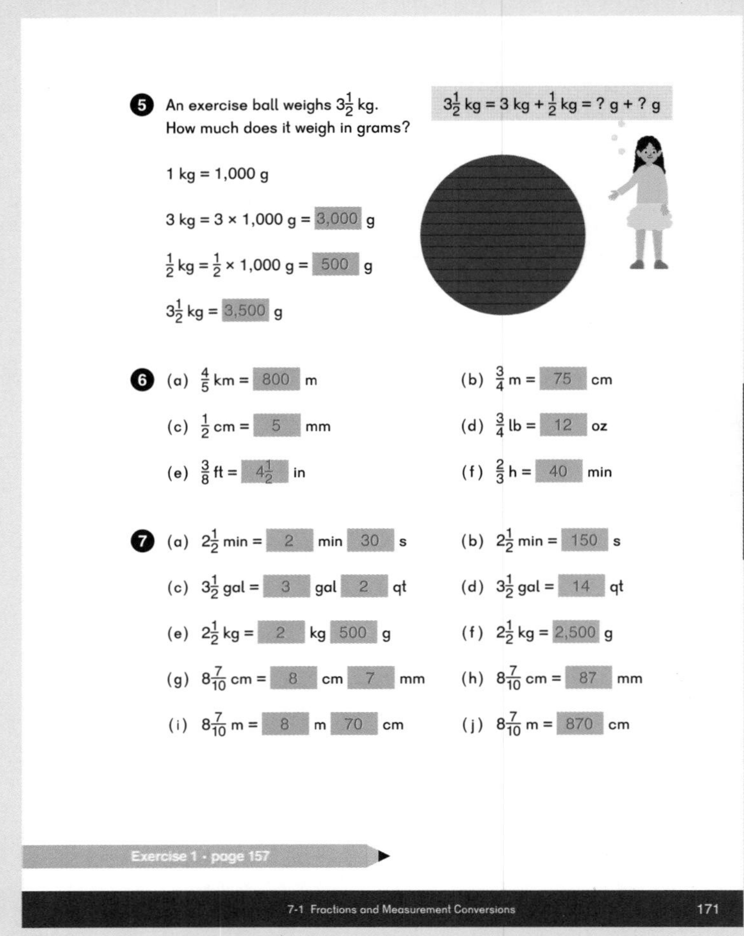

❺ An exercise ball weighs $3\frac{1}{2}$ kg. How much does it weigh in grams?

$3\frac{1}{2}$ kg = 3 kg + $\frac{1}{2}$ kg = ? g + ? g

1 kg = 1,000 g

3 kg = 3 × 1,000 g = 3,000 g

$\frac{1}{2}$ kg = $\frac{1}{2}$ × 1,000 g = 500 g

$3\frac{1}{2}$ kg = 3,500 g

❻ (a) $\frac{4}{5}$ km = 800 m (b) $\frac{3}{4}$ m = 75 cm

(c) $\frac{1}{2}$ cm = 5 mm (d) $\frac{3}{4}$ lb = 12 oz

(e) $\frac{3}{8}$ ft = $4\frac{1}{2}$ in (f) $\frac{2}{3}$ h = 40 min

❼ (a) $2\frac{1}{2}$ min = 2 min 30 s (b) $2\frac{1}{2}$ min = 150 s

(c) $3\frac{1}{2}$ gal = 3 gal 2 qt (d) $3\frac{1}{2}$ gal = 14 qt

(e) $2\frac{1}{2}$ kg = 2 kg 500 g (f) $2\frac{1}{2}$ kg = 2,500 g

(g) $8\frac{7}{10}$ cm = 8 cm 7 mm (h) $8\frac{7}{10}$ cm = 87 mm

(i) $8\frac{7}{10}$ m = 8 m 70 cm (j) $8\frac{7}{10}$ m = 870 cm

Exercise 1 • page 157

7-1 Fractions and Measurement Conversions 171

Activities

● **Match**

Materials: Conversion Match Cards (BLM), multiple sets

Lay cards in a faceup array. Have students find two Conversion Match Cards (BLM) that show equivalent measurements.

▲ **Memory**

Materials: Conversion Match Cards (BLM), multiple sets

Play using the same rules as **Match**, but arrange the cards facedown in an array.

Exercise 1 • page 157

Lesson 2 Fractions and Area

Objective

- Find the area of rectangles with fractional side lengths.

Lesson Materials

- Square pieces of paper

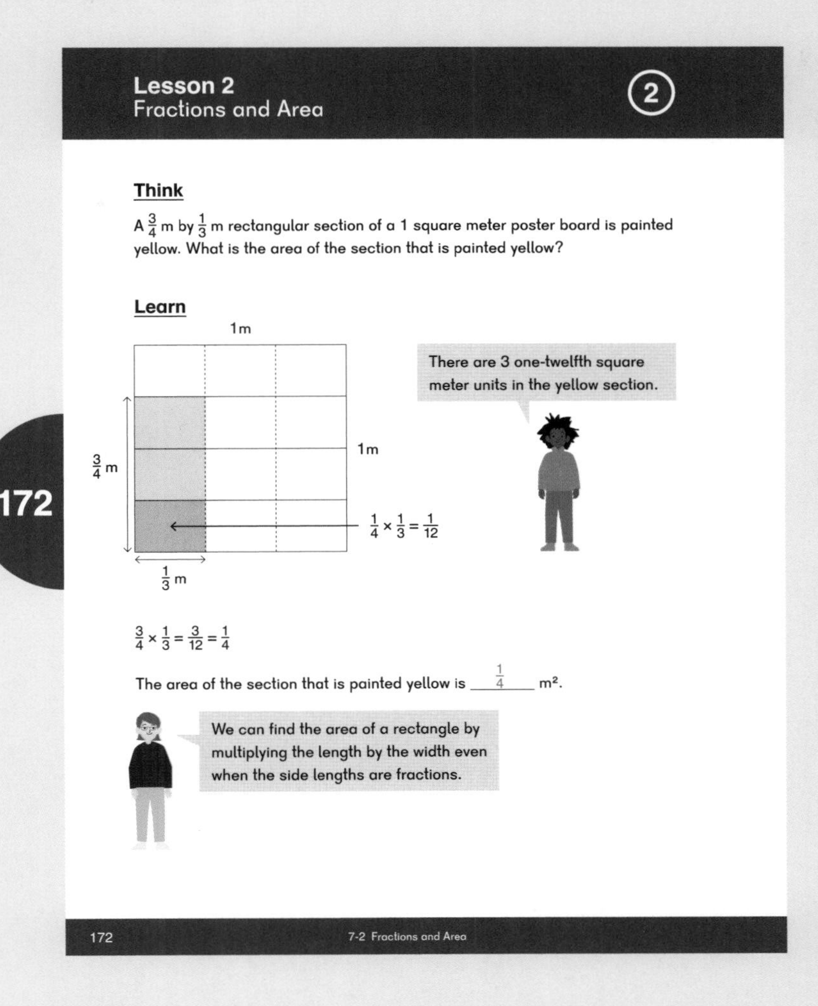

Think

Provide students with square pieces of paper and pose the **Think** problem. Tell students the paper represents the poster that is 1 m on each side. They can fold, color, or shade the square paper to find the section of poster board that is painted yellow.

Discuss student solutions.

Learn

Have students compare their solutions from **Think** with the one shown in the textbook. If necessary, provide them with another square paper to fold and color so that they have one that looks like the textbook example.

Students should see that one unit is $\frac{1}{4}$ m × $\frac{1}{3}$ m = $\frac{1}{12}$ m². Even though the units are not shown in the calculation in the textbook, it is important that students see that $\frac{1}{12}$ m² is the area of one unit, and since 3 units are shaded, the area of the shaded part is $\frac{3}{12}$ m² = $\frac{1}{4}$ m².

Applying prior knowledge of the area formula for rectangles with whole number measurements, students should realize that multiplying length by width will also give the area of rectangles with fractional side lengths.

Do

❶—❷ Discuss the given models and problems with students.

❶ Ask students:

- "What is the area of two of the smaller squares?" ($\frac{2}{4}$, or $\frac{1}{2}$ in²)
- "What is the area of 3 of the smaller squares?" ($\frac{3}{4}$ in²)

❷ Alex prompts students to first express the mixed numbers as improper fractions:

$2\frac{1}{2} \times 1\frac{1}{2} = \frac{5}{2} \times \frac{3}{2} = \frac{15}{4} = 3\frac{3}{4}$ in²

Sofia avoids using improper fractions by recalling that the areas of smaller rectangles can be added to find the area of the figure.

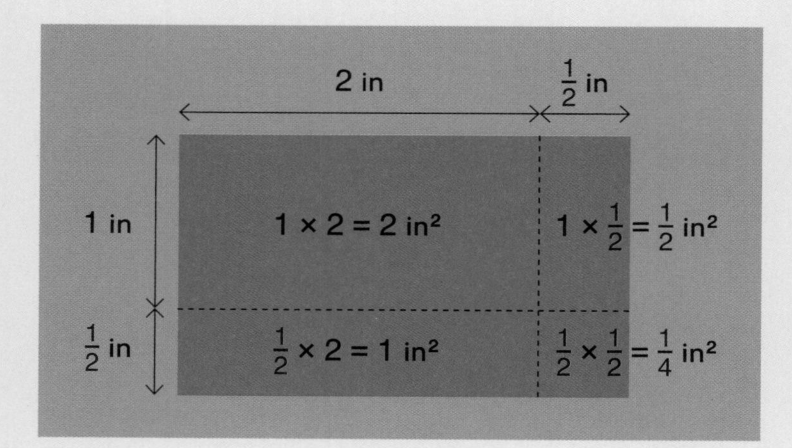

$2 + \frac{1}{2} + 1 + \frac{1}{4} = 3\frac{3}{4}$ in²

❸—❺ Most students should be able to solve these problems independently.

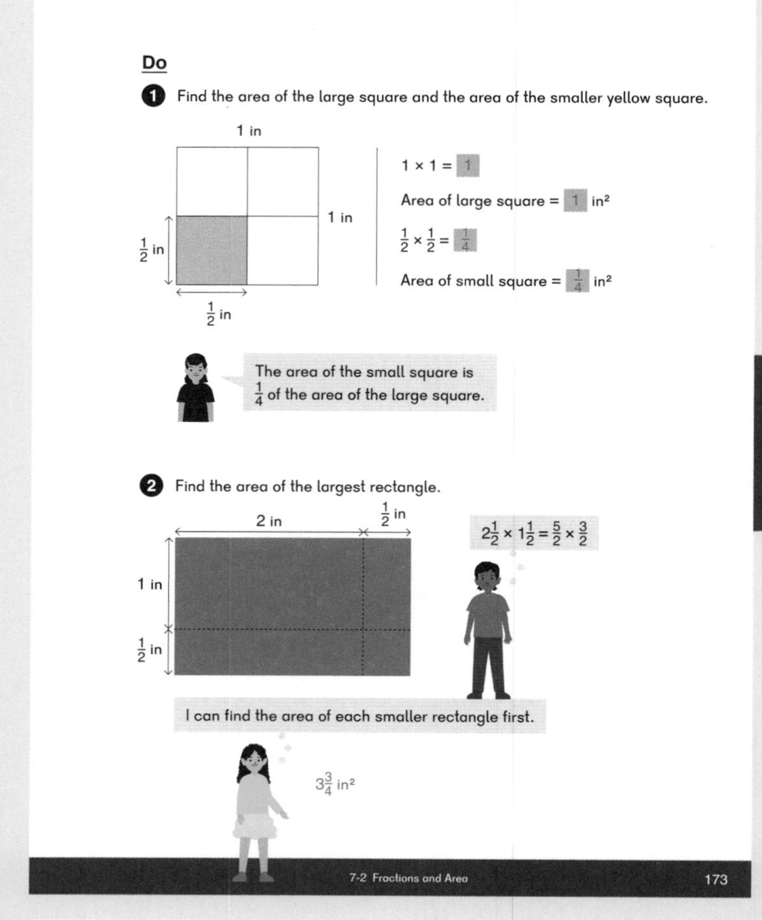

173

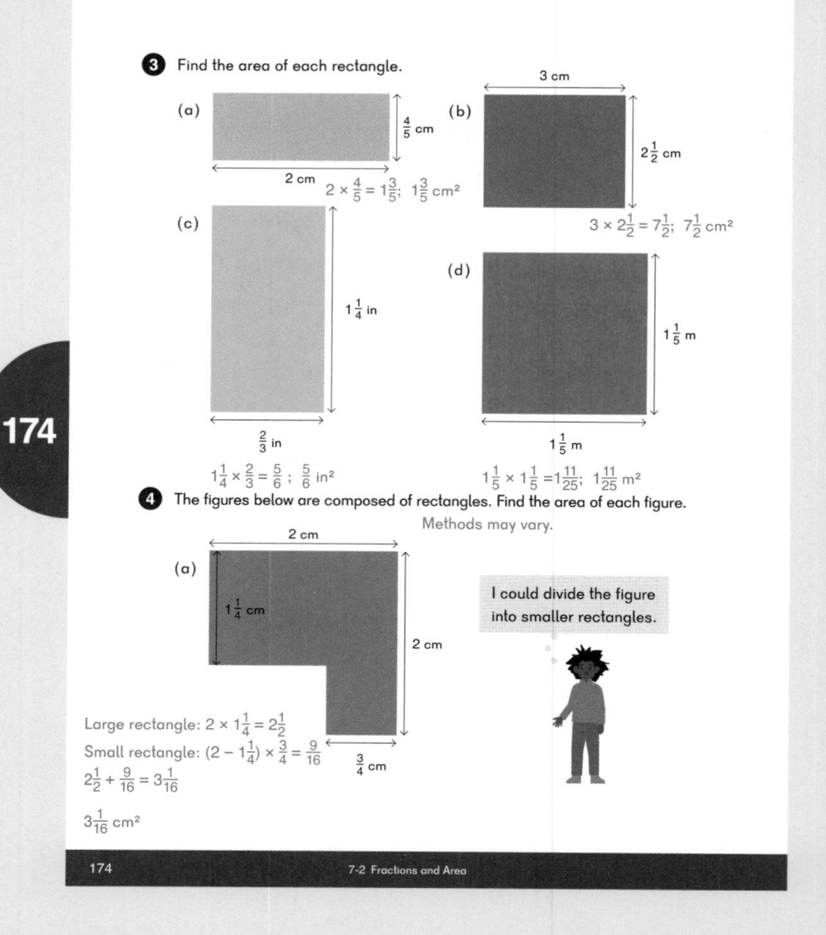

174

4 (b) The solution in the answer overlay is based on Emma's suggestion. Students may solve the problem by partitioning into smaller rectangles as well.

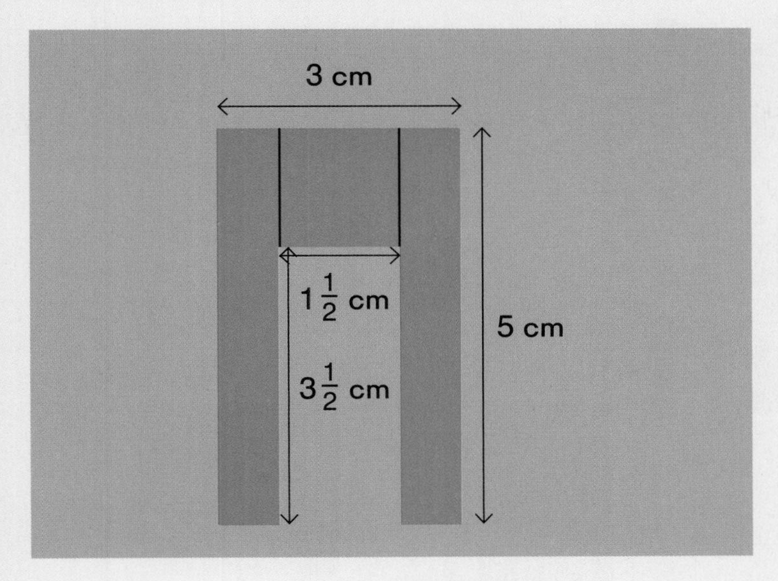

Legs:
$3\text{ cm} - 1\frac{1}{2}\text{ cm} = 1\frac{1}{2}\text{ cm}$

$\frac{3}{2}\text{ cm} \div 2 = \frac{3}{4}\text{ cm}$

$2 \times \frac{3}{4} \times 5 = 7\frac{1}{2}\text{ cm}^2$

Middle:
$5 - 3\frac{1}{2} = 1\frac{1}{2}\text{ cm}$

$1\frac{1}{2} \times 1\frac{1}{2} = \frac{9}{4} = 2\frac{1}{4}\text{ cm}^2$

Area of figure: $7\frac{1}{2} + 2\frac{1}{4} = 9\frac{3}{4}\text{ cm}^2$

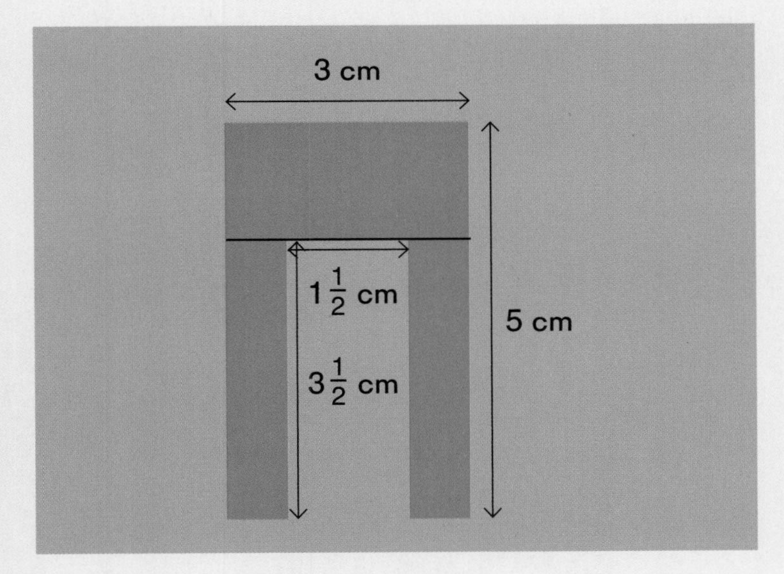

Top rectangle:
$5 - 3\frac{1}{2} - 1\frac{1}{2}\text{ cm}$

$3 \times 1\frac{1}{2} = 4\frac{1}{2}\text{ cm}^2$

Legs:
$3\text{ cm} - 1\frac{1}{2}\text{ cm} = 1\frac{1}{2}\text{ cm}$

$\frac{3}{2}\text{ cm} \div 2 = \frac{3}{4}\text{ cm}$

$2 \times 3\frac{1}{2} \times \frac{3}{4} = 5\frac{1}{4}\text{ cm}^2$

Area of figure: $5\frac{1}{4} + 4\frac{1}{2} = 9\frac{3}{4}\text{ cm}^2$

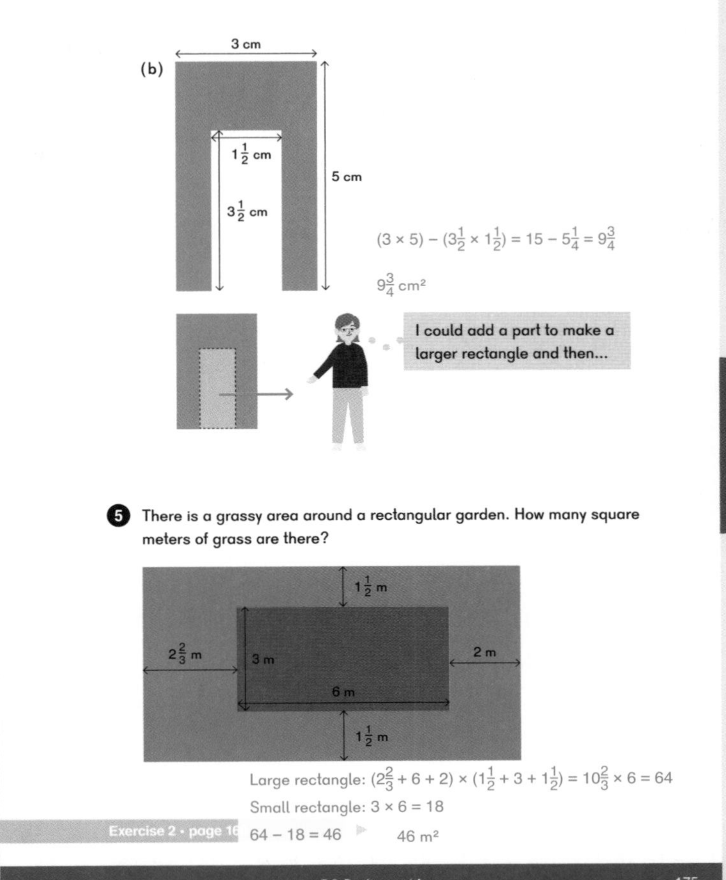

175

Activity

▲ Picture Frames

Materials: Ruler, construction paper

Give each student a piece of construction paper, a ruler, and a pair of scissors. Have them create one picture frame each by measuring and then folding to cut a rectangle from the interior of the piece of construction paper.

The cut-out rectangle should have mixed number side lengths. Have students calculate the area of their frame.

◀ Exercise 2 • page 160

Objective

- Practice concepts from Lessons 1 and 2.

After students complete the **Practice** in the textbook, have them continue to practice skills using activities from the chapter.

Activity

▲ Measure the School

Materials: Measuring tape

Provide students with measuring tape and have them measure rooms or spaces in the building. Students can compute the area in different square units: feet and inches, or meters and centimeters.

Exercise 3 • page 163

176

Lesson 3
Practice A

P 3

1. Jason played tennis for $\frac{2}{3}$ of an hour. How many minutes did he play tennis?
   $\frac{2}{3} \times 60$ min = 40 min

2. Maria needs $\frac{3}{8}$ lb of flour for a muffin recipe. She wants to double the recipe. How many ounces of flour does she need?
   $\frac{3}{8}$ lb × 2 = $\frac{6}{8}$ lb; $\frac{6}{8} \times 16$ ounces = 12 ounces

3. Last week Jackie ran $\frac{4}{5}$ km every day for 6 days. How far did she run in meters?
   $6 \times \frac{4}{5}$ km = $\frac{24}{5}$ km; $\frac{24}{5} \times 1{,}000$ m = 4,800 m

4. Danny had $\frac{3}{4}$ qt of apple juice and 2 qt of lemonade. He mixed $\frac{2}{3}$ of each juice to make fruit punch. How many cups of fruit punch does he have?
   $(\frac{2}{3} \times \frac{3}{4}) + (\frac{2}{3} \times 2) = 1\frac{5}{6}$ qt; $1\frac{5}{6} \times 4$ c = $7\frac{1}{3}$ c

5. Find the area of each figure.

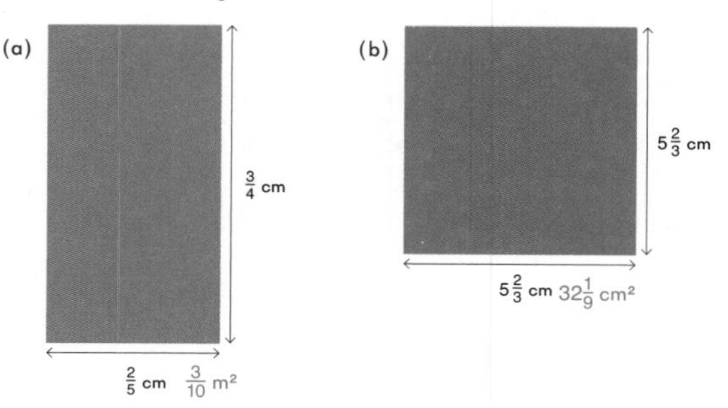

(a) $\frac{3}{10}$ m²
(b) $32\frac{1}{9}$ cm²

Methods may vary.

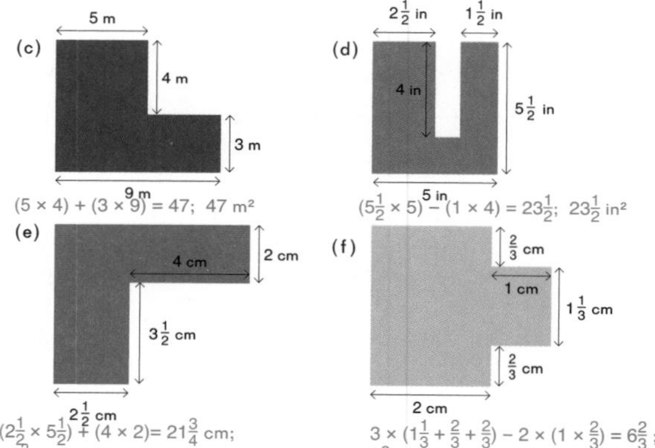

(c) $(5 \times 4) + (3 \times 9) = 47$; 47 m²

(d) $(5\frac{1}{2} \times 5) - (1 \times 4) = 23\frac{1}{2}$; $23\frac{1}{2}$ in²

(e) $(2\frac{1}{2} \times 5\frac{1}{2}) + (4 \times 2) = 21\frac{3}{4}$ cm; $21\frac{3}{4}$ cm²

(f) $3 \times (1\frac{1}{3} + \frac{2}{3} + \frac{2}{3}) - 2 \times (1 \times \frac{2}{3}) = 6\frac{2}{3}$; $6\frac{2}{3}$ cm²

6. There is a grassy area around a rectangular pond.

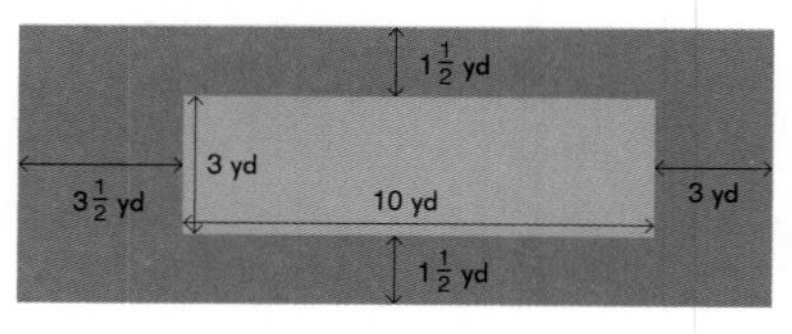

(a) How many square yards of grass are there?
$(3\frac{1}{2} + 10 + 3) \times (1\frac{1}{2} + 1\frac{1}{2} + 3) - (3 \times 10) = 99 - 30 = 69$ yd²

(b) How many square feet are in one square yard?
3 ft × 3 ft = 9 ft²; 1 square yard = 9 square feet.

(c) How many square feet of grass are there?
69 × 9 = 621 ft²

Exercise 3 • page 163

177

Objective

- Find the area of a triangle when the height is given inside of the triangle.

Lesson Materials

- Area of a Triangle 1 (BLM)

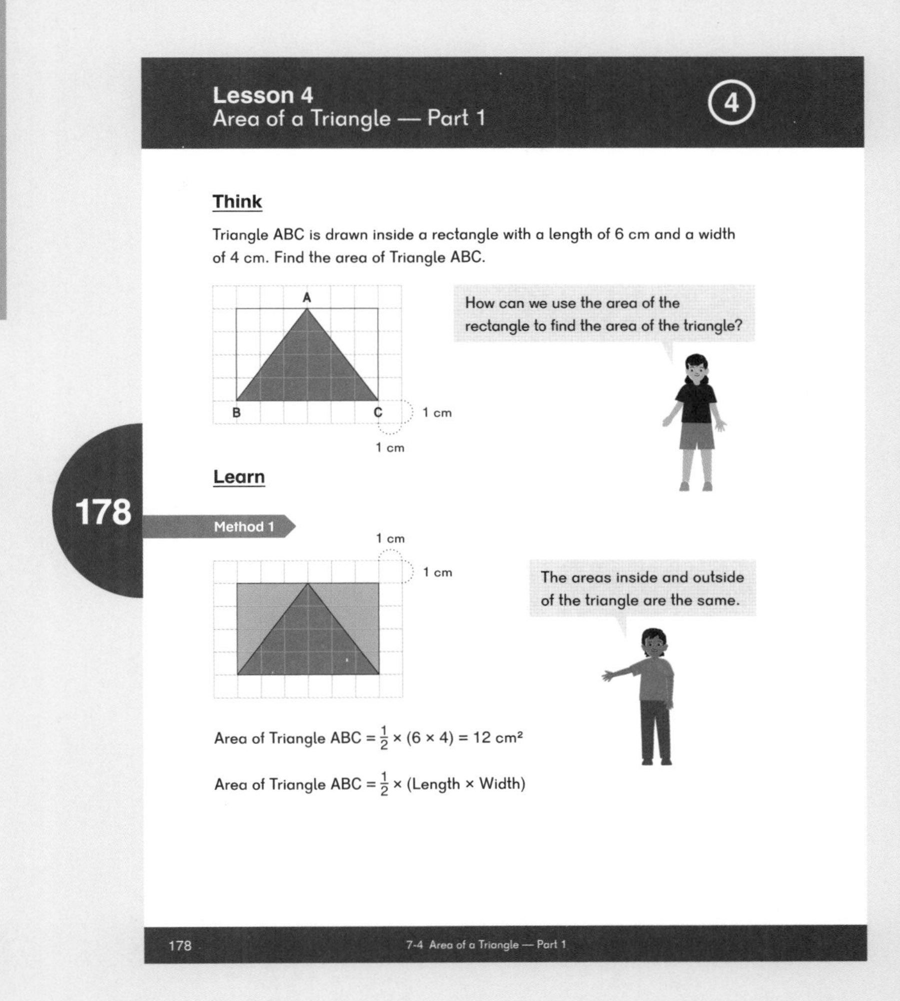

Think

Provide students with Area of a Triangle 1 (BLM) and pose the **Think** problem.

Discuss Mei's question. Students can fold, shade, or cut Area of a Triangle 1 (BLM) to find their answers. Students may also try to match partial squares to make full squares and count the squares.

Discuss student solutions.

Learn

Have students compare their solutions to the three methods shown in **Learn**.

Method 1

The base of the triangle is one side of the related rectangle, which is the rectangle that has the same length base and height as the triangle.

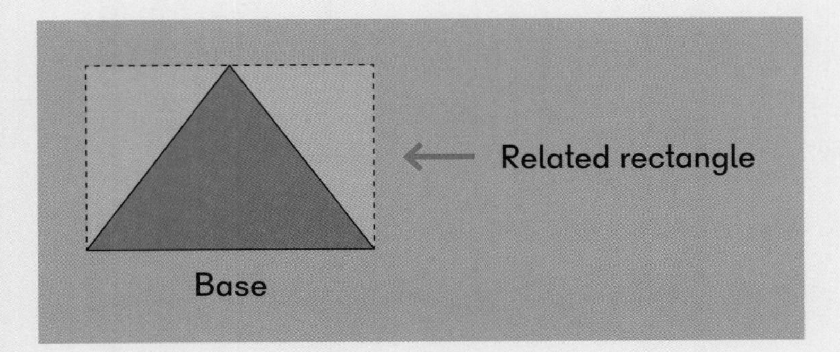

Alex cuts out the related rectangle, and then the triangle. The parts of the rectangle that are cut away will directly overlay the remaining triangle.

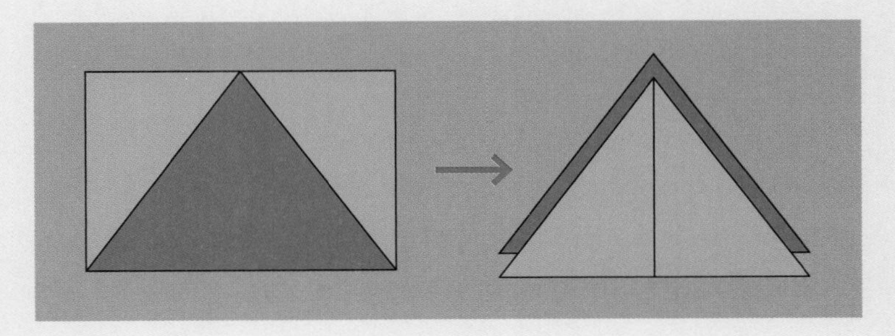

Since the light green and dark green triangles together make up the whole rectangle, each triangle is one half of the rectangle.

Method 2

Sofia cuts out the triangle, and then cuts the triangle in half. The parts of the triangle are put together and form one half of the original rectangle.

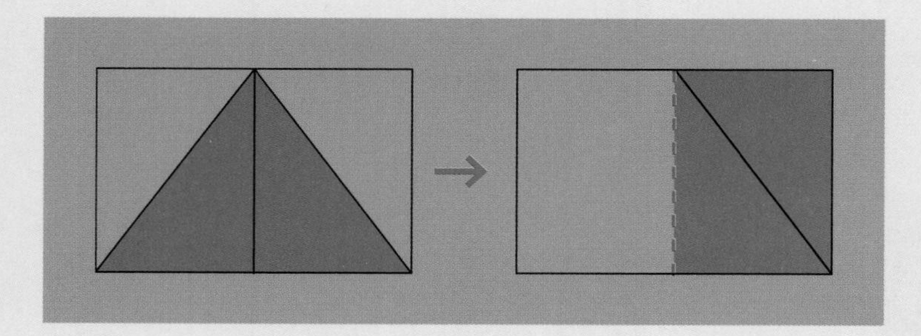

Method 3

Dion cuts the triangle in half horizontally. He can then cut the top part of the triangle in half, as in Method 2, to form one half of the rectangle in a different way.

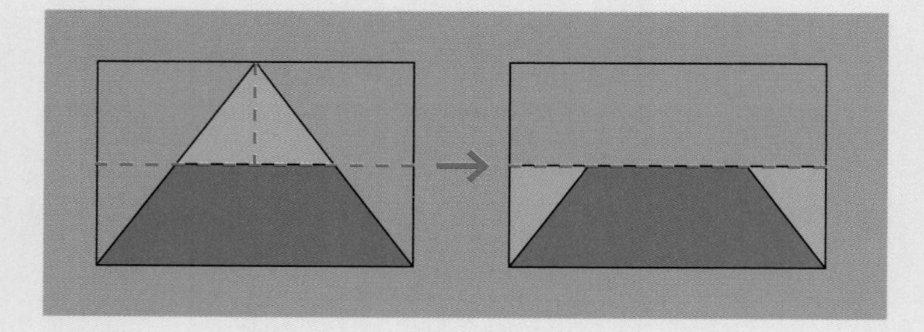

Point out that the related rectangle has the same base and height as the triangle. We can see that the area of the triangle is half of the area of the related rectangle by cutting and moving pieces.

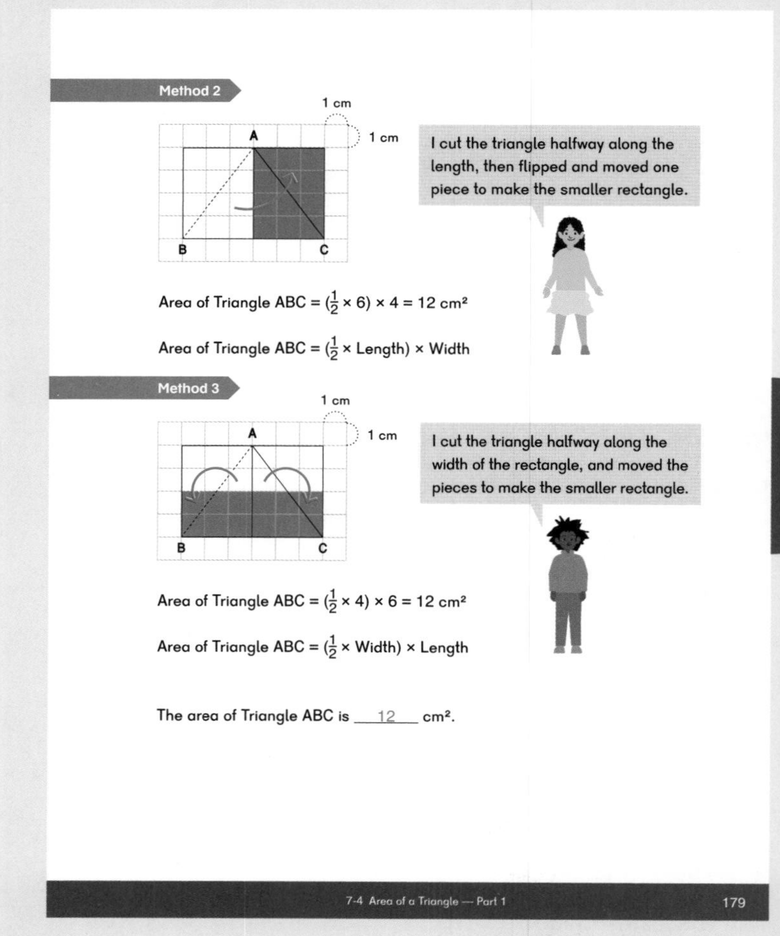

Method 2

1 cm

1 cm

A

B

C

I cut the triangle halfway along the length, then flipped and moved one piece to make the smaller rectangle.

Area of Triangle ABC = $(\frac{1}{2} \times 6) \times 4 = 12$ cm²

Area of Triangle ABC = $(\frac{1}{2} \times \text{Length}) \times \text{Width}$

Method 3

1 cm

1 cm

A

B

C

I cut the triangle halfway along the width of the rectangle, and moved the pieces to make the smaller rectangle.

Area of Triangle ABC = $(\frac{1}{2} \times 4) \times 6 = 12$ cm²

Area of Triangle ABC = $(\frac{1}{2} \times \text{Width}) \times \text{Length}$

The area of Triangle ABC is __12__ cm².

7-4 Area of a Triangle — Part 1 179

179

Mei introduces the terms "base" and "height" of a triangle.

Emma helps students understand that any side of the triangle can be considered the base regardless of the orientation of the triangle. Students learn that height is always perpendicular to the base.

Have students draw an acute triangle, choose one side as the base, then draw a perpendicular line for the height. Next, have them rotate the triangle and consider another side the base and draw another height. Have them do the same for the third side.

With base and height defined, we can now derive a formula to find the area of a triangle using those terms. To find the area of a rectangle, we use the formula: Area = Length × Width. To find the area of a triangle, we use the formula: Area = $\frac{1}{2}$ × Base × Height.

Ask students their thoughts about Dion's question. Do not tell them the answer yet as they will discover it when they complete Lesson 5.

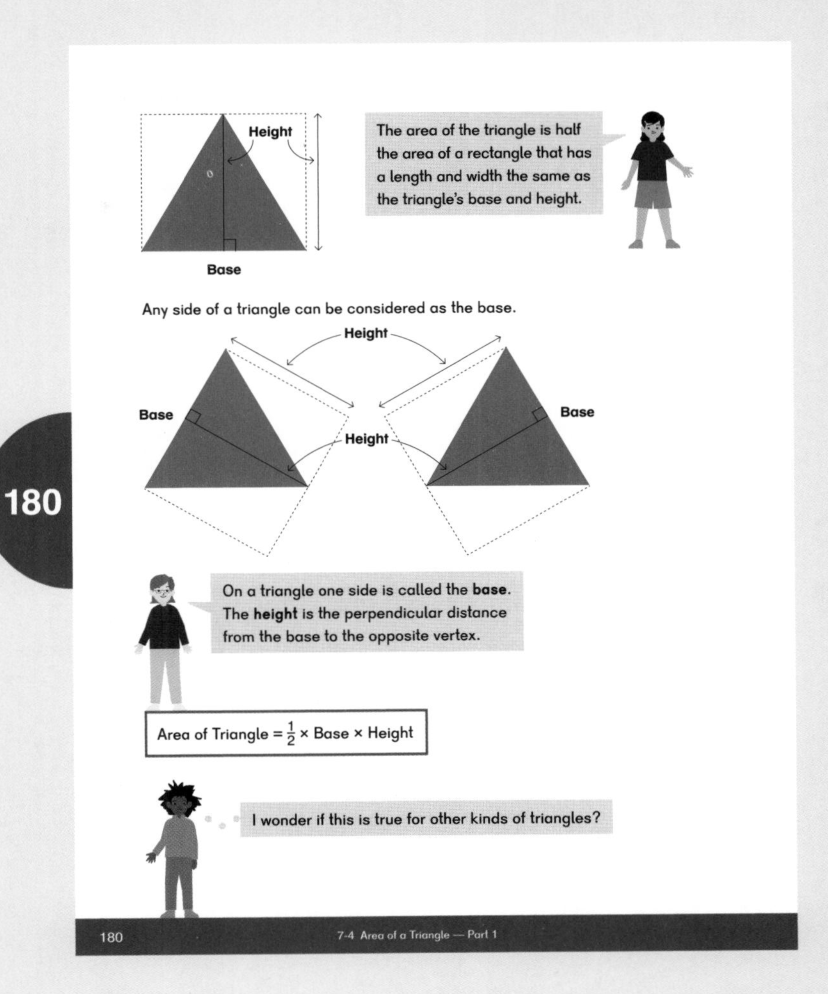

Do

❶ (a) Ask students:

- “Which side should we make the base?” (BC or CD)
- “Why?” (Because we know the length of these sides.)
- “Then what is the height?” (5 cm if the base is BC and 6 cm if the base is CD.)

Each calculation reinforces the formula $\frac{1}{2}$ × Base × Height. Alex helps students understand that regardless of which side is used as the base, the formula will always work.

❷—❹ Discuss the problems with students.

❷ Students can see from ❶ that the formula works for right triangles and acute triangles that are not isosceles. This is an example with an obtuse triangle. They can only use the side opposite the obtuse angle as the base. They will learn how to find the area if one of the other sides is the base in the next chapter.

❸—❹ Most students should be able to solve these problems independently.

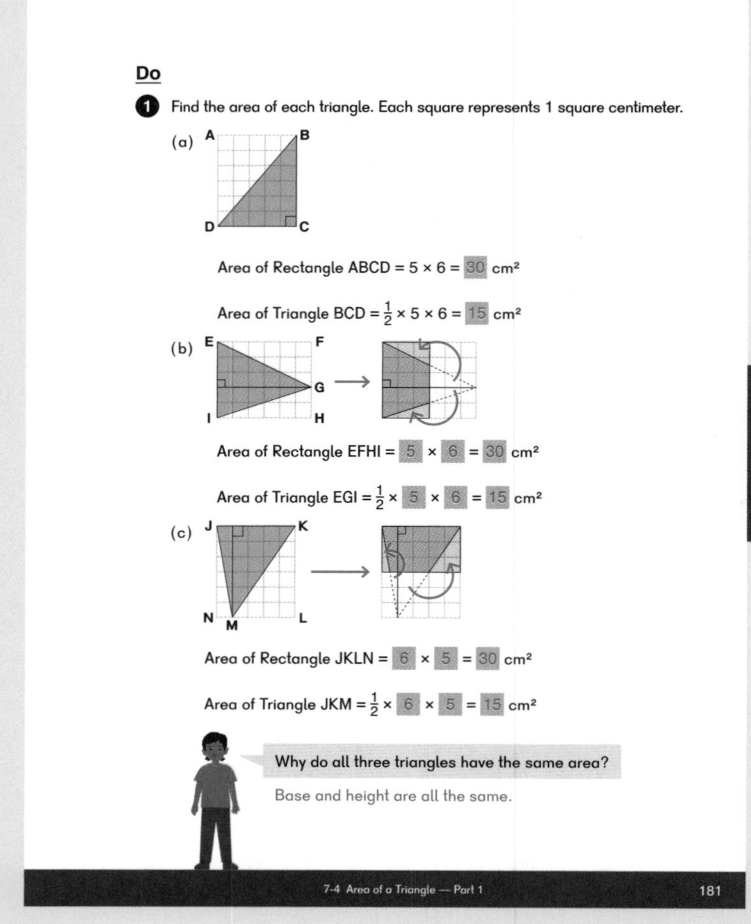

Do

❶ Find the area of each triangle. Each square represents 1 square centimeter.

(a)

Area of Rectangle ABCD = 5 × 6 = 30 cm²

Area of Triangle BCD = $\frac{1}{2}$ × 5 × 6 = 15 cm²

(b)

Area of Rectangle EFHI = 5 × 6 = 30 cm²

Area of Triangle EGI = $\frac{1}{2}$ × 5 × 6 = 15 cm²

(c)

Area of Rectangle JKLN = 6 × 5 = 30 cm²

Area of Triangle JKM = $\frac{1}{2}$ × 6 × 5 = 15 cm²

Why do all three triangles have the same area?

Base and height are all the same.

7-4 Area of a Triangle — Part 1 181

181

❷ Find the area of the triangle. Each square represents 1 square centimeter.

$\frac{1}{2}$ × 10 × 3 = 15; 15 cm²

❸ Identify a base and the corresponding height for each triangle.

(a) Base = DF

Height = DE

(b) Base = JL

Height = KM

(c) Base = QS

Height = PR

182 7-4 Area of a Triangle — Part 1

182

❹ (b) If students write the equation $\frac{1}{2} \times 3 \times 2$, remind them that multiplication can be done in any order. They could also write $\frac{1}{2} \times 2 \times 3$, or calculate without rewriting.

It is easier to calculate $\frac{1}{2}$ of 2 first, then multiply by 3.

(e) Both the base and height are odd numbers. Students may find it easier to first multiply 7×5, then multiply 35 by $\frac{1}{2}$, than to multiply either 5 or 7 by $\frac{1}{2}$ first and then multiply that number by the measure of the other given side.

(f) Students should know that it is the entire length of the side that is the base. Some students may also solve the problem by finding the area of the two right triangles and adding them together.

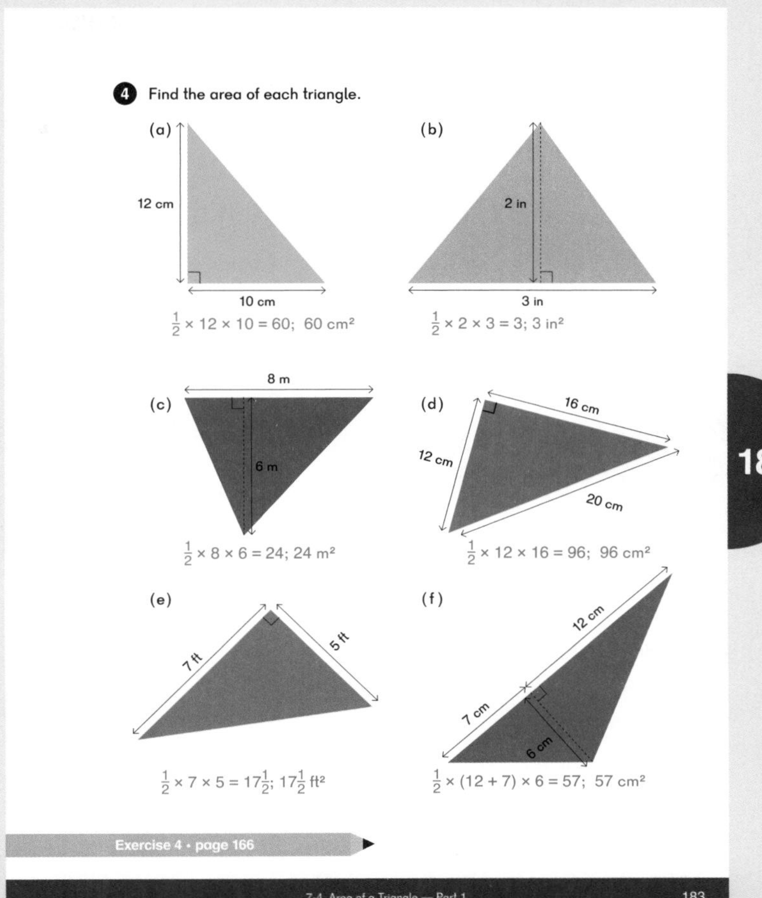

Objective

- Find the area of a triangle when the height for a given base falls outside the triangle.

Lesson Materials

- Area of a Triangle 2 (BLM), extra copies

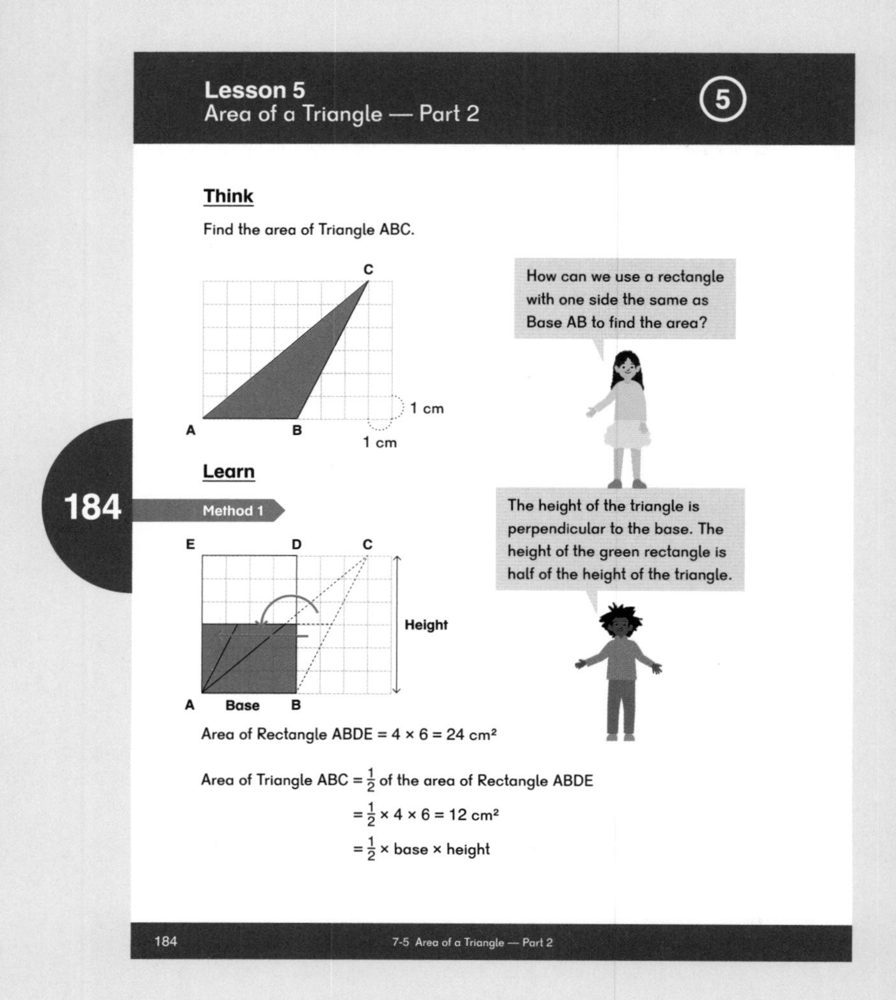

Think

Provide students with Area of a Triangle 2 (BLM) and pose the **Think** problem.

Students can fold, shade, or cut Area of a Triangle 2 (BLM) to find their answers.

Ask students:

- "If we want a whole number for the base, which side should we use as the base?"
- "Can you outline the rectangle with Base AB that Sofia is talking about?"
- "Do you think that it is possible to cut the triangle up and rearrange the pieces into a rectangle that is one-half the area of the related rectangle, as in the previous lesson?"

Discuss student solutions.

Learn

Have students compare their solutions to the two methods shown in **Learn**.

Method 1

Dion makes a smaller rectangle with the Base AB. He can partition the triangle and put it inside of the rectangle with Base AB to see that it is $\frac{1}{2}$ the area of the related rectangle. We can see the calculation from the picture: ($\frac{1}{2}$ of the height) × the base. We know that we can multiply in any order: $\frac{1}{2}$ × Base × Height.

Dion sees that the formula for the area of a triangle still works if we can determine the height.

Method 2

Emma finds the area of a larger right triangle, ACD, that she makes from the given height and a perpendicular line to the Base AB. Then she finds the area of Triangle BCD, the smaller right triangle she created.

Area of Triangle ABC = Area of Triangle ACD − Area of Triangle BCD.

Alex finds that the difference in the areas of the two triangles is the same as the difference in the bases of the two triangles multiplied by $\frac{1}{2}$ of the height.

We can see that the formula still works in cases where the height is outside of the base.

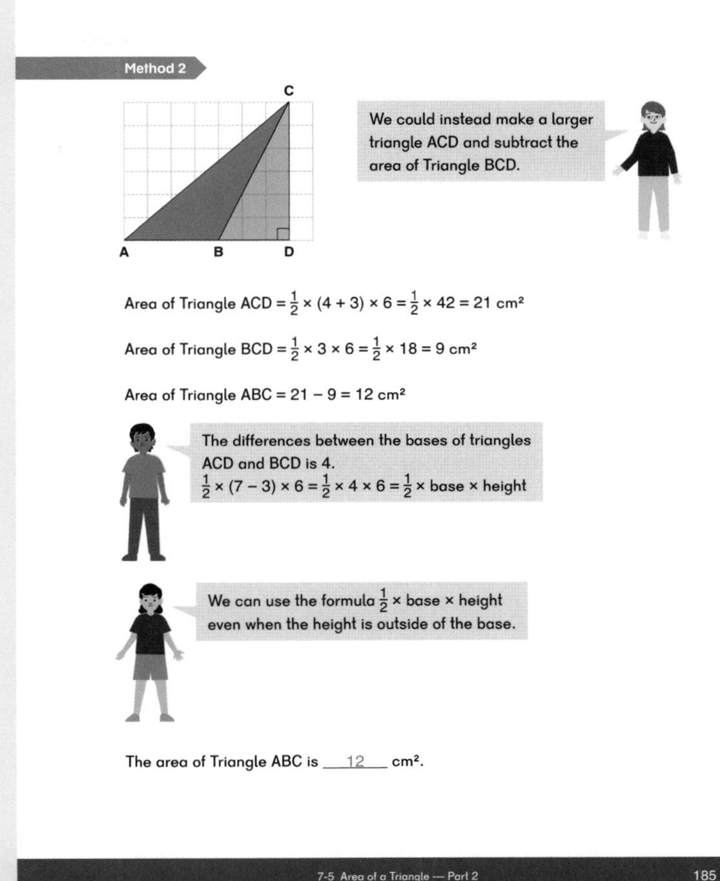

Do

❶—❷ Discuss the problems and given models with students. Have them point out a base and height with measurements they can use on each triangle in the problems.

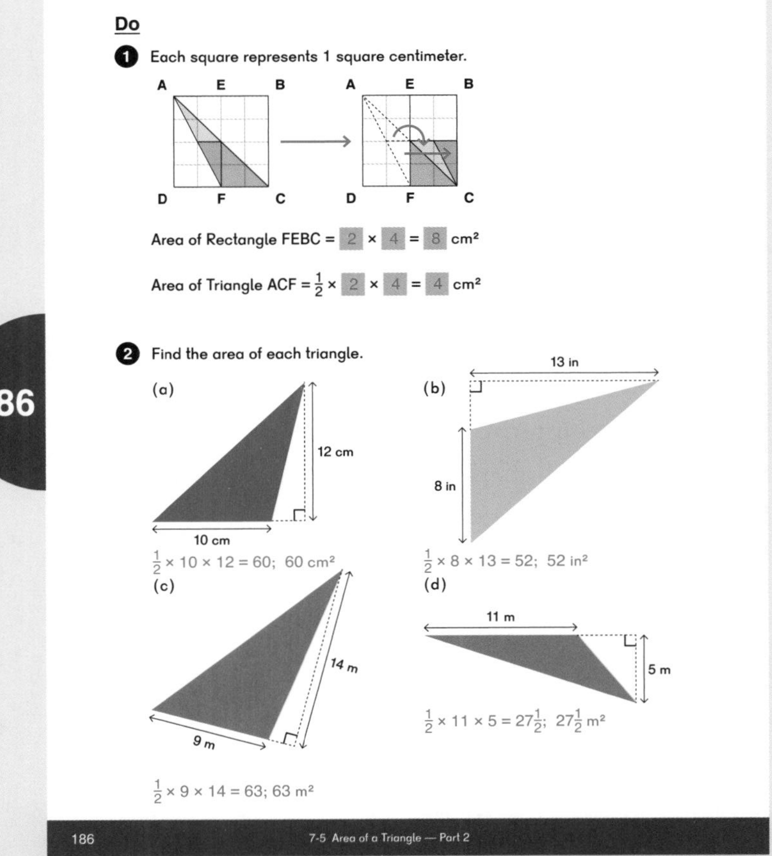

❸—❻ Students should be able to solve the problems independently.

❸ The length of the extended part of the base is given. Students should use the length of the base of the colored triangle to calculate the area of the triangle.

❹ Make sure students realize that triangles with the same length base and height have the same area.

Remind students that the distance between opposite points of parallel lines is always the same so the height will always be the same.

Students may find it surprising that every triangle with Base AB and its third point on Line CE has the same area regardless of how far they extend the top point along the line parallel to the base.

❺ The bases of the two triangles are the same. The height of Triangle EHG is twice that of Triangle EFG. Students should see that the area of Triangle EHG is twice the area of Triangle EFG.

❻ The heights of Triangle JKL and Triangle JKM are the same. The base of Triangle JKM is three times as long as the base of Triangle JKL.

Students should see that the area of Triangle JKM is three times the area of Triangle JKL.

Ask students if the answer to this question will always apply: "If the base of a larger triangle that shares the height of a smaller triangle is 100 times as long as the base of the smaller triangle, will the area of the larger triangle be 100 times the area of the smaller triangle?" (Yes, because the formula is $\frac{1}{2}$ × Base × Height. Multiplying a base by a given factor will result in an area which is that factor times the area of the smaller triangle.)

Exercise 5 • page 171

❸ Find the area of each triangle.

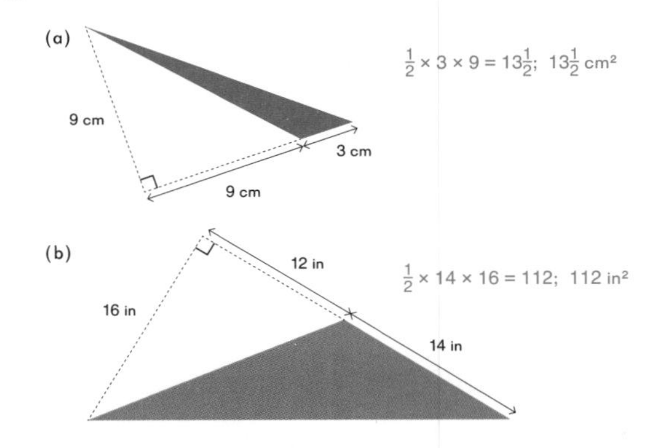

(a) $\frac{1}{2} \times 3 \times 9 = 13\frac{1}{2}$; $13\frac{1}{2}$ cm²

(b) $\frac{1}{2} \times 14 \times 16 = 112$; 112 in²

❹ Triangles ABC, ABD, and ABE share the same base AB. Each triangle has a vertex on the same line parallel to the base. Find the area of each triangle. What do you notice about the area of each triangle?

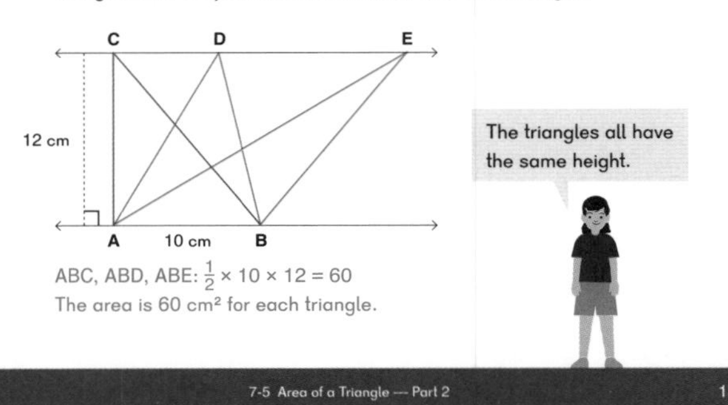

ABC, ABD, ABE: $\frac{1}{2} \times 10 \times 12 = 60$

The area is 60 cm² for each triangle.

The triangles all have the same height.

❺ Triangles EFG and EHG share the same base, EG. The height of Triangle EHG is twice as long as the height of Triangle EFG. Find the area of each triangle in square units and compare the areas.

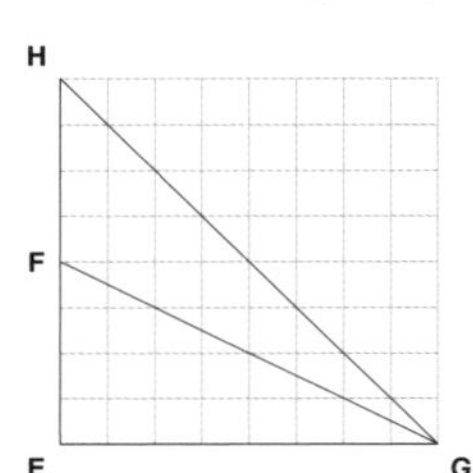

EFG: $\frac{1}{2} \times 8 \times 4 = 16$ square units; EHG: $\frac{1}{2} \times 8 \times 8 = 32$ square units

The area of triangle EHG is twice the area of EFG.

❻ Triangles JKL and JKM share the same height, JK. The base of Triangle JKM is three times as long as the base of Triangle JKL. Find the area of each triangle and compare the areas.

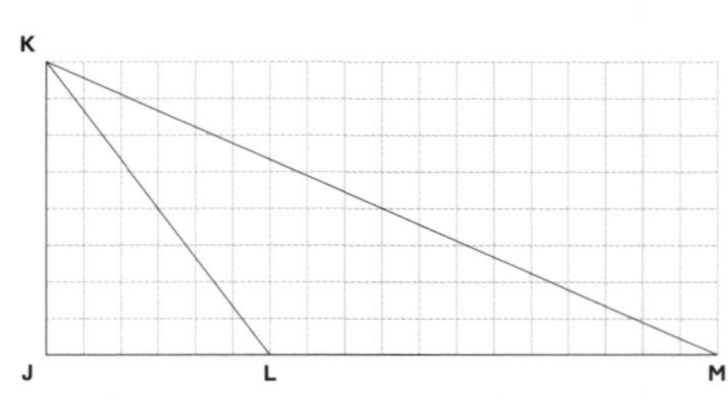

JKL: $\frac{1}{2} \times 6 \times 8 = 24$ square units; JKM: $\frac{1}{2} \times 18 \times 8 = 72$ square units

The area of triangle JKM is three times the area of JKL.

Exercise 5 • page 171

Lesson 6 Area of Complex Figures

Objective

- Find the area of complex figures composed of rectangles and triangles.

Lesson Materials

- Area of Complex Figures (BLM)

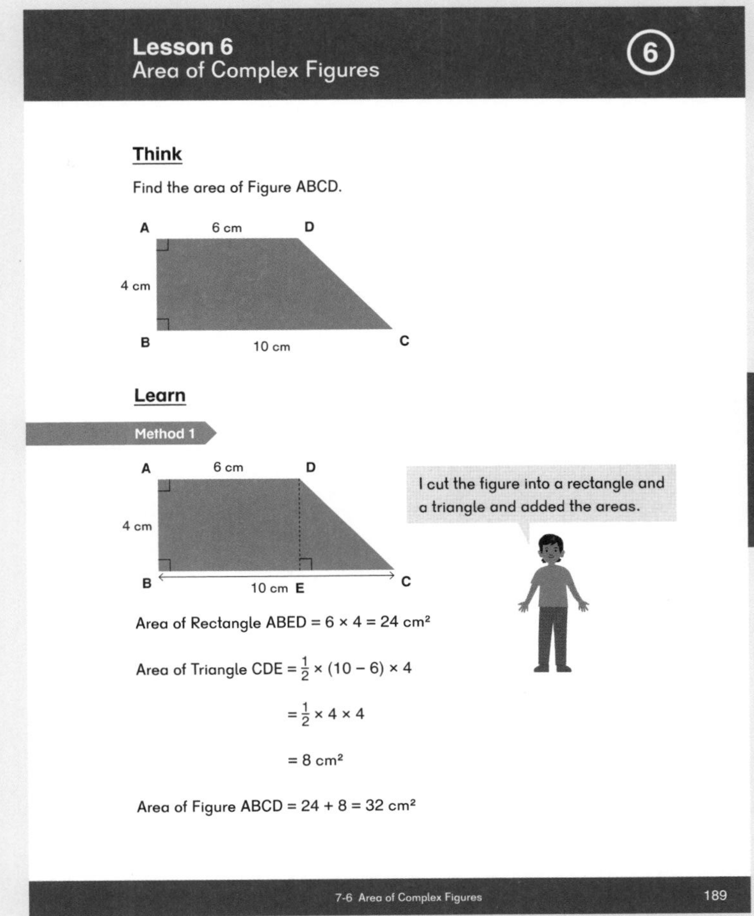
Lesson 6
Area of Complex Figures

6

Think

Find the area of Figure ABCD.

A 6 cm D
4 cm
B 10 cm C

Learn

Method 1

A 6 cm D
4 cm
B 10 cm E C

I cut the figure into a rectangle and a triangle and added the areas.

Area of Rectangle ABED = $6 \times 4 = 24$ cm²

Area of Triangle CDE = $\frac{1}{2} \times (10 - 6) \times 4$

$= \frac{1}{2} \times 4 \times 4$

$= 8$ cm²

Area of Figure ABCD = $24 + 8 = 32$ cm²

7-6 Area of Complex Figures 189

189

Think

Provide students with Area of Complex Figures (BLM) and pose the **Think** problem.

Ask students:

- "What is the name of this shape?" (Quadrilateral or Trapezoid.)
- "How is this different from the problem you solved in the previous lesson?" (It is not a triangle.)
- "How can we change the shape into a shape we know how to find the area of?" (We can cut it to make a rectangle and a triangle, or add a triangle to make a bigger rectangle.)

Students can fold, shade, or cut Area of Complex Figures (BLM) to find their answers.

Discuss student solutions.

Learn

Have students discuss the **Learn** examples and compare their methods from **Think** with the two methods in the textbook.

Method 1

Alex partitioned the figure into a rectangle and triangle. Since DE is perpendicular to BC, ABED is a rectangle, so CE must be 4 cm.

Method 2

Sofia finds the area of the whole rectangle and subtracts the triangle part of the figure.

Students might also have solved this problem by partitioning the figure into two triangles.

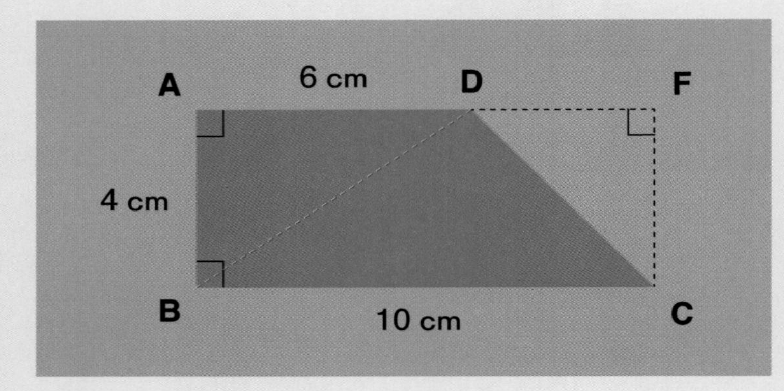

$\frac{1}{2} \times 10 \times 4 + \frac{1}{2} \times 6 \times 4$

$= 20 + 12$

$= 32$

32 cm²

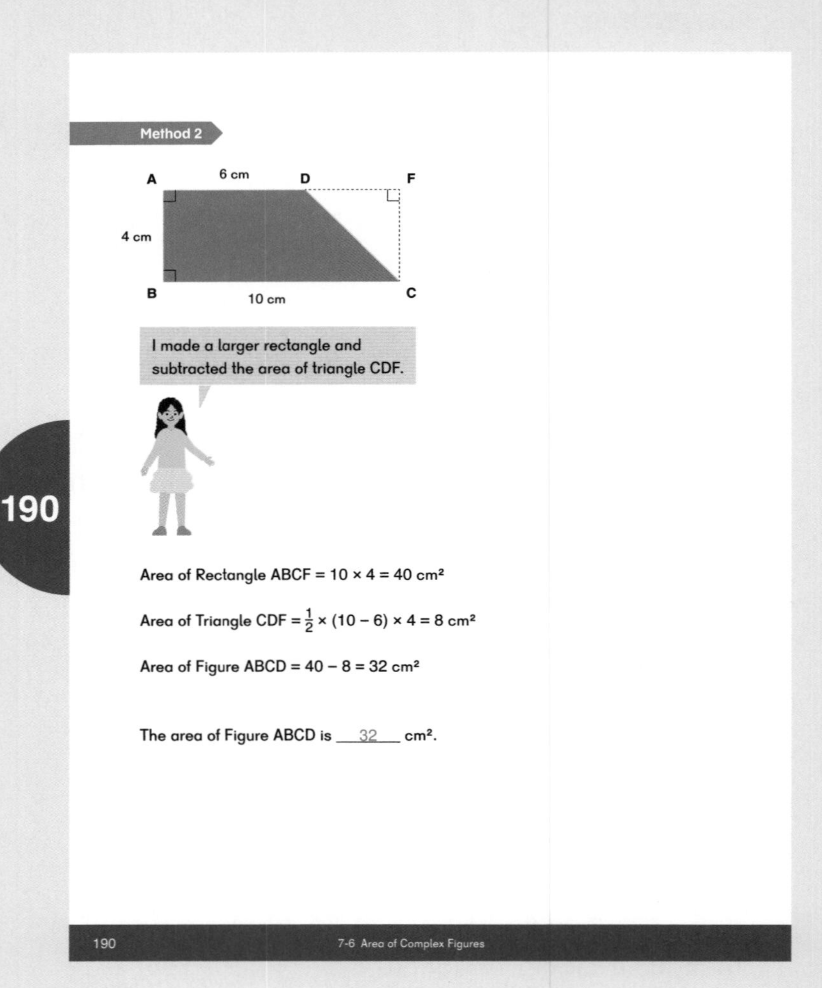

Do

❶–❷ Discuss the problems with students.

Ask students:

- "What information is given?"
- "Which side should we use as the base? Can we find its length?"
- "What is the length of the corresponding height?"
- "Which method can you use?"
- "Which method seems more efficient for each problem?"

❶ (a) We can find the length of the rectangle by adding 10 cm and 6 cm, and using that for the base of the triangle. The height is then 8 cm.

(b) We can find the length of the bottom side of the triangle using the given lengths. (12 cm – 4 cm = 8 cm)

❷ (a) Enough information is provided so that students can use either Method 1 or Method 2 from **Learn**. The solution using Method 2 is given in the answer overlay.

Solution using Method 1:

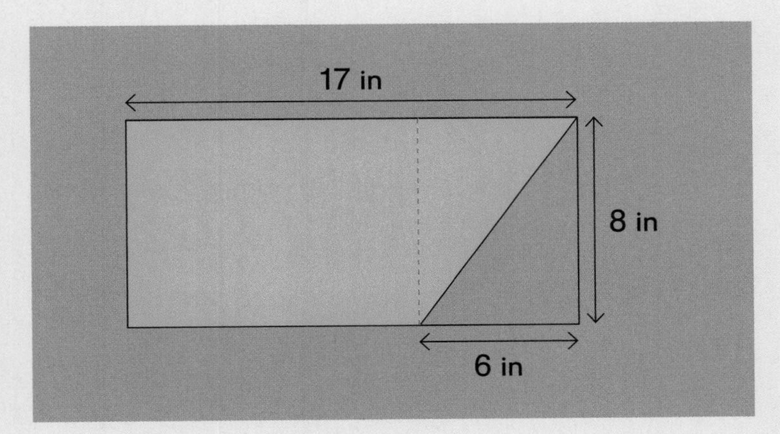

Area of rectangle:
$8 \times (17 - 6) = 88 \text{ in}^2$

Area of triangle:
$\frac{1}{2} \times 6 \times 8 = 24 \text{ in}^2$

Total area of the shaded part:
$88 \text{ in}^2 + 24 \text{ in}^2 = 112 \text{ in}^2$

Methods may vary.

Do

❶ Find the area of the shaded part of each rectangle.

(a) 10 cm, 6 cm, 8 cm

$\frac{1}{2} \times (10 + 6) \times 8 = 64$; 64 cm^2

(b) 12 cm, 10 cm, 4 cm

$\frac{1}{2} \times (12 - 4) \times 10 = 40$; 40 cm^2

❷ Find the area of the shaded part of each rectangle.

(a) 17 in, 8 in, 6 in

Triangle: $\frac{1}{2} \times 6 \times 8 = 24$
Rectangle: $17 \times 8 = 136$
$136 - 24 = 112$; 112 in^2

(b) 12 m, 20 m, 14 m

Triangle: $\frac{1}{2} \times 14 \times (20 - 12) = 56$
Rectangle: $20 \times 14 = 280$
$280 - 56 = 224$; 224 m^2

7-6 Area of Complex Figures 191

191

❸—❹ Students should be able to solve the problems independently.

❸ Ensure that students understand that the line on the left side of the figure is showing the height of the figure. Since the height and base of the figure are both 18 cm, students could draw the large square enclosing the shape and think about Method 2 from **Learn**. They can then subtract the area of the white triangles:

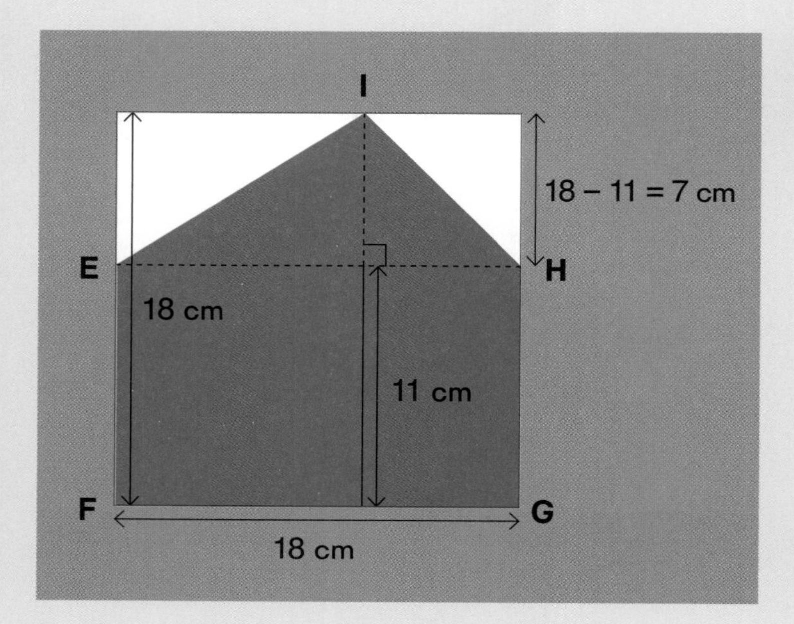

Area of whole rectangle: $18 \times 18 = 324$ cm²

Area of white triangles: $\frac{1}{2} \times 18 \times 7 = 63$ cm²

Area of Figure EFGHI = $324 - 63 = 261$ cm²

Activity

▲ Copy Me

Materials: Graph paper, ruler

Students take turns being the Original and the Copier(s). The Original draws a figure made up of rectangles and triangles on a piece of graph paper using a ruler. They calculate the area of the figure. They then try to describe their figure to the Copier(s), who attempts to draw a copy of the figure from the information provided. For example, for the figure shown in **Think** and **Learn**:

- The figure is a quadrilateral, but not a rectangle.
- The figure is composed of two common shapes.
- It has an area of 32 cm².

The Copier(s) must then draw a shape that fits the description given.

Have students compare their drawings to the Original's drawing.

192

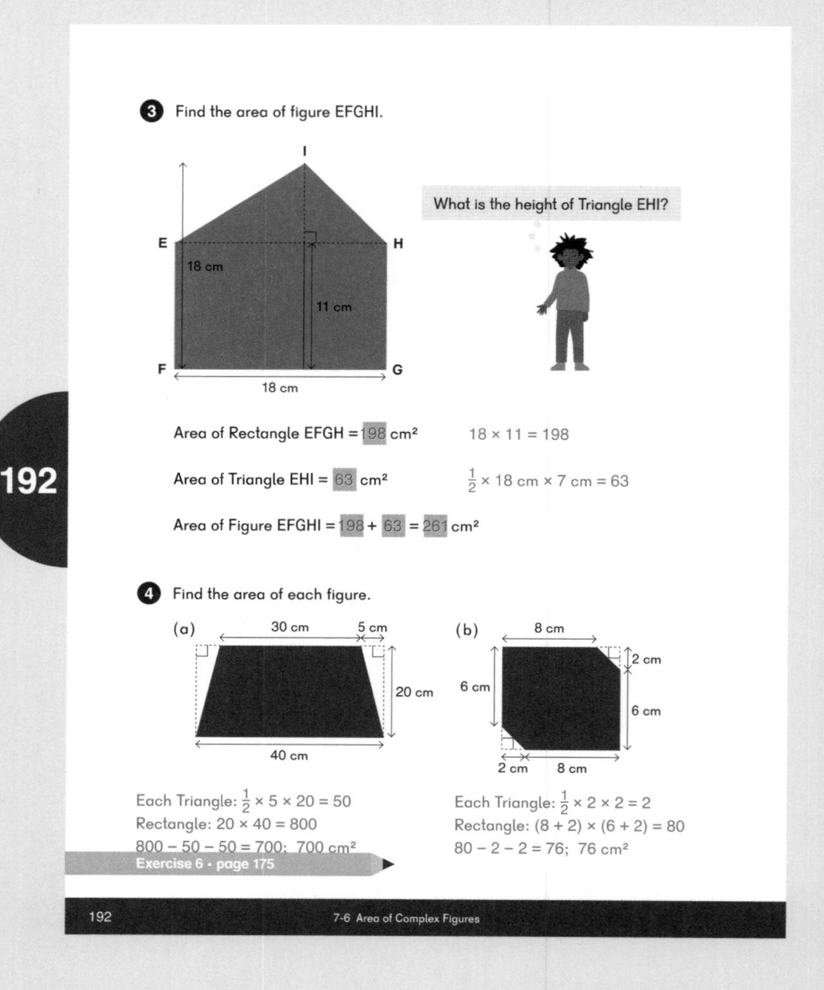

❸ Find the area of figure EFGHI.

Area of Rectangle EFGH = 198 cm² $18 \times 11 = 198$

Area of Triangle EHI = 63 cm² $\frac{1}{2} \times 18 \text{ cm} \times 7 \text{ cm} = 63$

Area of Figure EFGHI = 198 + 63 = 261 cm²

❹ Find the area of each figure.

(a) Each Triangle: $\frac{1}{2} \times 5 \times 20 = 50$
Rectangle: $20 \times 40 = 800$
$800 - 50 - 50 = 700$; 700 cm²

(b) Each Triangle: $\frac{1}{2} \times 2 \times 2 = 2$
Rectangle: $(8 + 2) \times (6 + 2) = 80$
$80 - 2 - 2 = 76$; 76 cm²

Exercise 6 • page 175

192 7-6 Area of Complex Figures

Exercise 6 • page 175

Objective

- Practice concepts from the chapter.

After students complete the practice in the textbook, have them continue to practice concepts using the activities from the chapter.

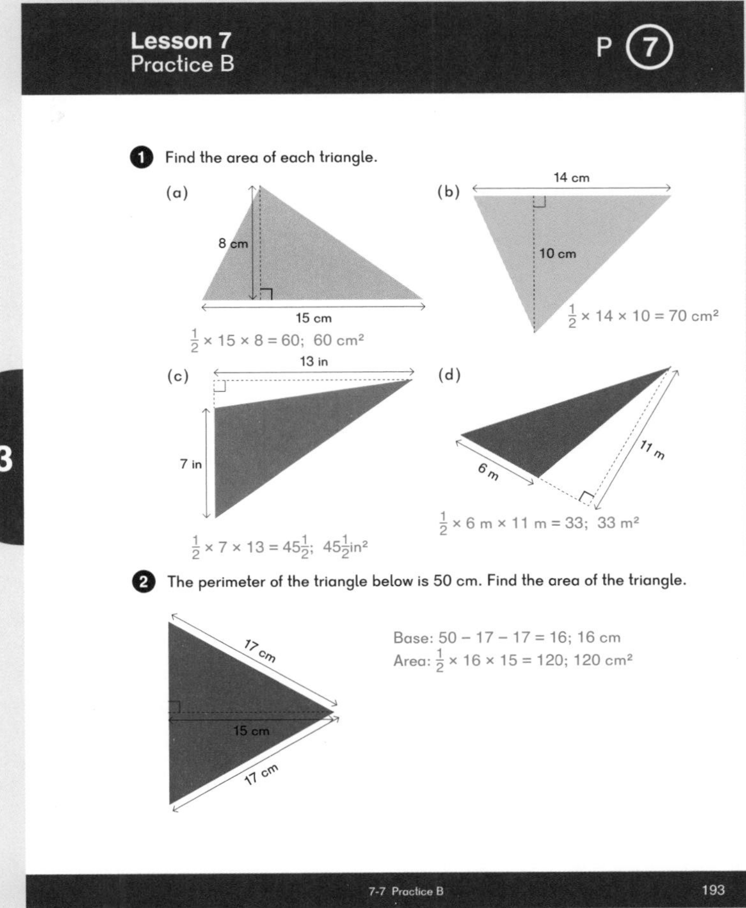

❸ (a) $(20 \times 12) - (\frac{1}{2} \times 3 \times 12) - (5 \times 9) = 177$
177 cm²

(b) $(10 \times 20) - (\frac{1}{2} \times 12 \times 10) - (5 \times 5) = 115$
115 cm²

❹ (a) Triangles: $(\frac{1}{2} \times 5 \times 9) = 22\frac{1}{2}$
$(\frac{1}{2} \times 12 \times 4) = 24$

Rectangle: $12 \times 9 = 108$

$108 - 24 - 22\frac{1}{2} = 61\frac{1}{2}$
$61\frac{1}{2}$ cm²

(b) Large triangle: $(\frac{1}{2} \times 12 \times 12) = 72$

Unshaded part: $(\frac{1}{2} \times 12 \times 2) = 12$

Shaded part: $72 - 12 = 60$
60 cm²

❺ (a) Triangle: $(\frac{1}{2} \times 13 \times 8) = 52$

Rectangle: $13 \times 16 = 208$

$208 - 52 = 156$
156 cm²

(b) Triangles: $\frac{1}{2} \times 4 \times 4 = 8$

$4 \times 8 = 32$
32 in²

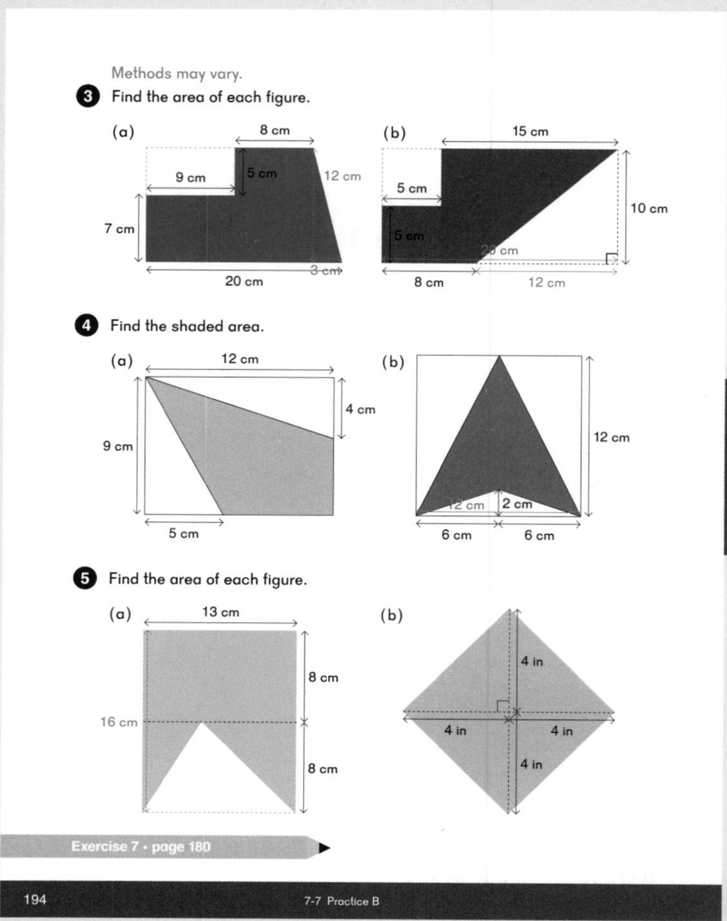
Methods may vary.

❸ Find the area of each figure.

❹ Find the shaded area.

❺ Find the area of each figure.

Exercise 7 • page 180

Exercise 7 • page 180

Brain Works

★ Orthocenters

Materials: Set square or straight edge

1. Draw any acute triangle with 3 different side lengths.
2. Draw three lines, one from each vertex, to determine the corresponding heights. The point where all three lines marking the heights meet is called the orthocenter.

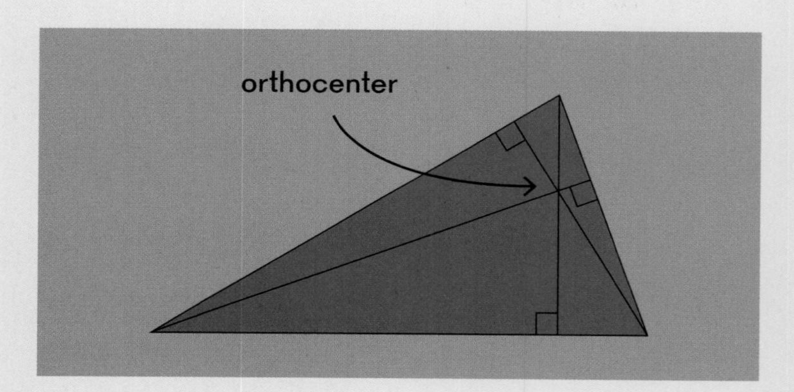

Extensions and questions for discussion:

- Draw different triangles.
- Draw an isosceles triangle. Where is the orthocenter? Inside the triangle.
- Draw an equilateral triangle. Where is the orthocenter? Inside the triangle.
- Draw an obtuse triangle. Where is the orthocenter? Outside the triangle.

Chapter 7 Measurement

Exercise 1

Basics

1. (a) 1 ft = 12 in (b) 1 lb = 16 oz
   (c) 1 yd = 3 ft (d) 1 qt = 4 c
   (e) 1 gal = 4 qt (f) 1 day = 24 h
   (g) 1 h = 60 min (h) 1 min = 60 s
   (i) 1 km = 1,000 m (j) 1 L = 1,000 mL
   (k) 1 kg = 1,000 g (l) 1 m = 100 cm
   (m) 1 cm = 10 mm (n) 1 L = 10 dL

2. (a) 3 L = 3 × 1,000 mL = 3,000 mL
   (b) $\frac{3}{8}$ L = $\frac{3}{8}$ × 1,000 mL = 375 mL
   (c) $3\frac{3}{8}$ L = 3,000 mL + 375 mL = 3,375 mL

3. Express $7\frac{3}{4}$ ft in inches.
   7 × 12 + $\frac{3}{4}$ × 12 = 84 + 9 = 93
   $7\frac{3}{4}$ ft = 93 in

Practice

4. (a) $4\frac{3}{10}$ km = 4 km 300 m
   (b) $2\frac{3}{4}$ lb = 2 lb 12 oz
   (c) $6\frac{3}{5}$ cm = 6 cm 6 mm

5. (a) $2\frac{3}{8}$ lb = 38 oz (b) $3\frac{4}{5}$ min = 228 s
   (c) $6\frac{3}{5}$ km = 6,600 m (d) $5\frac{3}{20}$ m = 515 cm
   (e) $4\frac{1}{2}$ gal = 18 qt (f) $5\frac{2}{3}$ yd = 17 ft
   (g) $2\frac{3}{4}$ kg = 2,750 g (h) $2\frac{1}{2}$ days = 60 h

6. A bag of beans weighs $2\frac{1}{2}$ lb. 12 ounces of beans were used for soup, and another $1\frac{1}{8}$ lb of beans were used to make chili. How many ounces of beans are still in the bag?
   $2\frac{1}{2}$ lb = 40 oz
   $1\frac{1}{8}$ lb = 18 oz
   40 oz − 12 oz − 18 oz = 10 oz
   10 oz

7. In a 2 h practice, a team spent 10 min on warm up, and $1\frac{2}{3}$ h on drills. How many minutes are left for stretching at the end?
   2 h = 120 min
   $1\frac{2}{3}$ h = 100 min
   120 min − 100 min − 10 min = 10 min
   10 min

8. A fathom is 6 ft. The sonar says that a submarine is at a depth of $18\frac{2}{3}$ fathoms. How many feet deep is the submarine?
   $18\frac{2}{3}$ × 6 ft = 112 ft
   112 ft

9. 1 mile is 5,280 ft. How many yards are in $\frac{3}{4}$ miles?
   $\frac{3}{4}$ × 5,280 ÷ 3 = 1,320
   1,320 yd

Exercise 2 • pages 160–162

Exercise 2

Basics

1 What is the area of a rectangle that is $\frac{3}{4}$ ft long and $\frac{2}{3}$ ft wide in square feet?

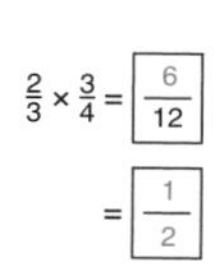

$\frac{2}{3} \times \frac{3}{4} = \frac{6}{12}$

$= \frac{1}{2}$

Area = $\frac{1}{2}$ ft²

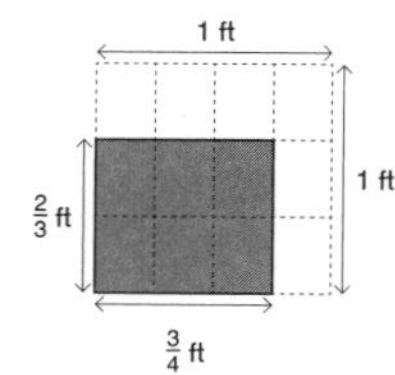

2 What is the area of a rectangle that is $2\frac{1}{5}$ m long and $1\frac{1}{2}$ m wide in square meters?

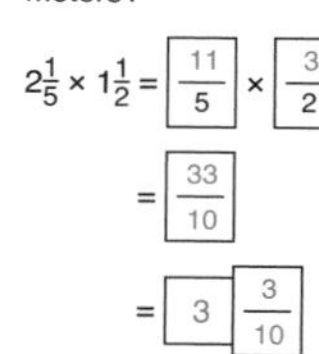

$2\frac{1}{5} \times 1\frac{1}{2} = \frac{11}{5} \times \frac{3}{2}$

$= \frac{33}{10}$

$= 3\frac{3}{10}$

Area = $3\frac{3}{10}$ m²

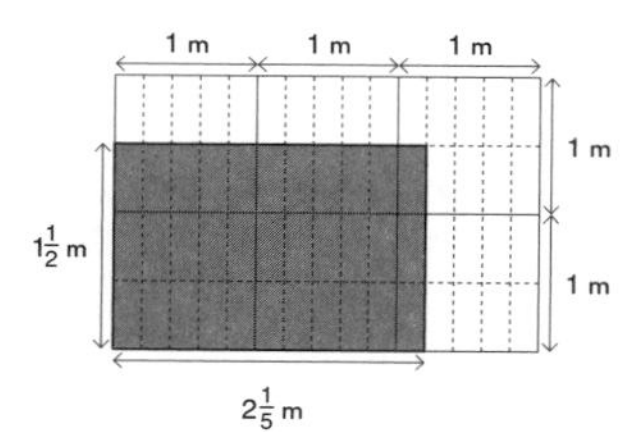

3 What is the area of a rectangle that is 4 in long and $2\frac{3}{8}$ in wide?

$4 \times 2\frac{3}{8} = 4 \times \frac{19}{8} = \frac{19}{2} = 9\frac{1}{2}$

Area = $9\frac{1}{2}$ in²

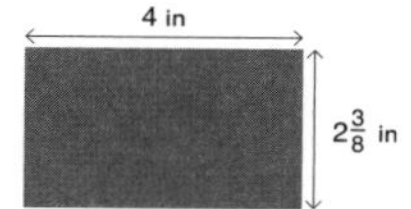

Practice

4 Find the area of each figure.

(a)

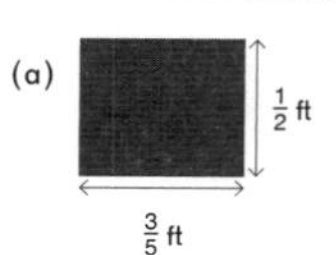

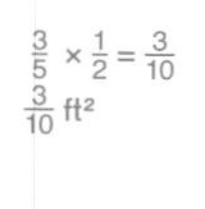

$\frac{3}{5} \times \frac{1}{2} = \frac{3}{10}$

$\frac{3}{10}$ ft²

(b)

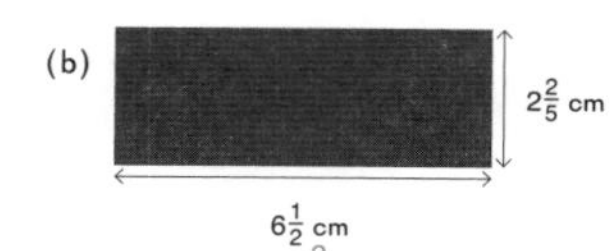

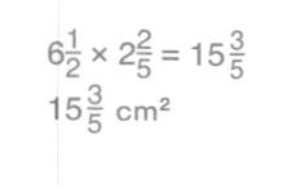

$6\frac{1}{2} \times 2\frac{2}{5} = 15\frac{3}{5}$

$15\frac{3}{5}$ cm²

(c)

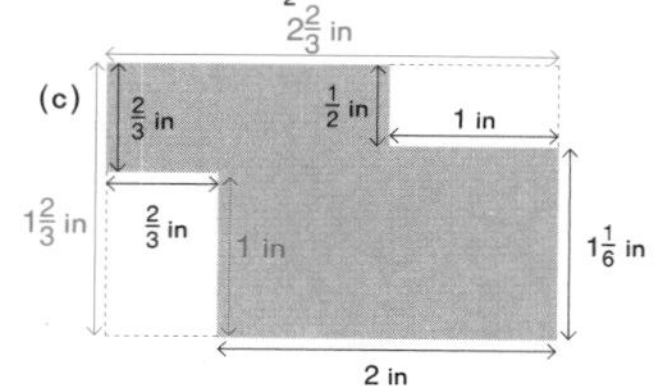

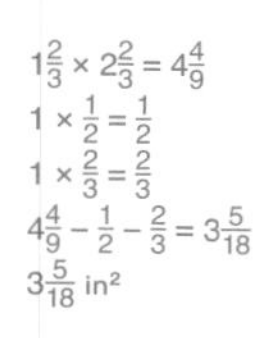

$1\frac{2}{3} \times 2\frac{2}{3} = 4\frac{4}{9}$

$1 \times \frac{1}{2} = \frac{1}{2}$

$1 \times \frac{2}{3} = \frac{2}{3}$

$4\frac{4}{9} - \frac{1}{2} - \frac{2}{3} = 3\frac{5}{18}$

$3\frac{5}{18}$ in²

5 The figure is made up of 3 identical rectangles. What is the area of the figure?

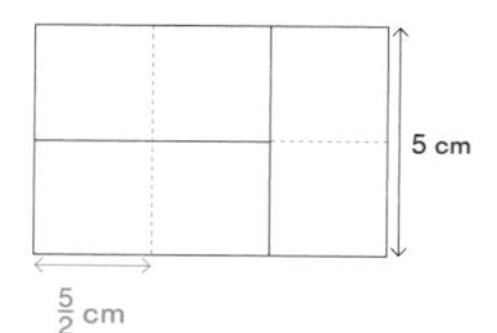

$5 \times \frac{15}{2} = 37\frac{1}{2}$

$37\frac{1}{2}$ cm²

6 A gravel path, $1\frac{1}{2}$ m wide, surrounds a grass lawn, $18\frac{1}{2}$ m by 11 m. A garden shed in the middle of the lawn is 5 m by $3\frac{1}{4}$ m.

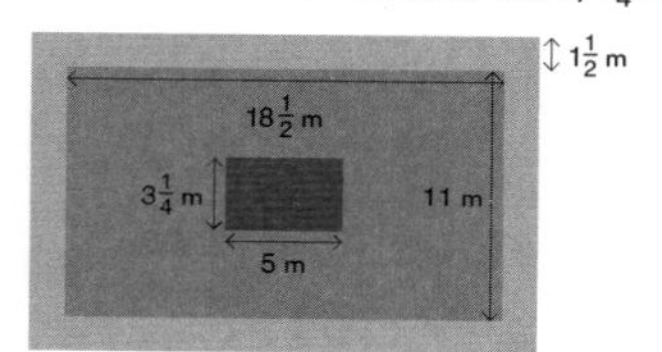

(a) What is the area of the path in square meters?

$18\frac{1}{2} + (2 \times 1\frac{1}{2}) = 21\frac{1}{2}$; $11 + (2 \times 1\frac{1}{2}) = 14$

Area of large rectangle: $21\frac{1}{2} \times 14 = 301$

Area of rectangle inside the path: $18\frac{1}{2} \times 11 = 203\frac{1}{2}$

$301 - 203\frac{1}{2} = 97\frac{1}{2}$

$97\frac{1}{2}$ m²

(b) What is the area that has grass growing in square meters?

Area of shed: $5 \times 3\frac{1}{4} = 16\frac{1}{4}$

$203\frac{1}{2} - 16\frac{1}{4} = 187\frac{1}{4}$

$187\frac{1}{4}$ m²

7 Aiden is painting a rectangular wall that is $15\frac{1}{5}$ ft by $12\frac{1}{2}$ ft. He needs 1 quart of paint for every 60 square feet of wall. How many 1-quart cans does he need to buy?

Area of wall: $15\frac{1}{5} \times 12\frac{1}{2} = \frac{76}{5} \times \frac{25}{2} = 190$; 190 ft²

$190 \div 60 = 3\frac{1}{6}$

4 cans

Exercise 3

Check

1. Anthony's cat slept for $\frac{2}{3}$ of the time between 6:00 a.m. one morning to 6:00 a.m. the next morning. How many hours did it sleep?

   $\frac{2}{3} \times 24 = 16$

   16 hours

2. Tyler read for $1\frac{2}{3}$ h in the afternoon and $\frac{3}{4}$ h before bed. How many minutes did he spend reading that day?

   $1\frac{2}{3} \times 60 \text{ min} + \frac{3}{4} \times 60 \text{ min} = 100 \text{ min} + 45 \text{ min} = 145 \text{ min}$

   145 min

3. Diego's time for a 100-m sprint was $\frac{3}{5}$ min. Adam took $\frac{5}{6}$ as long as Diego to complete the same sprint. How many seconds did Adam take to sprint 100 meters?

   $\frac{5}{6} \times \frac{3}{5} \times 60 = 30$

   30 s

4. The area of a rectangle is 2 ft². One side is $\frac{3}{4}$ ft long. What is the length of the other side in inches?

   $2 \div \frac{3}{4} = 2\frac{2}{3}$

   $2\frac{2}{3} \times 12 \text{ in} = 32 \text{ in}$

   32 in

5. A recipe calls for $\frac{2}{3}$ of a stick of butter. Natasha wants to double the recipe. 4 sticks of butter weigh 1 pound. How many ounces of butter will she use?

   1 stick of butter is $\frac{1}{4}$ lb.

   $2 \times \frac{2}{3} = \frac{4}{3}$; $\frac{4}{3}$ sticks of butter are needed.

   $\frac{4}{3} \times \frac{1}{4} \text{ lb} = \frac{1}{3} \text{ lb}$

   $\frac{1}{3} \times 16 = \frac{16}{3} = 5\frac{1}{3}$

   $5\frac{1}{3}$ oz

6. A rectangle is $2\frac{1}{6}$ ft long and $1\frac{2}{3}$ ft wide.

   (a) What is its area in square feet?

   $2\frac{1}{6} \times 1\frac{2}{3} = \frac{13}{6} \times \frac{5}{3} = \frac{65}{18} = 3\frac{11}{18}$

   $3\frac{11}{18}$ ft²

   (b) What is its area in square inches?

   $2\frac{1}{6} \times 12 \text{ in} = 26 \text{ in}$

   $1\frac{2}{3} \times 12 \text{ in} = 20 \text{ in}$

   $26 \times 20 = 520$

   520 in²

Challenge

7. When four identical right triangles are arranged as follows, a square inside a square is formed. What is the area of the shaded part of the figure in square inches?

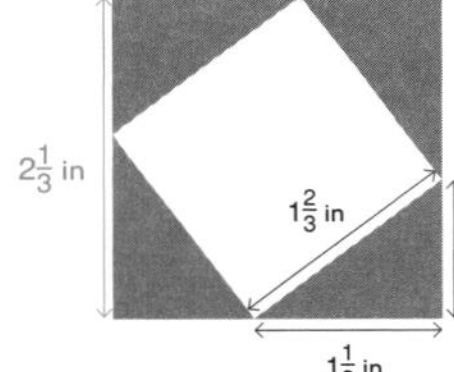

   $2\frac{1}{3} \times 2\frac{1}{3} = \frac{7}{3} \times \frac{7}{3} = \frac{49}{9}$

   $1\frac{2}{3} \times 1\frac{2}{3} = \frac{5}{3} \times \frac{5}{3} = \frac{25}{9}$

   $\frac{49}{9} - \frac{25}{9} = \frac{24}{9} = \frac{8}{3} = 2\frac{2}{3}$

   $2\frac{2}{3}$ in²

8. In medieval times, a "moment" was $\frac{1}{10}$ of a "point." A point was 15 minutes.

   (a) How many minutes is a moment?

   $\frac{1}{10} \times 15 = 1\frac{1}{2}$

   $1\frac{1}{2}$ min

   (b) How many seconds is a moment?

   $1\frac{1}{2} \times 60 = 90$

   90 s

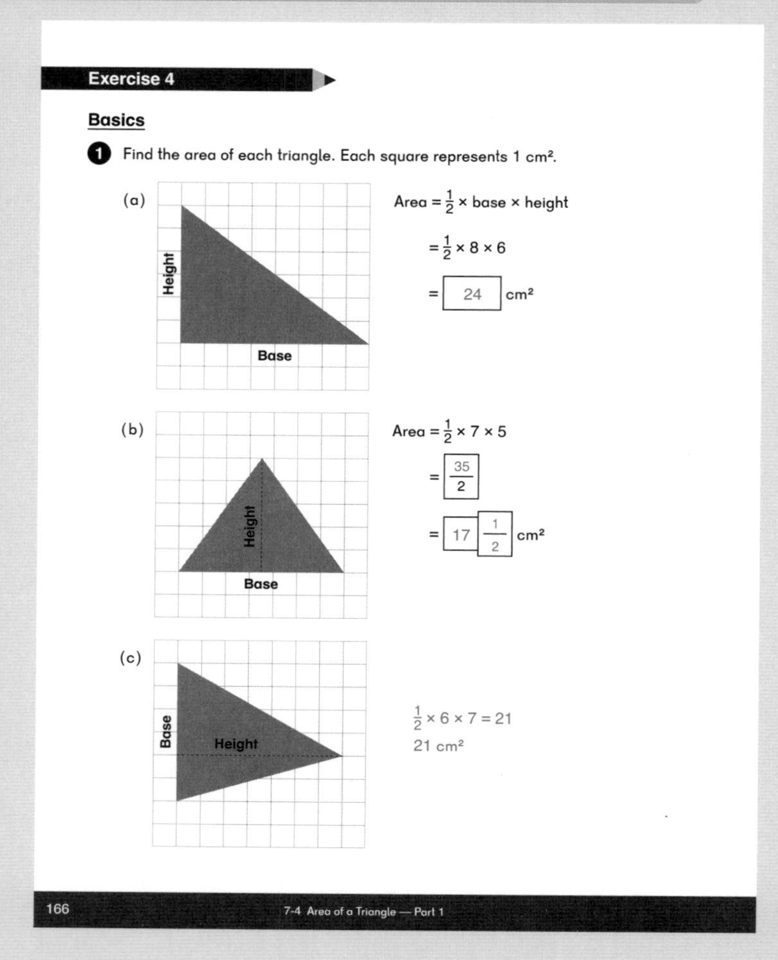

Exercise 4

Basics

1. Find the area of each triangle. Each square represents 1 cm².

(a) Area = $\frac{1}{2}$ × base × height

= $\frac{1}{2}$ × 8 × 6

= 24 cm²

(b) Area = $\frac{1}{2}$ × 7 × 5

= $\frac{35}{2}$

= $17\frac{1}{2}$ cm²

(c) $\frac{1}{2}$ × 6 × 7 = 21

21 cm²

166 7-4 Area of a Triangle — Part 1

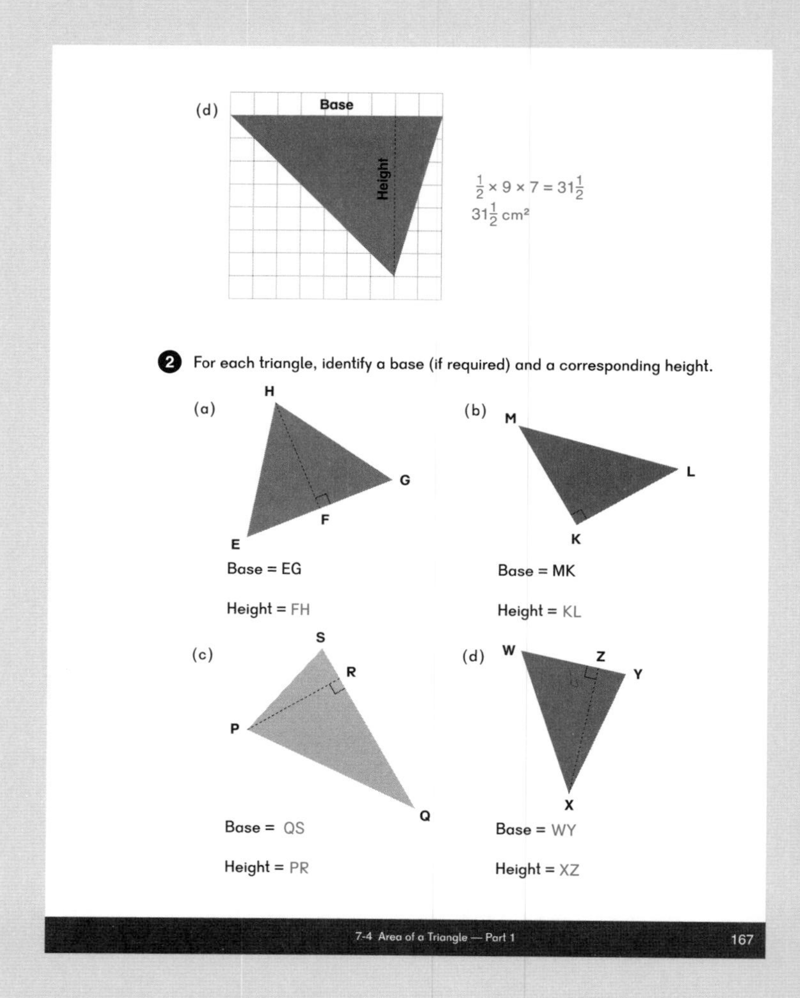

(d) $\frac{1}{2}$ × 9 × 7 = $31\frac{1}{2}$

$31\frac{1}{2}$ cm²

2. For each triangle, identify a base (if required) and a corresponding height.

(a) Base = EG

Height = FH

(b) Base = MK

Height = KL

(c) Base = QS

Height = PR

(d) Base = WY

Height = XZ

7-4 Area of a Triangle — Part 1 167

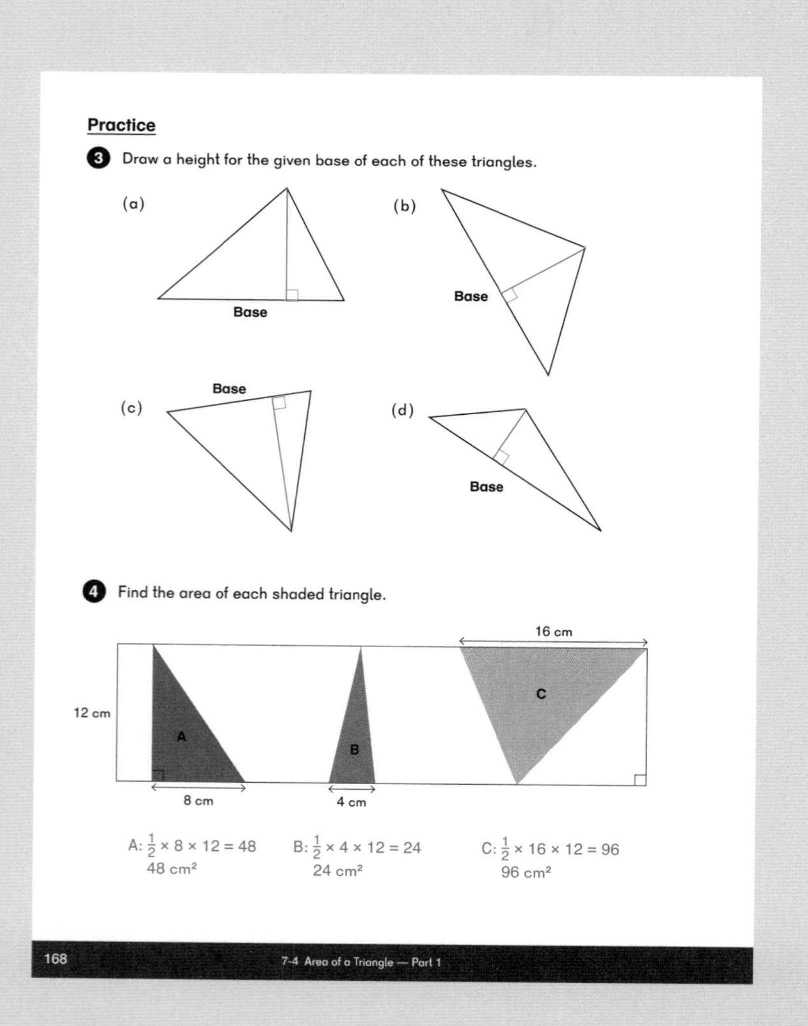

Practice

3. Draw a height for the given base of each of these triangles.

(a) (b) (c) (d)

4. Find the area of each shaded triangle.

A: $\frac{1}{2}$ × 8 × 12 = 48
48 cm²

B: $\frac{1}{2}$ × 4 × 12 = 24
24 cm²

C: $\frac{1}{2}$ × 16 × 12 = 96
96 cm²

168 7-4 Area of a Triangle — Part 1

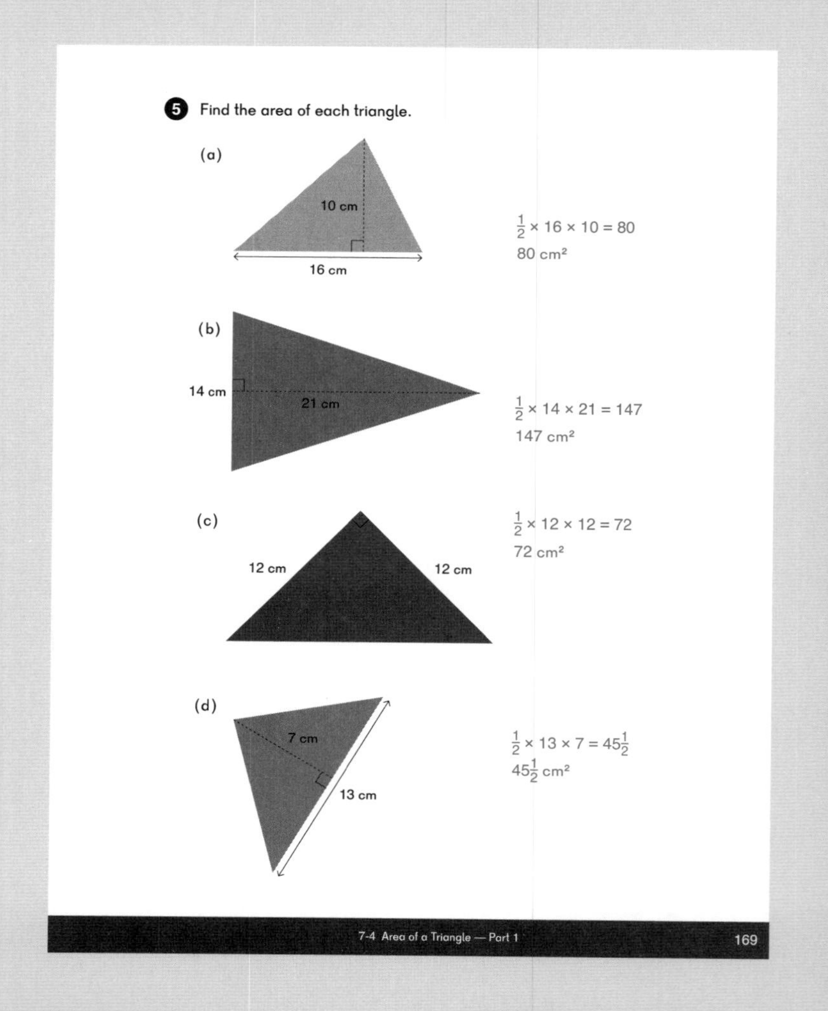

5. Find the area of each triangle.

(a) $\frac{1}{2}$ × 16 × 10 = 80
80 cm²

(b) $\frac{1}{2}$ × 14 × 21 = 147
147 cm²

(c) $\frac{1}{2}$ × 12 × 12 = 72
72 cm²

(d) $\frac{1}{2}$ × 13 × 7 = $45\frac{1}{2}$
$45\frac{1}{2}$ cm²

7-4 Area of a Triangle — Part 1 169

6 Find the area of each triangle.

(a)

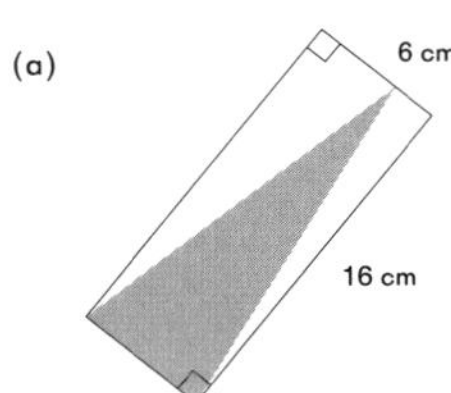

$\frac{1}{2} \times 6 \times 16 = 48$

48 cm²

(b)

7 cm
13 cm
4 cm

$\frac{1}{2} \times 17 \times 7 = 59\frac{1}{2}$

$59\frac{1}{2}$ cm²

Challenge

7 (a) A triangle has a base of 5 cm and an area of 20 cm². What is its height?

$\frac{1}{2} \times 5 \times ? = 20$

$5 \times ? = 40$

$? = 8$

8 cm

(b) A triangle has a height of 3 cm and an area of $7\frac{1}{2}$ cm². What is its base?

$\frac{1}{2} \times ? \times 3 = 7\frac{1}{2} = \frac{15}{2}$

$5 \times 3 = 15$, so ? must be 5.

5 cm

Exercise 5

Basics

1. Find the area of each triangle. Each square represents 1 cm².

(a) Area $= \frac{1}{2} \times$ base $\times$ height

$= \frac{1}{2} \times 6 \times 7$

$=$ 21 cm²

(b) Area $= \frac{1}{2} \times 5 \times 5$

$= \frac{25}{2}$

$= 12\frac{1}{2}$ cm²

(c) $\frac{1}{2} \times 3 \times 8 = 12$

12 cm²

7-5 Area of a Triangle — Part 2 171

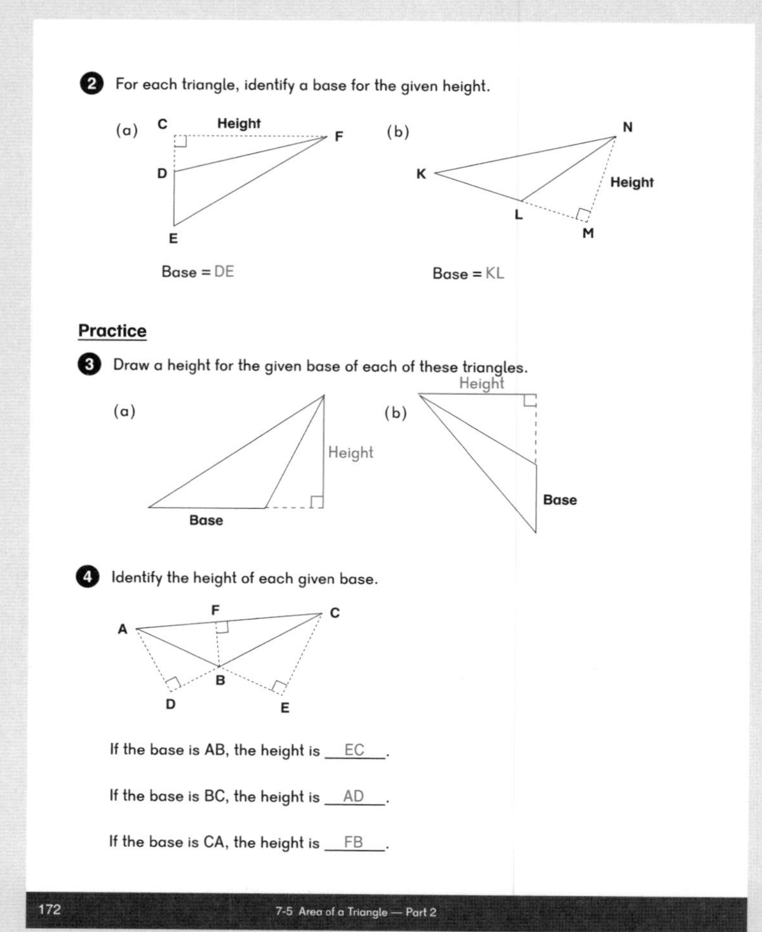

2. For each triangle, identify a base for the given height.

(a) Base = DE

(b) Base = KL

Practice

3. Draw a height for the given base of each of these triangles.

4. Identify the height of each given base.

If the base is AB, the height is EC.

If the base is BC, the height is AD.

If the base is CA, the height is FB.

172 7-5 Area of a Triangle — Part 2

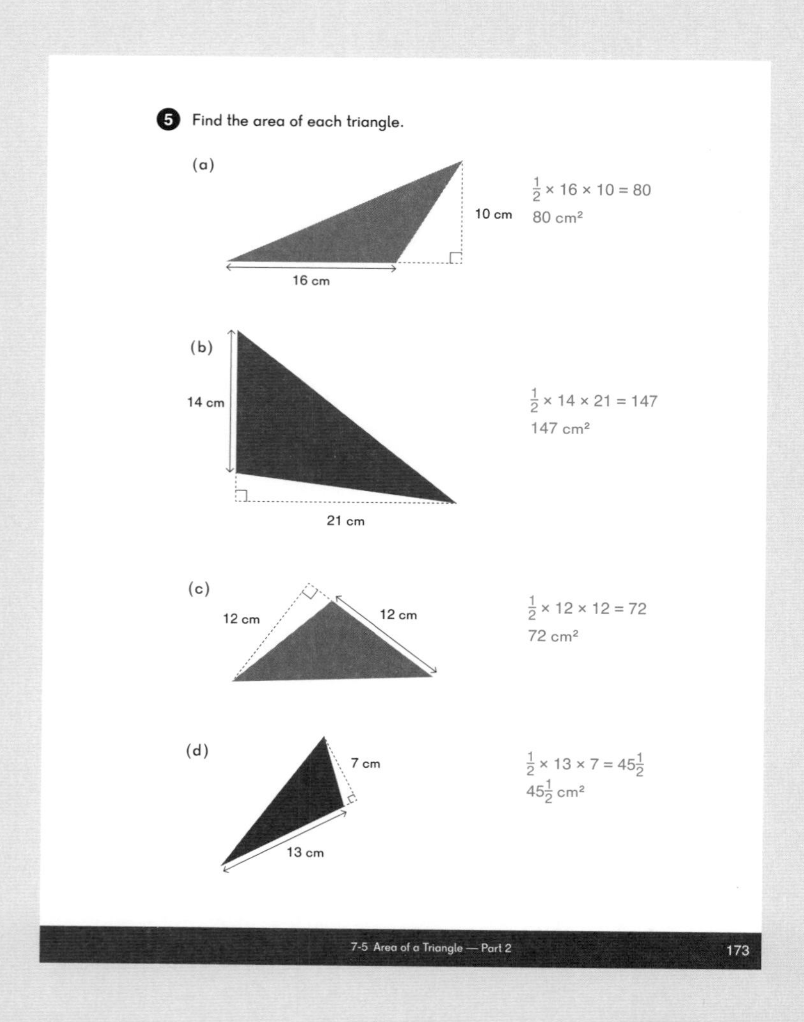

5. Find the area of each triangle.

(a) $\frac{1}{2} \times 16 \times 10 = 80$

80 cm²

(b) $\frac{1}{2} \times 14 \times 21 = 147$

147 cm²

(c) $\frac{1}{2} \times 12 \times 12 = 72$

72 cm²

(d) $\frac{1}{2} \times 13 \times 7 = 45\frac{1}{2}$

$45\frac{1}{2}$ cm²

7-5 Area of a Triangle — Part 2 173

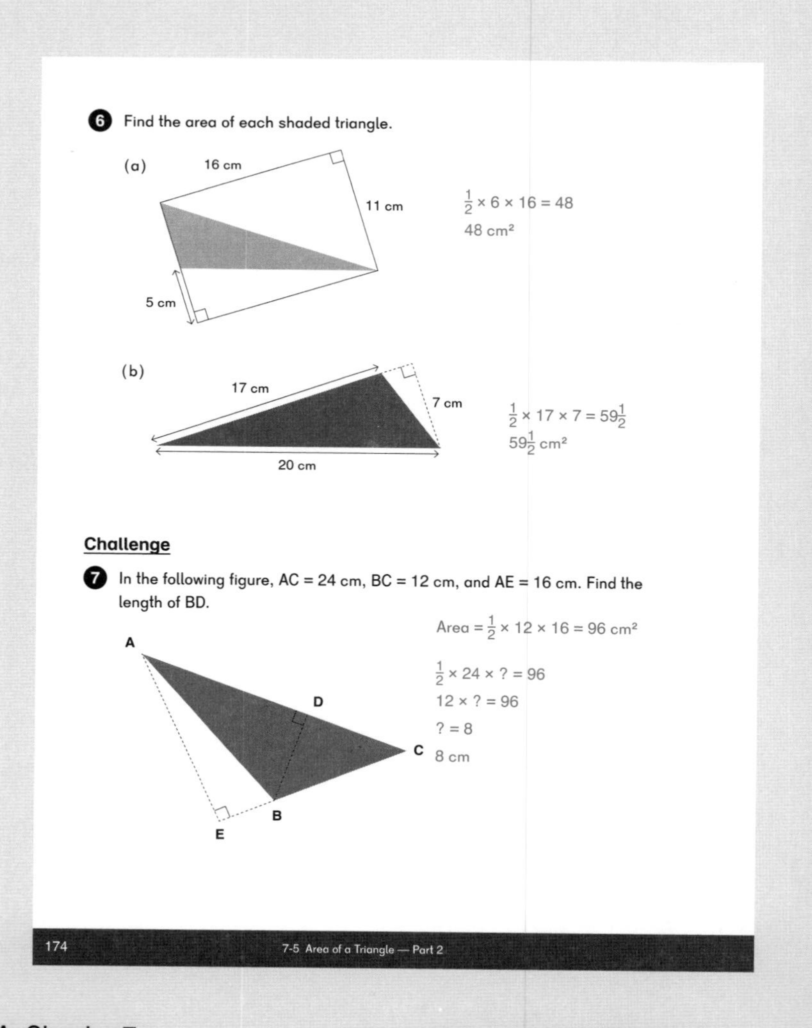

6. Find the area of each shaded triangle.

(a) $\frac{1}{2} \times 6 \times 16 = 48$

48 cm²

(b) $\frac{1}{2} \times 17 \times 7 = 59\frac{1}{2}$

$59\frac{1}{2}$ cm²

Challenge

7. In the following figure, AC = 24 cm, BC = 12 cm, and AE = 16 cm. Find the length of BD.

Area $= \frac{1}{2} \times 12 \times 16 = 96$ cm²

$\frac{1}{2} \times 24 \times ? = 96$

$12 \times ? = 96$

$? = 8$

8 cm

174 7-5 Area of a Triangle — Part 2

Exercise 6

Basics

1 Find the area of the shaded figures. Each square represents 1 cm^2.

(a)

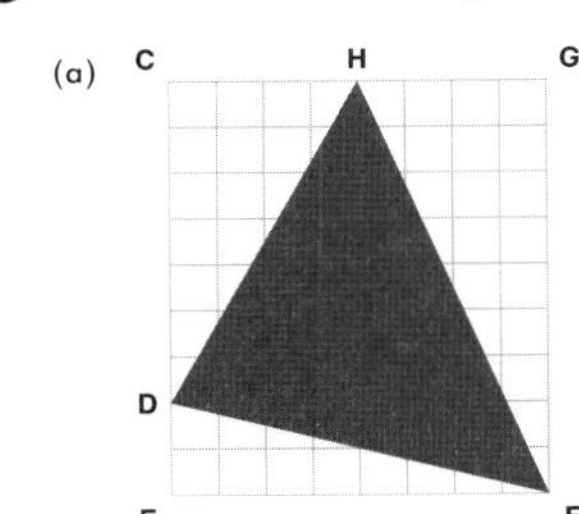

Area of Rectangle CEFG:
$9 \times 8 = 72$ cm^2

Area of Triangle CDH:
$\frac{1}{2} \times 4 \times 7 = 14$ cm^2

Area of Triangle DEF:
$\frac{1}{2} \times 2 \times 8 = 8$ cm^2

Area of Triangle HFG:
$\frac{1}{2} \times 4 \times 9 = 18$ cm^2

Area of Triangle HDF:
$72 - 14 - 8 - 18 = 32$ cm^2

(b)

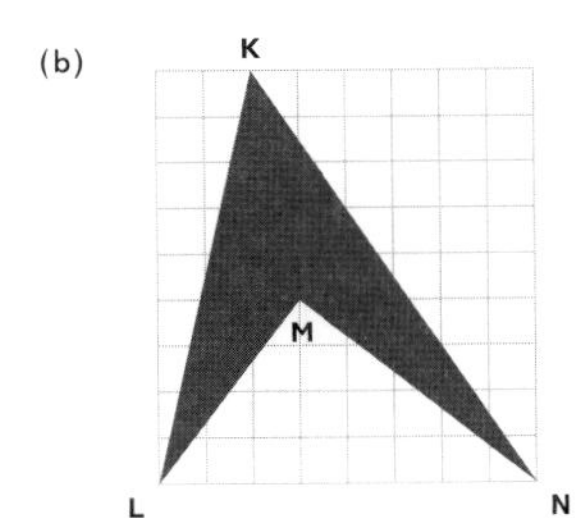

Area of Triangle LKN:
$\frac{1}{2} \times 8 \times 9 = 36$ cm^2

Area of Triangle LMN:
$\frac{1}{2} \times 8 \times 4 = 16$ cm^2

Area of Figure KLMN:
$36 - 16 = 20$ cm^2

2 Find the area of the shaded figure.

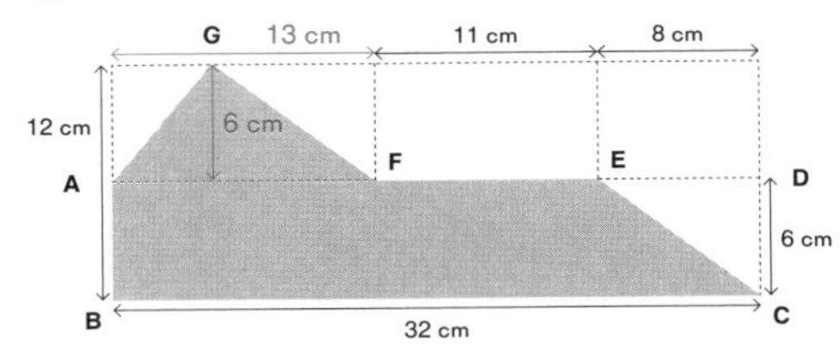

Area of Rectangle ABCD: $32 \times 6 = 192$ cm^2

Area of Triangle AFG: $\frac{1}{2} \times 13 \times 6 = 39$ cm^2

Area of Triangle CDE: $\frac{1}{2} \times 8 \times 6 = 24$ cm^2

Area of Figure ABCEFG: $192 + 39 - 24 = 207$ cm^2

3 The figure below is made up of two squares, ABCG and FCDE. Find the area of the shaded part.

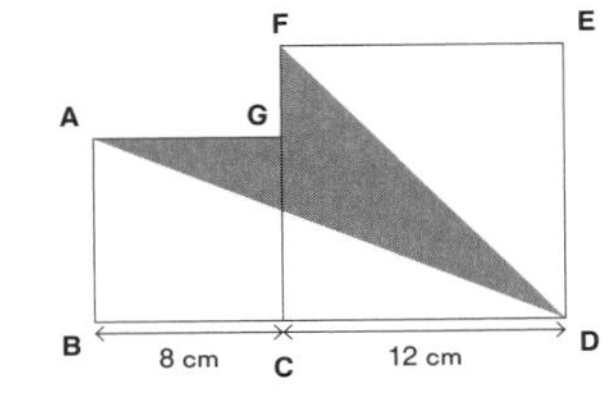

Area of Triangle ABD:
$\frac{1}{2} \times 20 \times 8 = 80$ cm^2

Area of Triangle FDE:
$\frac{1}{2} \times 12 \times 12 = 72$ cm^2

Area of both squares:
$8 \times 8 + 12 \times 12 = 208$ cm^2

Area of Figure ADFG:
$208 - 80 - 72 = 56$ cm^2

Practice

4 Find the area of the shaded figure. Each square represents 1 cm^2.

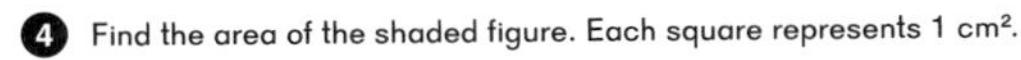

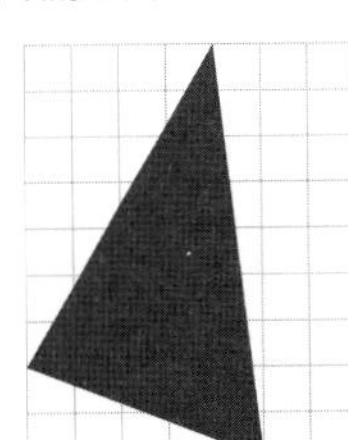

$9 \times 5 = 45$

$\frac{1}{2} \times 7 \times 4 = 14$

$\frac{1}{2} \times 2 \times 5 = 5$

$\frac{1}{2} \times 1 \times 9 = 4\frac{1}{2}$

$45 - 14 - 5 - 4\frac{1}{2} = 21\frac{1}{2}$

$21\frac{1}{2}$ cm^2

5 Find the area of the shaded figure.

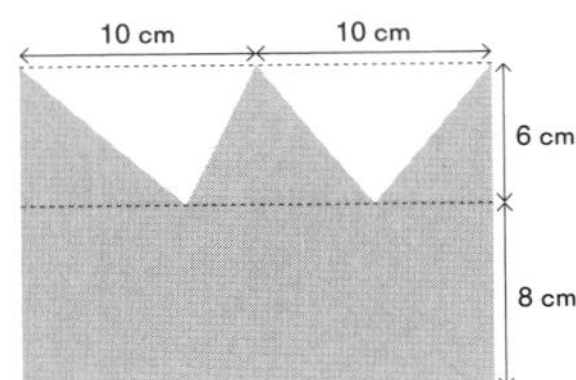

$20 \times 14 = 280$

$2 \times \frac{1}{2} \times 10 \times 6 = 60$

$280 - 60 = 220$

220 cm^2

6 4 identical triangles are cut from the corners of a rectangular paper that is 20 cm long and 12 cm wide. What is the area of the paper left?

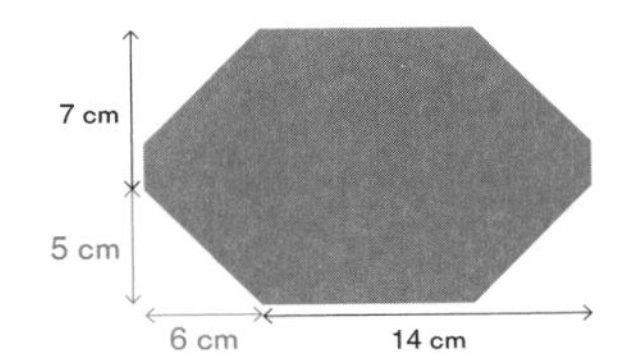

$20 \times 12 = 240$

$4 \times \frac{1}{2} \times 5 \times 6 = 60$

$240 - 60 = 180$

180 cm^2

7 The figure below shows two squares. Find the area of the shaded triangle.

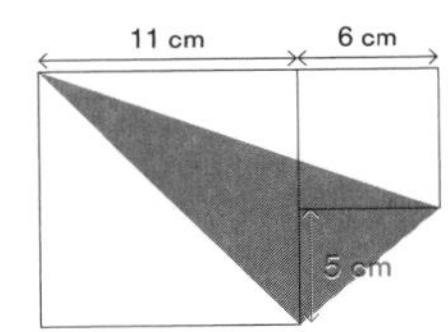

$\frac{1}{2} \times 11 \times 11 = 60\frac{1}{2}$

$\frac{1}{2} \times 17 \times 6 = 51$

$11 \times 11 + 6 \times 6 = 157$

$\frac{1}{2} \times 6 \times 5 = 15$

$157 - 51 - 60\frac{1}{2} + 15 = 60\frac{1}{2}$

$60\frac{1}{2}$ cm^2

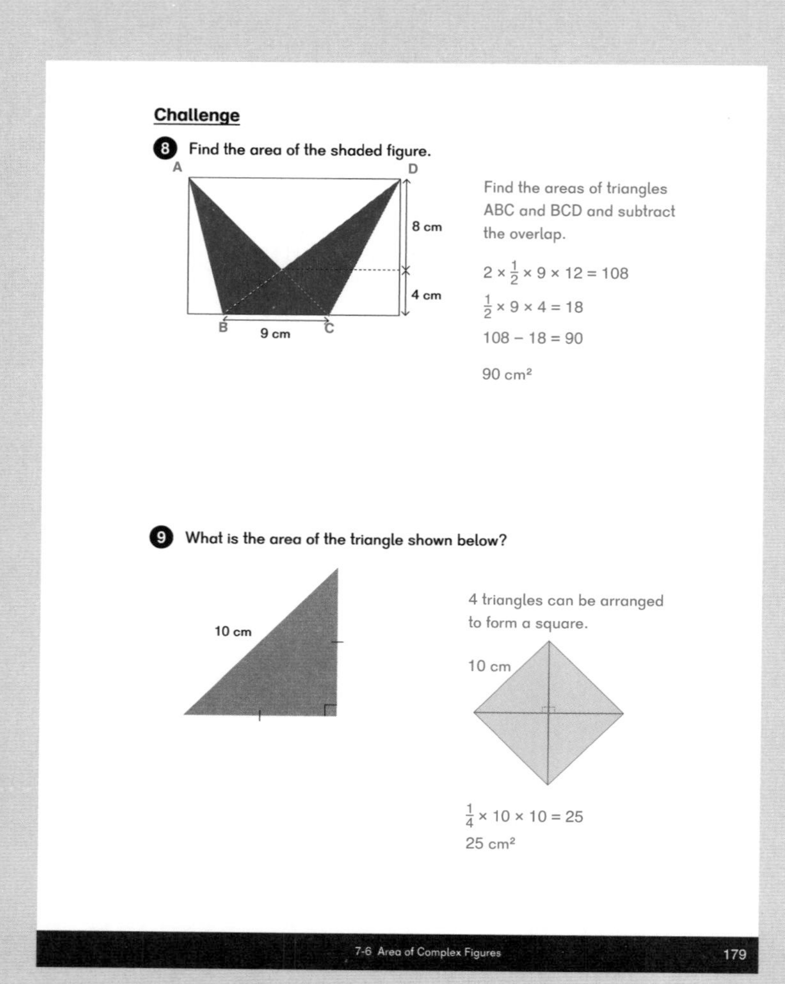

Challenge

8. Find the area of the shaded figure.

Find the areas of triangles ABC and BCD and subtract the overlap.

$2 \times \frac{1}{2} \times 9 \times 12 = 108$

$\frac{1}{2} \times 9 \times 4 = 18$

$108 - 18 = 90$

90 cm²

9. What is the area of the triangle shown below?

4 triangles can be arranged to form a square.

$\frac{1}{4} \times 10 \times 10 = 25$

25 cm²

Exercise 7 • pages 180–184

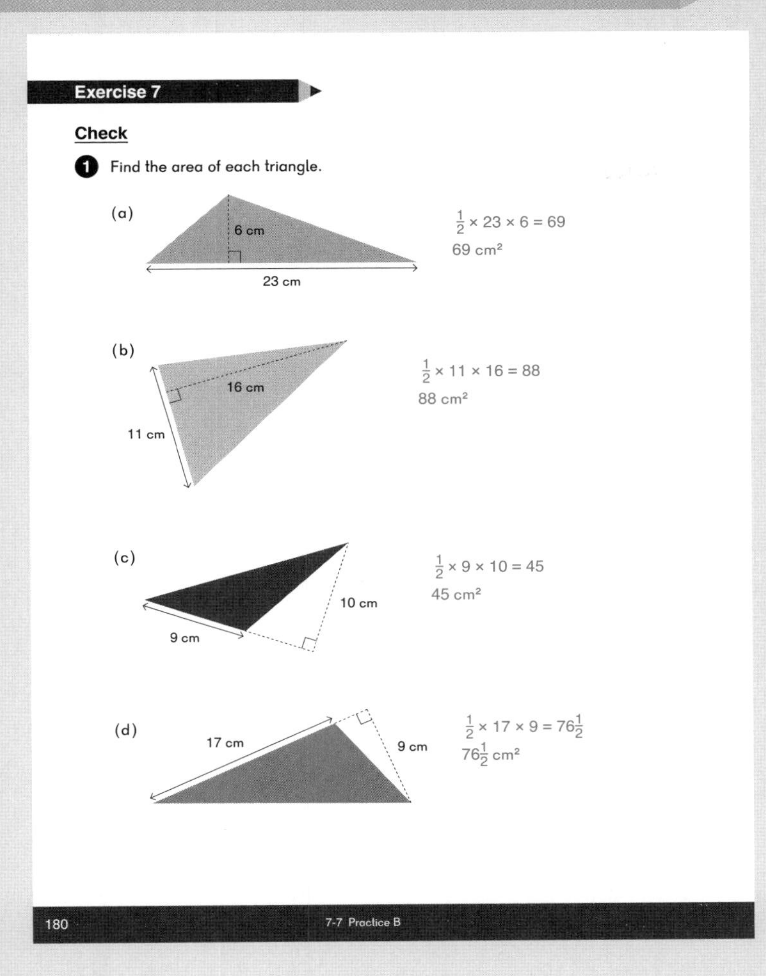

Exercise 7

Check

1. Find the area of each triangle.

(a) $\frac{1}{2} \times 23 \times 6 = 69$

69 cm²

(b) $\frac{1}{2} \times 11 \times 16 = 88$

88 cm²

(c) $\frac{1}{2} \times 9 \times 10 = 45$

45 cm²

(d) $\frac{1}{2} \times 17 \times 9 = 76\frac{1}{2}$

$76\frac{1}{2}$ cm²

180 7-7 Practice B

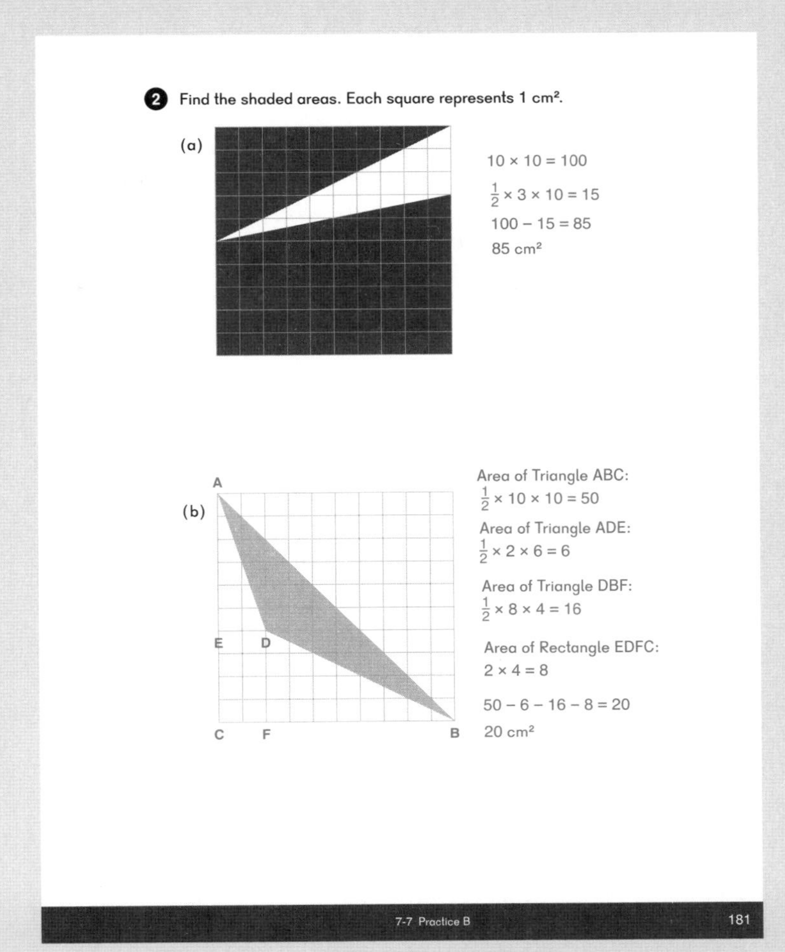

2. Find the shaded areas. Each square represents 1 cm².

(a) $10 \times 10 = 100$

$\frac{1}{2} \times 3 \times 10 = 15$

$100 - 15 = 85$

85 cm²

(b) Area of Triangle ABC:

$\frac{1}{2} \times 10 \times 10 = 50$

Area of Triangle ADE:

$\frac{1}{2} \times 2 \times 6 = 6$

Area of Triangle DBF:

$\frac{1}{2} \times 8 \times 4 = 16$

Area of Rectangle EDFC:

$2 \times 4 = 8$

$50 - 6 - 16 - 8 = 20$

20 cm²

7-7 Practice B 181

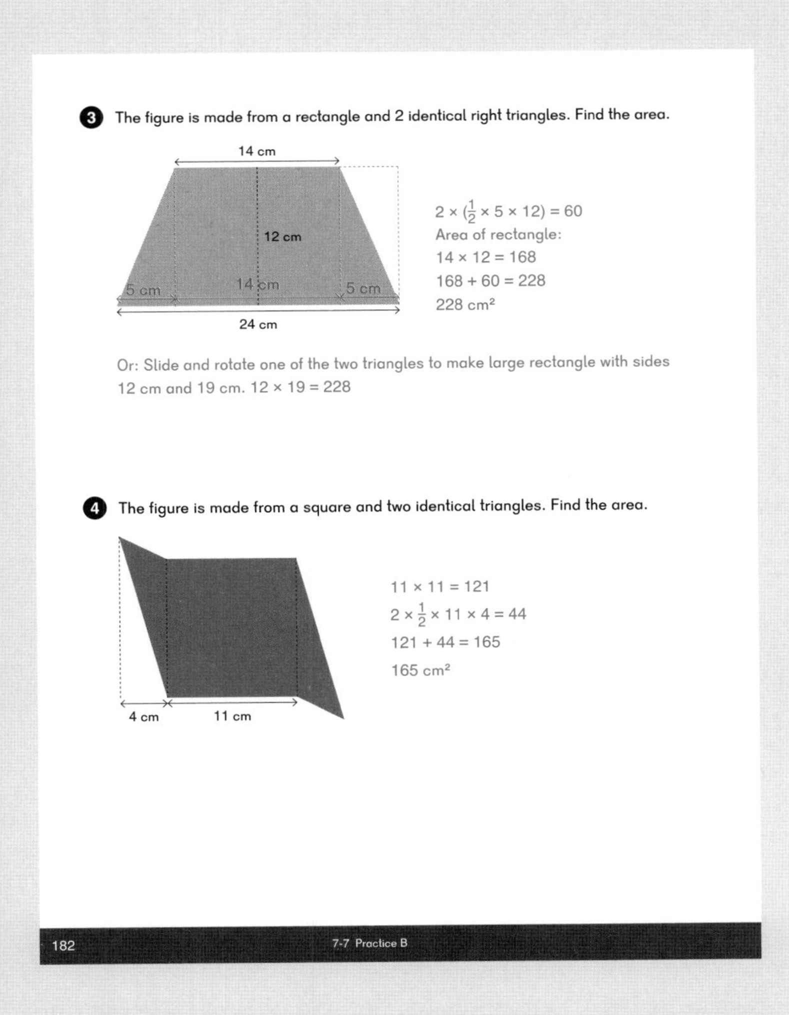

3. The figure is made from a rectangle and 2 identical right triangles. Find the area.

$2 \times (\frac{1}{2} \times 5 \times 12) = 60$

Area of rectangle:

$14 \times 12 = 168$

$168 + 60 = 228$

228 cm²

Or: Slide and rotate one of the two triangles to make large rectangle with sides 12 cm and 19 cm. $12 \times 19 = 228$

4. The figure is made from a square and two identical triangles. Find the area.

$11 \times 11 = 121$

$2 \times \frac{1}{2} \times 11 \times 4 = 44$

$121 + 44 = 165$

165 cm²

182 7-7 Practice B

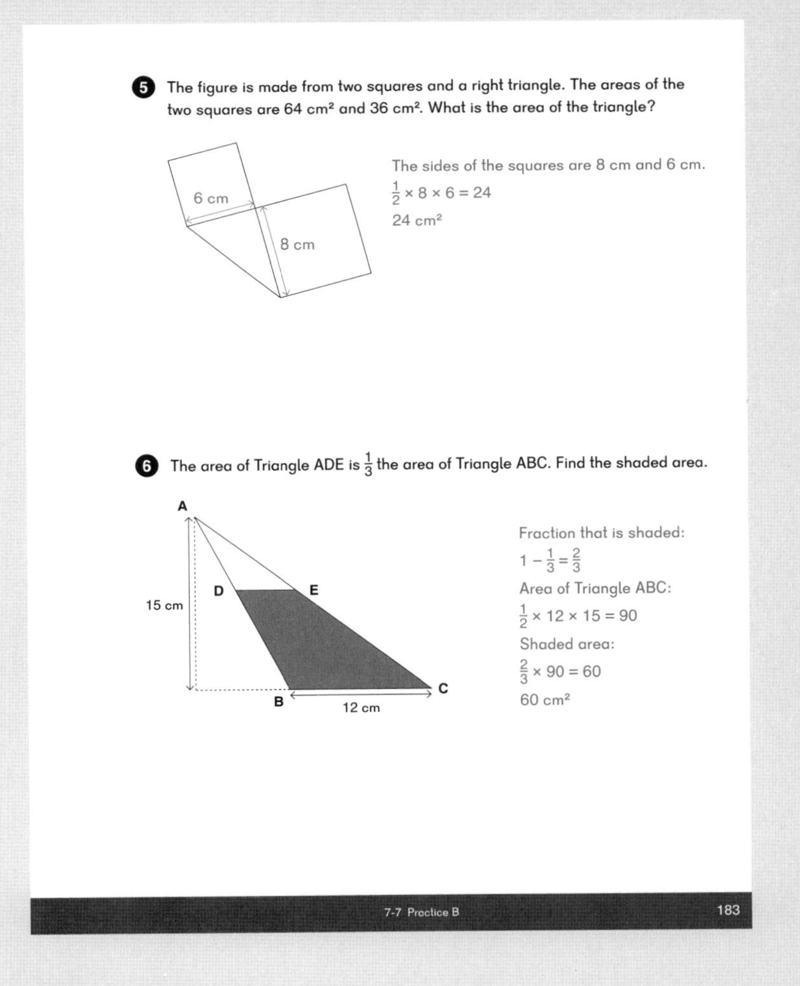

5. The figure is made from two squares and a right triangle. The areas of the two squares are 64 cm² and 36 cm². What is the area of the triangle?

The sides of the squares are 8 cm and 6 cm.

$\frac{1}{2} \times 8 \times 6 = 24$

24 cm²

6. The area of Triangle ADE is $\frac{1}{3}$ the area of Triangle ABC. Find the shaded area.

Fraction that is shaded:

$1 - \frac{1}{3} = \frac{2}{3}$

Area of Triangle ABC:

$\frac{1}{2} \times 12 \times 15 = 90$

Shaded area:

$\frac{2}{3} \times 90 = 60$

60 cm²

7-7 Practice B 183

Challenge

7 The figure below shows three squares. Find the area of the shaded part.

Area of Rectangle ABCD: $17 \times 8 = 136$

Area of Triangle EBC: $\frac{1}{2} \times 13 \times 8 = 52$

Area of Triangle FGD: $\frac{1}{2} \times 12 \times 4 = 24$

Area of Square AEHF: $4 \times 4 = 16$

$136 - 52 - 24 - 16 = 44$

44 cm²

8 The area of triangle ABC is 3 times the area of Triangle ABD. Triangle DBE is an isosceles right triangle. Find the area of Triangle DBE.

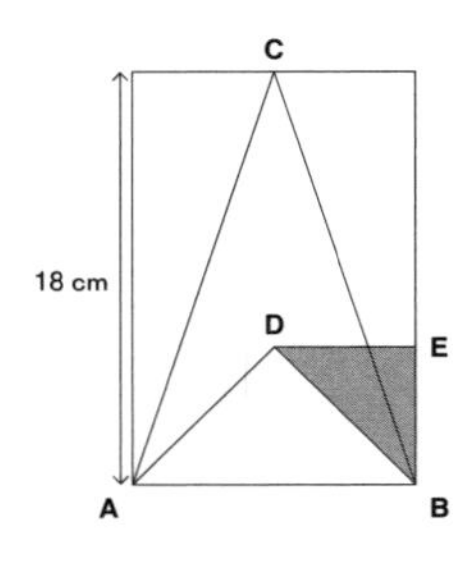

Triangles ABC and ABD have the same base, so if ABC is 3 times the area of ABD, then its height is 3 times the height of ABD. BE is therefore 6 cm.

Area = $\frac{1}{2} \times 6 \times 6 = 18$ cm²

Suggested number of class periods: 9–10

	Lesson	Page	Resources	Objectives
	Chapter Opener	p. 259	TB: p. 195	Investigate volume.
1	Cubic Units	p. 260	TB: p. 196 WB: p. 185	Understand the meaning of volume. Find the volume of solid figures by counting unit cubes.
2	Volume of Cuboids	p. 262	TB: p. 200 WB: p. 189	Derive a formula for finding the volume of a cuboid.
3	Finding the Length of an Edge	p. 265	TB: p. 205 WB: p. 192	Find the length of a missing edge of a cuboid given the volume and the length of the other two sides, or the area of the corresponding base.
4	Practice A	p. 268	TB: p. 209 WB: p. 195	Practice volume concepts from Lessons 1–3.
5	Volume of Complex Shapes	p. 270	TB: p. 212 WB: p. 199	Find the volume of complex solid figures composed of two cuboids.
6	Volume and Capacity — Part 1	p. 273	TB: p. 216 WB: p. 202	Relate volume to capacity. Find the capacity of a container, or the volume of water in a cuboid-shaped container, and express it in L and mL.
7	Volume and Capacity — Part 2	p. 276	TB: p. 220 WB: p. 205	Find the volume of a solid by displacement.
8	Practice B	p. 278	TB: p. 223 WB: p. 208	Practice finding the volume of solids.
	Review 2	p. 280	TB: p. 225 WB: p. 212	Review concepts from Chapters 1–8.
	Workbook Solutions	p. 285		

Students have learned:

- To find the area of rectangles and compound rectilinear figures using a given length and width (Dimensions Math 3B and 4B).
- To measure the capacity of containers and convert between units of measurement, for example 1,000 mL = 1 L (Chapter 7).
- The attributes of cubes and cuboids, and how to identify nets of cubes and cuboids (Dimensions Math 4B).

In this chapter, students will use these skills to:

- Find the volume of cuboids and figures composed of cuboids.
- Find unknown lengths of cuboids given the volume and two other lengths or the area of one side.
- Convert between cubic centimeters and milliliters.

Volume of Solids and Cuboids

Students will learn the volume of a solid is a measure of the amount of space a solid occupies. Lesson 1 begins with students determining the volume of a solid figure by building that figure from 1 cubic centimeter unit cubes (1 cm^3). The volume of a 1-cm cube is 1 cm × 1 cm × 1 cm = 1 cm^3. 1 cm^3 should be read as 1 cubic centimeter (not one centimeter cubed), and is a unit of volume. We use cubic units to measure volume.

Students will learn that they can find the volume of a cuboid by multiplying the area of one face, called the base, by the length of the side perpendicular to that face, called the height: Volume of a Cuboid = Area of Base × Height.

Since the area of the base (one face) is the length × width of the rectangular face, they also know: Volume of a Cuboid = Length × Width × Height.

Example:

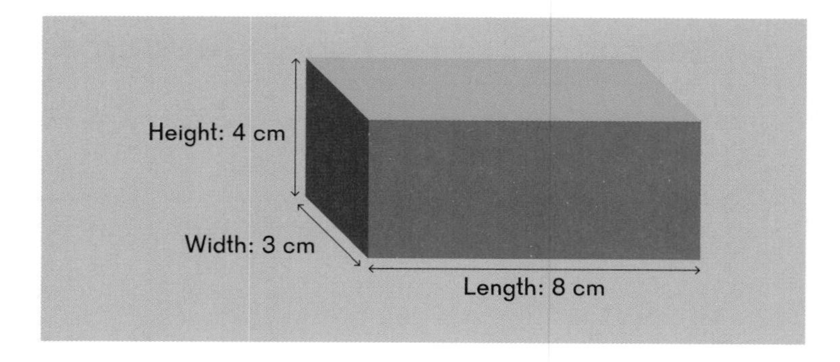

Volume = Area of Base × Height
= (8 × 3) × 4
= 96 cm^3

Volume = Length × Width × Height
= 8 × 3 × 4
= 96 cm^3

Students should understand both of these formulas and how they are related.

Finding the Length of an Edge

In Lesson 3, students will be given the volume of a cuboid and two edge lengths. They will then determine the missing edge length by dividing the volume by the product of the two given edge lengths. They will also be given the volume of the cuboid and the area of one face, and determine the length of the edge perpendicular to the given face by dividing the volume by the given area.

Example:

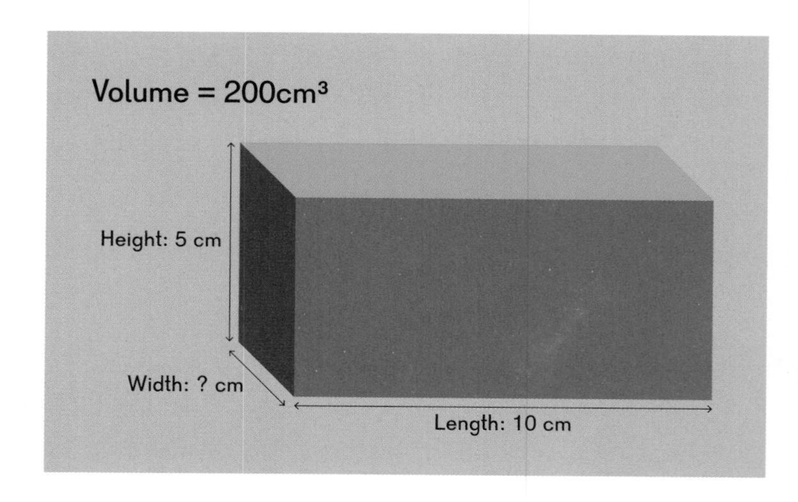

Volume = Length x Width × Height
$200 \text{ cm}^3 = 10 \times ? \text{ cm} \times 5 \text{ cm}$

We can then divide the volume by the product of the lengths of the other two edges:
$\frac{200}{10 \times 5} = \frac{200}{50} = 4 \text{ cm}$

We can also think of if it this way:
$\frac{200}{10 \times 5} = 200 \div 10 \div 5 = 4 \text{ cm}$

Volume of Composite Figures

As students found areas of composite figures composed of rectangles (or rectilinear shapes) in Dimensions Math 4B, they will now find the volume of a three-dimensional shape composed of cuboids.

Students should understand that although the strategies look different, the underlying idea for finding the volume of the solid figure is finding a way to distinguish the different cuboids in the shape. From there, students can use the formula for the volume of a cuboid and add the volumes to find the volume of the shape.

Method 1

Partition the solid figure into cuboids.

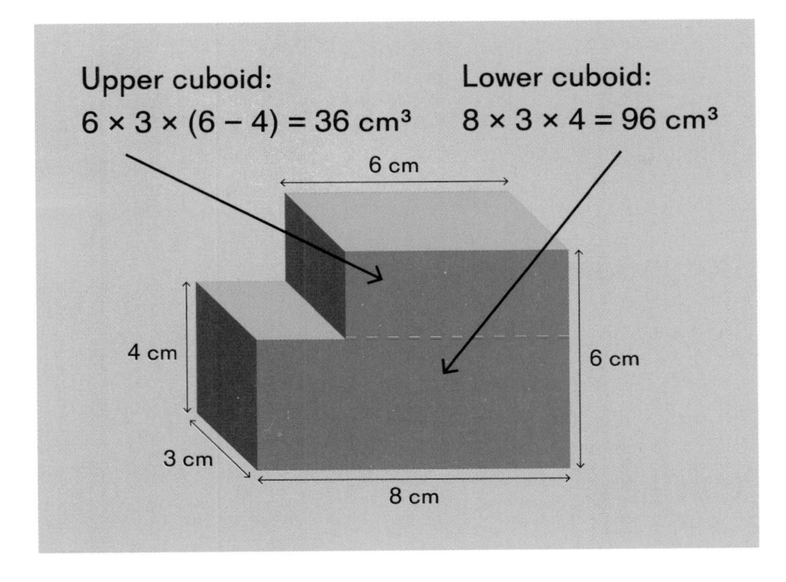

Total volume: $36 \text{ cm}^3 + 96 \text{ cm}^3 = 132 \text{ cm}^3$

In this example we could partition the solid figure into a left and right cuboid.

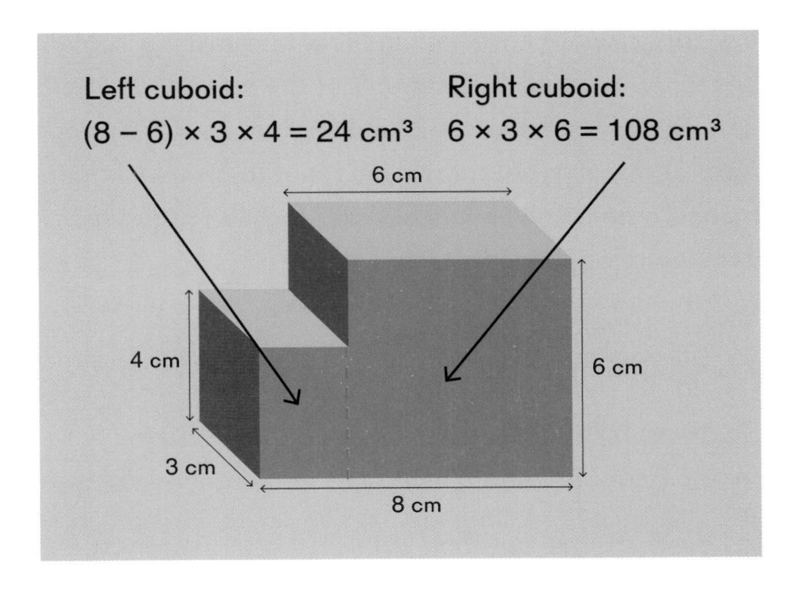

Total volume: $24 \text{ cm}^3 + 108 \text{ cm}^3 = 132 \text{ cm}^3$

Method 2

Think of the shape as a larger cuboid from which a smaller cuboid has been cut away. Find the total volume of the larger cuboid and subtract the missing part.

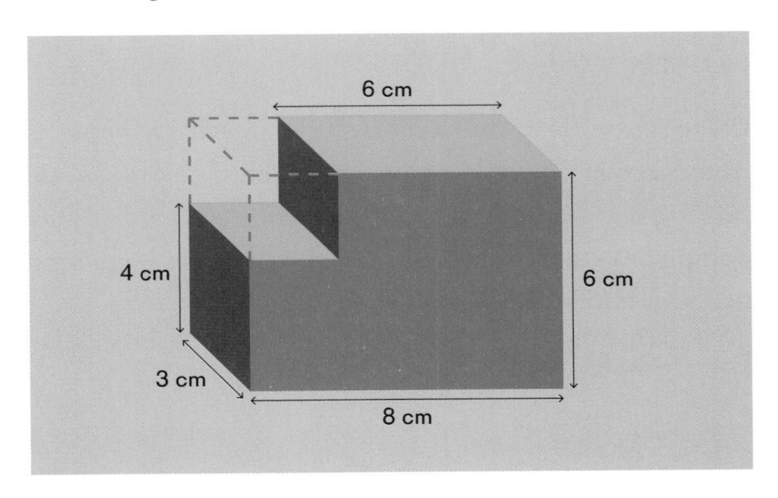

Volume of whole cuboid: $8 \times 6 \times 3 = 144 \text{ cm}^3$

Volume of missing part: $(8 - 6) \times 3 \times (6 - 4) = 12 \text{ cm}^3$

Total volume: $144 - 12 = 132 \text{ cm}^3$

Volumes can be added or subtracted as long as they are expressed in the same units of measurement. These strategies are similar to what students learned to do when finding the area of compound figures.

Volume and Capacity

In Dimensions Math 4A, Students learned to find the capacity of containers in liters and milliliters. In Lesson 6, students will learn that the volume of liquids can be expressed in cubic centimeters as well as in units of capacity. Students will learn to convert liquid measurements given in liters and milliliters to cubic centimeters and vice versa.

1 mL = 1 cm^3
1 L = 1,000 cm^3

Students will find the volume of water placed in rectangular containers using the formula for volume.

In Lesson 6, the textbook will use the terms cuboid-shaped or cube-shaped container or tank. In Lesson 7, the textbook will use the more common term "rectangular" tank, even though a rectangle is a two dimensional shape. A rectangular tank is simply a tank in which all the sides are rectangular.

Students will solve problems involving the volume of solids by understanding the displacement of a liquid by a solid.

Using a container and water, students will see that when a solid object is placed in water, it displaces, or pushes out of place, a volume of water. If the object is completely submerged, the volume of water displaced is equal to the volume of the object.

For example:

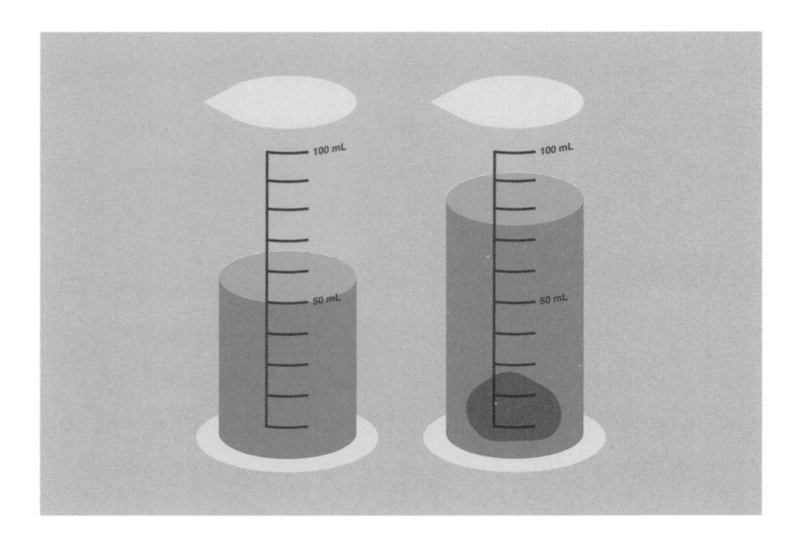

The addition of the rock raises the water level to a new height.

The difference in the water levels before and after the rock is added is equal to the volume of the rock.

Volume of water in beaker: 50 mL

Volume of water and rock in beaker: 75 mL

Volume of the rock: 75 mL – 50 mL = 25 mL

Materials

- 1-cm centimeter cubes
- 1 liter measuring cube
- 100 mL beakers or liquid measuring cups with mL markings
- Bricks
- Centimeter cubes
- Counters, 8 per student
- Liter measuring cup
- Rocks, marbles, or other solids
- Tank
- Unit cubes
- Whiteboard

Blackline Masters

- Checkerboard
- Isometric Dot Paper
- Large Cuboid

Storybooks

- *Archimedes Takes a Bath* by Joan Lexau
- *Mr. Archimedes' Bath* by Pamela Allen

Activities

Fewer games and activities are included in this chapter as students will be working with cubes, beakers, and other manipulatives. The included activities can be used after students complete the **Do** questions, or anytime additional practice is needed.

Objective

- Investigate volume.

Lesson Materials

- 1-cm centimeter cubes or unit cubes from a base-ten set

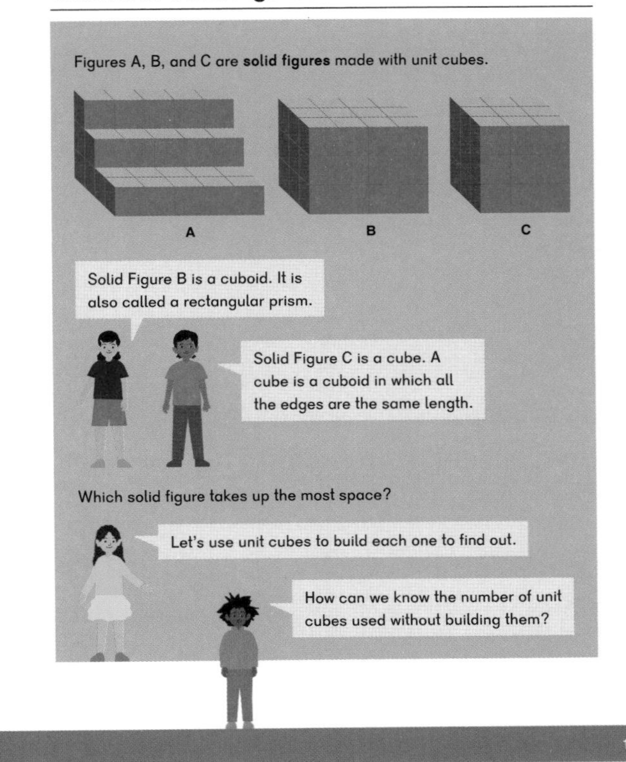

Discuss Mei's and Alex's comments and review the terms with students.

Provide students with centimeter cubes and have them build the three solid figures. Once students have built the figures in the **Chapter Opener**, and have answered Dion's question for each of them, have them build other solid figures with the cubes and state the total number of cubes in their solid.

For Figure A, students may see:

- "There are 7 rows of 5 cubes so it is 7 × 5 = 35 cubes."
- "If you look at the side layer there are 7 cubes and if you look at the front layer there are 5 layers so it is 7 × 5 = 35."
- "If you look at the back layer + middle layer + 2 front rows it is 15 + 10 + 5 + 5 = 35."

Activity

▲ Visualizing Solid Figures

Materials: Unit cubes, Isometric Dot Paper (BLM)

Drawing three-dimensional solids on paper can help students understand how volume is represented in two dimensions and understand when to assume that there are "hidden cubes." Provide students with the Isometric Dot Paper (BLM) and have them draw a single cube. Once they can draw a single cube, have them draw the solid figures depicted in the **Chapter Opener**.

★ To extend, have students build and then draw solid figures of less than 20 cubes.

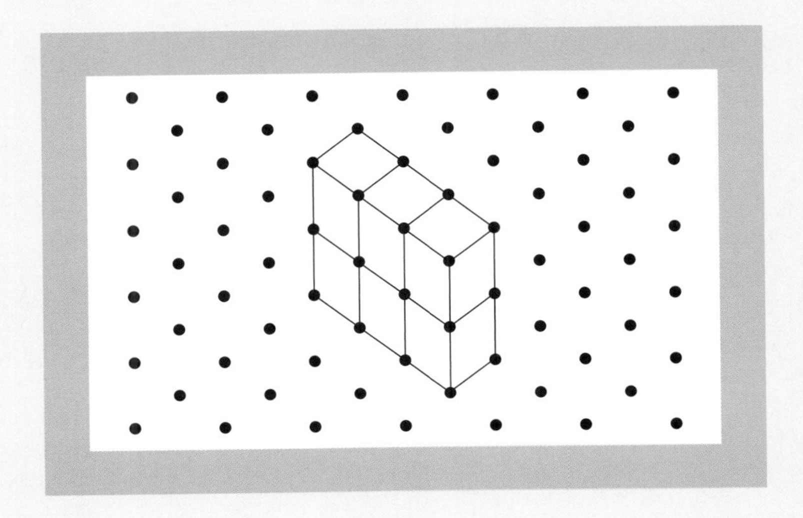

Objectives

- Understand the meaning of volume.
- Find the volume of solid figures by counting unit cubes.

Lesson Materials

- Large Cuboid (BLM)
- 1-cm cubes, 60 per student or pair of students

Think

Provide students with Large Cuboid (BLM), tape, and 1-cm cubes and pose the **Think** problem. Have them build the cuboid from the net first.

Have students start with 5 cubes and ask them how many cubes they think will be needed to fill the whole cuboid and why. Have them fill the cuboid to see how many cubes are needed.

Learn

Ensure students have filled in their cuboids with no gaps between the net and the unit cubes. As Mei shows, students' cuboids should hold 60 unit cubes.

Discuss the terms "volume" and "cubic units."

Linear units, such as inches and centimeters, measure length, which is one-dimensional.

Square units measure area, since they cover two dimensions (length and width), and are abbreviated with the superscript 2. Cubic units measure volume, since they cover three dimensions, and are abbreviated with the superscript 3.

Dion relates cubic centimeters to the notation, cm^3.

196

Lesson 1
Cubic Units ①

Think

How many 1-cm cubes will fill up a cuboid made from this net?

1 cm
1 cm

Learn

We filled the inside of the cuboid with 60 1-cm cubes.

196 8-1 Cubic Units

197

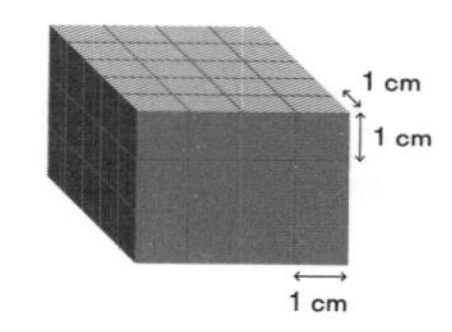

The amount of space a solid figure occupies is called the **volume** of the solid figure. We measure volume in **cubic units**. The volume of a unit cube is 1 cubic unit.

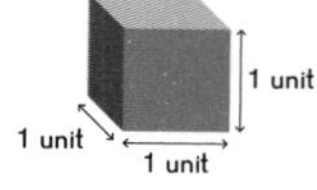

We are measuring the amount of three-dimensional space a solid figure takes up. We need units that take up three dimensions.

Some units of volume are **cubic centimeters** (cm^3), **cubic meters** (m^3), **cubic inches** (in^3), and **cubic feet** (ft^3).

We need sixty 1-cm cubes to fill the cuboid. The volume of the cuboid is 60 cm^3.

8-1 Cubic Units 197

Do

❷ Students can build the figures as needed. Building the figures will be especially helpful to see that there are hidden cubes in (b) – (d). The hidden cubes are ones with a cube on top of them and in front of them.

Students may also think about the layers of each shape in (b) – (d) in order to find the total number of cubes. In (b), the top layer has 3 × 2 cubes. Since there are 3 layers, students can think 3 × (3 × 2) cubic units.

In (d), the top layer is 7 cubes. The figure has 3 layers of 7 cubes. 3 × 7 = 21 cubic units.

❸–❹ Students should be able to solve these problems independently. They can use multiplication to find the volume of each figure.

❸ Examples:

(b) The front layer has 3 × 5 = 15 cubes, there are 3 layers behind it that each have 4 × 5 = 20 cubes so the number of cubes is 3 × 5 + 3 × 20 = 75.

(c) The top layer has 4 cubes, the next layer down has 2 × 4 cubes, etc.

Exercise 1 • page 185

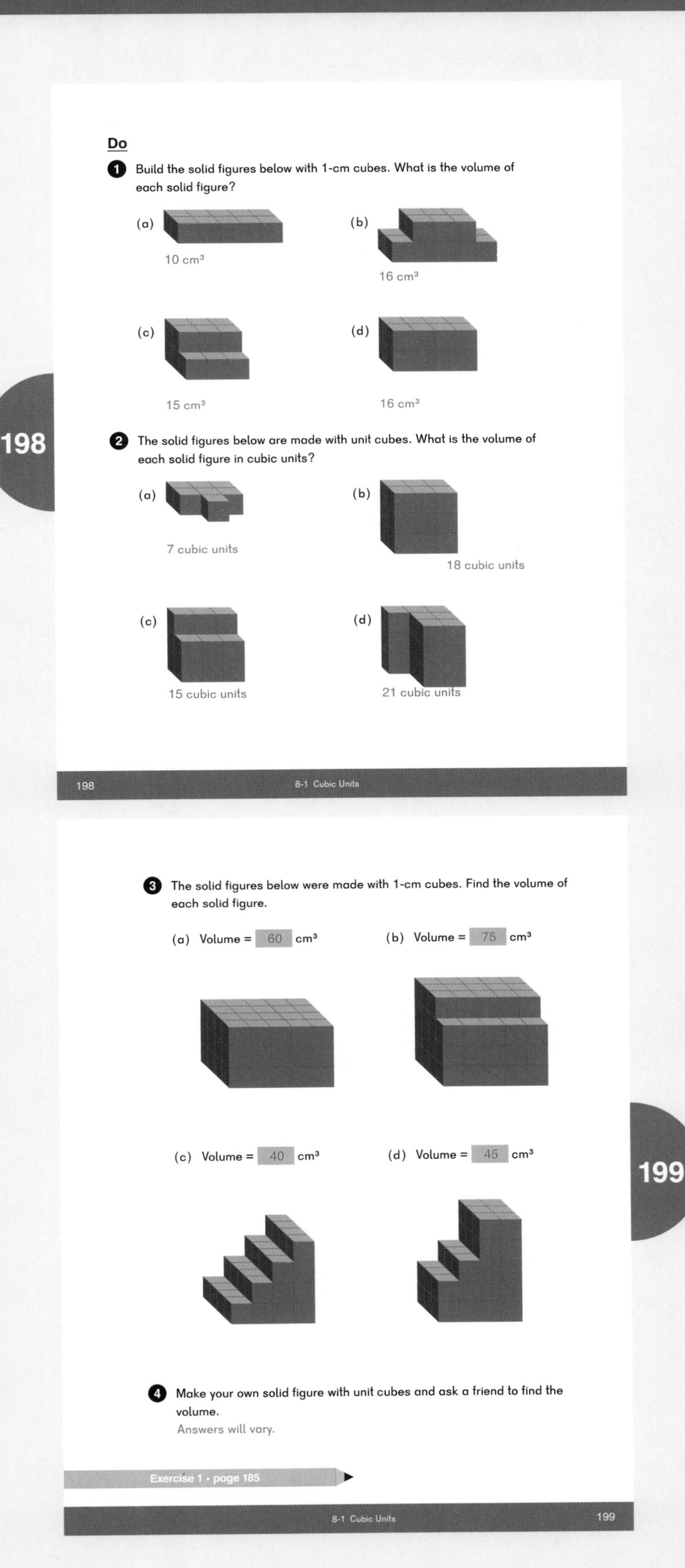
198

Do

❶ Build the solid figures below with 1-cm cubes. What is the volume of each solid figure?

(a) 10 cm³ (b) 16 cm³

(c) 15 cm³ (d) 16 cm³

❷ The solid figures below are made with unit cubes. What is the volume of each solid figure in cubic units?

(a) 7 cubic units (b) 18 cubic units

(c) 15 cubic units (d) 21 cubic units

198 8-1 Cubic Units

❸ The solid figures below were made with 1-cm cubes. Find the volume of each solid figure.

(a) Volume = 60 cm³ (b) Volume = 75 cm³

(c) Volume = 40 cm³ (d) Volume = 45 cm³

❹ Make your own solid figure with unit cubes and ask a friend to find the volume.
Answers will vary.

Exercise 1 • page 185

8-1 Cubic Units 199

199

Objective

- Derive a formula for finding the volume of a cuboid.

Lesson Materials

- Unit cubes, 10 per student

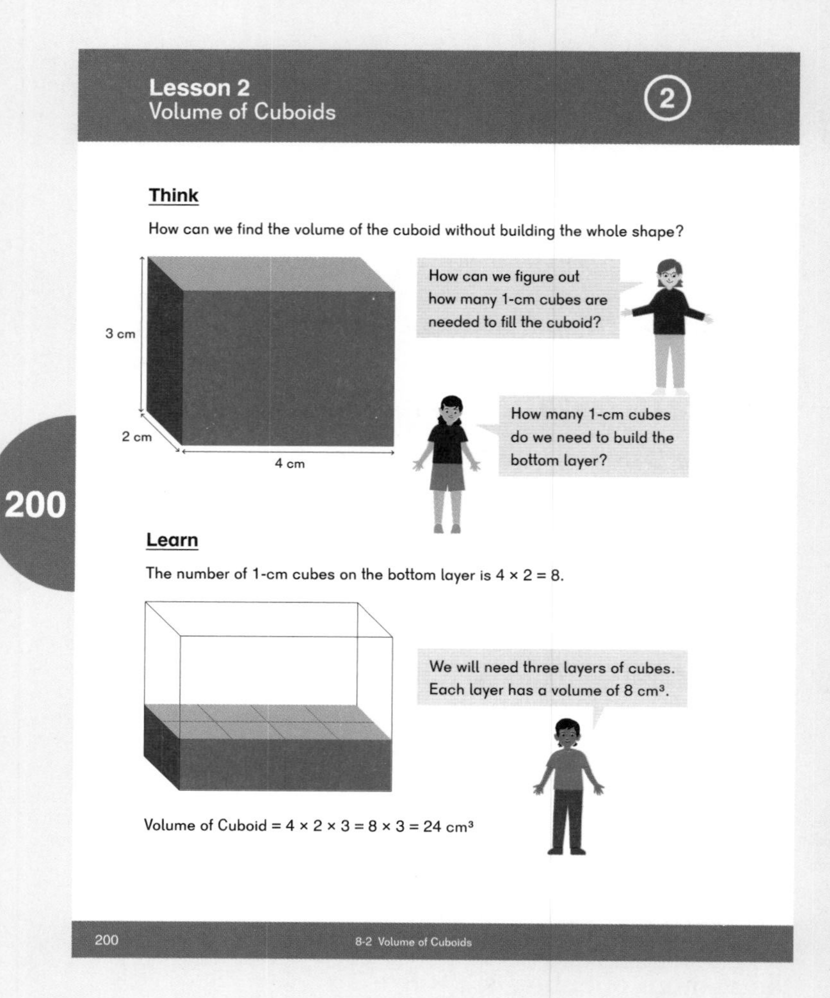

Think

Pose the **Think** problem and have students use the unit cubes to find the volume of the bottom layer. They will not have enough cubes to build the whole shape. Students should think about how to solve the problem with only the bottom layer of cubes.

Discuss student solutions.

Learn

Have students compare their solutions from **Think** with the one in the textbook. Alex knows that if the height of the cuboid is 3 cm, he will need 3 layers of cubes to build the solid figure.

Have students look at the top (or bottom) of the cuboid and see that it is a rectangle. They should realize that the area in square centimeters, found by multiplying the length by the width, is the same as the number of cubes in that layer.

Students should see that if they know the area of the base, they can multiply that by the height to find the volume of the cuboid.

Dion points out that any face can be considered the base of a cuboid. All of these formulas use the area of a face and the length of a side perpendicular to the face. If we think of the front face as the base, we see that its area is $4 \times 3 = 12$. The width gives the number of layers, each of which are made up of 12 cubes.

Do

❶–❸ Discuss the problems and Emma's comments for ❷ with students.

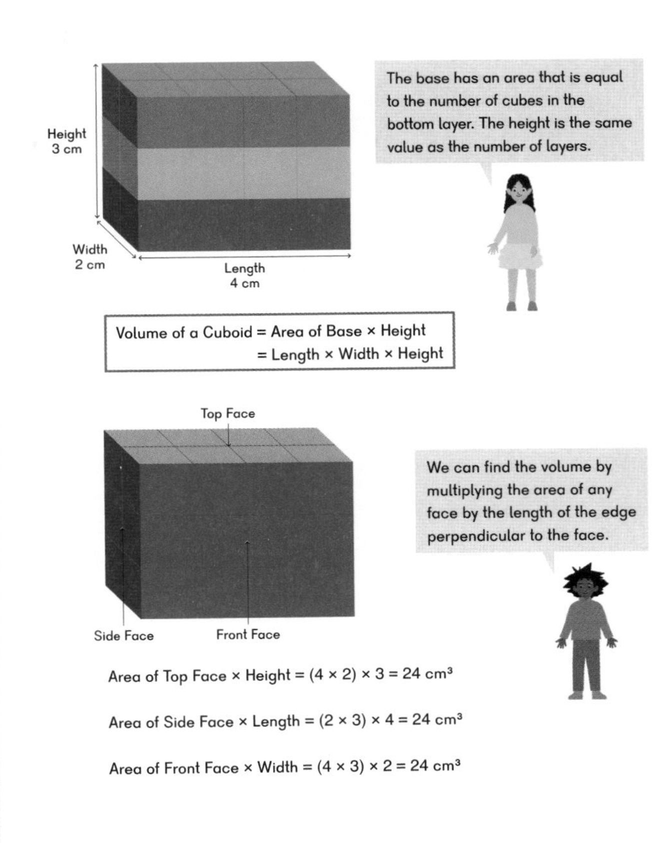

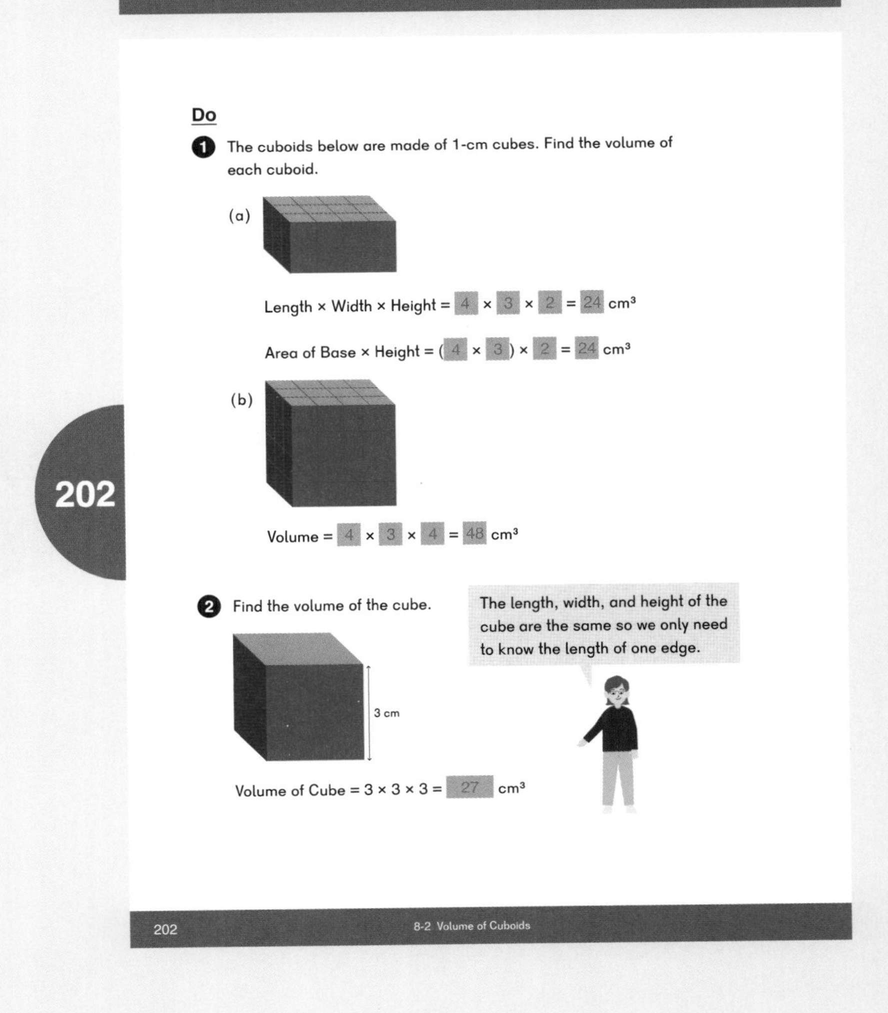

❸ Cubes that show the three dimensions are given. Students should think about how many cubes it will take to fill the cuboid.

❹—❻ Students should be able to solve these problems independently.

❹ Students are given the length of each edge, and should no longer need to see each individual cube. They should be using the formula and the dimensions given to find the volume.

❺ Students are only given the area of a base, and the length of a side perpendicular to the base, so they do not need to calculate the area of the base.

❻ The units of measurement are different. First convert yards to feet to solve the problem.

Exercise 2 • page 189

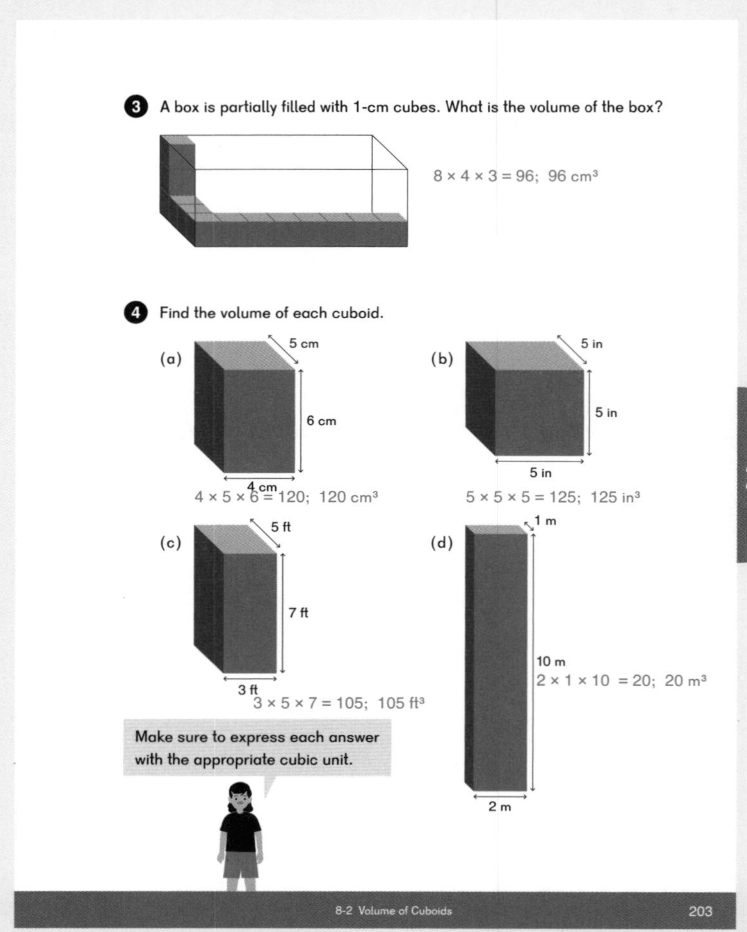

203

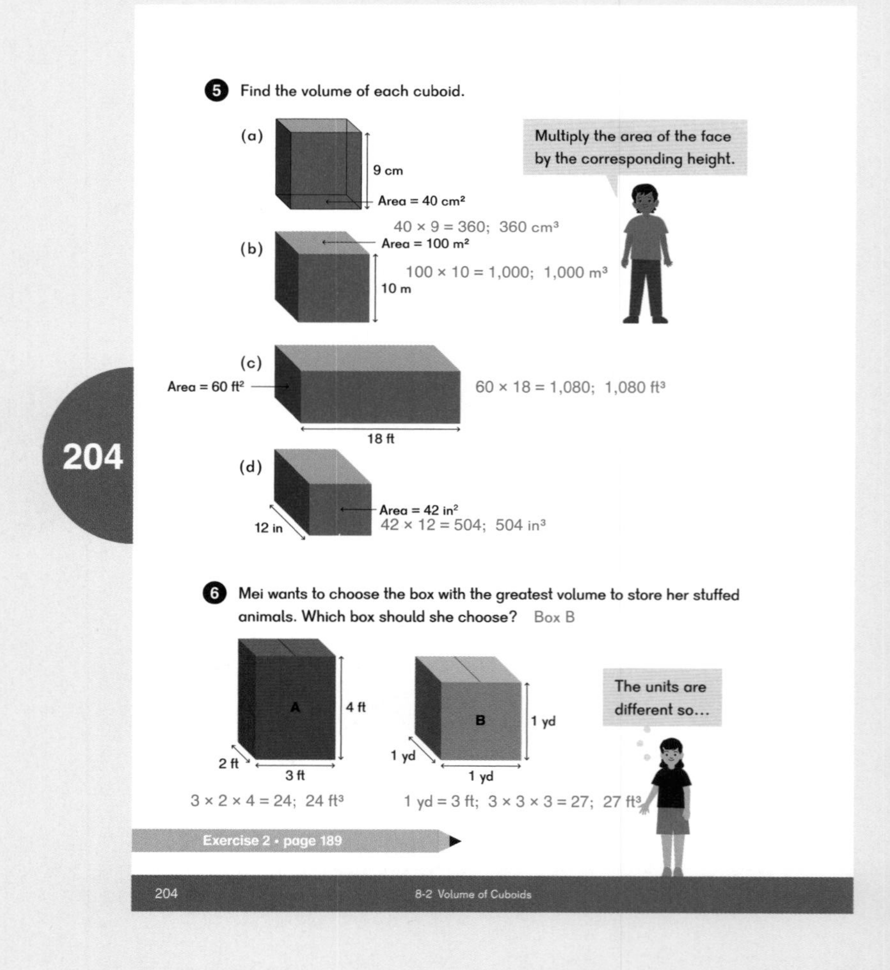

204

Objective

- Find the length of a missing edge of a cuboid given the volume and the length of the other two sides, or the area of the corresponding base.

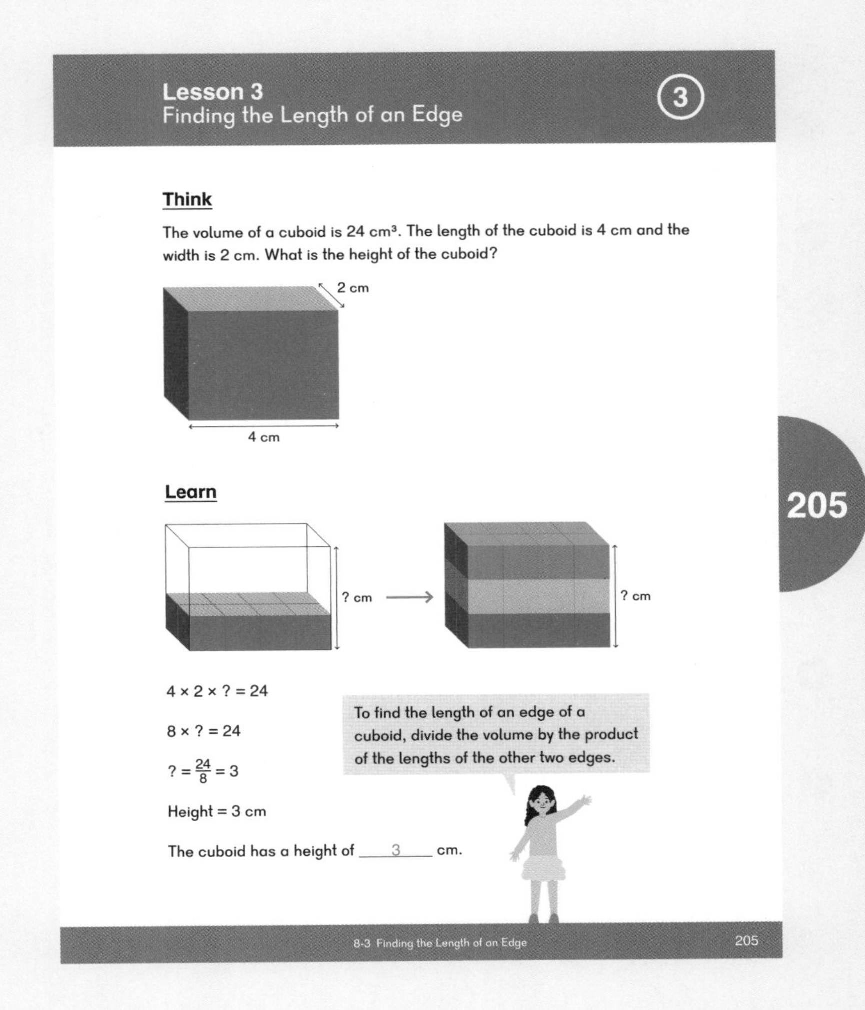

205

Think

Pose the **Think** problem and give students time to find solutions independently.

Ask students how this problem is similar to and different from the **Think** problem in the previous lesson. (In both **Think** problems we were finding the volume of cuboids. In the previous lesson, we were given the measurements and found the volume. Here, we are given the volume and need to find the length of the missing side.)

Discuss student solutions.

Learn

Have students compare their solution from **Think** with the one in the textbook. If we know the length and the width, we can find the area of the base: $4 \times 2 = 8$.

Because Volume = Area of Base × Height, we can find the missing height by using division.

$24 = 8 \times ?$
$24 \div 8 = ?$
$24 \div 8$ can be shown as a fraction $\frac{24}{8}$, so $24 \div (4 \times 2)$ can be shown as:

$\frac{24}{4 \times 2}$

Students should realize that this represents a step in the calculation.

Do

❶—❸ Discuss the problems with students. The layer that students should use to find the area is shown.

❶ The calculations are combined into a single equation.

$$\frac{36}{4 \times 3} = \frac{36}{12} = 3$$

Students can write the problems as missing factor problems first, then divide to find the missing factor.

❷ The dimensions of one face are given. Volume = area of side face × length, so we can write 5 × 4 × length = 60. To find the length we divide 60 by 5 × 4.

❹—❼ Students should be able to solve these problems independently.

❹ The base has to be the face for which we are given both dimensions. In (b), students should see that it is either the top or bottom face. Divide the volume by the area of the base to find the missing dimension.

206

Do

❶ The volume of a cuboid is 36 cm³. It has a length of 4 cm and a height of 3 cm. What is the width of the cuboid?

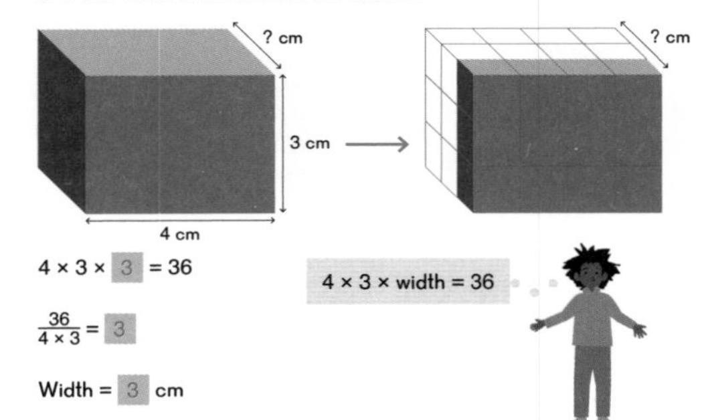

4 × 3 × 3 = 36

$\frac{36}{4 \times 3}$ = 3

Width = 3 cm

4 × 3 × width = 36

❷ The volume of a cuboid is 60 cm³. It has a width of 5 cm and a height of 4 cm. What is the length of the cuboid?

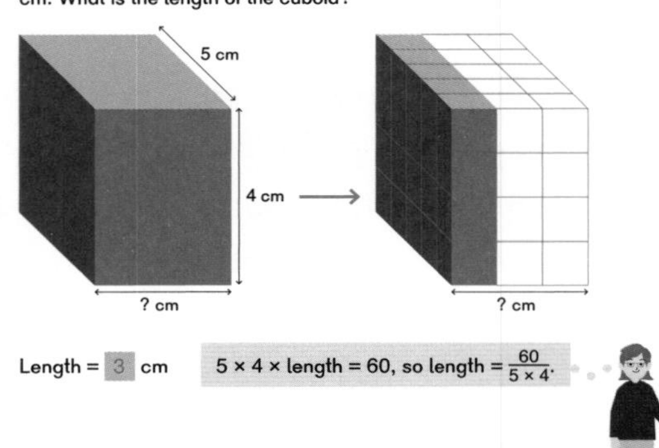

Length = 3 cm

5 × 4 × length = 60, so length = $\frac{60}{5 \times 4}$.

207

❸ The volume of this cuboid is 40 cm³. The area of the base is 10 cm². What is the height?

10 × 4 = 40

$\frac{40}{10}$ = 4

Height = 4 cm

Area of Base = 10 cm²

❹ Find the length of the unknown edge of each cuboid.

(a) Volume = 168 in³ $\frac{168}{4 \times 6}$ = 7

AB = 7 in

(b) Volume = 343 m³ $\frac{343}{7 \times 7}$ = 7

CD = 7 m

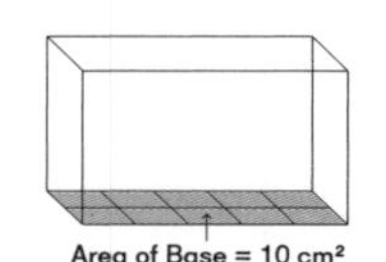

(c) Volume = 360 ft³ $\frac{360}{45}$ = 8

EF = 8 ft

(d) Volume = 140 yd³ $\frac{140}{28}$ = 5

GH = 5 yd

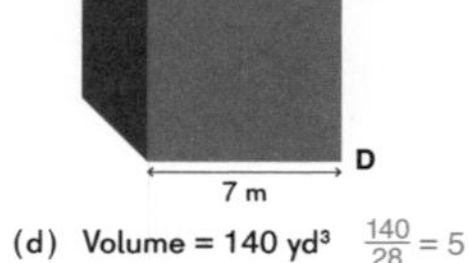

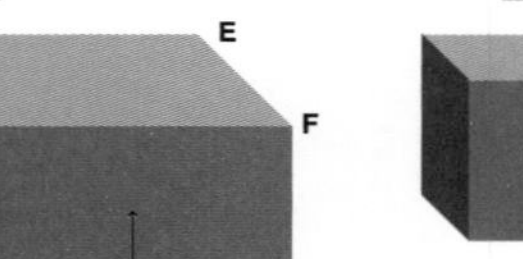

❺ Since the figure is a cuboid, we know that all the edges have to be the same length. We are not given the area or the length of two of the edges.

❻ Students are given the volume and the height. They divide to find the area of the base.

❼ 1 m = 100 cm

The number of 1-cm cubes on the bottom layer is $100 \times 100 = 10{,}000$.

The height is 100 cm so the number of layers of 1-cm cubes is $10{,}000 \times 100 = 1{,}000{,}000$.

Exercise 3 • page 192

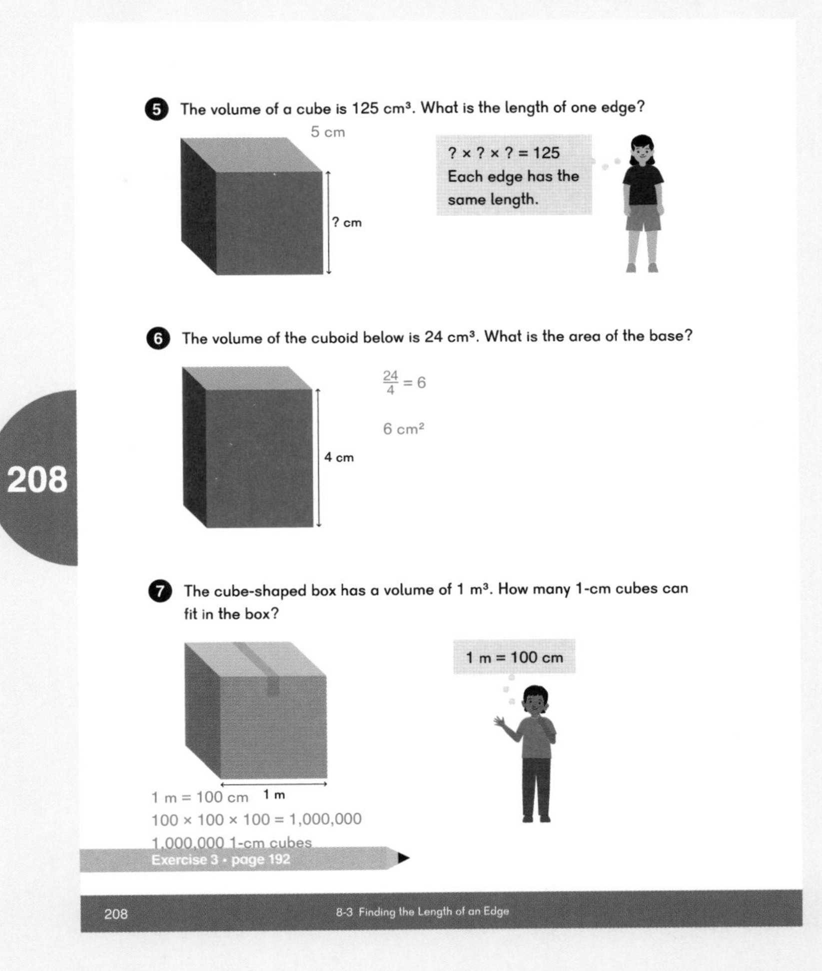

208

❺ The volume of a cube is 125 cm³. What is the length of one edge?

5 cm

? cm

? × ? × ? = 125
Each edge has the same length.

❻ The volume of the cuboid below is 24 cm³. What is the area of the base?

$\frac{24}{4} = 6$

6 cm²

4 cm

❼ The cube-shaped box has a volume of 1 m³. How many 1-cm cubes can fit in the box?

1 m = 100 cm

1 m

1 m = 100 cm
100 × 100 × 100 = 1,000,000
1,000,000 1-cm cubes

Exercise 3 • page 192

208 8-3 Finding the Length of an Edge

Objectives

- Practice volume concepts from Lessons 1–3.

❶–❸ Students should express the area using cubic units for the measurement unit given.

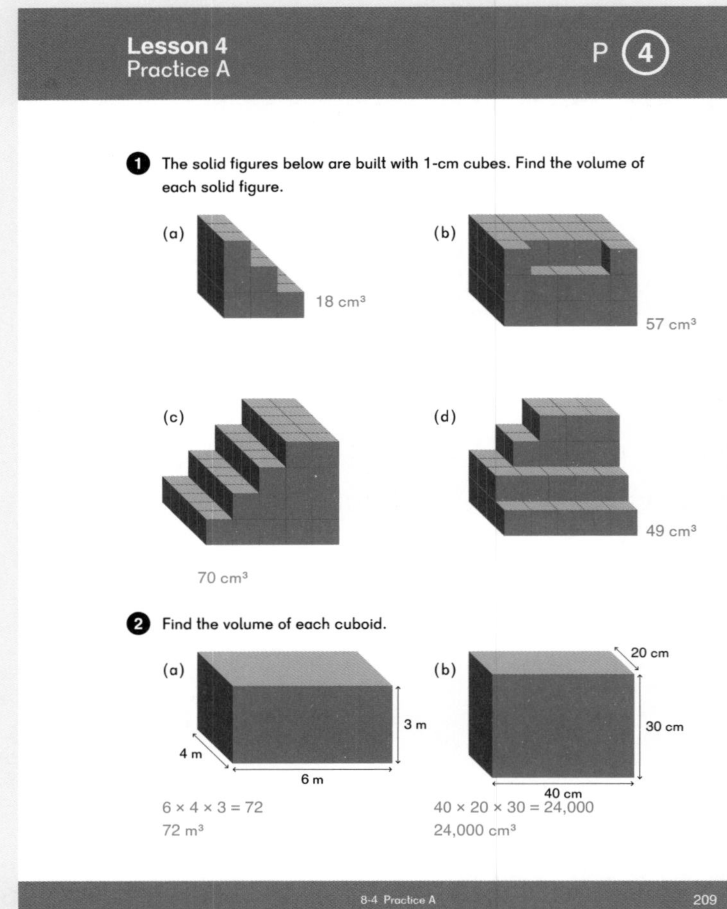

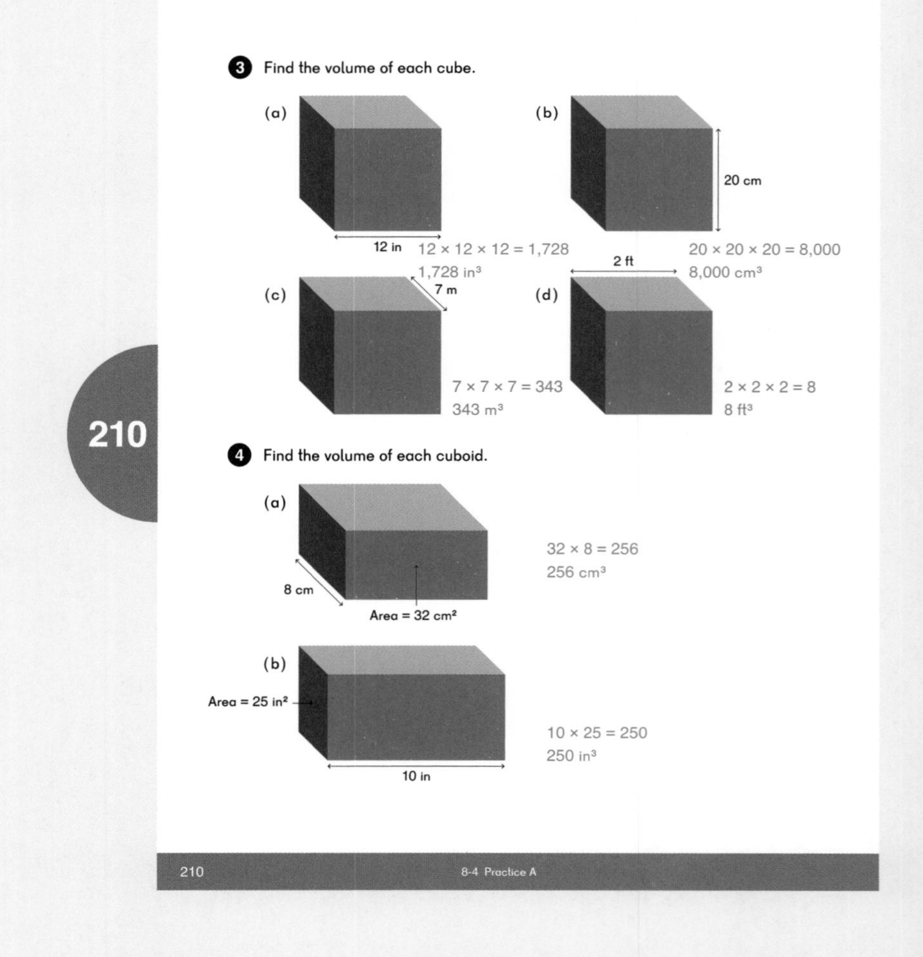

7 (a) This is the first time students are not given a drawing of the cuboid. They should be able to solve the problem without a drawing.

(b) Students should realize they cannot solve this by dividing the total volume by the volume of each 2 cm cube (i.e., 2,160 ÷ 8 does not give a correct answer). There will be a gap in the height that is not filled. If students struggle, provide a drawing of the box with tick marks for each centimeter.

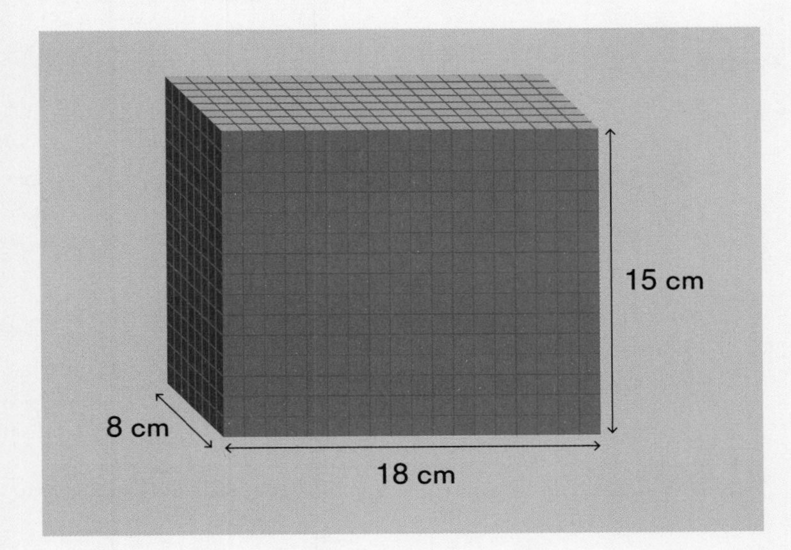

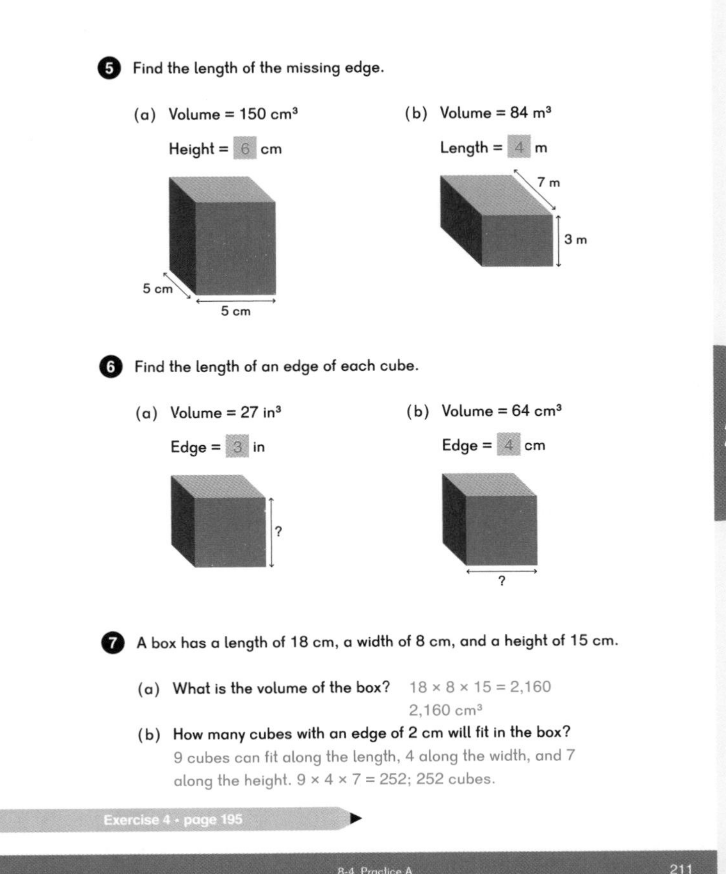

5 Find the length of the missing edge.

(a) Volume = 150 cm³

Height = 6 cm

(b) Volume = 84 m³

Length = 4 m

6 Find the length of an edge of each cube.

(a) Volume = 27 in³

Edge = 3 in

(b) Volume = 64 cm³

Edge = 4 cm

7 A box has a length of 18 cm, a width of 8 cm, and a height of 15 cm.

(a) What is the volume of the box? 18 × 8 × 15 = 2,160
2,160 cm³

(b) How many cubes with an edge of 2 cm will fit in the box?
9 cubes can fit along the length, 4 along the width, and 7 along the height. 9 × 4 × 7 = 252; 252 cubes.

Exercise 4 • page 195

8-4 Practice A 211

211

Exercise 4 • page 195

Objective

- Find the volume of complex solid figures composed of two cuboids.

Lesson Materials

- Centimeter cubes

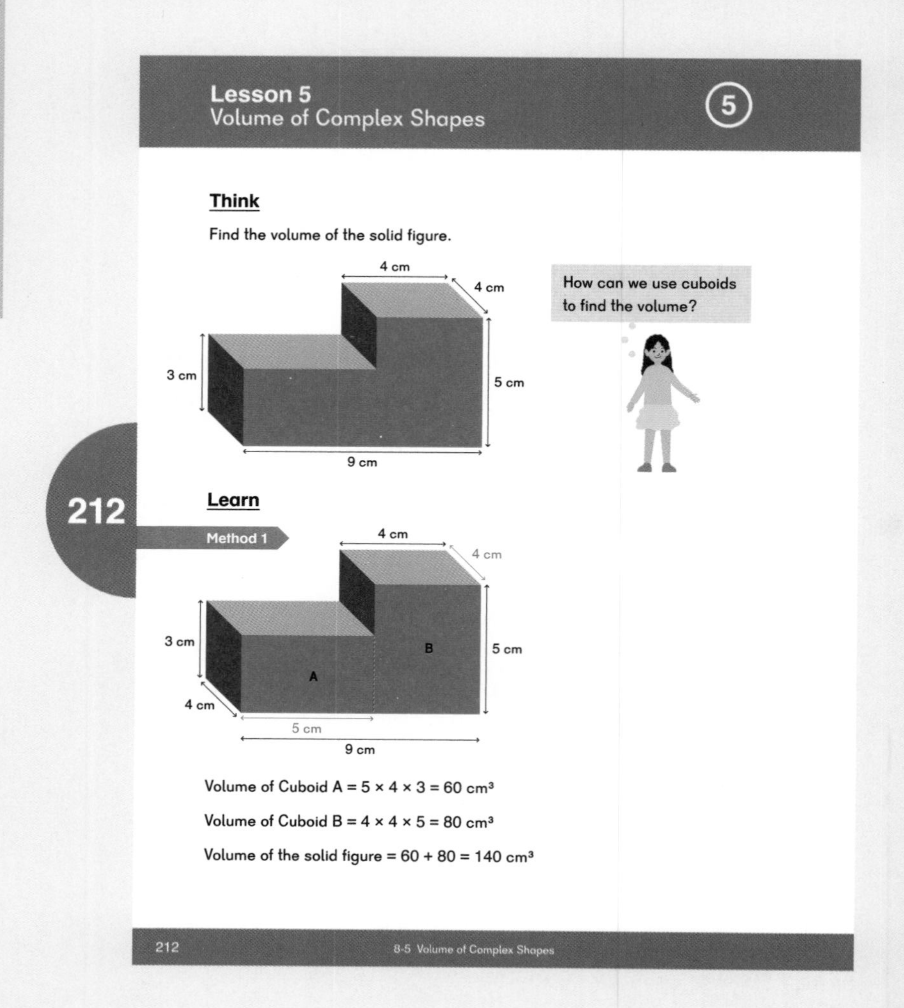

Think

Pose the **Think** problem and give students time to solve the problem independently.

Learn

Students should relate finding the volume of the figure to what they did in Chapter 7 when they found the area of two-dimensional figures. Have students compare their solutions from **Think** with the three methods in the textbook.

Methods 1 and 2

The solid figure has been partitioned into smaller cuboids. We calculate the missing side lengths and then the volume of each cuboid. Finally, we add the volume of the two cuboids together to get the total volume.

Method 3

Earlier, we found the area of a two-dimensional shape by thinking of the shape as having a part that was cut away. Similarly, we can find the volume of a solid figure by imagining it as a larger cuboid that has a missing part. We can then find the volume of the whole figure and subtract the part that was removed.

Discuss the differences and similarities of the three methods.

Students may say:

- "They are all different methods."
- "Methods 1 and 2 are similar. Both methods are splitting the figure into two cuboids."
- "Method 3 is different because the method is imagining a large cuboid and subtracting the small cuboid that is not there."
- "All the methods are similar because they are seeing a figure composed of cuboids."

Students should see that volume can be added or subtracted, just like any other measurement they have learned, such as length or area.

Some students may find the area of the front face using a strategy for finding the area of a rectilinear figure, then multiplying that by the depth (4 cm).

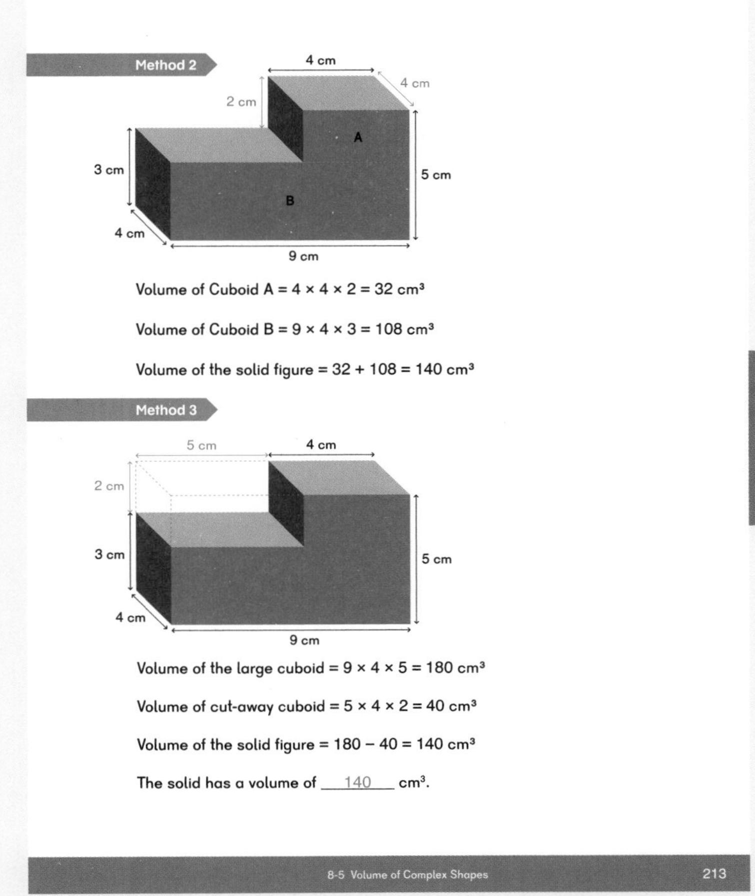

Method 2

Volume of Cuboid A = $4 \times 4 \times 2 = 32$ cm³

Volume of Cuboid B = $9 \times 4 \times 3 = 108$ cm³

Volume of the solid figure = $32 + 108 = 140$ cm³

Method 3

Volume of the large cuboid = $9 \times 4 \times 5 = 180$ cm³

Volume of cut-away cuboid = $5 \times 4 \times 2 = 40$ cm³

Volume of the solid figure = $180 - 40 = 140$ cm³

The solid has a volume of 140 cm³.

8-5 Volume of Complex Shapes 213

213

Do

❶–❸ Discuss the problems with students.

❶ Provide students with centimeter cubes.

❷ Ask students to solve the problem with two of the three methods from **Learn**.

❸ Students should be able to solve the problems independently. They will need to find some lengths that are not provided using the given lengths.

Exercise 5 • page 199

214

Do

❶ Use unit cubes to build the solid figure below.

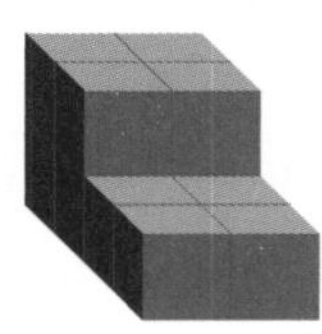

(a) In what different ways can you divide the solid figure into 2 cuboids?
Answers will vary.

(b) What is the fewest number of cubes that need to be added to change the figure into a cuboid?
4

(c) What is the volume of the figure?
12 cubic units

❷ Find the volume of the solid figure below in two different ways.

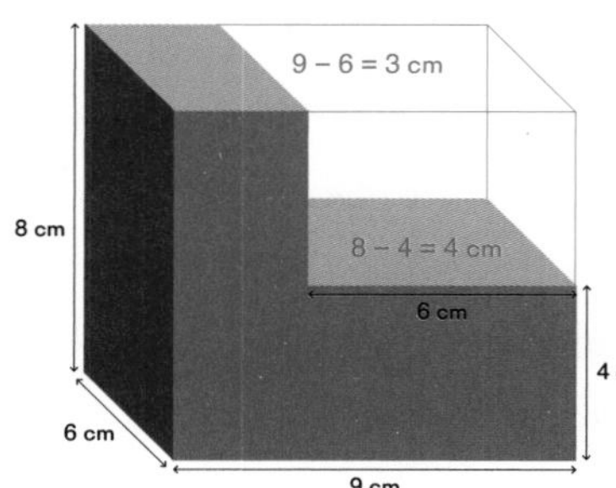

Method 1: Volume of top cuboid:
4 × 3 × 6 = 72;
Volume of bottom cuboid:
9 × 6 × 4 = 216; 72 + 216 = 288;
Method 2: Volume of left cuboid:
3 × 6 × 8 = 144
Volume of right cuboid: 6 × 6 × 4 = 144;
144 + 144 = 288;
Method 3: Volume of large cuboid:
9 × 6 × 8 = 432;
Volume of small cuboid:
6 × 6 × 4 = 144; 432 − 144 = 288;
288 cm³

Methods may vary.

❸ Find the volume of each solid figure.

(a)

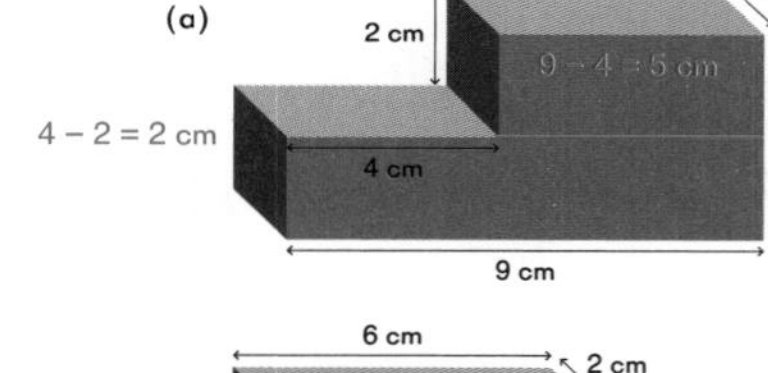

Volume of top cuboid:
5 × 3 × 2 = 30
Volume of bottom cuboid:
9 × 3 × 2 = 54
Volume of solid figure:
30 + 54 = 84
84 cm³

(b)

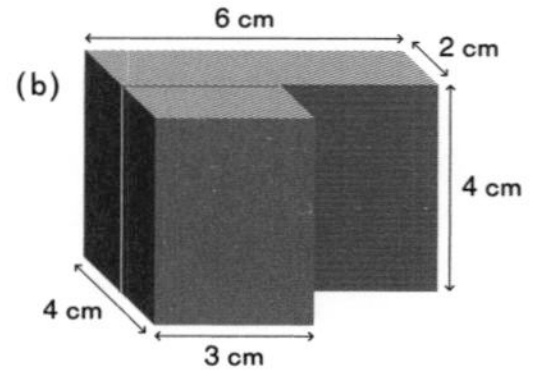

Volume of back cuboid:
6 × 2 × 4 = 48
Volume of front cuboid:
3 × 2 × 4 = 24
Volume of solid figure:
48 + 24 = 72
72 cm³

(c)

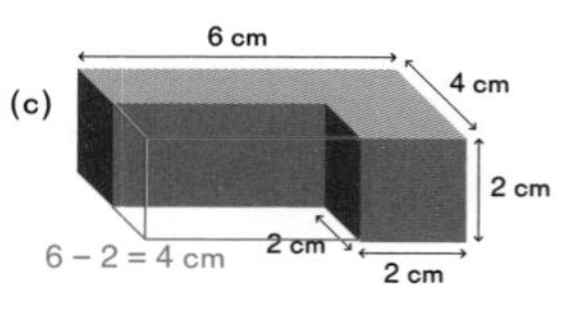

Volume of large cuboid:
6 × 4 × 2 = 48
Volume of small cuboid:
4 × 2 × 2 = 16
Volume of solid figure:
48 − 16 = 32
32 cm³

(d)

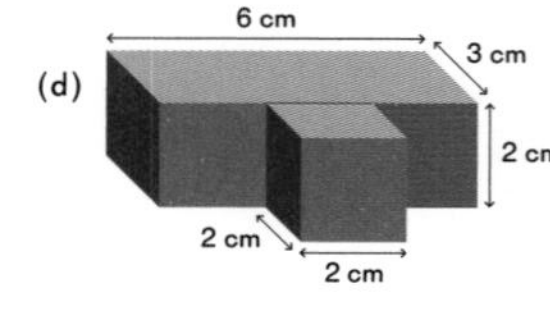

Volume of back cuboid:
6 × 3 × 2 = 36
Volume of front cuboid:
2 × 2 × 2 = 8
Volume of solid figure:
36 + 8 = 44
44 cm³

Exercise 5 • page 199

215

Objectives

- Relate volume to capacity.
- Find the capacity of a container, or the volume of water in a cuboid-shaped container, and express it in L and mL.

Lesson Materials

- Centimeter cubes
- 1 liter measuring cube
- Liter measuring cup

216

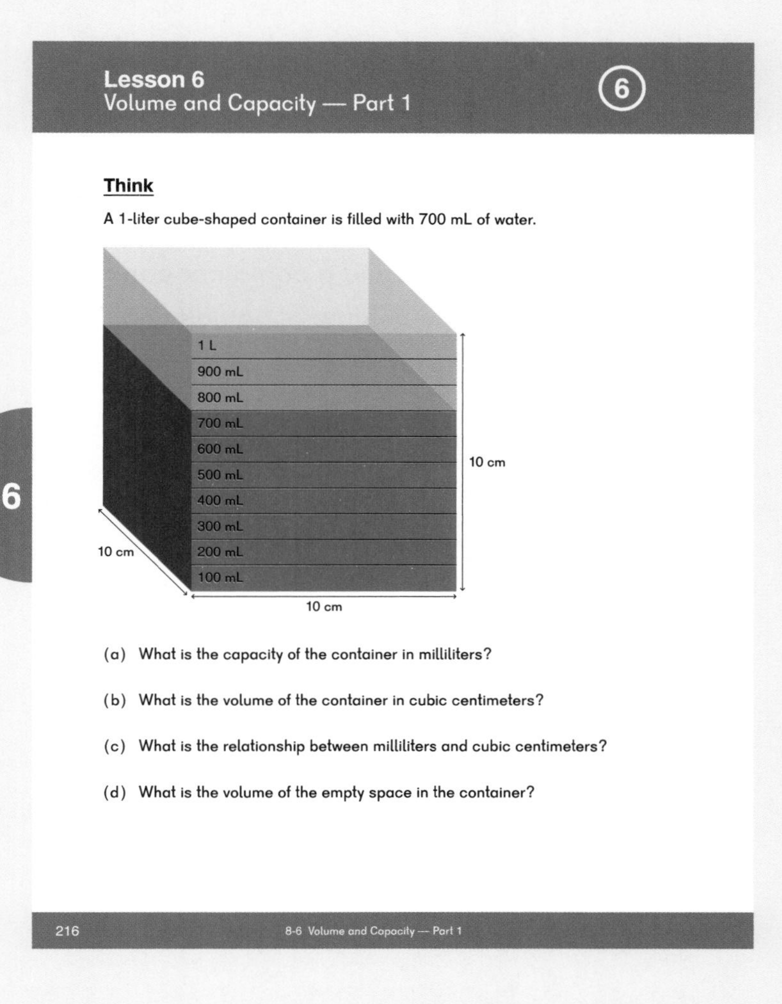

Lesson 6
Volume and Capacity — Part 1 (6)

Think

A 1-liter cube-shaped container is filled with 700 mL of water.

(a) What is the capacity of the container in milliliters?

(b) What is the volume of the container in cubic centimeters?

(c) What is the relationship between milliliters and cubic centimeters?

(d) What is the volume of the empty space in the container?

216 8-6 Volume and Capacity — Part 1

Think

Show students the 1 L measuring cube and tell them it has a capacity of 1 L, as given by the measurements on the side. Ask them for the capacity of the cube in milliliters.

Have a student measure the sides of the container. They should find that each side is 10 cm long.

Show students the centimeter cube, and ask them how many will fit along the side.

Pose the **Think** problem.

After students find that 1 L, or 1,000 mL, is equal to 1,000 cm^3, show them the 1 liter measuring cup and ask them how many cubic centimeters of liquid it can hold. Even though the cup is not a cube, it still holds the same volume of water as the thousand cube. 1 mL of water in any shape has a volume of 1 cm^3 and 1 L of any shape has a volume of 1,000 cm^3.

Learn

Have students compare their answers from **Think** with the methods in the textbook.

(c) Students have used liters and milliliters to measure the capacity of liquid a container can hold. We can also express the volume of liquids in cubic centimeters.

(d) **Method 1**

If we know the capacity of the container and the volume of the water already in the container, so we can subtract to find the volume of the empty space.

Method 2

We can also calculate the volume of the empty space just as we calculated the volume of other cuboids: Length × Width × Height.

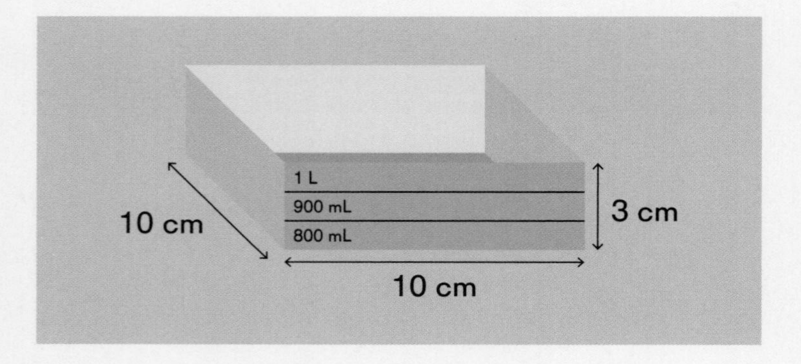

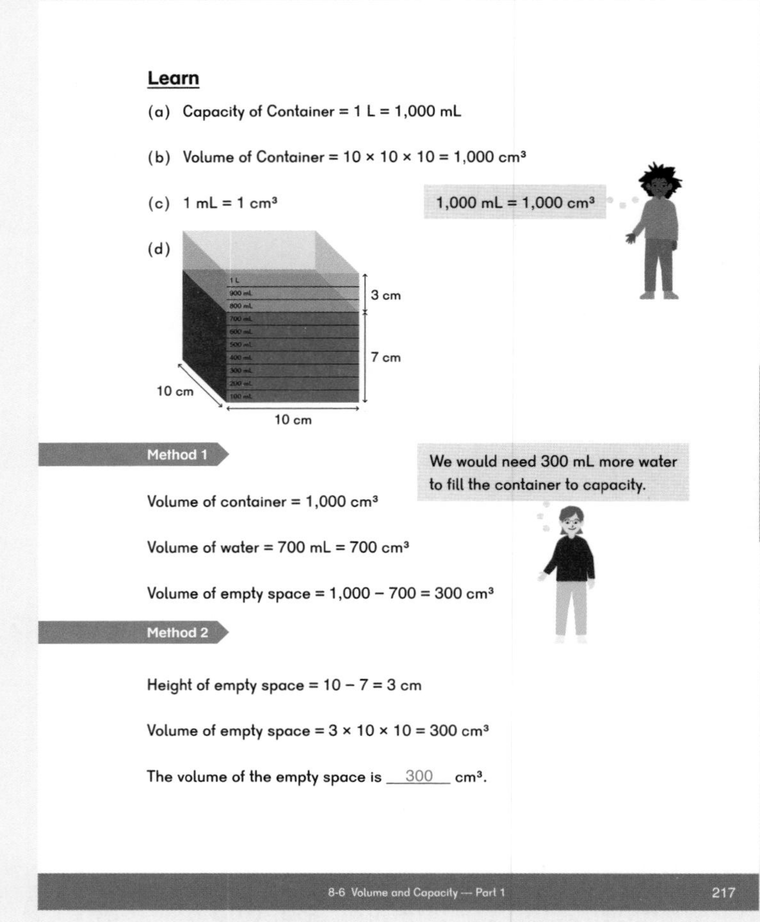

217

Do

❶—❸ Discuss the problems with students. Remind students how to convert L and mL to mL only, and mL to L if needed.

Ensure that they are converting liters to milliliters or cubic centimeters correctly.

Ask students:

- "What units are we given?"
- "What units are we asked to find?"

❹—❺ Students should be able to solve the problems independently.

❺ Students should realize they need to first express $1\frac{1}{2}$ L as milliliters and then cubic centimeters, to find the volume of water.

Exercise 6 • page 202

218

Do

1 Write each amount in cubic centimeters.

(a) 750 mL = 750 cm³ (b) 2 L = 2,000 cm³

(c) 1 L 300 mL = 1,300 cm³ (d) 3 L 25 mL = 3,025 cm³

2 Write each amount in liters and milliliters.

(a) 650 cm³ = 650 mL

(b) 4,000 cm³ = 4 L

(c) 1,850 cm³ = 1 L 850 mL

(d) 2,005 cm³ = 2 L 5 mL

3 A cube-shaped container measures 15 cm by 15 cm by 15 cm. It is filled with 3 L of water.

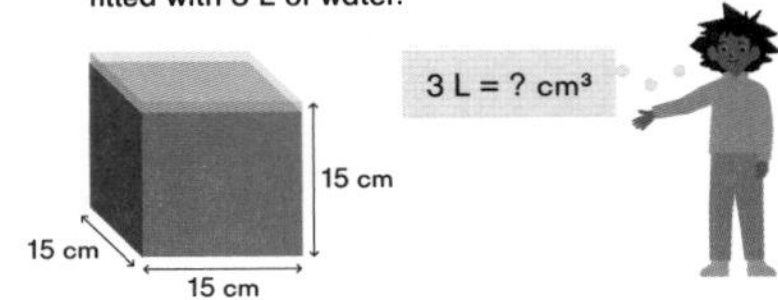

(a) What is the capacity of the container in milliliters?
15 × 15 × 15 = 3,375; 3,375 cm³ = 3,375 mL

(b) How many more milliliters of water is needed for the container to be completely full?
3 L = 3,000 mL
3,375 − 3,000 = 375; 375 mL

4 A cuboid-shaped fish tank measures 30 cm by 15 cm by 20 cm. It is filled with water to a height of 10 cm.

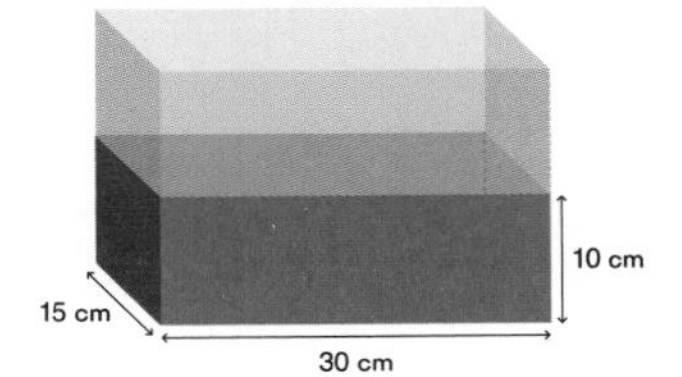

(a) What is the volume of water in the fish tank in cubic centimeters?
30 × 15 × 10 = 4,500; 4,500 cm³

(b) What is the volume of water in liters and milliliters?
4,500 mL; 4 L 500 mL

(c) What is the capacity of the fish tank in liters and milliliters?
30 × 15 × 20 = 9,000; 9 L

(d) What is the volume of the empty space in the tank in cubic centimeters?
9,000 − 4,500 = 4,500; 4,500 cm³

219

5 The area of the bottom side of a cuboid-shaped fish tank is 100 cm². There is $1\frac{1}{2}$ L of water in the tank. What is the height of the water?

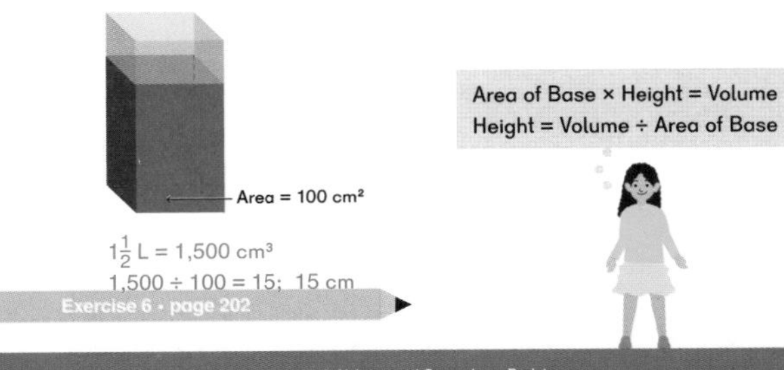

$1\frac{1}{2}$ L = 1,500 cm³
1,500 ÷ 100 = 15; 15 cm

Exercise 6 • page 202

Objective

- Find the volume of a solid by displacement.

Materials

- Liter measuring cup
- Rocks, marbles, or other solids
- 100 mL beakers or liquid measuring cups with mL markings

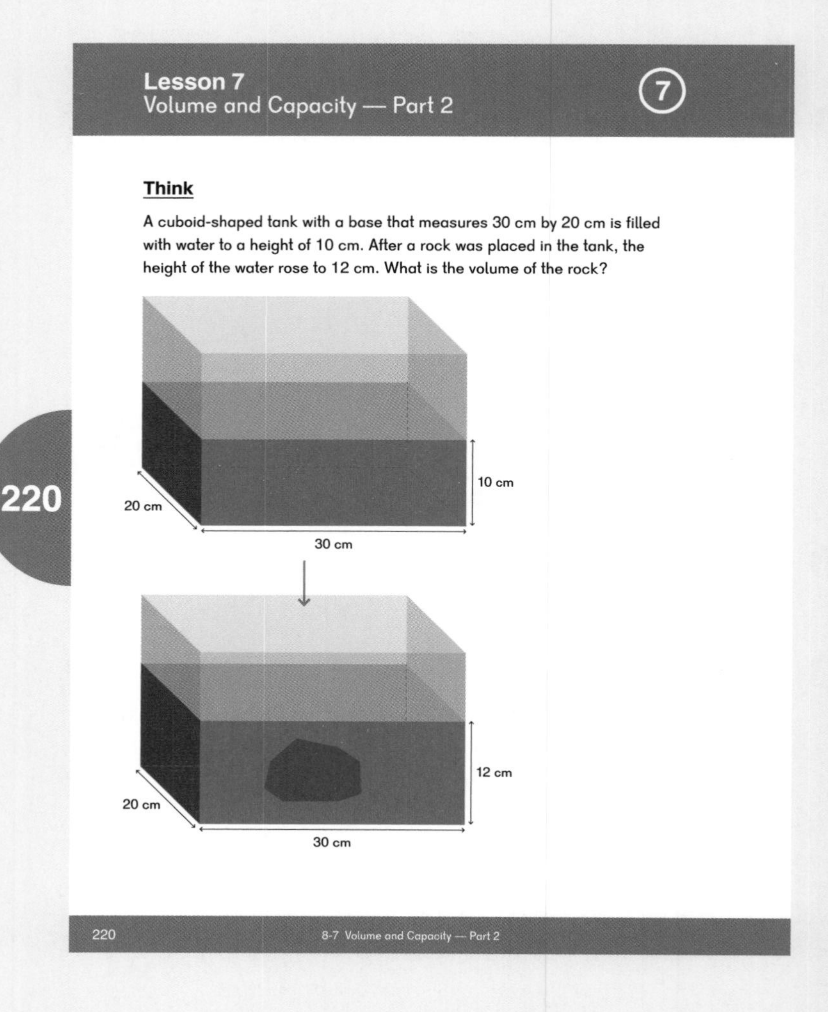

Think

Show students an irregularly shaped object, such as a rock, and ask them how we could find its volume. Ask students what would happen if they filled a bathtub or small pool to the top and then tried to get in. (The tub overflows.)

Provide students with beakers, water, and small solid objects. Have them fill the beakers to 50 mL, add their objects, and note what happens to the water level in the beaker.

Ask students:

- "What is the volume of water in the beaker at first?" (50 mL)
- "What is the volume of water with the object?" (Answers vary.)
- "What is the difference in volume?" (Answers vary.)
- "What do you think the difference in water levels tells us about the object?" (How much space the object takes up, which is its volume.)

If using different objects, have students repeat the experiment with other objects.

Pose the **Think** problem and allow students time to find a solution independently.

Learn

Have students compare the two methods shown in **Learn** with their own solutions from **Think**.

Method 1

If we know the volume of the water with and without the rock, we can subtract to find the volume of the rock.

Method 2

We can also calculate the volume of the rock by finding the volume of a cuboid with a height equal to the difference between the height of the two water levels before and after the rock was placed in the tank.

Do

❶—❸ Discuss the problems with students.

Activity

▲ Investigate Archimedes

A classic story about Archimedes discovering how to use water to find the volume of an object is told in *Archimedes Takes a Bath* by Joan Lexau and *Mr. Archimedes' Bath* by Pamela Allen.

Students may find non-fiction books on Archimedes interesting as well.

Exercise 7 • page 205

221

Learn

Method 1

Volume of the water in the tank before the rock was put in
$= 20 \times 30 \times 10 = 6{,}000\ \text{cm}^3$

Volume of the water and the rock together $= 30 \times 20 \times 12 = 7{,}200\ \text{cm}^3$

Volume of the rock $= 7{,}200 - 6{,}000 = 1{,}200\ \text{cm}^3$

Method 2

2 cm

20 cm

30 cm

Difference between the height of water before and after the rock was put in
$= 12 - 10 = 2$ cm

Volume of rock $= 30 \times 20 \times 2 = 1{,}200\ \text{cm}^3$

The rock has a volume of __1,200__ cm^3.

8-7 Volume and Capacity — Part 2 221

222

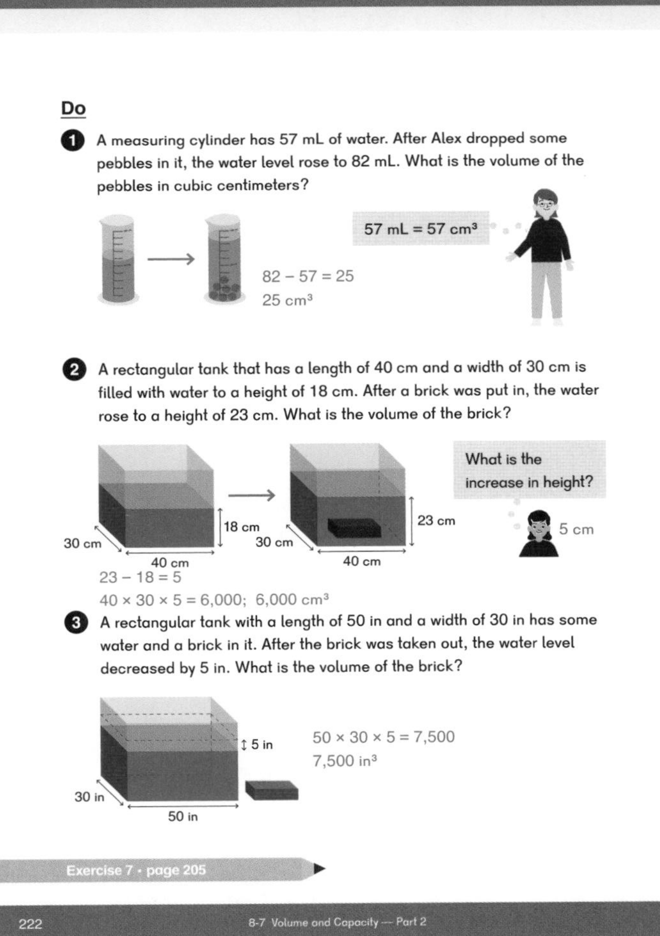

Do

❶ A measuring cylinder has 57 mL of water. After Alex dropped some pebbles in it, the water level rose to 82 mL. What is the volume of the pebbles in cubic centimeters?

57 mL = 57 cm^3

$82 - 57 = 25$
25 cm^3

❷ A rectangular tank that has a length of 40 cm and a width of 30 cm is filled with water to a height of 18 cm. After a brick was put in, the water rose to a height of 23 cm. What is the volume of the brick?

What is the increase in height?

5 cm

18 cm, 30 cm, 40 cm, 23 cm, 30 cm, 40 cm

$23 - 18 = 5$
$40 \times 30 \times 5 = 6{,}000$; 6,000 cm^3

❸ A rectangular tank with a length of 50 in and a width of 30 in has some water and a brick in it. After the brick was taken out, the water level decreased by 5 in. What is the volume of the brick?

5 in, 30 in, 50 in

$50 \times 30 \times 5 = 7{,}500$
7,500 in^3

Exercise 7 • page 205

222 8-7 Volume and Capacity — Part 2

Objective

- Practice finding the volume of solids.

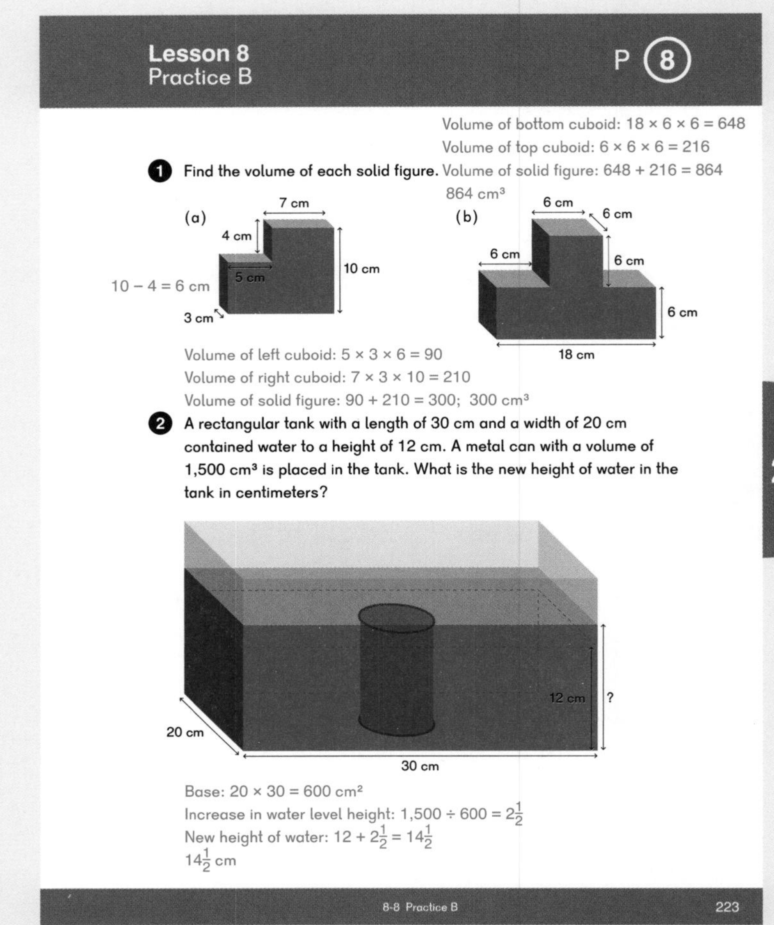
Lesson 8
Practice B
P 8

1 Find the volume of each solid figure.

(a)
7 cm, 4 cm, 5 cm, 10 cm, 3 cm
10 − 4 = 6 cm

Volume of left cuboid: $5 \times 3 \times 6 = 90$
Volume of right cuboid: $7 \times 3 \times 10 = 210$
Volume of solid figure: $90 + 210 = 300$; 300 cm³

(b)
6 cm, 6 cm, 6 cm, 6 cm, 6 cm, 18 cm

Volume of bottom cuboid: $18 \times 6 \times 6 = 648$
Volume of top cuboid: $6 \times 6 \times 6 = 216$
Volume of solid figure: $648 + 216 = 864$
864 cm³

2 A rectangular tank with a length of 30 cm and a width of 20 cm contained water to a height of 12 cm. A metal can with a volume of 1,500 cm³ is placed in the tank. What is the new height of water in the tank in centimeters?

20 cm, 30 cm, 12 cm, ?

Base: $20 \times 30 = 600$ cm²
Increase in water level height: $1,500 \div 600 = 2\frac{1}{2}$
New height of water: $12 + 2\frac{1}{2} = 14\frac{1}{2}$
$14\frac{1}{2}$ cm

8-8 Practice B 223

After students complete the **Practice** in the textbook, have them continue to practice skills using the activity in this lesson.

2 The volume of the object is given and students will have to find the new height. This is the first time the answer is a mixed number.

3 Student need to find the volume of a single object given the displacement of volume by multiple identical objects. They can find the volume of the 8 marbles in all, then divide to find the volume of a single marble.

4 The volume of water stays the same. Find the volume of the rectangular tank first, then find the height of the water in the cube-shaped tank:

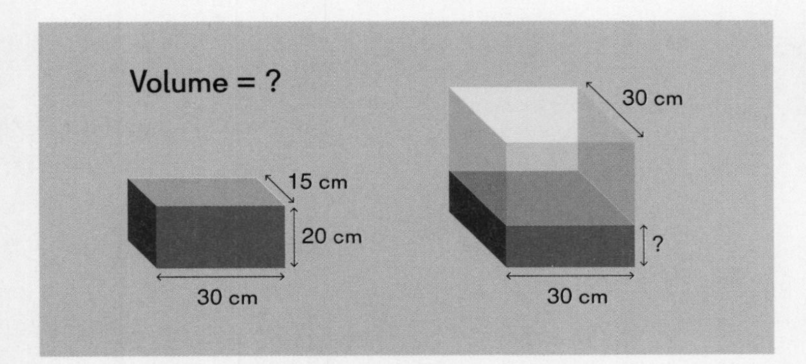

5 2,500 cm³ causes a 2 cm rise in height. The length of the tank is given.

To find the missing width, we can divide:

$\frac{2,500}{20} \div 2 = 2,500 \div 20 \div 2$

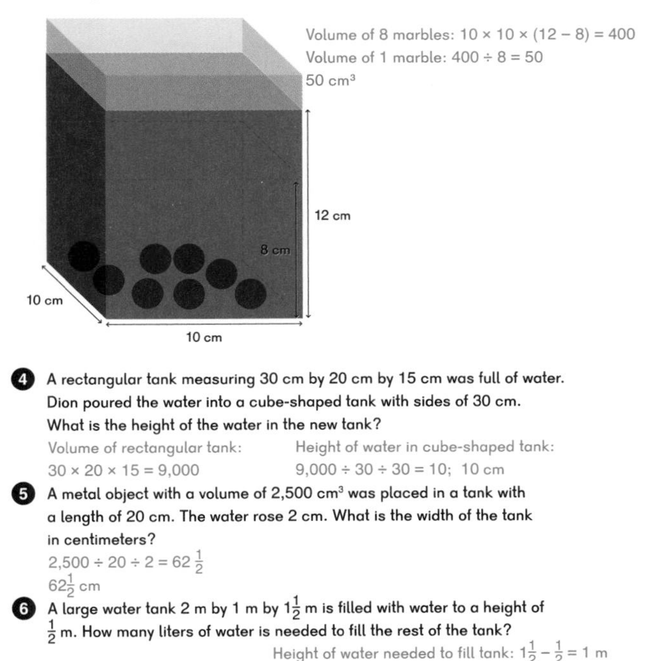

224

3 A rectangular container with a length of 10 cm and a width of 10 cm is filled with water to a height of 8 cm. After 8 identical marbles were added the height of the water rose to 12 cm. What is the volume of one marble?

Volume of 8 marbles: 10 × 10 × (12 − 8) = 400
Volume of 1 marble: 400 ÷ 8 = 50
50 cm³

4 A rectangular tank measuring 30 cm by 20 cm by 15 cm was full of water. Dion poured the water into a cube-shaped tank with sides of 30 cm. What is the height of the water in the new tank?

Volume of rectangular tank: 30 × 20 × 15 = 9,000
Height of water in cube-shaped tank: 9,000 ÷ 30 ÷ 30 = 10; 10 cm

5 A metal object with a volume of 2,500 cm³ was placed in a tank with a length of 20 cm. The water rose 2 cm. What is the width of the tank in centimeters?

$2,500 \div 20 \div 2 = 62\frac{1}{2}$
$62\frac{1}{2}$ cm

6 A large water tank 2 m by 1 m by $1\frac{1}{2}$ m is filled with water to a height of $\frac{1}{2}$ m. How many liters of water is needed to fill the rest of the tank?

Height of water needed to fill tank: $1\frac{1}{2} - \frac{1}{2} = 1$ m
Water needed to fill tank: 2 × 1 × 1 = 2 m³
2 m³ = 2,000 L; 2,000 L

Exercise 8 • page 208

224 8-8 Practice B

Activity

▲ Displacement

Materials: Tank, water, bricks, rocks

Fill a tank halfway with water. Mark the height of the water with a marker or tape. Put a brick or large rock in the tank and mark the new height of the water. Have students find the volume of the brick or rock in several different ways.

Exercise 8 • page 208

Brain Works

★ Checkerboard

Materials: Checkerboard (BLM), 8 counters

Ask students if they can place the 8 counters on the Checkerboard (BLM) such that there is only one in each column, row, and diagonal.

There are multiple solutions. Example solution:

Review 2

Objective

- Review concepts from Chapters 1–8.

Review 2 is an end-of-book review and covers content from Dimensions Math 5A.

Review 2

R 2

1. Find the values. Express each answer in simplest form.

(a) $4\frac{5}{6} + 4\frac{3}{5}$ $9\frac{13}{30}$

(b) $9\frac{7}{10} - 4\frac{5}{6}$ $4\frac{13}{15}$

2. Estimate and then find the actual values, expressed in simplest form.

Estimations may vary. Actual values provided.

(a) 432×65 28,080

(b) $8,671 \times 24$ 208,104

(c) $78 \times 7,342$ 572,676

(d) $8,956 \div 27$ $331\frac{19}{27}$

(e) $3,816 \div 42$ $90\frac{6}{7}$

(f) $98,532 \div 24$ $4,105\frac{1}{2}$

3. Find the values. Express each answer in simplest form.

(a) $12 \times \frac{3}{8}$ $4\frac{1}{2}$

(b) $14 \times \frac{5}{7}$ 10

(c) $\frac{8}{3} \times 24$ 64

(d) $\frac{1}{9} \times \frac{1}{8}$ $\frac{1}{72}$

(e) $\frac{7}{10} \times \frac{5}{21}$ $\frac{1}{6}$

(f) $\frac{8}{5} \times \frac{10}{4}$ 4

(g) $5\frac{5}{6} \times \frac{3}{5}$ $3\frac{1}{2}$

(h) $3\frac{2}{5} \times 3\frac{1}{3}$ $11\frac{1}{3}$

(i) $1\frac{4}{5} \times 2\frac{2}{9}$ 4

(j) $\frac{3}{4} \times \frac{5}{7} \times \frac{4}{3} \times \frac{7}{5}$ 1

(k) $\frac{2}{3} \times 9 + \frac{2}{3} \times 3$ 8

(l) $15 - 8 \times \frac{1}{2} + 2\frac{4}{5}$ $13\frac{4}{5}$

(m) $3\frac{6}{7} \times 8 - 1\frac{1}{4} \times 8$ $20\frac{6}{7}$

(n) $\frac{2}{4} \times (3\frac{1}{2} - 2\frac{2}{3}) + 6\frac{1}{2}$ $6\frac{11}{12}$

4. Find the missing numbers.

(a) $\frac{7}{8} \times 1\frac{1}{7} =$ 1

(b) $\frac{4}{5} \times$ $\frac{5}{4}$ $= 1$

(c) $\frac{1}{7}$ $\times 7 = 1$

(d) $1 = 4\frac{2}{3} \times$ $\frac{3}{14}$

5. Find the missing numbers.

(a) $\frac{3}{5}$ h = 36 min

(b) $\frac{7}{10}$ km = 700 m

(c) $3\frac{1}{4}$ gal = 13 qt

(d) $5\frac{3}{4}$ ft = 69 in

(e) $3\frac{1}{4}$ L = 3,250 mL

(f) $2\frac{3}{5}$ m = 260 cm

Alternate solutions for some problems:

7

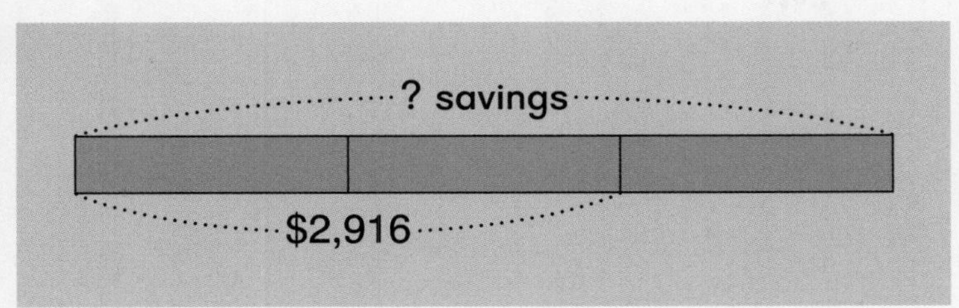

2 units ⟶ \$2,916
1 unit ⟶ $\frac{\$2,916}{2}$ = \$1,458
3 units ⟶ \$1,458 × 3 = \$4,374

She had \$4,374 at first.

8

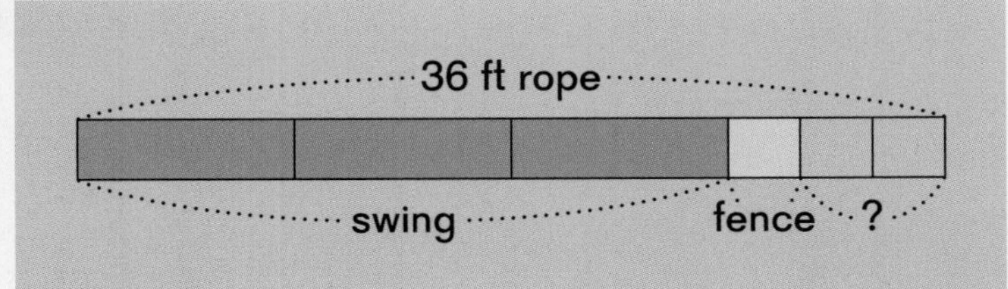

4 units ⟶ 36 ft

1 unit ⟶ $\frac{36}{4} = 9$ ft

$\frac{2}{3}$ unit ⟶ $\frac{2}{3} \times 9 = 6$ ft

He had 6 ft of rope left.

11 4 dinner rolls ⟶ $\frac{2}{3}$ cup
1 dinner roll ⟶ $\frac{2}{3} \div 4 = \frac{2}{3} \times \frac{1}{4} = \frac{1}{6}$ cup

1 dinner roll uses $\frac{1}{6}$ cup of flour.

12

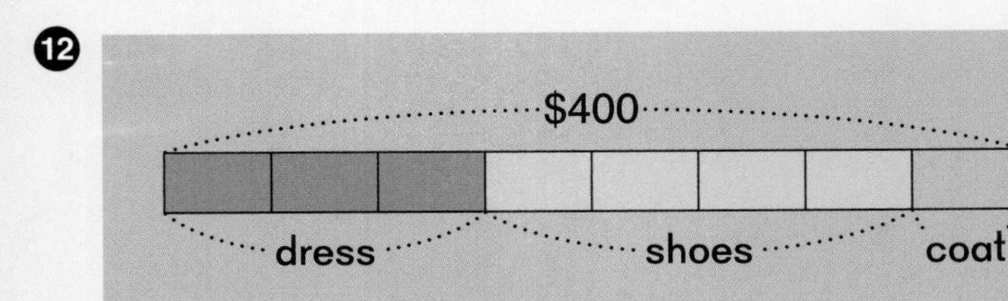

8 units ⟶ \$400
1 unit ⟶ $\frac{\$400}{8}$ = \$50

The coat cost \$50.

227

6 Find the values. Express each answer in simplest form.

(a)	$\frac{1}{8} \div 5$	$\frac{1}{40}$
(b)	$\frac{1}{3} \div 12$	$\frac{1}{36}$
(c)	$\frac{9}{10} \div 3$	$\frac{3}{10}$
(d)	$\frac{3}{5} \div 6$	$\frac{1}{10}$
(e)	$\frac{15}{9} \div 5$	$\frac{1}{3}$
(f)	$\frac{1}{9} \div 4$	$\frac{1}{36}$
(g)	$6 \div \frac{1}{10}$	60
(h)	$12 \div \frac{1}{4}$	48
(i)	$6 \div \frac{3}{8}$	16
(j)	$9 \div \frac{3}{7}$	21
(k)	$\frac{5}{7} \div 10 \times \frac{20}{3}$	$\frac{10}{21}$
(l)	$\frac{3}{5} \times 10 \div \frac{1}{3}$	18
(m)	$4\frac{3}{4} - 2 \div \frac{1}{2}$	$\frac{3}{4}$
(n)	$7 \div (\frac{5}{6} - \frac{2}{3}) \times 75$	3,150

228

7 Gina spent $\frac{2}{3}$ of her savings on a car. The car cost \$2,916. How much were her savings to begin with?
$2,916 \div \frac{2}{3} = 4,374$
\$4,374

8 Barry had a rope that was 36 ft long. He used $\frac{3}{4}$ of it to make a swing and $\frac{1}{3}$ of the remainder to repair a fence. How much rope does he have left?
$\frac{3}{4} \times 36 = 27$; $36 - 27 = 9$; $\frac{2}{3} \times 9 = 6$; 6 ft

9 A carpenter cut a 21-ft long board into pieces that are each $\frac{3}{4}$ ft long. How many $\frac{3}{4}$-ft long pieces are there?
$21 \div \frac{3}{4} = 28$
28 pieces

10 $\frac{4}{5}$ kg of pumpkin seeds are placed equally into 8 bags. How many kilograms of pumpkin seeds are in each bag?
$\frac{4}{5} \div 8 = \frac{1}{10}$; $\frac{1}{10}$ kg

11 It takes $\frac{2}{3}$ cups of flour to make 4 dinner rolls. How much flour does it take to make 1 dinner roll?
$\frac{2}{3} \div 4 = \frac{1}{6}$; $\frac{1}{6}$ cups

12 Sasha had \$400. She spent $\frac{3}{8}$ of it on a dress and $\frac{4}{5}$ of the remainder on shoes. She spent what was left on a coat. How much did the coat cost?
Spent on dress: $400 \times \frac{3}{8} = 150$; Remainder: $400 - 150 = 250$
Spent on shoes: $250 \times \frac{4}{5} = 200$; Left: $250 - 200 = 50$; \$50

13 $\frac{2}{3}$ of the coins in Caleb's coin collection are gold coins, $\frac{1}{3}$ of the remainder are silver coins, and the rest are copper coins. He has 100 copper coins. How many coins does he have in his collection?
1 smaller unit ⟶ $100 \div 2 = 50$; 3 smaller units ⟶ $3 \times 50 = 150$
1 larger unit ⟶ 150; 3 larger units ⟶ $3 \times 150 = 450$; 450 coins

14 $\frac{3}{7}$ of Eli's stamps were French stamps and the rest were Spanish stamps. He gave $\frac{1}{3}$ of his Spanish stamps to Mia. What fraction of the stamps that he started with does he have left?
Stamps given away: $(1 - \frac{3}{7}) \times \frac{1}{3} = \frac{4}{21}$; Fraction of stamps left: $1 - \frac{4}{21} = \frac{17}{21}$

13 From the bar model, students can see that $\frac{1}{3}$ of the remaining coins means each unit can be divided into thirds.

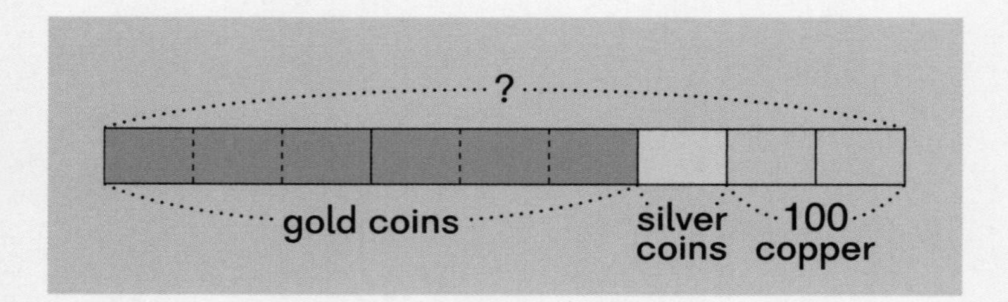

2 units ⟶ 100 coins
1 unit ⟶ $\frac{100}{2}$ = 50 coins
9 units ⟶ 50 coins × 9 = 450 coins

He had 450 coins in all.

14

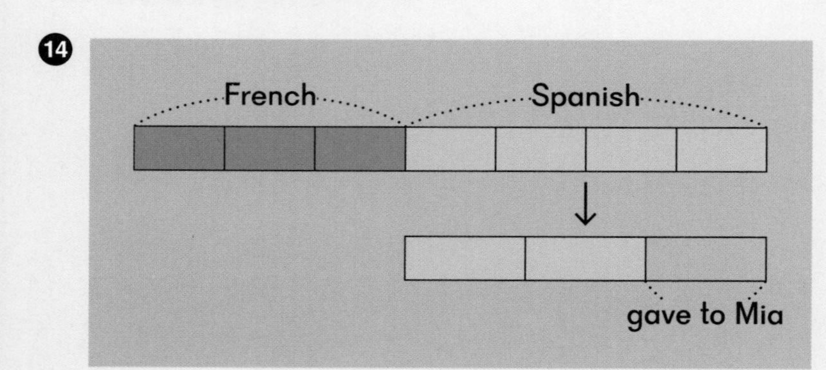

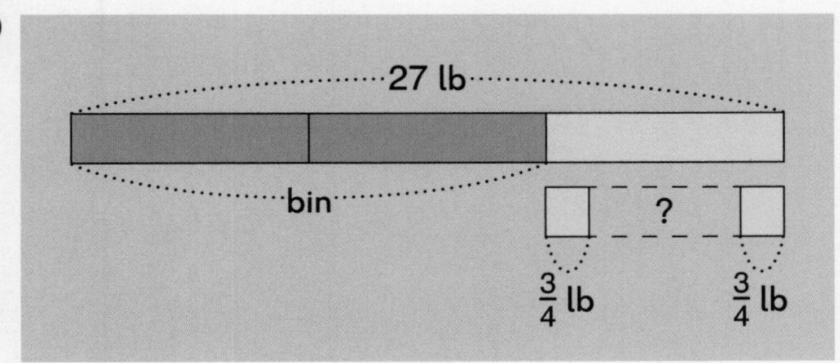

3 units $\longrightarrow$ 27

1 unit $\longrightarrow \frac{27}{3} = 9$

Number of bags: $9 \div \frac{3}{4} = 12$

16

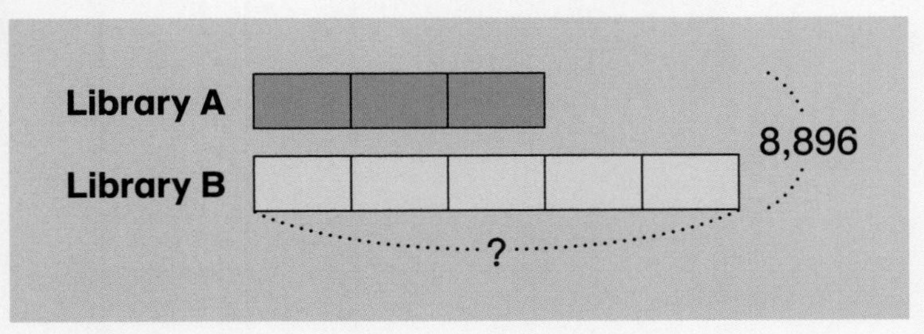

15 An employee at a market has 27 lb of grapes. She puts $\frac{2}{3}$ of the grapes in a bin and packs the remainder of the grapes into bags. Each bag has $\frac{3}{4}$ lb of grapes. How many bags of grapes are there?

Grapes in bin: $\frac{2}{3} \times 27 = 18$ lb; Remainder: $27 - 18 = 9$ lb

Bags of grapes: $9 \div \frac{3}{4} = 12$; 12 bags

16 There were 8,896 books in two libraries. After $\frac{1}{4}$ of the books were transferred from Library A to Library B, there were $\frac{3}{5}$ as many books in Library A as in Library B. How many books are now in Library B?

1 unit $\longrightarrow 8{,}896 \div 8 = 1{,}112$

5 units $\longrightarrow 5 \times 1{,}112 = 5{,}560$; 5,560 books

17 Find the area of each figure.

(a)

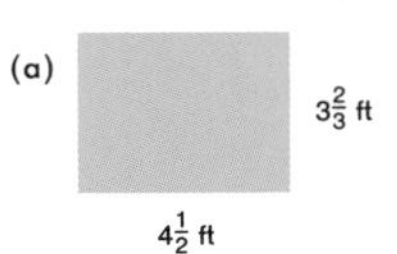

$4\frac{1}{2} \times 3\frac{2}{3} = 16\frac{1}{2}$; $16\frac{1}{2}$ ft²

(b)

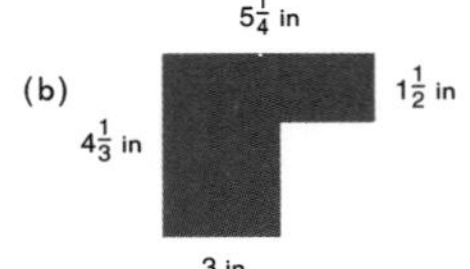

$4\frac{1}{3} \times 3 + 1\frac{1}{2} \times (5\frac{1}{4} - 3) = 16\frac{3}{8}$; $16\frac{3}{8}$ in²

(c)

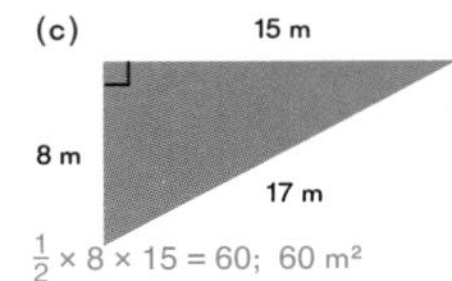

$\frac{1}{2} \times 8 \times 15 = 60$; 60 m²

(d)

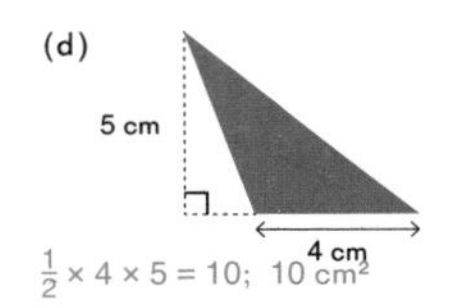

$\frac{1}{2} \times 4 \times 5 = 10$; 10 cm²

(e)

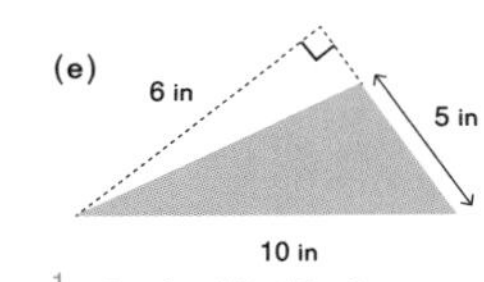

$\frac{1}{2} \times 5 \times 6 = 15$; 15 in²

(f)

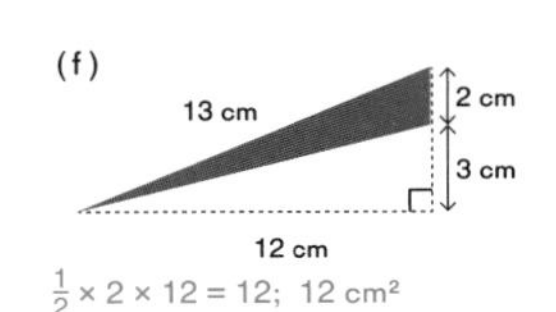

$\frac{1}{2} \times 2 \times 12 = 12$; 12 cm²

18 Find the shaded area of each figure.

(a)

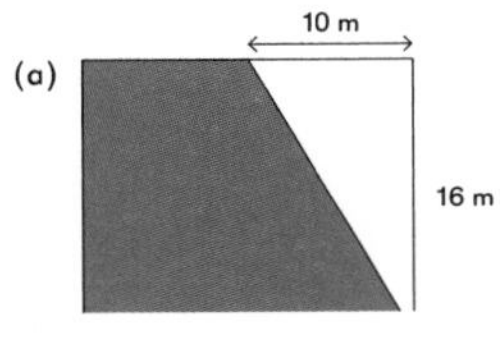

Rectangle: $20 \times 16 = 320$

Triangle: $\frac{1}{2} \times 10 \times 16 = 80$

$320 - 80 = 240$; 240 m²

(b)

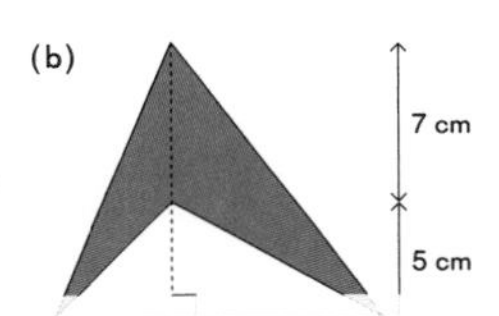

Large triangle: $\frac{1}{2} \times 18 \times 12 = 108$

Small triangle: $\frac{1}{2} \times 18 \times 5 = 45$

$108 - 45 = 63$; 63 cm²

19 Find the volume of each solid figure. Figure (a) is a cube.

(a)

$15 \times 15 \times 15 = 3{,}375$; 3,375 in³

(b)

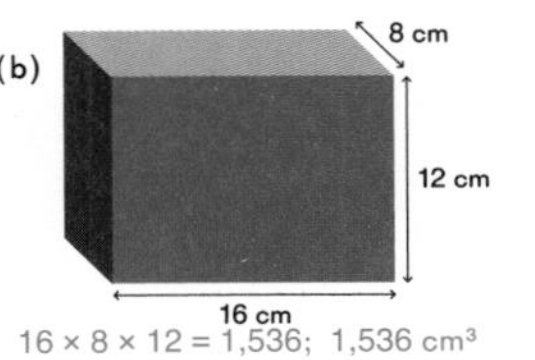

$16 \times 8 \times 12 = 1{,}536$; 1,536 cm³

(c)

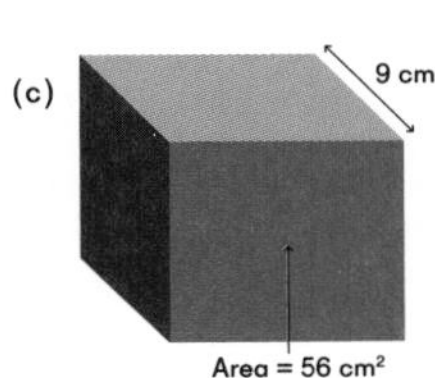

$56 \times 9 = 504$

504 cm³

(d)

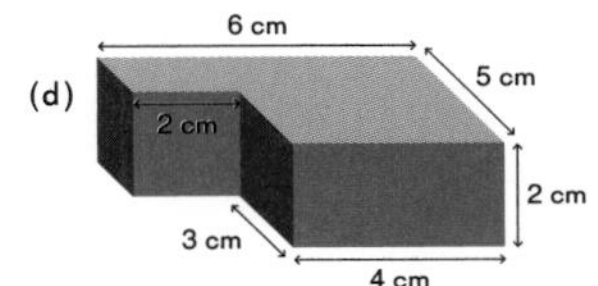

Left cuboid: $2 \times (5 - 3) \times 2 = 8$

Right cuboid: $4 \times 5 \times 2 = 40$

$8 + 40 = 48$; 48 cm³

Exercise 9 • page 212

20 The cuboid has a volume of 960 cm³. Find the length of the Edge AB.

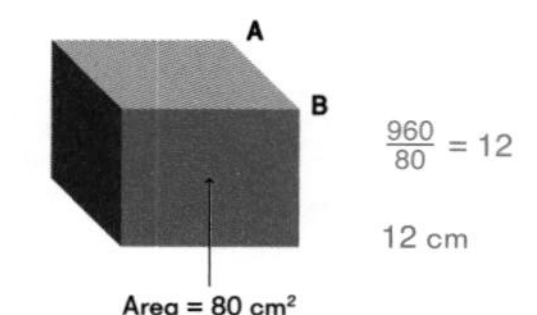

$\frac{960}{80} = 12$

12 cm

21 A rectangular container that measures 24 cm by 12 cm by 20 cm is filled to the top with water. 2 L of water are emptied from the container. How much water is left in the container?

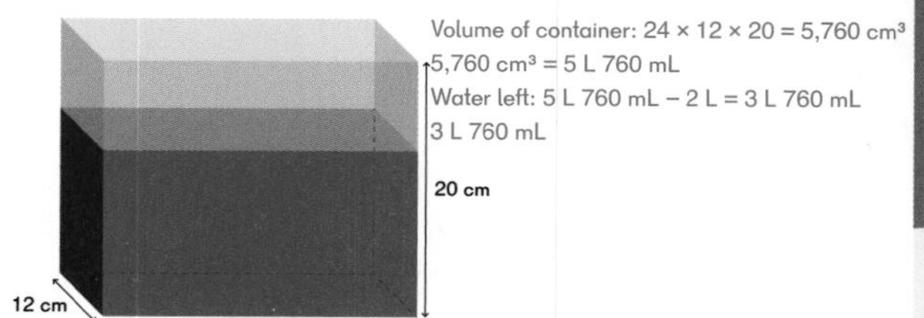

Volume of container: $24 \times 12 \times 20 = 5{,}760$ cm³

5,760 cm³ = 5 L 760 mL

Water left: 5 L 760 mL − 2 L = 3 L 760 mL

3 L 760 mL

22 A rectangular fish tank has a length of 48 in, width of 12 in, and height of 16 in. It is filled with water to a height of 10 in. After some rocks are placed in the tank the water level rose to a height of 14 in. What is the volume of the rocks?

Increase in volume of water: $48 \times 12 \times (14 - 10) = 2{,}304$

2,304 in³

Exercise 9 • page 212

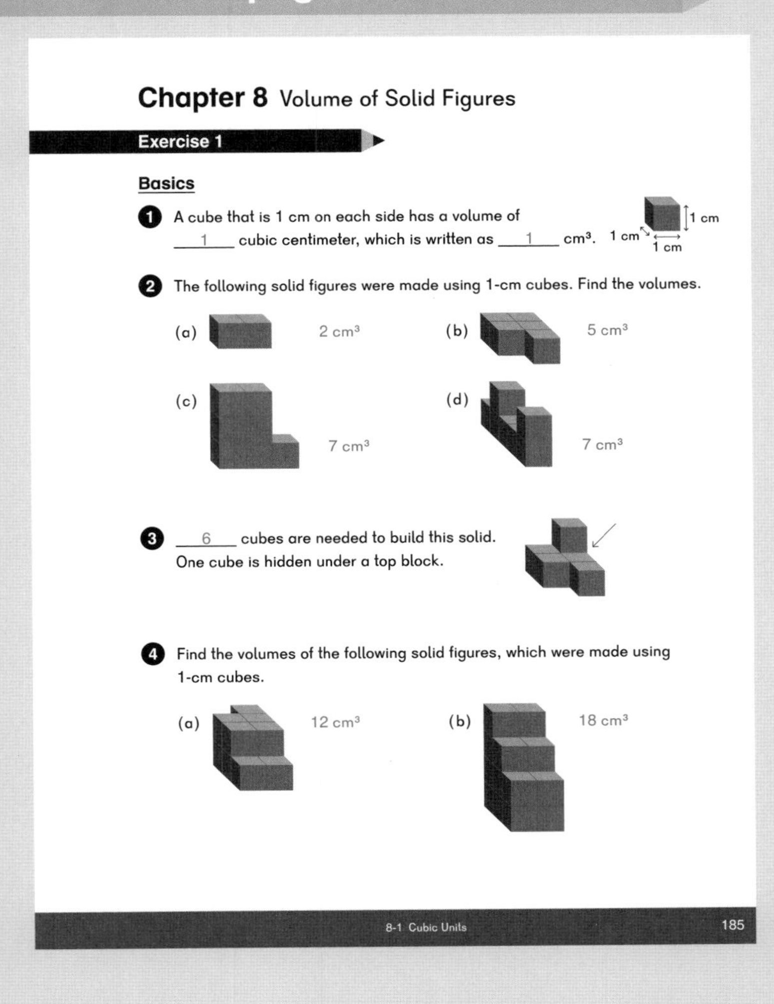

Chapter 8 Volume of Solid Figures

Exercise 1

Basics

1. A cube that is 1 cm on each side has a volume of __1__ cubic centimeter, which is written as __1__ cm³.

2. The following solid figures were made using 1-cm cubes. Find the volumes.

(a) 2 cm³ (b) 5 cm³

(c) 7 cm³ (d) 7 cm³

3. __6__ cubes are needed to build this solid.
One cube is hidden under a top block.

4. Find the volumes of the following solid figures, which were made using 1-cm cubes.

(a) 12 cm³ (b) 18 cm³

8-1 Cubic Units 185

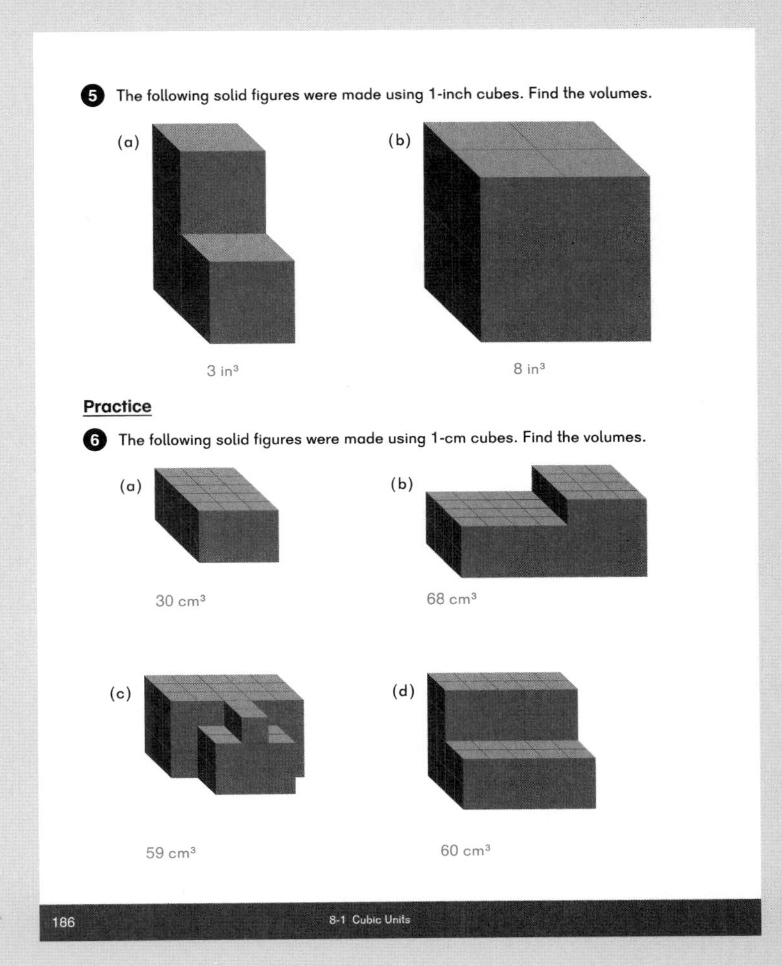

5. The following solid figures were made using 1-inch cubes. Find the volumes.

(a) 3 in³ (b) 8 in³

Practice

6. The following solid figures were made using 1-cm cubes. Find the volumes.

(a) 30 cm³ (b) 68 cm³

(c) 59 cm³ (d) 60 cm³

186 8-1 Cubic Units

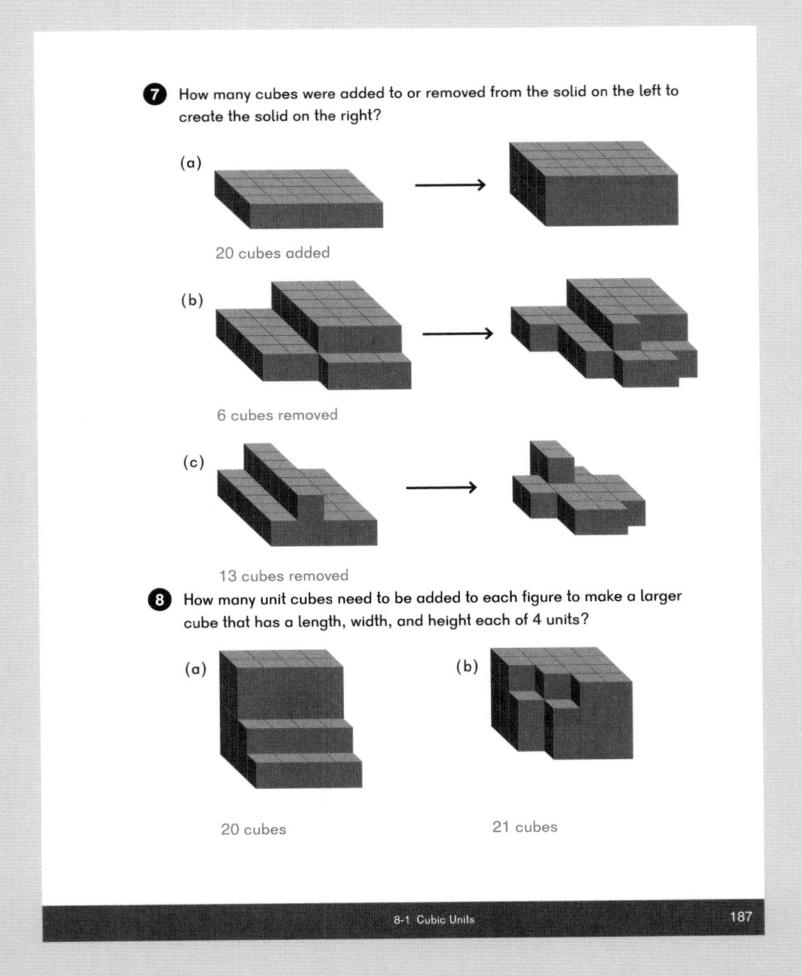

7. How many cubes were added to or removed from the solid on the left to create the solid on the right?

(a) 20 cubes added

(b) 6 cubes removed

(c) 13 cubes removed

8. How many unit cubes need to be added to each figure to make a larger cube that has a length, width, and height each of 4 units?

(a) 20 cubes (b) 21 cubes

8-1 Cubic Units 187

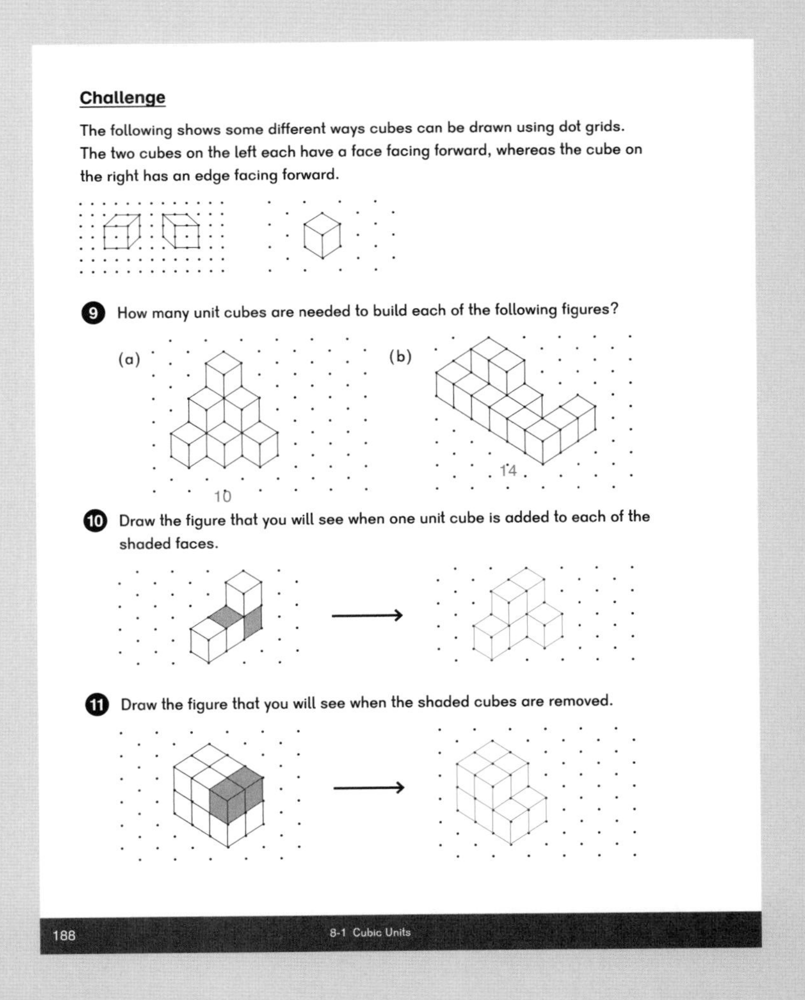

Challenge

The following shows some different ways cubes can be drawn using dot grids. The two cubes on the left each have a face facing forward, whereas the cube on the right has an edge facing forward.

9. How many unit cubes are needed to build each of the following figures?

(a) 10 (b) 14

10. Draw the figure that you will see when one unit cube is added to each of the shaded faces.

11. Draw the figure that you will see when the shaded cubes are removed.

188 8-1 Cubic Units

Exercise 2 • pages 189–191

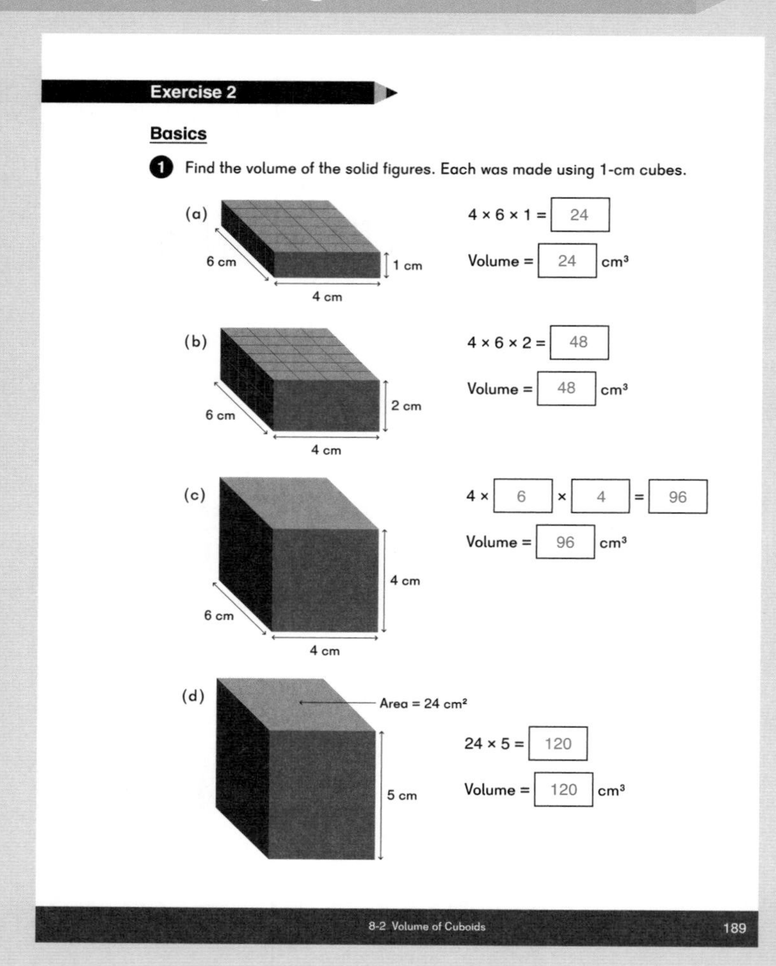

Exercise 2

Basics

1. Find the volume of the solid figures. Each was made using 1-cm cubes.

(a) 6 cm, 4 cm, 1 cm

$4 \times 6 \times 1 =$ 24

Volume = 24 cm³

(b) 6 cm, 4 cm, 2 cm

$4 \times 6 \times 2 =$ 48

Volume = 48 cm³

(c) 6 cm, 4 cm, 4 cm

$4 \times$ 6 $\times$ 4 $=$ 96

Volume = 96 cm³

(d) Area = 24 cm², 5 cm

$24 \times 5 =$ 120

Volume = 120 cm³

8-2 Volume of Cuboids 189

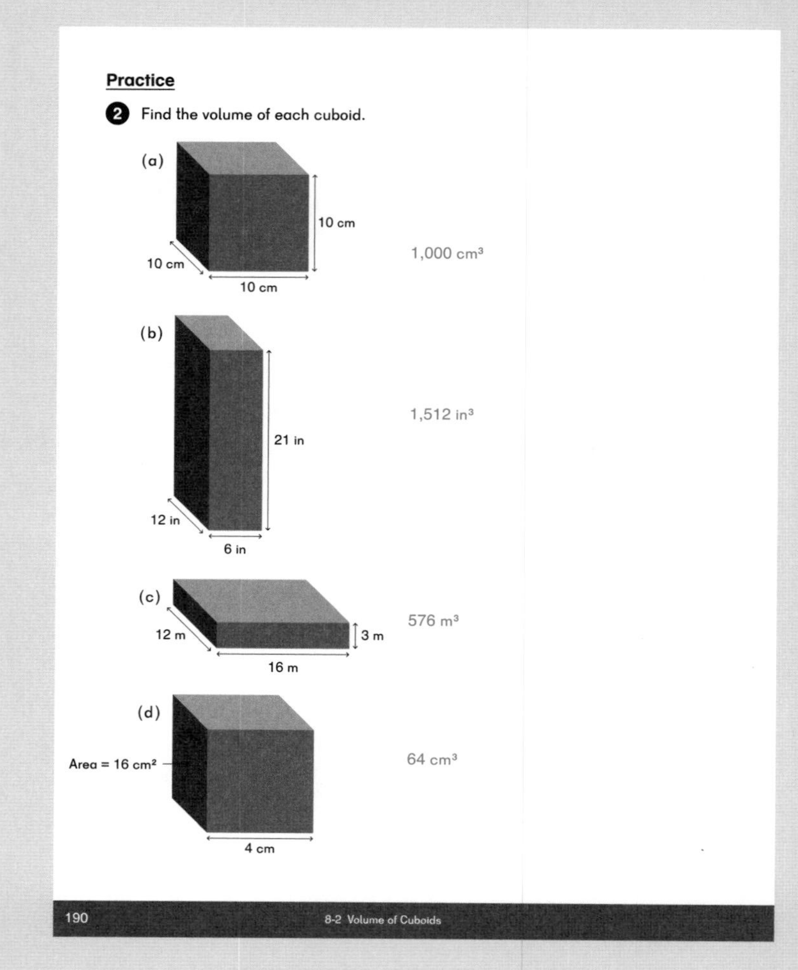

Practice

2. Find the volume of each cuboid.

(a) 10 cm, 10 cm, 10 cm — 1,000 cm³

(b) 12 in, 6 in, 21 in — 1,512 in³

(c) 12 m, 16 m, 3 m — 576 m³

(d) Area = 16 cm², 4 cm — 64 cm³

190 8-2 Volume of Cuboids

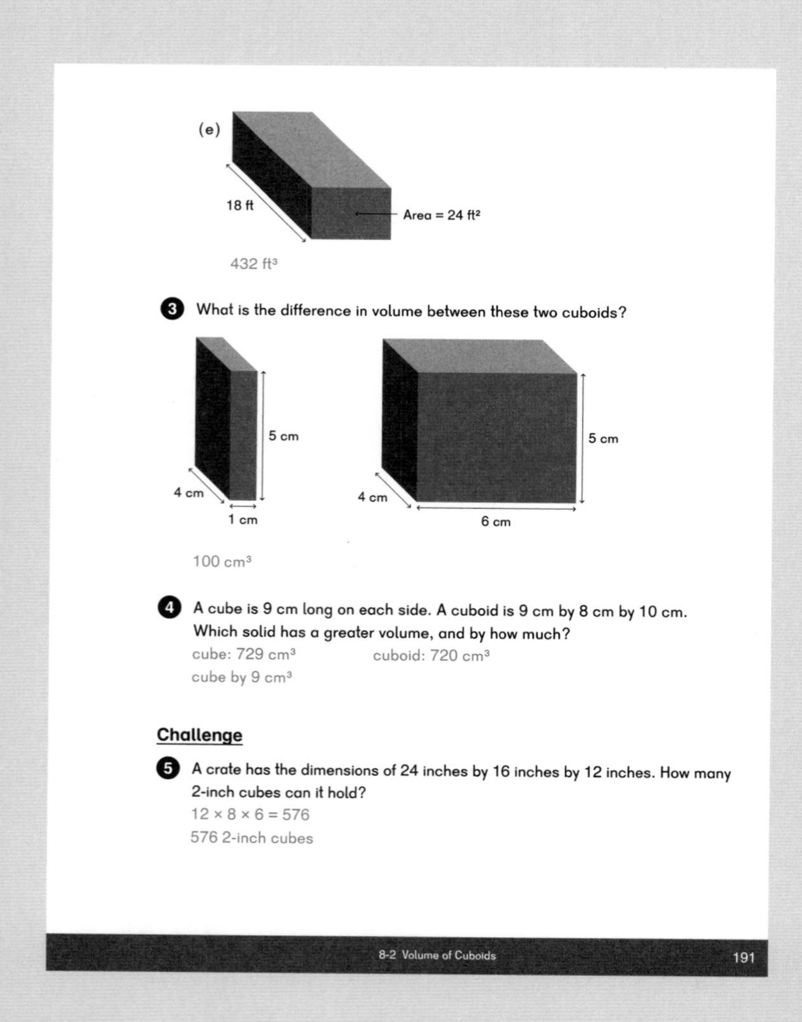

(e) 18 ft, Area = 24 ft²

432 ft³

3. What is the difference in volume between these two cuboids?

4 cm, 1 cm, 5 cm — 4 cm, 6 cm, 5 cm

100 cm³

4. A cube is 9 cm long on each side. A cuboid is 9 cm by 8 cm by 10 cm. Which solid has a greater volume, and by how much?

cube: 729 cm³ cuboid: 720 cm³

cube by 9 cm³

Challenge

5. A crate has the dimensions of 24 inches by 16 inches by 12 inches. How many 2-inch cubes can it hold?

$12 \times 8 \times 6 = 576$

576 2-inch cubes

8-2 Volume of Cuboids 191

Exercise 3 • pages 192–194

Exercise 3

Basics

1. The volume of this cuboid is 96 cm³. The bottom face is 6 cm by 4 cm. What is the height of the cuboid?

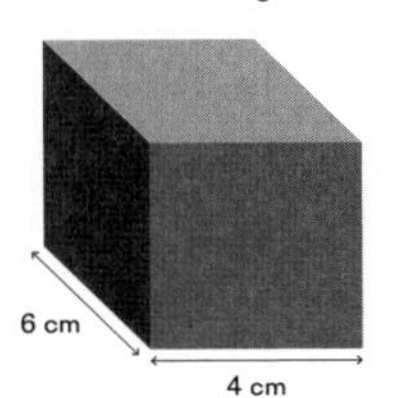

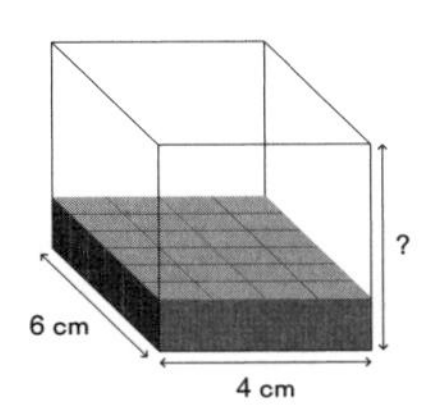

Number of 1-cm cubes in the bottom layer: 6×4

Number of layers of cubes: $96 \div (6 \times 4) = \frac{96}{6 \times 4} =$ [4]

Height = [4] cm

2. The volume of this cuboid is 432 cm³. Its height is 6 cm and its length is 12 cm. What is the width of the cuboid?

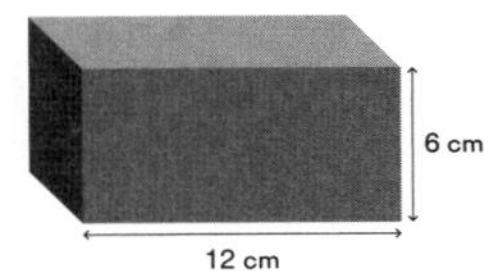

$12 \times 6 \times \text{Width} = 432$

Width = $\frac{432}{12 \times 6} =$ [6]

Width = [6] cm

3. The volume of a cuboid is 84 cm³. The top face has an area of 28 cm². What is the height of the cuboid?

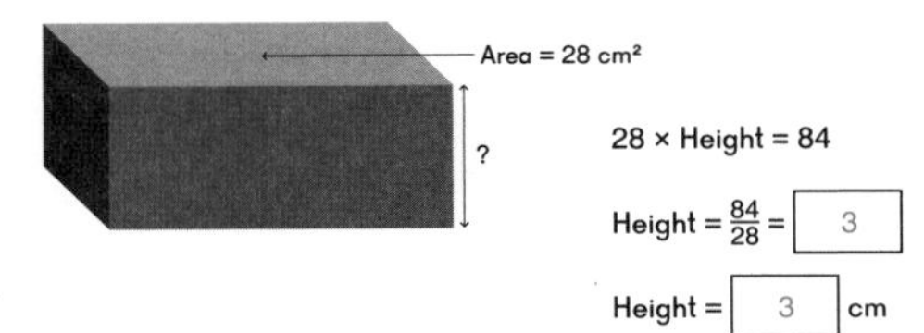

$28 \times \text{Height} = 84$

Height = $\frac{84}{28} =$ [3]

Height = [3] cm

Practice

4. Find the length of the unknown edge of each cuboid.

(a) Volume = 600 cm³

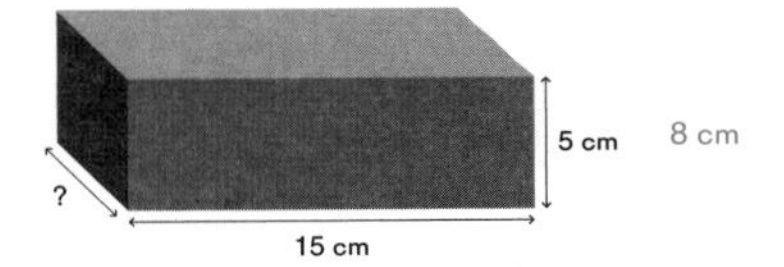

8 cm

(b) Volume = 352 in³

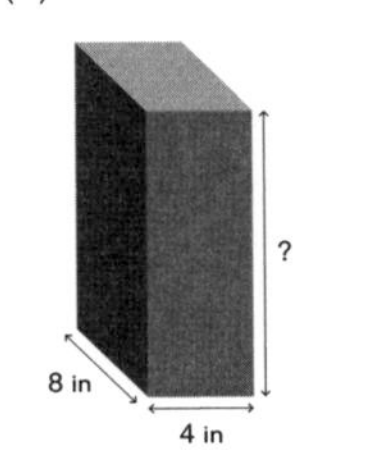

11 in

(c) Volume = 252 m³

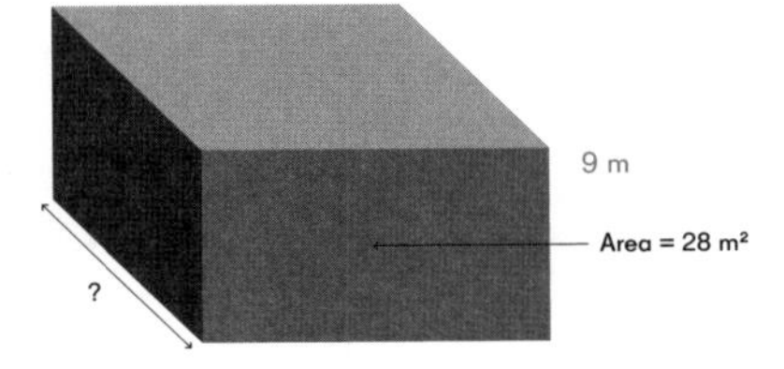

9 m

(d) Volume = 540 cm³

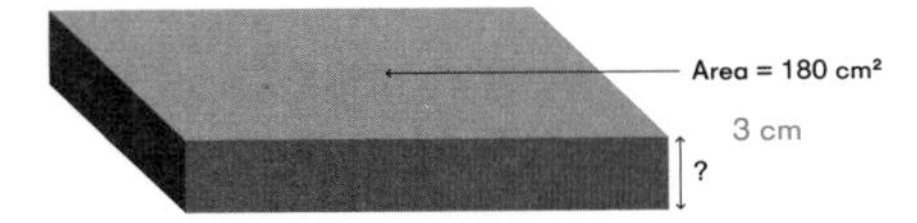

3 cm

5. A shipping container is 20 ft long and 8 ft wide with a volume of 1,360 ft³. How high is it in feet?

$\frac{1,360}{20 \times 8} = 8\frac{1}{2}$

$8\frac{1}{2}$ ft

Challenge

6. A rectangular container has a volume of 468 cm³. The base is a square with an area of 36 cm². How many 2-cm cubes can fit in the container?

Height: 13 cm

6 2-cm cubes can fit along the height and 3 along the width and length.

$3 \times 3 \times 6 = 54$

54 2-cm cubes

Exercise 4

Check

1. The following solid figures were made using 1-cm cubes. Find the volumes.

(a) (b)

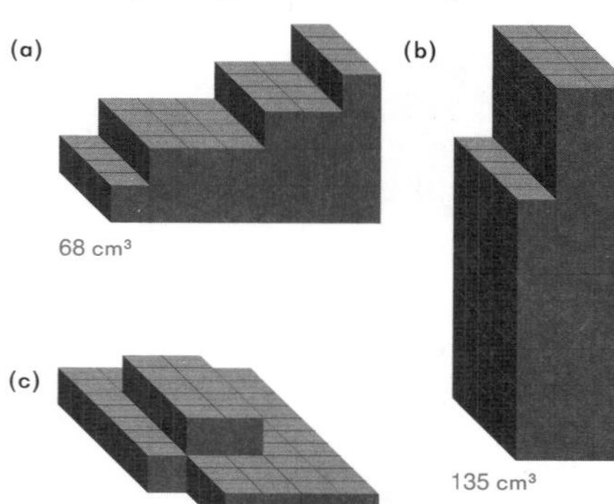

68 cm³

135 cm³

(c)

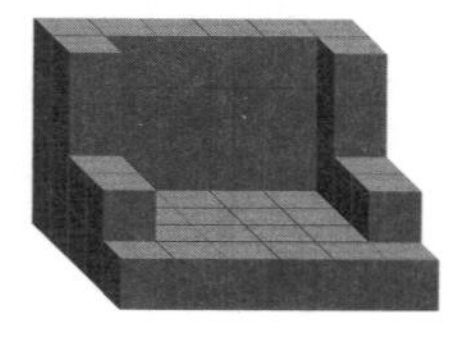

57 cm³

2. How many cubes need to be added to the figure below to make a cuboid with a base area of 30 square units and a height of 4 units?

62 cubes

3. Find the volume of each cuboid.

(a) (b)

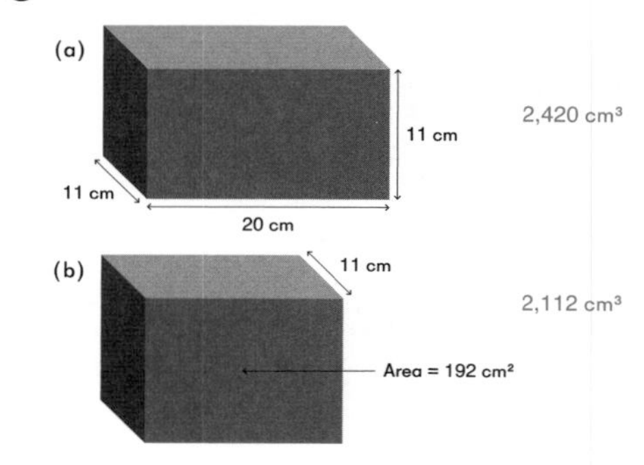

(a) 2,420 cm³

(b) 2,112 cm³

4. Find the length of the unknown edge of each cuboid.

(a) Volume = 2,100 cm³

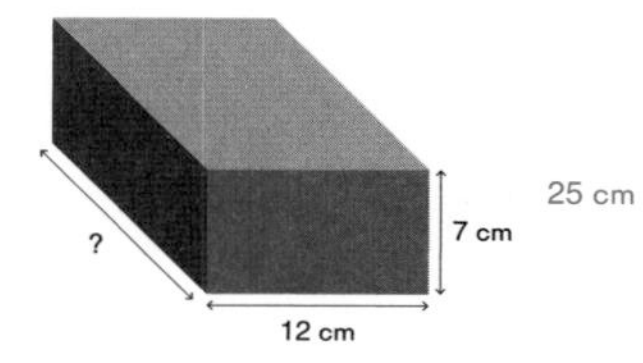

25 cm

(b) Volume = 1,920 cm³

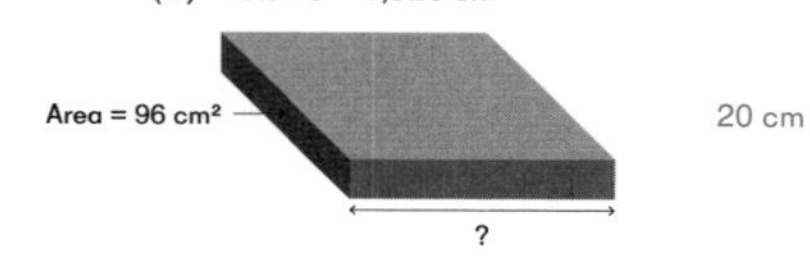

20 cm

5. The base of a crate has an area of 1,200 ft². The volume of the crate is 30,000 ft³. What is its height?

$\frac{30,000}{1,200} = 25$

25 ft

6. A solid is made up of 8 cubes each with an edge of 4 cm. What is the volume of the solid?

8 × 4 × 4 × 4 = 512

512 cm³

7. Each layer of a structure forms a square. The bottom layer has 100 1-cm cubes. The next layer up has 81 cubes, and the next layer up has 64 cubes. This pattern continues until the top layer has 16 cubes.

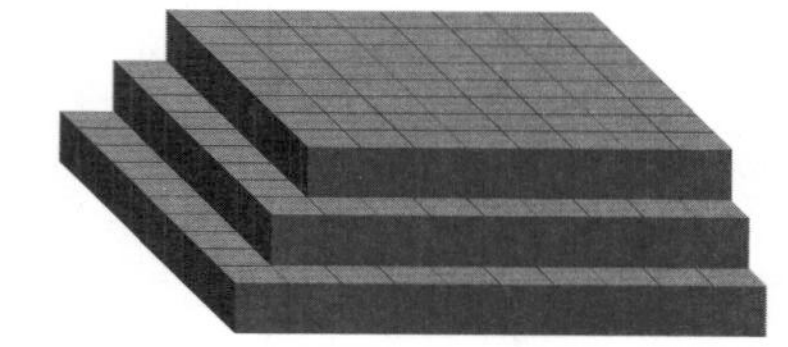

(a) What is the volume of the entire structure?

100 + 81 + 64 + 49 + 36 + 25 + 16 = 371

371 cm³

(b) How many more cubes need to be added to have a larger cube with sides 10 cm long?

10 × 10 × 10 = 1,000

1,000 − 371 = 629

629 more cubes

Challenge

8. 3 metal cubes are 3 cm, 4 cm, and 5 cm long. They were melted and recast into one new cube. What is the length of the new cube?

(3 × 3 × 3) + (4 × 4 × 4) + (5 × 5 × 5) = 27 + 64 + 125 = 216

216 is less than 1,000, so it will be a length between 6 and 9.

Students can try 6 × 6 × 6 and see that works.

6 cm

9. How many 2-cm cubes can be put in a rectangular container measuring 20 cm by 15 cm by 12 cm?

The number of cubes along the 20 cm edge is 10, along the 12-cm edge is 6, and the greatest number along the 15 cm edge is 7.

10 × 6 × 7 = 420

420 2-cm cubes

10. Twenty-four 4-cm cubes are used to make a solid. If 2-cm cubes were used instead, how many cubes would be needed?

4 × 4 × 4 = 64, and 2 × 2 × 2 = 8. The 4-cm cube is 8 times larger.

So 8 times as many 2-cm cubes are needed.

8 × 24 = 192

192 2-cm cubes

Exercise 5 • pages 199–201

Exercise 5

Basics

1. A block with a width of 6 cm, a length of 9 cm, and a height of 7 cm is placed on top of another block with the same width, but with a length of 15 cm and a height of 5 cm. What is the volume of the structure?

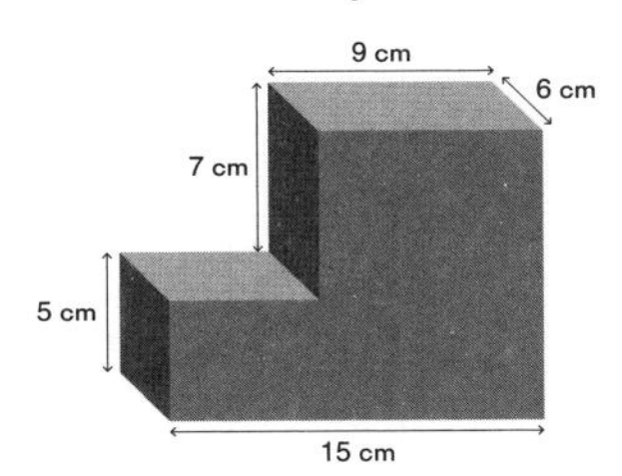

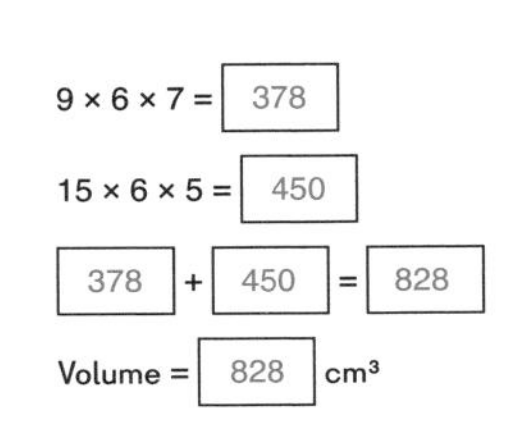

$9 \times 6 \times 7 =$ 378

$15 \times 6 \times 5 =$ 450

378 + 450 = 828

Volume = 828 cm³

2. Two cubes with lengths of 5 cm are cut from a cuboid that is 12 cm by 5 cm by 15 cm. What is the volume of the remaining solid?

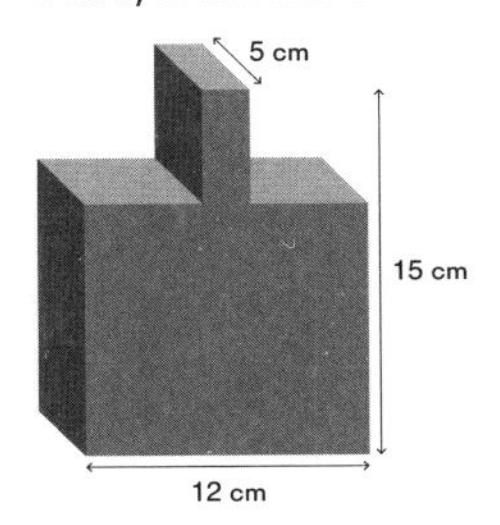

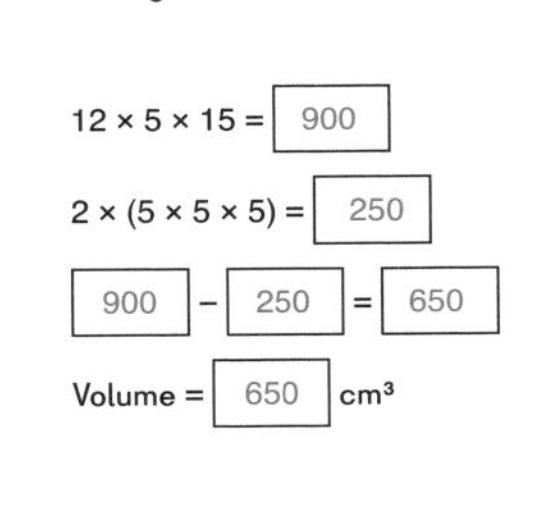

$12 \times 5 \times 15 =$ 900

$2 \times (5 \times 5 \times 5) =$ 250

900 − 250 = 650

Volume = 650 cm³

Practice

Methods may vary.

3. Find the volume of each solid figure.

(a)

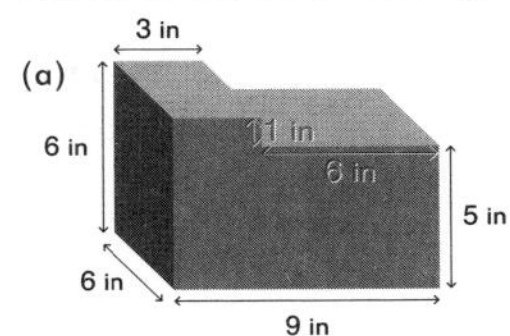

$(9 \times 6 \times 6) - (6 \times 6 \times 1)$
$= 324 - 36$
$= 288$

288 in³

(b)

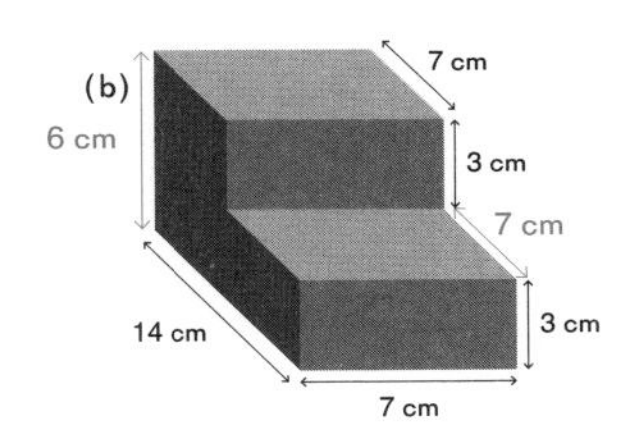

$(7 \times 14 \times 3) + (7 \times 7 \times 3)$
$= 294 + 147$
$= 441$

441 cm³

(c)

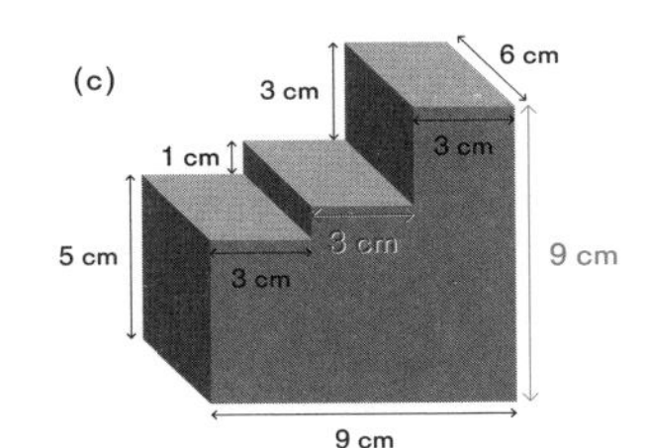

$(9 \times 6 \times 9) - (3 \times 6 \times 4) - (3 \times 6 \times 3)$
$= 486 - 72 - 54$
$= 360$

360 cm³

(d)

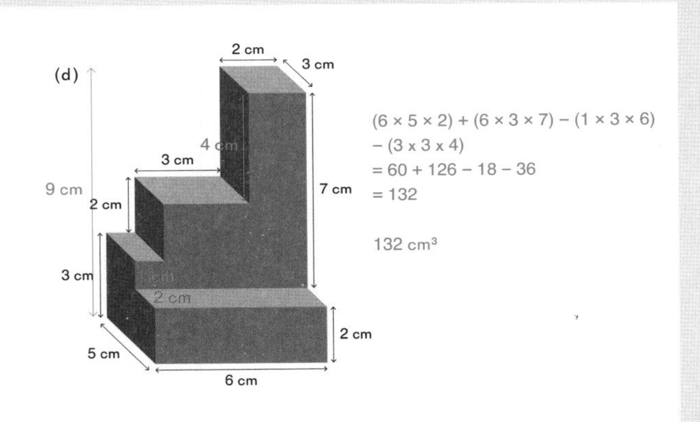

$(6 \times 5 \times 2) + (6 \times 3 \times 7) - (1 \times 3 \times 6)$
$- (3 \times 3 \times 4)$
$= 60 + 126 - 18 - 36$
$= 132$

132 cm³

4. A cuboid has a cuboid hole in it. The front and back faces of the hole are squares. Find the volume of the remaining solid.

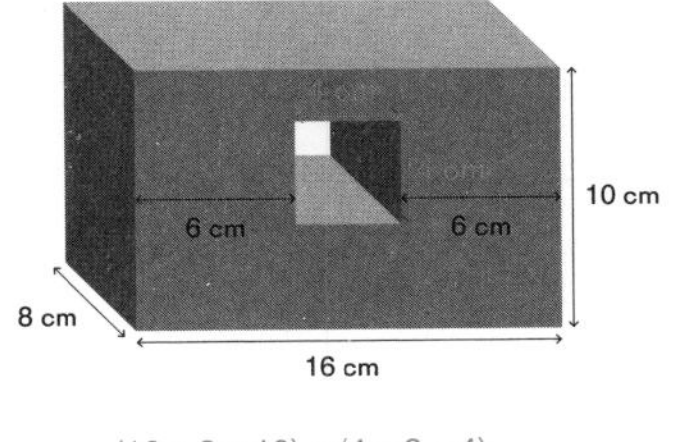

$(16 \times 8 \times 10) - (4 \times 8 \times 4)$
$= 1{,}280 - 128$
$= 1{,}152$

1,152 cm³

Exercise 6

Basics

1

10 cm

10 cm

10 cm

$1 \text{ cm}^3 = 1 \text{ mL}$

(a) What is the volume of this tank in cubic centimeters? $1{,}000 \text{ cm}^3$

(b) What is its capacity in milliliters? 1,000 mL

(c) What is its capacity in liters? 1 L

2 (a) $40 \text{ cm}^3 =$ [40] mL

(b) $400 \text{ cm}^3 =$ [400] mL

(c) $4{,}000 \text{ cm}^3 =$ [4,000] mL = [4] L

(d) $4{,}030 \text{ cm}^3 =$ [4,030] mL = [4] L [30] mL

(e) 850 mL = [850] cm^3

(f) 1 L 850 mL = [1,850] mL = [1,850] cm^3

(g) 1 L 85 mL = [1,085] mL = [1,085] cm^3

3 A rectangular tank is partially filled with water to a depth of 8 cm. Find the volume of water in the tank in liters and milliliters.

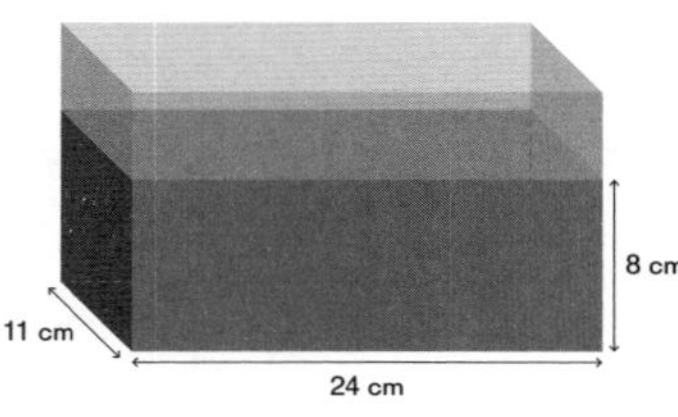

$24 \times 11 \times 8 =$ [2,112]

Volume = [2,112] cm^3

Volume = [2] L [112] mL

Practice

4 A rectangular container, 20 cm long and 10 cm wide, contains 1 L 400 mL of water. What is the height of the water?

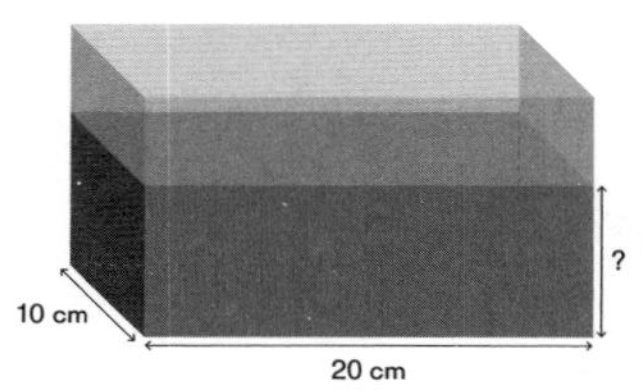

$\frac{1{,}400}{20 \times 10} = 7$

7 cm

5 A rectangular container, 20 cm by 30 cm by 42 cm, is filled completely with water. 18 L of water is then poured out. What is the height of the water left in the container?

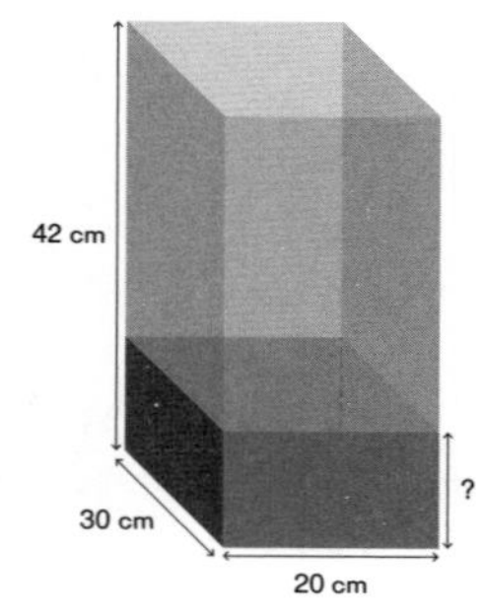

$20 \times 30 \times 42 = 25{,}200 = 25 \text{ L } 200 \text{ mL}$

$25 \text{ L } 200 \text{ mL} - 18 \text{ L} = 7 \text{ L } 200 \text{ mL} = 7{,}200 \text{ cm}^3$

$\frac{7{,}200}{20 \times 30} = 12$

12 cm

6 A rectangular tank 15 cm long, 10 cm wide, and 40 cm high is $\frac{4}{5}$ full of water. How many more liters and milliliters of water are needed to fill the tank completely?

$\frac{1}{5} \times 40 = 8$

$15 \times 10 \times 8 = 1{,}200$

$1{,}200 \text{ cm}^3 = 1 \text{ L } 200 \text{ mL}$

1 L 200 mL

or:

$15 \times 10 \times 40 = 6{,}000 \text{ cm}^3$

$6{,}000 \text{ cm}^3 = 6{,}000 \text{ mL}$

$\frac{1}{5} \times 6{,}000 = 1{,}200 \text{ mL}$

1 L 200 mL

7 A bottle containing 2 L of water is poured into a rectangular tank with a base area of 240 cm^2 and a height of 12 cm until the tank is $\frac{2}{3}$ full. How much water is left in the bottle?

$\frac{2}{3} \times 12 = 8$

$240 \times 8 = 1{,}920$

$2{,}000 - 1{,}920 = 80$

80 mL

or:

$\frac{2}{3} \times 240 \times 12 = 1{,}920$

$2{,}000 - 1{,}920 = 80$

80 mL

Exercise 7

Basics

1 A rectangular tank with a base area of 30 cm by 20 cm is filled with water to a height of 12 cm.

(a) An object is placed in the tank and the water rises to 15 cm. What is the volume of the object?

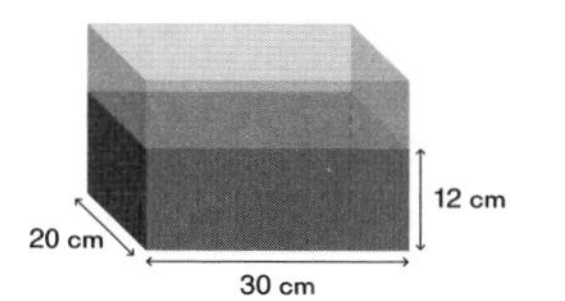

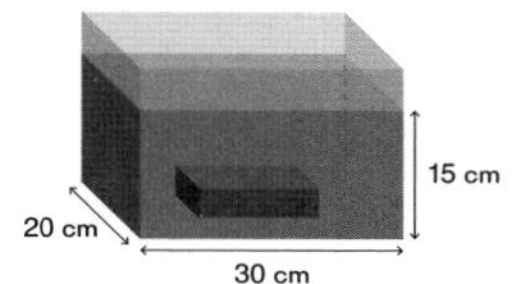

Increase in height of water level = 15 − 12 = 3

Volume of water displaced = 30 × 20 × 3 = 1,800

Volume of object = 1,800 cm^3

(b) Another object with a volume of 1,200 cm^3 is added to the tank. What will be the new height of the water?

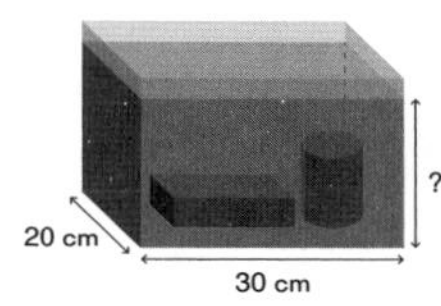

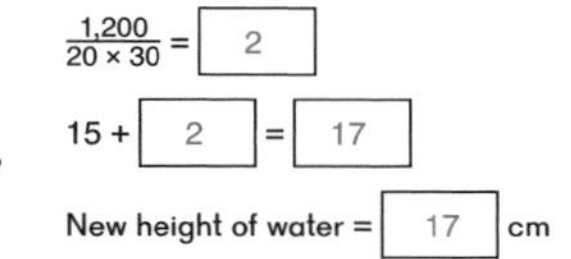

$\frac{1,200}{20 \times 30}$ = 2

15 + 2 = 17

New height of water = 17 cm

Practice

2 A measuring cylinder had 500 mL of water in it. After 20 identical glass marbles were added, the water level was 840 mL.

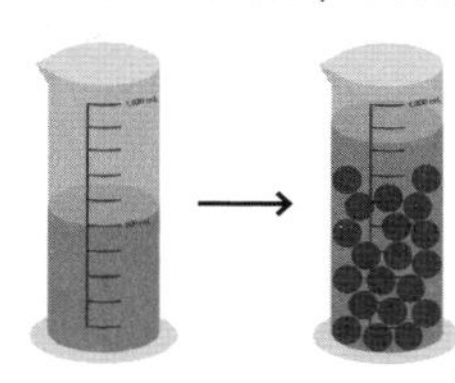

(a) What is the volume of the 20 marbles?

840 − 500 = 340

340 cm^3

(b) What is the volume of a single marble?

340 ÷ 20 = 17

17 cm^3

3 A cubical container with sides of 30 cm was $\frac{2}{3}$ filled with water. After an object was placed in it, the water level rose to 4 cm from the top. What is the volume of the object?

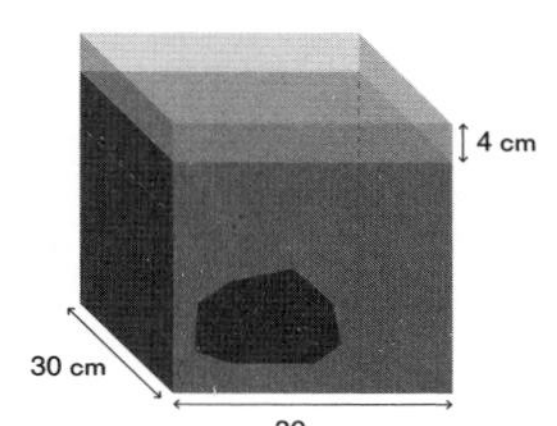

30 − 4 = 26

$\frac{2}{3}$ × 30 = 20

26 − 20 = 6

The water rose 6 cm.

30 × 30 × 6 = 5,400

5,400 cm^3

4 William put water in a rectangular tank and then added identical game tokens until the water rose by 2 cm. The base of the tank measures 10 cm by 8 cm. He added 12 game tokens in all. What is the volume of 1 game token?

10 × 8 × 2 = 160

$\frac{160}{12} = 13\frac{1}{3}$

$13\frac{1}{3}$ cm^3

5 A rectangular container, 30 cm long and 10 cm wide, contains 2 L 400 mL of water. Two identical cuboids with the dimensions of 10 cm by 3 cm by 5 cm are in the water. What is the height of the water?

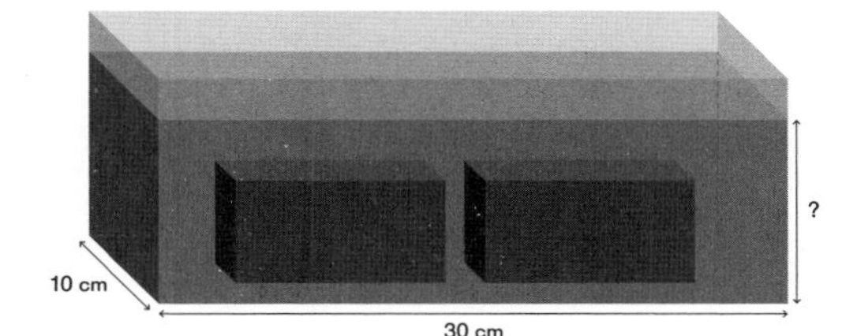

$\frac{2,400}{10 \times 30}$ = 8

2 × (10 × 5 × 3) = 300

$\frac{300}{10 \times 30}$ = 1

8 + 1 = 9

9 cm

Exercise 8

Check Methods may vary.

1. Find the volume of each solid figure.

(a) 12 cm, 15 cm, 5 cm, 6 cm, 10 cm, 6 cm, 7 cm

$(12 \times 5 \times 7) + (6 \times 10 \times 7)$
$= 420 + 420$
$= 840$
840 cm³

(b) 6 cm, 5 cm, 5 cm, 7 cm, 8 cm, 15 cm, 20 cm

$(20 \times 5 \times 15) - (7 \times 5 \times 8) + (6 \times 5 \times 5)$
$= 1{,}500 - 280 + 150$
$= 1{,}370$
1,370 cm³

2. (a) 64 cm³ = 64 mL

(b) 3,420 cm³ = 3 L 420 mL

(c) 6,007 cm³ = 6 L 7 mL

(d) 98 mL = 98 cm³

(e) 6 L = 6,000 cm³

(f) 1 L 20 mL = 1,020 cm³

(g) $4\frac{1}{2}$ L = 4,500 cm³

3. A rectangular tank measuring 30 cm by 25 cm by 20 cm is $\frac{3}{4}$ filled with water. Some of the water is then poured into a cubical tank with sides of 15 cm to fill it up. What is the volume of the water in liters and milliliters that is left in the rectangular tank?

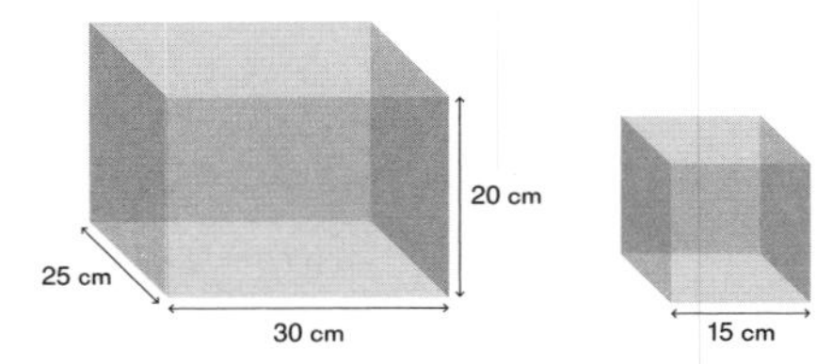

$\frac{3}{4} \times 20 = 15$
$15 \times 25 \times 30 = 11{,}250$
$15 \times 15 \times 15 = 3{,}375$
$11{,}250 - 3{,}375 = 7{,}875$
7 L 875 mL

4. The container below is filled with water to a depth of 12 cm. What is the volume of water in liters and milliliters?

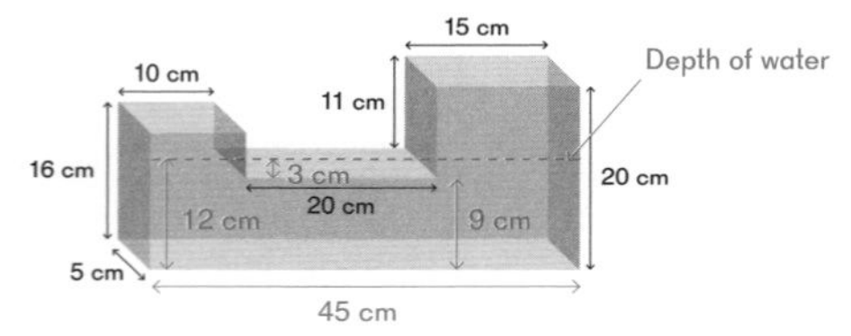

$(45 \times 5 \times 12) - (20 \times 5 \times 3)$
$= 2{,}700 - 300$
$= 2{,}400$
2,400 cm³
2 L 400 mL

5. A rectangular tank measuring 50 cm by 40 cm by 40 cm is half filled with water. When 4 metal cubes each with an edge of 10 cm are placed in the water, the water level rises. What is the new height of the water?

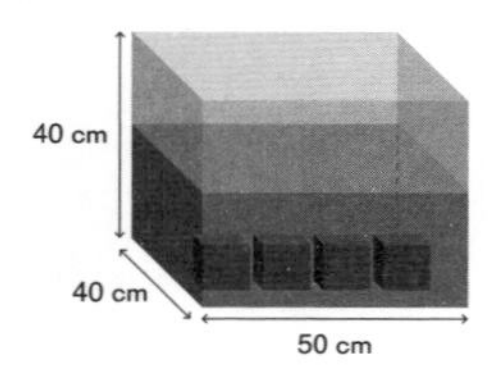

Water level before = 20 cm
$4 \times 1{,}000 = 4{,}000$
$\frac{4{,}000}{40 \times 50} = 2$
$20 + 2 = 22$
22 cm

Challenge

6. A solid cube with an edge 30 cm long has 3 square holes with sides 10 cm long cut all the way through to the other side as shown. What is the volume of the remaining solid?

Subtract volume of each hole and add back in the overlap twice.
$30 \times 30 \times 30 = 27{,}000$
$10 \times 10 \times 30 = 3{,}000$
$10 \times 10 \times 10 = 1{,}000$
$27{,}000 - (3 \times 3{,}000) + (2 \times 1{,}000) = 20{,}000$
20,000 cm³

7. A rectangular tank with a base 30 cm by 20 cm is $\frac{1}{2}$ filled with water. After 3 L of water is added to it, it becomes $\frac{3}{5}$ filled with water. What is the height of the water in the tank when it is $\frac{3}{5}$ filled?

$\frac{3}{5} - \frac{1}{2} = \frac{1}{10}$
3 L $\longrightarrow \frac{1}{10}$ filled
Capacity of tank = 30 L
$\frac{30{,}000}{30 \times 20} = 50$
Height of tank is 50 cm.
$\frac{3}{5} \times 50 = 30$
30 cm

Exercise 9

Check

1. Use the following number to answer the questions: three hundred ninety-four million, eight hundred one thousand.

   (a) Write the number in numerals.
   394,801,000

   (b) What is the value of the digit 9?
   90,000,000

   (c) Divide the number by 1,000. What is the new value of the digit 9?
   90,000

2. Find the values. Express fractions in simplest form.

   (a) $21 - 14 \div 7 + 3 \times 9$ 46

   (b) $8 - 3 \div 4 + 1 \times 2$ $9\frac{1}{4}$

   (c) $(2\frac{1}{2} + \frac{2}{3} + 1\frac{5}{6}) \div \frac{1}{5}$ 25

   (d) $\frac{1}{2} \times \frac{3}{5} + \frac{1}{4} \div \frac{1}{6}$ $1\frac{4}{5}$

3. Ms. Perez earned $6,942 a month for the past 4 years. How much did she earn in all during those 4 years?
   6,942 × 4 × 12 = 333,216
   $333,216

4. The area of a rectangle is 1,568 in². One side measures $2\frac{1}{3}$ feet. What is the length of the other side in inches?
   $2\frac{1}{3}$ feet = 28 in
   1,568 ÷ 28 = 56
   56 in

5. A bottle can hold 3 L of water. It had $2\frac{1}{2}$ L of water at first and then $\frac{3}{4}$ L was poured out. 785 mL was then added. How many more milliliters of water are needed to fill the bottle?
   $3 - (2\frac{1}{2} - \frac{3}{4}) = 1\frac{1}{4}$ L
   $1\frac{1}{4} \times 1{,}000 = 1{,}250$ mL
   1,250 − 785 = 465
   465 mL

6. Daniel spent $\frac{1}{3}$ of his money on roller blades and $\frac{1}{6}$ of the remainder on a helmet. He had $155 left. How much money did he have at first?

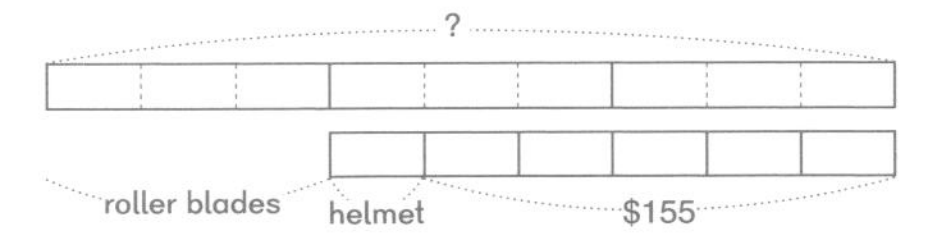

   $\frac{1}{6} \times \frac{2}{3} = \frac{1}{9}$
   roller blades + helmet = 4 out of 9 units
   5 units ⟶ 155
   1 unit ⟶ 155 ÷ 5 = 31
   9 units ⟶ 9 × 31 = 279
   $279

7. Some bags of rice have a total weight of 30 kg. Each bag of rice weighs $\frac{3}{5}$ kg. How many bags of rice are there?
   $30 \div \frac{3}{5} = 50$
   50 bags

8. A rectangular city block is twice as long as it is wide. The distance around the block is $\frac{3}{4}$ mile. How wide is the city block?
   $\frac{3}{4} \div 6 = \frac{1}{8}$
   $\frac{1}{8}$ mile

9. What fraction of the triangle is shaded?

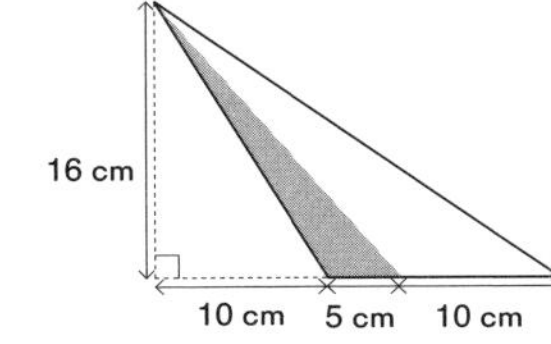

   $\frac{1}{2} \times 15 \times 16 = 120$
   $\frac{1}{2} \times 5 \times 16 = 40$
   $\frac{40}{120} = \frac{1}{3}$

   Or: Since the base of the shaded triangle is $\frac{1}{3}$ the base of the entire triangle, and the heights are the same, the area of the shaded part is $\frac{1}{3}$ the area of the entire triangle.

10. Find the shaded area in square meters.

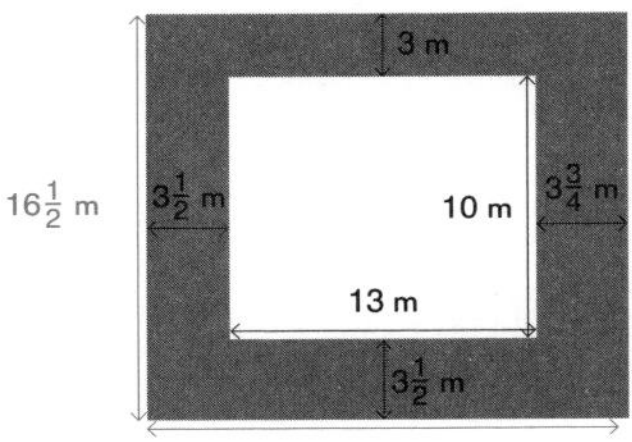

   $16\frac{1}{2} \times 20\frac{1}{4} = 334\frac{1}{8}$
   10 × 13 = 130
   $334\frac{1}{8} - 130 = 204\frac{1}{8}$
   $204\frac{1}{8}$ m²

11. Find the area of the following figure.

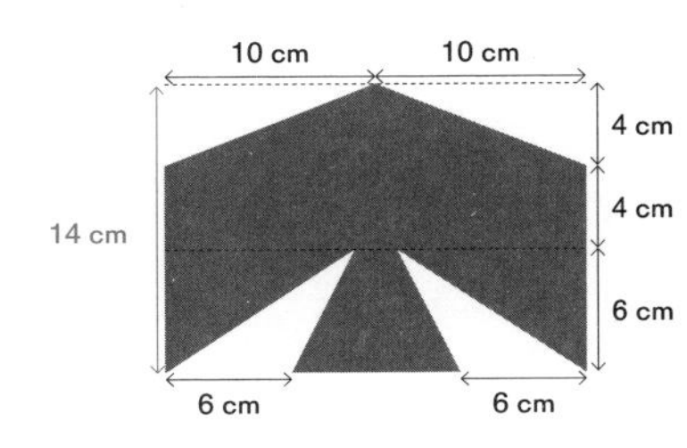

   14 × 20 = 280
   $2 \times \frac{1}{2} \times 10 \times 4 = 40$
   $2 \times \frac{1}{2} \times 6 \times 6 = 36$
   280 − 40 − 36 = 204
   204 cm²

12. A rectangular tank measuring 45 cm by 40 cm by 24 cm was $\frac{1}{2}$ filled with water. When a stone was placed in the tank, the tank became $\frac{3}{4}$ filled.

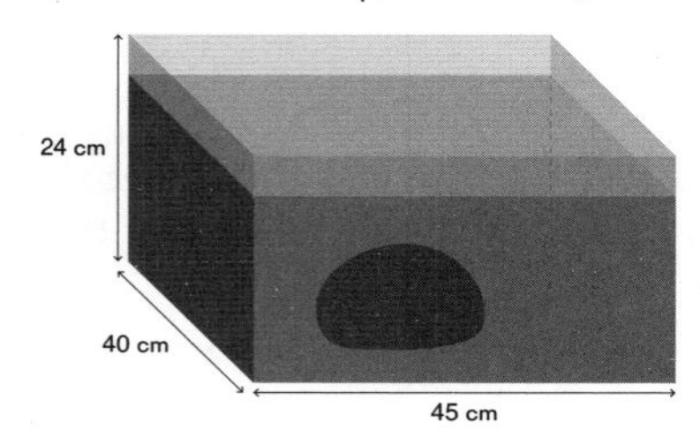

(a) Find the capacity of the tank in liters and milliliters.

$45 \times 40 \times 24 = 43{,}200$

43 L 200 mL

(b) Find the volume of the stone.

$\frac{1}{2} \times 24 = 12$; $\frac{3}{4} \times 24 = 18$

Water rises 6 cm.

$45 \times 40 \times 6 = 10{,}800$

10,800 cm³

Challenge

13. The figure shows two identical squares of sides 12 cm overlapping each other. Find the area of the overlapping part.

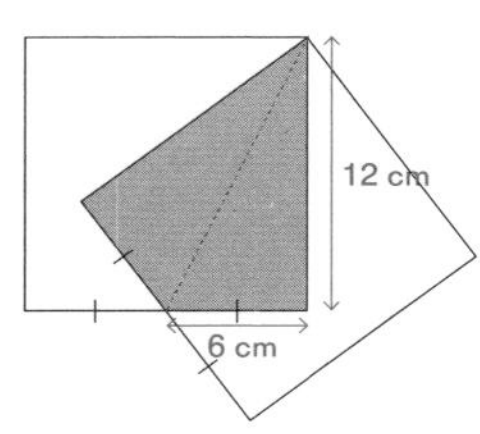

$2 \times \frac{1}{2} \times 6 \times 12 = 72$

72 cm²

14. A 4-digit multiple of 17 is made up of 4 different digits. What is the least number it could be?

If a number is a multiple of 17, that number + 17 is a multiple of 17.
Find the first 4-digit number that is a multiple of 17.
$1{,}000 \div 17$ is 58 with a remainder of 14, so 1,003 is the smallest 4-digit multiple of 17.
$1{,}003 + 17 = 1{,}020$
$1{,}020 + 17 = 1{,}037$
1,037 has 4 different digits, so the answer is 1,037.

15. How many unit cubes are needed to build each of the following solids?

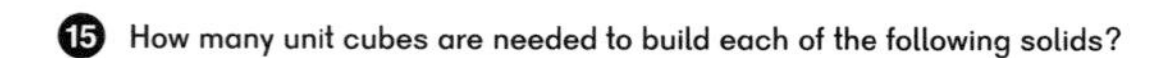

= 1 unit cube

(a)

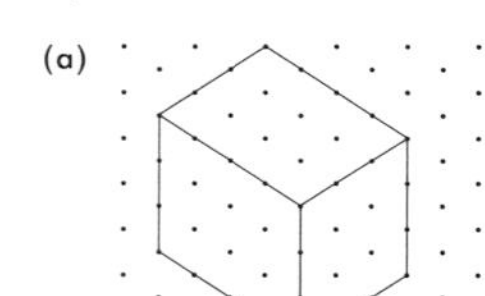

36

(b)

48

16. Complete the drawing of each cuboid. Then give the volume in cubic units.

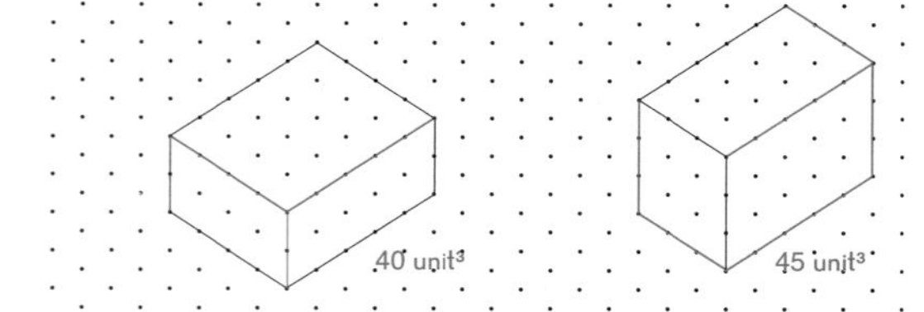

40 unit³

45 unit³

17. Draw a solid figure with a volume of 64 cubic units.

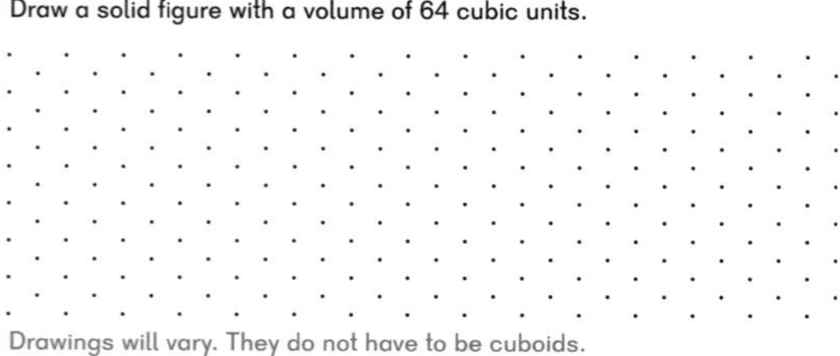

Drawings will vary. They do not have to be cuboids.

Blackline Masters for 5A

All Blackline Masters used in the guide can be downloaded from dimensionsmath.com.
This lists BLMs used in the **Think** and **Learn** sections.
BLMs used in **Activities** are included in the Materials list within each chapter.

Area of a Triangle 1	**Chapter 7:** Lesson 4
Area of a Triangle 2	**Chapter 7:** Lesson 5
Area of Complex Figures	**Chapter 7:** Lesson 6
Large Cuboid	**Chapter 8:** Lesson 1
Shaded Dots	**Chapter 2:** Chapter Opener, Lesson 2
Stars	**Chapter 2:** Lesson 2

Notes

